Mammals of Oklahoma

An Oklahoma Museum of Natural History Publication

Fox squirrel, painted by George Miksch Sutton. *Courtesy of W. R. Johnson*

MAMMALS OF OKLAHOMA

WILLIAM CAIRE

JACK D. TYLER

BRYAN P. GLASS

MICHAEL A. MARES

Illustrated by Zenith Marsh

University of Oklahoma Press : Norman and London

Financial assitance provided by
Oklahoma Department of Wildlife Conservation
Nongame Wildlife Program

Library of Congress Cataloging-in-Publication Data

Mammals of Oklahoma / William Caire . . . [et al.] ; illustrated by
Zenith Marsh. — 1st ed.
  p. cm.
"An Oklahoma Museum of Natural History publication."
Includes index.
ISBN 0-8061-2217-X (alk. paper)
  1. Mammals—Oklahoma. I. Caire, William, 1946–
QL719.O5M37 1989
599.09766—dc20   89-40212
                                                            CIP

The paper in this book meets the guidelines for permanence and durability of the
Committee on Production Guidelines for Book Longevity of the Council on Library
Resources, Inc. ⊚

Dedicated to the late
J. Keever Greer
who first recognized the need for such a work
and who worked hard to see it begin
and to all of our families and friends who continually
encouraged us to finish what he started

Contents

Tables

Authors' Preface

Some seventy million years ago, mammals supplanted reptiles as the dominant form of vertebrate life on earth. Through succeeding epochs they diversified greatly, filling niches left vacant by their reptilian predecessors. During the age of the mammals, most of what is now Oklahoma was undergoing a period of erosion, rather than deposition, so there is very little fossil evidence of the mammals that inhabited the state during most of the Tertiary period. Only in the western counties and the Panhandle are there Pliocene and Pleistocene deposits, and these reveal a fauna considerably different from that which exists today. The history of the fossil predecessors of our recent mammalian fauna must be sought beyond our own political boundaries and is far beyond the intended scope of this book.

Assembled in the volume are accounts of all species known to occur in Oklahoma, the means for their identification, range maps, and pertinent life-history information. A work of this type has been needed for many years. The last such publication (Blair, 1939) dealt with 80 species; the present work encompasses 106 (including 4 introduced species).

All four authors have edited and examined the various portions of the book, but each individual is responsible for the content and veracity of the sections he compiled and wrote, as shown in the Table of Contents. Obviously, however, we are directly responsible for only a small part of this assemblage of data. Many of the specimens, particularly the earlier ones, were collected by surveying or exploratory expeditions during the nineteenth and early twentieth centuries, but the greatest number by far have been accumulated by students in Oklahoma's own institutions of higher learning as part of their studies. Collections at the following state schools were instrumental in the completion of the manuscript: the University of Oklahoma; Oklahoma State University; Central State University; Cameron University; and East

Central, Southeastern, Northeastern, and Northwestern Oklahoma state universities. We gratefully acknowledge the diligent and skillful help lent by hundreds of former students. We are indebted for technical assistance to personnel of the Oklahoma Department of Wildlife Conservation, particularly Byron Moser, assistant director; Richard Hatcher, furbearer biologist; and nongame wildlife biologists Dana Base, Laura Pollard, and John Skeen. Paul Moore of the Wildlife Department and Ken Johnston of the Oklahoma Geological Survey provided several photographs.

The profound influence of the late J. Keever Greer should not pass unnoticed. It was Dr. Greer who, as director of the Oklahoma Museum of Natural History and head of the Oklahoma Biological Survey at the University of Oklahoma, planted the seeds of the ideas that ultimately evolved into this book. In spite of his untimely death during the early stages of writing, his efforts provided the impetus for completion of this work.

This book would not have been possible without the generous assistance of several organizations and numerous individuals. The Oklahoma Museum of Natural History and the Oklahoma Biological Survey offered financial and logistic support throughout the project. Funds awarded by the Research Associates of the University of Oklahoma made possible visits to various collections and production of the manuscript and most of the artwork. Faculty research grants from Central State University and Cameron University aided in fieldwork and data collection. Vehicles and facilities that contributed to the completion of this project were provided by the University of Oklahoma Zoology Department and the Central State University and Cameron University biology departments. Zenith Marsh of the University of Oklahoma Zoology Department made most of the original drawings of the individual species and the final drawings of the figures (from those compiled and sketched by W. Caire) in the identification key. The entire manuscript was typed by Sonya Johnson, Oklahoma Museum of Natural History technical manuscript specialist. Also at the University of Oklahoma, Janet Braun helped with various aspects of manuscript preparation and data compilation. The computerization of all the data and of the extensive manuscript, a task of fundamental importance to this volume's completion, was done by Dan Hough. Leslie Nitikman aided in verifying capture localities. At Central State University, numerous individuals assisted in various ways. Facilities and release time were made available through the College of Mathematics and Science by Dean David Hart and Vice President of Academic Affairs James Perry. Warren Smith, chairman of the Biology Department, provided facilities and contributed to the etymology of Oklahoma mammal names. Terry Harrison, George Goodman, and Doyle McCoy provided considerable information and a critical evaluation of the physiognomic section. National Institute of Health Grants (E-819, HD-01833) allowed Bryan Glass to conduct research on Oklahoma bats, and the information he gathered provided the baseline data for the species accounts.

At Cameron University, President Don Davis provided encouragement and enabled financial assistance, and Joyce Grimes, Judie Morris, and Sharon Whitrock typed several of the species accounts. Kathryne Sites assisted in typing at Central State University. Trips to the National Archives in Washington, D.C.; the University of Kansas Museum of National History; the Fort Worth County Museum; the University of Texas Memorial Museum; the American Museum of Natural History; and the United States National Museum, and to repositories in the Los Angeles vicinity and in Oklahoma, were funded by Cameron University and Central State University research funds. Dan Russell, curatorial assistant at the American Museum, and Cathy Blount, museum specialist with the U.S. Fish and Wildlife Service at the National Museum, rendered assistance at those institutions. We acknowledge a sincere debt of gratitude to all these people and many others throughout Oklahoma and at museums across the United States who aided us in various ways. Dr. Kenneth Hoving, vice-provost for research administration of the University of Oklahoma, supported this project throughout its duration. Dr. Bruce M. Bell, former director of the Oklahoma Museum of Natural History, also supported this work in its early stages. We are also indebted to the late Dr. George M. Sutton for his subtle yet continual encouragement of our efforts.

Oklahoma is often visualized as a flat tableland lacking in environmental diversity. In fact the state includes a wide variety of habitats supporting a large number of species. The natural environments of the state have changed greatly from their pristine condition, and several of the species herein discussed either have been extirpated from the state or are now only uncommon residents. The mammal fauna of Oklahoma is a unique and renewable natural resource for the state. We hope that an awareness and appreciation of these many species will aid the citizens of the state in continuing efforts aimed toward the conservation of the mammals of Oklahoma.

WILLIAM CAIRE
Edmond, Oklahoma
JACK D. TYLER
Lawton, Oklahoma
BRYAN P. GLASS
Stillwater, Oklahoma
MICHAEL A. MARES
Norman, Oklahoma

Part One

Mammalogy in Oklahoma

Introduction

William Caire

The primary objective of this book is to acquaint the public with the mammals of Oklahoma. At the same time, sufficient technical information is included to be useful to the professional mammalogist.

Material contained herein is the result of a great deal of field work, a thorough literature review, and examination of nearly twenty thousand specimens from Oklahoma deposited in museums throughout the United States. It is felt that those few specimens that inadvertently might have been overlooked will not appreciably change the distribution maps or alter our knowledge of the mammals of Oklahoma. Appendix 1 lists the localities where specimens have been collected, together with their various repositories. The history and development of mammalogy are detailed in a separate section. A general description of the topography, climate, and vegetation of Oklahoma can be found in the section on the physiognomic regions. The zoogeography section discusses broader patterns of mammalian distribution in Oklahoma.

An illustrated key is included to aid in the identification of Oklahoma mammals to order and species levels. Each couplet contains information on both skin and skull characters. Incorporated in the key are several species of unverified occurrence in Oklahoma, but which are known to occur in contiguous states. Their inclusion should aid in the recognition of these species if by chance one should be collected. Also included are keys to recently extirpated species. A glossary precedes the key and is intended to aid readers unfamiliar with the more technical terms employed by mammal taxonomists.

Nomenclature used in the checklist of species and in the species accounts follows closely the arrangement of Jones *et al.* (1986) and Honacki *et al.* (1982). A conservative approach has been followed in adopting name changes for various families, genera, and species. In several cases, the changes pro-

3

posed by some authors are still being evaluated, and it was deemed prudent to follow the established names until the new combinations are more widely accepted. For instance, the order Marsupialia is retained until it is determined whether one or several orders exist (Jones *et al.*, 1986).

The treatment of the species of *Blarina* is in agreement with Jones *et al.* (1986), who chose to separate *carolinensis* and *hylophaga* from *brevicauda*. This taxonomic problem is discussed in the individual species accounts.

In the order Chiroptera, use of the genus *Lasiurus* for the tree bats also follows Jones *et al.* (1986) instead of Hall (1981), who selected the older genus *Nycteris* rather than *Lasiurus*, even though the latter has been recognized by the International Commission on Zoological Nomenclature. The specific epithet *leibii* is used rather than *subulatus* for the small-footed myotis. Western populations of *M. leibii* have been considered by Van Zyll de Jong (1984, 1985) to belong to a separate species, *M. ciliolabrum;* however, we retain *M. leibii* until more Oklahoma specimens have been examined. Conservative use of *M. keenii* is continued in place of *M. septentrionalis*, a name suggested by Van Zyll de Jong (1979, 1985). *Tadarida* is also retained as the generic name of the free-tailed bats over *Nyctinomops* proposed by Freeman (1981).

Glass (1986) argues for the term Xenarthra and against Edentata as the ordinal name of the armadillos and their relatives. His suggestion is followed here.

The present work differs from Jones *et al.* (1986) and Honacki *et al.* (1982) by retaining the western chipmunks in the genus *Eutamias* rather than lumping them with *Tamias*, the genus of the eastern species. However, strong evidence is presented by Levenson *et al.* (1985) for *Tamias* to be used as the single generic name. The arrangement of Jones *et al.* (1986) and Honacki *et al.* (1982) is followed in the use of Cricetidae as a familial name distinct from Muridae.

The taxonomy concerning the gophers in Oklahoma is still somewhat controversial, and our conservative approach delays our adoption of all the recently proposed nomenclatural changes. We do, however, acknowledge that considerable evidence has been presented by various workers for at least two taxonomic changes. Bohlin and Zimmerman (1982) and Cothran and Zimmerman (1985) have presented considerable evidence for the recognition of *Geomys breviceps* at the species level. We also acknowledge that Honeycutt and Williams (1982) suggest a return to the use of *Cratogeomys* instead of *Pappogeomys* as the generic name for the yellow-faced pocket gopher.

Similarly, we conserve the generic name *Perognathus* for the hispid pocket mouse even though Hafner and Hafner (1983) suggest that the spiny-rumped pocket mice should be referred to as *Chaetodipus*.

In the Order Carnivora, the genus *Vulpes* is treated as distinct from *Canis* even though some support is offered against this by Van Gelder (1978). Jones *et al.* (1986) are followed in the use of *Ursus arctos* instead of the numerous taxa listed by Hall (1981). Mead (1968) offers strong evidence, which we accept, for the recognition of *Spilogale putorius* and *S. gracilis* as distinct species. Specific problems in regard to these latter two forms are mentioned in those accounts. Considerable disagreement exists in the use of *Felis* and *Lynx* for the generic name of the cats, but this book follows Jones *et al.* (1986) in employing *Felis*.

For the deer, the genus *Odocoileus* is chosen instead of *Dama* (as used by Hall, 1981). Antilocapridae is retained as a distinct family and not included with the Bovidae as recommended by O'Gara and Matson (1975) and accepted by Honacki *et al.* (1982).

Each species account begins with the currently recognized specific name followed by the common name and a brief synonymy. The species accounts are arranged in the same sequence as listed by Jones *et al.* (1986) down to the level of genus. However, the species within each genus are alphabetical in order to facilitate referencing. The synonymy includes the original name and citation and the reference to the first usage of the name as currently recognized. Each species account contains a short description of the mammal and contrasts it with other similar species. These descriptive comments may be used in conjunction with the identification key. Pen-and-ink drawings of each animal provide readers unfamiliar with it an idea of the general appearance. Also included in each account is a discussion of the species' distribution in Oklahoma, its generally preferred habitat, comments on reproduction, and various other ecological information.

No attempt has been made to detail the extent of geographic variation of each species. However, near the end of each account are listed the various subspecies and references to sources of additional information.

The distribution map included with each species account contains a closed dot in the center of each county from which a specimen has been examined. More precise locality information is available in Appendix 1. The distribution maps of several species (such as antelope and grizzly bear) have crosshatchings which represent the probable past distributions of the species before their extirpation by man's activities. The open dots seen on some maps are significant sight records (made by the authors or other individuals we feel are competent to correctly identify the species) or literature records of specimens we did not examine.

Domesticated species, exotic species, and species of unverified occurrence are discussed in separate sections. The domesticated species are listed with brief comments. The few species that may eventually be found in Oklahoma are discussed in more depth to facilitate their recognition.

Appendix 2 contains an etymology of scientific names for the mammals of Oklahoma. This was included to help those not familiar with scientific names learn them more quickly.

Appendix 3 contains a list of scientific names and common names for the various plant species mentioned throughout the text.

History of Mammalogy in Oklahoma

Bryan P. Glass

Progress in our knowledge of the mammals of Oklahoma may be roughly divided into four periods: early exploration, the territorial period, statehood to World War II, and the post–World War II period. The periods from territorial days until World War II have been well summarized by Blair (1939), and most of the information given below for that time span has been taken from that publication.

The region today known as Oklahoma was incorporated into the United States when the Louisiana Territory was purchased from France in 1803. At that time it was an unknown land to most people living in the original states. Although much of the northern part of the purchase area was known to French trappers and "mountain men," what was to become Oklahoma was not an area where fur-bearing animals were known to be abundant. Coronado is presumed to have traversed part of the Oklahoma Panhandle in 1541, but it was the designation of parts of Oklahoma as a territory for the relocation of various Indian tribes that brought this part of North America to the attention of the government and citizens of the settled states.

When the Five Civilized Tribes (Cherokee, Chickasaw, Choctaw, Creek, and Seminole) were moved from their tribal homelands in the southeastern United States to the land set aside as Indian Territory, Fort Gibson became the main western terminus for this forced emigration. The territory within which these tribes were distributed constituted approximately the eastern half of present-day Oklahoma. Later, the western part of the state was designated as Oklahoma Territory and became a focus for resettlement of various Plains Indian tribes during the post–Civil War period.

In pre–Civil War times only two expeditions that passed through Oklahoma seem to have left any accounts concerning mammals. Washington Irving (1835) joined a military expedition that toured an area from Fort Gibson to about the center of the state, probably to the vicinity of Shawnee and Oklahoma City, and returned to Fort Gibson. In his book *A Tour of the Prairies*, Irving noted the presence of deer, bear, bison, wolves, elk, beaver, prairie dogs, skunks, and mustangs. Most of his accounts were of hunts, but he did give an interesting, factual account of a prairie dog town, replete with anthropomorphic interpretations of the animals' behavior.

Captain Randolph B. Marcy in 1852 commanded a military expedition to explore the Red River of the South from Otter Creek to its source (Marcy, 1854). As an appendix to his report he included a list of mammals encountered: antelope, deer, black bear, beaver, buffalo, otter, raccoon, skunk, civet, gray wolf, prairie wolf, "large lobos wolf," red fox, wild cat, panther, fox squirrel, striped squirrel, flying squirrel, rabbit, jackass rabbit, small prairie rabbit, prairie dog, and opossum.

After the Civil War, Oklahoma, except for the Panhandle, was officially reserved for Indian occupation until 1889. By a quirk of political geography, the Panhandle was not included within the boundaries of any defined political unit until 1893, when it was united with the Oklahoma Territory. The state as we know it today was created in 1907 by merging into one constitutional unit the Indian Territory, Oklahoma Territory, and the Panhandle. The Panhandle was then divided into three counties, as it is today.

Preceding these political changes there was increasing pressure from citizens to open parts of the region to white settlement, and this agitation culminated with the great land runs of 1889 and 1893. With territorial status achieved, a number of institutions and agencies commenced biological exploration of the newly opened lands. A party from the American Museum of Natural History under the leadership of Charles P. Rowley spent several weeks in October and November of 1889 in the western part of the Panhandle collecting several bison from the small southern herd, which was exterminated that year or the year following (Roe, 1970). The museum party collected a number of small mammals that are now deposited in the American Museum of Natural History. Their operations centered around a "Howard Ranch," the location of which is now in doubt. However, correspondence from Rowley to the museum director, and data tags on some of the small mammals he collected, indicate that the location was near the sources of the Beaver River (that is, Currumpa [Corrumpa] and Cienequilla [Seneca] creeks) in the southwestern part of what is now Cimarron County (Glass, 1971). Roe (1970) indicated that a rancher named Lee Howard was involved in the killing of the last extensive herd of bison in 1887–88 somewhere in the Canadian Divide region between the Canadian and North Canadian river basins. This is probably the same Howard mentioned by Rowley.

During the territorial period, Thaddeus Surber made collections for the Field Museum of Natural History in Chicago in what are now Cleveland and

Woods counties, and in the Arbuckle Mountains. He also collected in north-eastern Oklahoma for the Museum of Comparative Zoology at Harvard University. The U.S. Bureau of Biological Survey (then in the Department of Agriculture, now incorporated into the U.S. Fish and Wildlife Service, U.S. Department of the Interior) sent expeditions under E. A. Preble, James H. Gaut, Vernon Bailey, D. E. Lantz, and others to work in the Ouachita and Wichita mountains and in Woodward County. Their collections, together with all other Biological Survey specimens, are now included with those of the Smithsonian Institution. A few collections, particularly of the larger species, were also made by the University of Kansas during this time.

Little collecting of mammals occurred in Oklahoma for many years following statehood. In 1917 the University of Oklahoma published *Geography of Oklahoma*, by L. C. Snider. A chapter on animal life was contributed by Howard Cross of the University of Oklahoma, with some assistance from H. H. Lane. Cross's discussion of the larger mammals covered essentially those accounted for earlier by Irving (1835) and Marcy (1854). However, in a systematic list of species presumed to occur in the state, he included several species that have not been verified to date; he did not include a record of specimens that he examined. The only other reports of Oklahoma mammals to appear during these years were published in a serial publication of the U.S. Biological Survey, *North American Fauna*. Some of these reports dealt with surveys of particular geographic areas and contained lists of mammals and other fauna and flora. Most, however, consisted of taxonomic revisions of mammalian groups, principally of genera. For many years these publications were the most important works available on North American mammals. Whenever a generic review appeared, the known specimens from Oklahoma were listed if that genus was represented in the state. In most cases these revisions contain the oldest, most reliable and complete listing of information on Oklahoma mammals to be found. Number 25 of this series, *Biological Survey of Texas*, was compiled by Vernon Bailey and published in 1905. Bailey's inventory included portions of present-day Oklahoma as well as Texas.

Beginning in 1924, R. Chester Hughes, of the Oklahoma A&M College (now Oklahoma State University), collected mammals, principally in the Arbuckle Mountains and in the vicinity of Stillwater in Payne County. His specimens formed the nucleus of the OSU collections, now consisting of over twelve thousand cataloged entries. A short time later, similar activity began at the University of Oklahoma in Norman, where H. L. Whitaker assembled substantial collections from southeastern Oklahoma. A further stimulus to the study of Oklahoma mammals occurred when H. H. T. Jackson of the U.S. Biological Survey, together with members of the Oklahoma Biological Survey (a state-funded agency established at the University of Oklahoma) undertook a survey of the fauna adjacent to the Salt Plains in northwestern

Oklahoma (Jackson and Warfel, 1933). G. A. Moore joined Hughes in collecting in north central Oklahoma as part of a course in field zoology. In northeastern Oklahoma, H. D. Chase of the University of Tulsa collected during that period.

George M. Sutton, of the University of Michigan, and George H. Lowery, from Louisiana State University, also collected in Oklahoma during the years immediately preceding World War II. The most significant contributions during this decade, however, were made by W. Frank Blair, who collected mammals in Oklahoma during the mid-1930s while he was a graduate student at the University of Michigan. His two papers (Blair and Hubbell, 1938; Blair, 1939) represent the end of the prewar period and the first attempt to compile a validated list of species for the state. More importantly, Blair recognized that distribution of species is not unpredictable or haphazard, but is linked to the habitat requirements of the species. His second paper was the only published list presumed to encompass every species known from Oklahoma. To substantiate his statements about distribution, he recorded the collections in which known specimens from Oklahoma were deposited, thereby validating those species for the state.

Following World War II, interest in the science of mammalogy accelerated in Oklahoma. Students of A. O. Weese at the University of Oklahoma began studying the ecology of mammals. B. P. Glass, who joined the faculty at Stillwater in 1946, immediately set about to enlarge the collections, anticipating the establishment of a Cooperative Wildlife Research Unit there in 1948. James Burns and, subsequently, the late J. Keever Greer were curators of mammals at the Oklahoma Museum of Natural History at the University of Oklahoma in the 1950s and 1960s. The University of Oklahoma Biological Station on Lake Texoma opened in 1951, and Howard McCarley of Southeastern State College in Durant taught mammalogy there during several summer sessions.

All of these activities attracted students to study mammals. Mammalogy is currently taught either annually or on a frequent basis at the University of Oklahoma (by M. A. Mares), Oklahoma State University (by B. P. Glass), Central State University (by W. Caire), Cameron University (by J. D. Tyler), and a few other state universities. As a result of these mammalogy courses and associated research, significant collections of mammals now exist in many of these institutions.

This book is intended to update and consolidate all of the information that has accrued since Blair's publication in 1939. *Mammals of Oklahoma* provides specific information in greater detail than is available in such general treatments as *Mammals of North America*, by Hall (1981), and *Guide to Mammals of the Plains States*, by Jones *et al.* (1985). References which discuss the mammals from states adjacent to Oklahoma and which may provide the reader with additional information on the mammals that occur in Oklahoma include *The Mammals of Kansas* (Bee *et al.*, 1981), *The Wild Mammals of Missouri* (Schwartz and Schwartz, 1981), *A Guide to Arkansas Mammals* (Sealander, 1979), *Texas Mammals East of the Balcones Fault Zone* (Schmidly, 1983), *The Mammals of Texas* (Davis, 1974), *Mammals of New Mexico* (Findley *et al.*, 1975), and *Distribution of Mammals in Colorado* (Armstrong, 1972).

Physiognomic Regions of Oklahoma

William Caire

Although Oklahoma is generally thought of as little more than flat grassland prairie, the state in fact embraces several areas that are quite diverse topographically, climatologically, and vegetatively. There are eastern and southwestern mountainous areas, scattered ranges of low hills in the central part of the state, and an elevated region of mesas in the western Panhandle. Equally important in affecting plant and animal variety is the pronounced rainfall gradient across Oklahoma. Relatively high precipitation along the eastern border grades into fairly xeric conditions in the west, resulting in nine major physiognomic regions (Fig. 1). These nine regions are not intended to be detailed descriptions of the vegetation, topography, or climate of Oklahoma, but are broadly characterized regions intended to be useful in correlating the general distributional patterns of the Oklahoma mammals with environmental conditions. The name of each region includes a plant life form as well as a topographic term. This combination of names should help the reader visualize the general nature of each of the nine regions. Much of the following is borrowed and condensed from Bruner (1931), Blair and Hubbell (1938), Gray and Galloway (1959), Morris *et al.* (1976), and Rhodes (1980). More detail can be obtained by consulting those works.

Piñon-Juniper Mesas. This physiognomic region (Fig. 2) is located in the extreme northwestern corner of the Panhandle and is locally referred to as the Black Mesa region. The general topography consists of deep canyon systems and remnants formed by the erosion of the surrounding areas by the Cimarron River and its tributaries. Some mesas, especially those adjacent to the Cimarron River, rise as much as 153 m (502 ft.) above the valley floor. The top of Black Mesa, the highest elevation in Oklahoma, is 1,516 m (4,974 ft.) above sea level. Mesa slopes are usually steep and often littered with angular talus fragments. A few high-level plains are present, and broad floodplains

12

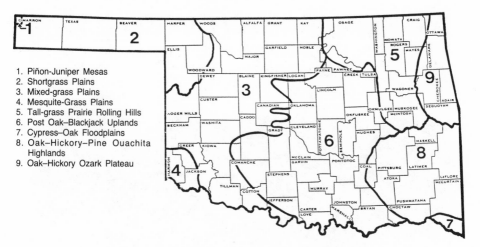

1. Piñon-Juniper Mesas
2. Shortgrass Plains
3. Mixed-grass Plains
4. Mesquite-Grass Plains
5. Tall-grass Prairie Rolling Hills
6. Post Oak–Blackjack Uplands
7. Cypress–Oak Floodplains
8. Oak–Hickory–Pine Ouachita Highlands
9. Oak–Hickory Ozark Plateau

Fig. 1. Major physiognomic regions of Oklahoma.

border the Cimarron River. Approximately 15 sq. km (9.3 sq. mi.) of sandstone mesas are covered with a Tertiary basaltic lava flow from a volcano in Colorado. The two main geological formations are the Morrison formation and the Dakota Sandstone. Soils consist primarily of limy and clay loams. Climatically the region is characterized by a mean annual temperature of 13° C (55° F), mean annual rainfall of 46 cm (18.1 in.), and a growing season of about 179 days.

Principal plant associations consist of either low scrub dominated by mixtures of thick-leaved hackberry (*Celtis reticulata*) and one-seeded juniper (*Juniperus monosperma*) or a mixture of piñon pine (*Pinus edulis*), juniper, and oaks (*Quercus undulata* and *Q. gambelii*). Most of the piñon pines grow on north-facing slopes. Western yellow pine (*Pinus ponderosa*) is present in a few canyons. Talus slopes are barren and have little or no vegetative cover. South-facing slopes often have woody cover of mesquite (*Prosopis glandulosa*) and prickly pear (*Opuntia* spp.). Intervening grasslands are typically dominated by shortgrasses such as blue grama (*Bouteloua gracilis*), hairy grama (*B. hirsuta*), and buffalo grass (*Buchloë dactyloides*). Scattered clumps of cholla cactus (*Opuntia imbricata*) and small soapweed (*Yucca glauca*) are common in the grasslands.

Shortgrass High Plains. The Shortgrass High Plains occupy the Panhandle region of Oklahoma outside the Piñon-Juniper Mesas region described above (Fig. 3). The eastern margin coincides with a sharply dissected and eroded break in the plains rising above the Mixed-grass Plains region described below. From that break this plain slopes upward from an elevation of 457 m

Fig. 2. Piñon-Juniper Mesas.

Fig. 3. Shortgrass High Plains.

(1,499 ft.) to about 1,220 m (4,003 ft.) at its western limits. Some of the most extensive geological formations in this region are the Ogallala, Laverne, Rush Springs Sandstone, and Marlow formations. The High Plains are underlain with Tertiary deposits consisting of loose, loamy, and clayey deposits having a high content of lime. Sandy and gravelly areas are especially common near streams and rivers. Many narrow, V-shaped valleys have been cut into the plains by various stream systems draining into the Beaver (North Canadian) and Cimarron rivers.

Climatically, the region is characterized by a mean annual temperature of about 13° C (55° F), an average annual rainfall of about 51 cm (20.1 in.), and a growing season that continues for about 190 days. The dominant climax vegetation consists of shortgrasses including blue grama (*Bouteloua gracilis*), hairy grama (*B. hirsuta*) and buffalo grass (*Buchloë dactyloides*). Other grasses are little bluestem (*Schizachyrium scoparium*), three-awn grama (*Aristida* spp.), and side-oats grama (*Bouteloua curtipendula*). Sandy areas adjacent to streams and rivers may support cottonwood (*Populus sargentii*), willows (*Salix amygdaloides* and *S. interior*), sand plum (*Prunus angustifolia*), sand sage (*Artemisia filifolia*), and small soapweed (*Yucca glauca*). On the steeper sloping outcrops of sandstone and gypsum, scattered one-seeded juniper (*Juniperus monosperma*) and small soapweed (*Y. glauca*) are common. Some areas of windblown sand are nearly devoid of vegetation.

Mixed-grass Plains. Excluding the Panhandle, the northwestern corner, and the extreme southwestern corner of Oklahoma, the western one-third of the state constitutes the most extensive physiognomic region in Oklahoma, the Mixed-grass Plains (Fig. 4). The eastern border is marked by interdigitating Post Oak–Blackjack Uplands. Rolling hills and plains dominate the topography. The average elevation is about 460 m (1,509 ft.). Permian Redbed deposits of red sandstones, siltstones, gypsum, and shale are locally common. Three of the most common geological formations are the Cloud Chief, Garber Sandstone, Hennessey Shale, and several gypsum formations. Numerous solution caves are located in the gypsum hills. Surface soils are generally loamy, subsurface soils, either reddish loamy or clayey. Quarternary silts and sandy deposits exist along almost all the major tributaries and rivers. The Cimarron, North Canadian, and Canadian rivers drain this area as they flow eastward toward the Arkansas River. The Washita River empties into the Red River to the south. Climatically, the Mixed-grass Plains is characterized by an average annual temperature of 15° C (59° F), an average annual rainfall of 69 cm (27.2 in.), and a growing season lasting about 210 days.

Vegetatively, this region is a transition area from the tall-grass prairies in the east to the shortgrass high plains in the west. Both sod and bunchgrass forms occur depending, in part, on local edaphic conditions. The dominant grasses include buffalo grass (*Buchloë dactyloides*), bluestems (*Andropogon*

Fig. 4. Mixed-grass Plains.

spp. and *Schizachyrium scoparium*) and grama grasses (*Bouteloua* spp.). Sandy areas along streams and rivers include sand sage (*Artemisia filifolia*), sand plum (*Prunus angustifolia*), and sumacs (*Rhus* spp.) as well as the grasses mentioned above. Some active sand dunes are either devoid of plants or support only scant vegetation, while others are well stabilized by shrubs, grasses, and weedy annuals. Dense stands of shin oaks (*Quercus havardii* and *Q. mohriana*) are found on sandy areas in the western sections of this region. Tamarisk (*Tamarix pentandra*), hackberries (*Celtis* spp.), American elm (*Ulmus americana*), chittamwood (*Bumelia lanuginosa*), and cottonwood (*Populus deltoides*) occur along many of the streams and rivers. Riparian forests, varying from almost pure stands of cottonwood in the west to mixed stands of considerable diversity in the east, extend upstream along the major rivers. Steep-walled ravines or canyons, often referred to as the Caddo Canyons, support isolated patches of forest composed of eastern trees such as black walnut (*Juglans nigra*), sugar maple (*Acer saccharum*), several oaks (*Quercus* spp.), and box elder (*Acer negundo*) as well as various mosses, ferns, and flowering herbs characteristic of regions much farther east.

Mesquite-Grass Plains. This physiognomic region is confined to the extreme southwestern corner of Oklahoma (Fig. 5). The Salt Fork of the Red River marks approximately the northern and eastern margins. Gently rolling low hills separated by level plains constitute the major topographic features. The average elevation is 457 m (1,499 ft.), and the entire region slopes southward toward the Red River. Several geological formations exist, including the Blaine Gypsum, Dog Creek Shale, and Duncan Sandstone. Red shales, sandstones, and gypsum strata are overlain in most areas with deep and fertile soils. Steep clay slopes and eroded gullies are locally common. Sand dunes are present in areas along both the Red River and the Salt Fork of the Red River. Average annual temperature is 17° C (62° F), average annual rainfall is 66 cm (26 in.), and the growing season is about 220 days.

Thorny shrubs such as mesquite (*Prosopis glandulosa*) dominate the vegetation of the region. Shortgrasses, including buffalo grass (*Buchloë dactyloides*), three-awn (*Aristida* spp.), and blue grama (*Bouteloua gracilis*), form a dense sod. Prickly pear cacti (*Opuntia leptocaulis* and *O. davisii*), small soapweed (*Yucca glauca*), and lotebush (*Condalia obtusifolia*) are patchy. Sandy areas adjacent to the Red River and along its tributaries support riparian vegetation, including cottonwood (*Populus deltoides*), willows (*Salix* spp.), and an admixture of a few other deciduous species and various grasses mentioned above.

Post Oak–Blackjack Uplands. This physiognomic region is the second most

Fig. 5. Mesquite-Grass Plains.

extensive in Oklahoma (Fig. 6). It is bounded on the south by the Red River, on the southeast by the Ouachita Highlands, and on the north and northeast by the Tall-grass Prairie Rolling Hills. The western margin is more complex and diffuse than depicted in the vegetation map (Fig. 1) because of considerable interdigitation with the Mixed-grass Plains region to the west, especially along major river systems. Pronounced escarpments and steep hills combine to form a rough topography, and the presence of the Wichita and Arbuckle mountains adds to the topographic complexity. The Washita, Canadian, North Canadian, and Cimarron rivers provide avenues of dispersal along which the more mesic vegetation in the east extends into the xeric western plains. Large expanses of this area are composed of Permian and Pennsylvanian sandstones, with clays and shales from numerous geologic formations scattered throughout. Older and more complicated geological formations and deposits exist in the Arbuckle and Wichita mountains. Soils are generally light-colored and sandy with subsoils of reddish sandy clay loam. The region has an average annual temperature of 16° C (61° F), an average annual rainfall of 102 cm (40.2 in.), and a growing season of about 220 days.

This physiognomic region represents an ecotone between the eastern deciduous forest and the western grasslands. The most characteristic plant association of this region is a scrub forest composed of blackjack oak (*Quercus marilandica*) and post oak (*Q. stellata*), with black hickory (*Carya texana*) in the central regions and mockernut hickory (*C. tomentosa*) in more mesic eastern portions. In mature forest areas, the trees are scattered, and grasses such as the bluestems (*Andropogon* spp. and *Schizachyrium scoparium*) and Indian grass (*Sorghastrum nutans*) are common. In disturbed areas, the young oaks and shrubs such as sumacs (*Rhus* spp.) and coralberry (*Symphoricarpos orbiculatus*), and woody vines such as greenbrier (*Smilax* sp.), form an often impenetrable secondary growth. Prairie vegetation is found in level areas within this region, while the scrub forest occurs primarily on the rougher terrain. Stream systems and bottomlands support a mesic forest that includes river birch (*Betula nigra*), willows (*Salix* spp.), buttonbush (*Cephalanthus occidentalis*), redbud (*Cercis canadensis*), American elm (*Ulmus americana*), oaks (*Quercus* spp.), cottonwood (*Populus deltoides*), sycamore (*Platanus occidentalis*), and various herbaceous species.

The Wichita and Arbuckle mountains are derived from a syncline that is eroded to the point of having its central igneous core exposed and has the original sedimentary strata tilted in opposite sequence on the north and south sides of the formation. They extend 80 km (49.7 mi.) in an east-west direction. The summits are approximately 396 m (1,299 ft.), rising about 122 m (400 ft.) above the surrounding lowland. Broad, intervening valleys are composed of beds of shales and softer limestones, while the ridges consist primarily of hard limestone strata. Many spring-fed tributaries drain to the

Fig. 6. Post Oak–Blackjack Uplands.

Washita River, and several limestone caves occur in the area. Mesic ravine forests include oaks (*Quercus* spp.), redbud (*Cercis canadensis*), American elm (*Ulmus americana*), cottonwood (*Populus deltoides*), and sycamore (*Platanus occidentalis*), as well as numerous mesic herbaceous forms, mosses, liverworts, and lichens.

The Wichita Mountains are a series of isolated peaks, some rising to elevations near 730 m (2,395 ft.) approximately 305 m (1,000 ft.) above the surrounding plains. The upper slopes of the higher peaks are steep and rugged, usually with a talus of large boulders and shallow soil. Lower hills and slopes are covered with a thin mantle of soil. Few caves exist in the Wichita Mountains. Most of the streams are intermittent, but a few are spring-fed and permanent. On the drier, south-facing slopes, a scrubby xeric forest of blackjack oak (*Quercus marilandica*) and post oak (*Q. stellata*) thrives. This dry oak forest is the most extensive vegetative type in the mountains. On the plains below the peaks, a Mixed-grass Plains vegetation predominates. In addition to oaks, several valleys contain such trees as American elm (*Ulmus americana*), black walnut (*Juglans nigra*), sugarberry (*Celtis laevigata*), white ash (*Fraxinus americana*), and chittamwood (*Bumelia lanuginosa*). Small stands of sugar maple (*Acer saccharum*) grow in a few protected spots, and live oaks (*Q. virginiana*) are not uncommon toward the western reaches of the mountain chain.

Tall-grass Prairie Rolling Hills. The Grand River and the Arkansas River form the approximate eastern and western margins, respectively, of this physiognomic region, a small portion of which extends south below the Arkansas River to the confluence of the North Canadian and Canadian rivers

Fig. 7. Tall-grass Prairie Rolling Hills.

(Fig. 7). Isolates of tall-grass prairie that occurred historically further west and south toward the Red River have mostly been lost to agriculture. Gently rolling hills (Osage Hills) with an occasional level plain dominate the topography. Differential weathering of the shale, sandstone, and limestone layers has produced rugged profiles in certain areas. Broad valleys underlain by shales are found between the few limestone and sandstone escarpments. Elevations vary from about 200 m (656 ft.) upward to 370 m (1,214 ft.). Principal geological formations are the Garber Sandstone, the Hennessey Shale, and the Flowerpot Shale. Soils are dark, heavily leached, and relatively shallow. The major drainage system is the Arkansas River, which flows along the western and southern margins. The Grand and Verdigris rivers drain the eastern area but eventually join the Arkansas to the south. Most tributaries of these rivers are sluggish and muddy and flow over broad floodplains. The mean annual temperature is 16° C (61° F), the mean annual rainfall 102 cm (40.2 in.), and the growing season is about 220 days.

The most extensive vegetative association is the tall-grass prairie, which occurs primarily on soils derived from shales. The dominant grasses include big bluestem (*Andropogon gerardi*), little bluestem (*Schizachyrium scoparium*), Indian grass (*Sorghastrum nutans*), and switch grass (*Panicum virgatum*). Drier soils on the larger limestone scarps have dry prairie associations, which are mixtures of tall-grasses and mid-grasses such as grama grasses (*Bouteloua* spp.) and bluestems (*Andropogon* spp. and *S. scoparium*). Persimmon (*Diospyros virginiana*) is common. Mesic ravines contain forest associations typical of the Ozark Plateau region to the east. The larger drainageways and stream systems support typical riparian vegetation that includes American elm (*Ulmus americana*), oaks (*Quercus* spp.), hackberries (*Celtis* spp.), cottonwood (*Populus deltoides*), sycamore (*Platanus occidentalis*), willows (*Salix* spp.), cattails (*Typha* spp.), and buttonbush (*Cephalanthus occidentalis*).

Oak-Hickory Ozark Plateau. That portion of the Ozark uplift occurring in northeastern Oklahoma contains this distinctive physiognomic region (Fig. 8). The western and southern margins are delimited by the Grand and Arkansas rivers, respectively. The topography consists of a deeply dissected plateau that includes the locally separated Cookson Hills and Boston Mountains. Boone Chert (cherty limestones and dolomites), the principal geological formation, consists of alternating layers of limestone and flint that have been eroded to form a rugged topography of hills, valleys, and prominent bluffs. The highest elevation is 462 m (1,516 ft.). The hills and bluffs extend 123 m (404 ft.) above the floodplains and valleys. Principal drainage systems are the Grand and Illinois rivers with their numerous clear, cold, and often spring-fed tributaries. Considerable drainage occurs underground, resulting in the formation of many sinks and caves. This area has a mean annual temperature of 16° C (61° F), a mean annual rainfall of 107 cm (42.1 in.), and a growing season lasting about 209 days.

Dry oak-hickory forests are the most widespread plant association. Dominant trees include oaks (*Quercus marilandica, Q. shumardii, Q. stellata,* and *Q. velutina*), black hickory (*Carya texana*), and winged elm (*Ulmus alata*). The lower vegetative stratum is composed of many species, including coralberry (*Symphoricarpos orbiculatus*), huckleberry (*Vaccinium vacillans*), and sassafras (*Sassafras albidum*). Many ravines contain a more mesic vegetation than that found on the slopes, including such plants as sugar maple (*Acer saccharum*), oaks (*Quercus alba* and *Q. muhlenbergii*), redbud (*Cercis canadensis*), dogwood (*Cornus florida*), basswood (*Tilia americana*), spicebush (*Benzoin aestivale*), pawpaw (*Asimina triloba*), mayapple (*Podophyllum peltatum*), and bloodroot (*Sanguinaria canadensis*). Juniper (*Juniperus virginiana*) mixed with oaks (*Quercus* spp.) and winged elm (*Ulmus alata*) are found on the more exposed limestone and chert bluffs where soil is sparse. Floodplains often have a rather open forest composed of maples (*Acer* spp.), elms (*Ulmus* spp.), river birch (*Betula nigra*), sycamore (*Platanus occidentalis*), and cottonwood (*Populus deltoides*).

Oak-Hickory-Pine Ouachita Highlands. Some of the most mountainous terrain in Oklahoma exists in this physiognomic region (Fig. 9). Collectively, the San Bois, Winding Stair, and Kiamichi mountains are usually referred to as the Ouachita Mountains and dominate the topography of this zone. These

Fig. 8. Oak-Hickory Ozark Plateau.

Fig. 9. Oak-Hickory-Pine Ouachita Highlands.

mountains consist of high, even-crested sandstone ridges that decrease in elevation from 878 m (2,881 ft.) near the Arkansas border to 231 m (758 ft.) in the west. The ridges in the east are as much as 554 m (1,818 ft.) high but westward decline to only 77 m (253 ft.) above the valley floors. Slopes are often littered with boulders and usually have very thin soils. Flint hills are locally common. Parallel series of broad, flat valleys extend in an east-west direction to the western edge of this region near Atoka. These valleys are often developed on the less resistant beds of shales or slates. The Jackfork Sandstone, Stanley Shale, Atoka and Antlers formations are the principal geological substrata. The principal rivers are the Kiamichi, Glover, Mountain Fork, and Little rivers, which drain into the Red River, and the San Bois, Fourche Maline, and Poteau rivers, which drain into the Arkansas. All have clear, swift tributaries. Climatically, the region is mild, having a mean annual temperature of 17° C (62° F), a mean annual rainfall of 127 cm (50 in.), and a growing season of some 220 days.

The most extensive vegetative association consists of open forests of shortleaf pine (*Pinus echinata*) mixed with oaks (*Quercus alba*, *Q. stellata*, *Q. phellos*, and *Q. marilandica*), mockernut hickory (*Carya tomentosa*), black hickory (*C. texana*), basswood (*Tilia americana*), and black locust (*Robinia pseudoacacia*). Ravines and more mesic areas contain fairly dense stands of vegetation which include maples (*Acer* spp.), hickories (*Carya* spp.), oaks (*Quercus* spp.), sweetgum (*Liquidambar styraciflua*), ferns, azaleas (*Rhododendron* spp.), gooseberry (*Ribes* spp.), and pawpaw (*Asimina triloba*). Streams and river bottoms support various vegetative types that include oaks, maples, pines, French mulberry (*Callicarpa americana*), tupelo or sourgum (*Nyssa sylvatica*), buttonbush (*Cephalanthus occidentalis*), and numerous herbs and ferns. In the few prairie areas that exist, the most common grasses are bluestems (*Andropogon* spp.), dropseed (*Sporobolus* spp.), and Indian grass (*Sorghastrum nutans*).

Cypress-Oak Floodplains. This small physiognomic region is restricted to the extreme southeastern corner of Oklahoma (Fig. 10). Practically all of the region is confined to the southern portion of McCurtain County. To the north it is bounded by the Oak-Hickory-Pine Ouachita Highland region, and to the west it grades into the Post Oak-Blackjack Uplands. Level plains varying in elevation from 92 to 154 m (302–505 ft.) are common topographical features. This region is a northern extension of the Mississippi Gulf Coastal Plain, and soils are composed of Cretaceous sands, sandy clays, and clays. Most of the streams are sluggish, mud-banked tributaries of Little River and Red River. The climate is characterized by an annual average temperature of 18° C (64° F), an average annual rainfall of 115 cm (45.3 in.), and a growing season of about 240 days.

Various forest types exist in this region. Along the Little River and other

Fig. 10. Cypress-Oak Floodplains.

small tributaries bald cypress (*Taxodium distichum*) swamps exist. Included in these swampy areas are various oak species (*Quercus phellos, Q. nigra, Q. alba*), willows (*Salix* spp.), and American holly (*Ilex opaca*). In other forest areas the principal tree is sweetgum (*Liquidambar styraciflua*), growing in association with tupelo (*Nyssa sylvatica*), various oaks (*Quercus* spp.), shortleaf pine (*Pinus echinata*), loblolly pine (*P. taeda*), and maples (*Acer* spp.). Shrubs and other low vegetation are often thick and include pawpaw (*Asimina triloba*), buttonbush (*Cephalanthus occidentalis*), palmetto (*Sabal glabra*), French mulberry (*Callicarpa americana*), alder (*Alnus serrulata*), and others. Vines, ferns, and shade-tolerant plants often cover the forest floor.

The nine regions described above are quite distinct with regard to their climate, topography, and dominant vegetative associations. By virtue of this diversity, Oklahoma hosts an exceptionally rich mammalian fauna.

Zoogeographical Affinities

Bryan P. Glass

Oklahoma's peculiar shape and extent stem from a haphazard political history. Consequently, the state encompasses within its boundaries a complex variety of physiognomic, edaphic, meteorological, and vegetative conditions that allow for an exceptional ecological diversity.

An act of Congress establishing the territory of Arkansas formed the eastern boundary. Another that defined the southern edge of the territory of Kansas concomitantly drew Oklahoma's northern border. The Louisiana Purchase, the Texas War of Independence, the United States–Mexican War, the transference of the Five Civilized Tribes from the Southeast into the Indian Territory, and later confinement of several plains tribes and others to reservations in Oklahoma Territory all played a part in outlining what is now the state of Oklahoma.

None of these historical events, however, included the present-day Oklahoma Panhandle, which lay outside the boundaries of all territories identified and ultimately owned by the United States. It was known as "No Man's Land" or the "Neutral Strip" and by other less savory epithets. When Oklahoma Territory was organized, Congress for the first time officially recognized and claimed it and designated it as Beaver County, Oklahoma Territory. At statehood the strip was divided into three nearly equal parts, which became, from west to east, Cimarron, Texas, and Beaver counties.

It is by this artifact of politics that Oklahoma reaches into what ecologically is Rocky Mountain foothills in the northwestern tip of the Panhandle and, at the other extreme, dips into southern pine forests and cypress-palmetto swamps of the Mississippi Gulf Coastal Plain. Elsewhere, the calcareous Ozark uplift of northeastern Oklahoma is covered with a mantle of oak-hickory hardwood forest typical of the eastern United States. Mesquite brush, prickly pear cactus and other xeric plants characterize the dry southwest.

27

Higher elevation, differing soil types, and lower rainfall have acted in concert to produce the central and western grasslands. Precipitation diminishes from east to west, and through the midsection of Oklahoma, prairie and forest compete and interlock in jigsawlike fashion. Because of this remarkable diversity of landscape, Oklahoma is home for an unusual variety of mammals.

Despite its size, however, Oklahoma has few, if any, truly indigenous species. Each physiognomic region has a composite assembly of species associated more closely with surrounding regions than with Oklahoma. Oklahoma resembles a vortex, with its center in the Great Plains, into which species are drawn. In most cases, these species also occur in other parts of the state. Several are species whose original range was continent-wide. The animal pathways leading into this vortex apparently originated from the Rocky Mountains, the Great Plains, the eastern deciduous forests, the Southeast and Gulf Coastal Plain, and the arid Southwest. With these regions as ecological units, Table 1 below gives the potential sources for the diverse species that compose Oklahoma's mammalian fauna.

TABLE 1.   Zoogeographical affinities of Oklahoma mammals.

CONTINENT-WIDE

Chiroptera
  Lasiurus cinereus
  Eptesicus fuscus
  Lasionycteris noctivagans
  Myotis lucifugus

Rodentia
  Castor canadensis
  Peromyscus leucopus
  Peromyscus maniculatus
  Ondatra zibethicus

Carnivora
  Canis lupus
  Vulpes vulpes
  Ursus americanus
  Procyon lotor
  Lutra canadensis
  Mephitis mephitis
  Mustela vison
  Felis concolor
  Felis rufus

Artiodactyla
  Odocoileus virginianus

EASTERN DECIDUOUS FORESTS

Insectivora
  Blarina hylophaga
  Scalopus aquaticus machrinoides

Chiroptera
  Myotis keenii septentrionalis
  Myotis leibii leibii
  Myotis sodalis
  Pipistrellus subflavus
  Lasiurus borealis
  Plecotus townsendii ingens

Lagomorpha
  Sylvilagus floridanus alacer

Rodentia
  Sciurus carolinensis
  Sciurus niger
  Glaucomys volans
  Tamias striatus
  Marmota monax
  Reithrodontomys humulis
  Zapus hudsonius
  Microtus pinetorum

Carnivora
  Urocyon c. cinereoargenteus

TABLE 1. Zoogeographical affinities of Oklahoma mammals (*continued*).

SOUTHEASTERN AND GULF COASTAL PLAIN

Marsupialia
Didelphis virginiana

Insectivora
Blarina (hylophaga/carolinensis)
Cryptotis parva
Scalopus aquaticus aereus

Chiroptera
Lasiurus seminolus
Myotis austroriparius
Plecotus rafinesquii
Nycticeus humeralis
Tadarida brasiliensis cynocephala

Xenarthra
Dasypus novemcinctus

Rodentia
Sciurus carolinensis
Sciurus niger
Glaucomys volans
Peromyscus attwateri
Peromyscus gossypinus
Ochrotomys nuttalli
Oryzomys palustris
Sigmodon hispidus
Reithrodontomys fulvescens
Baiomys taylori
Neotoma floridana

Carnivora
Canis niger
Urocyon c. cinereoargenteus
Spilogale putorius

ROCKY MOUNTAINS

Chiroptera
Myotis leibii melanorhinus
Plecotus townsendii pallescens

Rodentia
Spermophilus variegatus grammurus
Eutamias quadrivittatus
Reithrodontomys megalotis
Peromyscus truei

Peromyscus difficilis
Peromyscus boylii
Neotoma albigula
Neotoma mexicana
Erethizon dorsatum bruneri

Carnivora
Urocyon cinereoargenteus scotti
Canis latrans
Ursus horribilis
Taxidea taxus
Spilogale gracilis

Artiodactyla
Odocoileus hemionus
Cervus elaphus

GREAT PLAINS

Insectivora
Scalopus aquaticus intermedius

Lagomorpha
Lepus californicus melanotis
Sylvilagus floridanus llanensis

Rodentia
Spermophilus spilosoma
Spermophilus tridecemlineatus
Cynomys ludovicianus
Geomys bursarius
Perognathus hispidus
Reithrodontomys montanus griseus
Reithrodontomys megalotis
Onychomys leucogaster
Neotoma micropus
Microtus ochrogaster haydeni

Carnivora
Canis latrans
Vulpes velox
Mustela frenata neomexicana
Mustela frenata longicauda
Mustela nigripes
Taxidea taxus

Artiodactyla
Bison bison
Antilocapra americana

TABLE 1.   Zoogeographical affinities of Oklahoma mammals (*continued*).

ARID SOUTHWEST	Rodentia
Insectivora	*Spermophilus spilosoma*
Notiosorex crawfordi	*Pappogeomys castanops*
	Perognathus flavus
Chiroptera	*Perognathus flavescens*
Myotis yumanensis	*Dipodomys ordii*
Myotis velifer	*Dipodomys elator*
Myotis leibii melanorhinus	*Peromyscus pectoralis*
Plecotus townsendii pallescens	*Neotoma albigula*
Pipistrellus hesperus	*Neotoma mexicana*
Antrozous pallidus	
Tadarida brasiliensis mexicana	Carnivora
Tadarida macrotis	*Canis latrans*
	Vulpes velox
Lagomorpha	*Bassariscus astutus*
Lepus californicus melanotis	*Conepatus mesoleucus figginsi*
Sylvilagus audubonii	*Taxidea taxus*
	Spilogale gracilis

Note that the area from which each species seems to derive determines its listing. It is not implied nor should it be assumed that in Oklahoma the species is confined to the ecological association named. In most cases this is not so. When a species is listed more than once, there is a real question about which of the possible sources is valid or if both are equally so. As might be expected, the shortest list is that for the Great Plains, the fauna of which contains components derived mostly from adjoining areas. In several cases a species may be represented in different source groups by identifiable subspecies. Where this illuminates rather than confuses, the subspecies have been named. For example, *Scalopus aquaticus intermedius*, *S. a. machrinus* (= *machroides*), and *S. a. aereus* are given for moles from the plains, eastern hardwoods, and Southeast, respectively.

The zoogeographical affinities suggested here are similar to but do not conform exactly with those presented by other researchers. Another recent explanation of the distributional patterns of mammals in the Great Plains has been presented by Armstrong *et al.* (1986).

Glossary

William Caire

ALVEOLUS—the socket or hole in which the root of a tooth is anchored.

ANTLER—a bony head ornament which is deciduous and branched.

AUDITORY BULLA—the capsule of bone, usually inflated, that contains the middle and inner ear.

BRAINCASE—the part of the skull surrounding the brain.

BROW TINE—the first tine, point, or spike of an antler that usually extends over the brow or is short and erect above the forehead.

CALCAR—a cartilaginous spur on the ankle of a bat to help support a patagium.

CANAL—a passage or perforation of some length in a bone.

CANINE—the tooth next to the incisors; the canine is rooted in the maxillary bone.

CARNASSIAL TEETH—the last premolar of the upper jaw and first molar of the lower jaw of carnivores, adapted for cutting rather than tearing.

CHEEK TEETH—the teeth behind the canines; premolars and molars.

CINGULUM—a shelflike ridge on the edge of a tooth near the base or gum line.

CONDYLOBASAL LENGTH—the distance from the anterior border of the incisive alveoli to the posterior border of the occipital condyles.

CORONOID PROCESS—usually the portion of the lower jaw dorsal and anterior to the mandibular condyle.

CUSP—a rounded or pointed elevation on the dorsal surface of a tooth.

CUSPIDATE—having cusps.

DECIDUOUS—periodically shed.

DENTAL FORMULA—a convenient way of designating the number of incisors, canines, premolars, and molars of a species, for example: I 3/3, C 1/1, P 4/4, M 3/3. This example is the maximum number for most placental mammals.

DENTINE—the calcareous material usually occurring beneath the outer enamel layer of a tooth; the ivory.

DIASTEMA—a vacant place or gap between teeth in a jaw; may be between the incisors and the cheek teeth or in front between the left and right incisors.

DIGITIGRADE—a form of stance wherein only the tips of the digits or phalanges rest on the ground.

ENAMEL—hard outer covering of a tooth; usually covers the dentine.

FENESTRATE (d) (bone)—perforated by openings, giving bone a lacelike structure.

FORAMEN—a shallow hole or perforation through a bone.

FORAMEN MAGNUM—large opening in the occipital region of the skull from which the spinal cord emerges.

FRONTAL—bone (usually paired) immediately in front of the parietals and behind the nasal.

FULVOUS—dull brownish yellow; rusty.

FUR HAIR—fine, dense hairs forming the undercoat of many mammals, especially in winter; may be several filaments emerging from a single follicle.

GREATEST LENGTH OF SKULL—distance from posterior margin of skull to anteriormost edge of rostrum.

GRIZZLED—grayish, or dark gray flecked with lighter gray.

GUARD HAIR—the overhairs of most mammals, usually longer, stouter and less dense than underhair or fur; only one guard hair emerges from a single follicle.

HARD PALATE—*see* PALATE

HORN—the keratinous sheath that covers a permanent bony core.

IMPERFORATE—not having a foramen or hole.

INCISOR—one of the teeth in front of the canine tooth; if in upper jaw, the incisors are rooted in the premaxillary bone.

INFRAORBITAL CANAL—a canal which extends from the orbit through the maxillary bone to the side of the rostrum.

INFRAORBITAL FORAMEN—a shallow perforation of the maxillary process.

INTERFEMORAL MEMBRANE—in bats, the fold of skin between the hind legs and including at least part of the tail; the uropatagium (see PATAGIUM).

INTERORBITAL REGION—the region of the skull between the rostrum and the braincase.

INTERPARIETAL—triangular- or pentagonal-shaped bone situated posterodorsally on the skull between the parietals and above and in front of the occipital region.

LABIAL RIDGE—a small shelf or ridge located on the labial (or lip) side of a tooth.

LACRYMAL FORAMEN—the passage which carries the tear duct to the nasal cavity; located on the front edge of the orbit.

LACRYMAL RIDGE—a beadlike structure often extending from the lacrymal bone up and along the dorsal rim of the orbit.

LORDOSIS—great flexure or suppleness of the back; as used in mammalogy, a dorsal flexure of "humping" of the back as the animal moves.

MANDIBLE—the lower jaw.

MARSUPIUM—the abdominal pouch of some female marsupials; encloses the mammary glands and nipples.

MASTOID BONE—the dense bone attached posterolateral to the tympanic bulla that houses the inner ear.

MAXILLA—the paired bone of the upper jaw lying lateral and posterior to the premaxillary bones; bears all the teeth except the incisors.

METACONID—a small lingual (on the tongue side) cusp located on the posterior margin of a lower tooth.

NASAL—paired bones, located on the anterodorsal surface of the skull, that roof the nasal chamber.

NASAL SEPTUM—a partition of bone and cartilage dividing the nasal cavity bilaterally.

OCCIPITAL—complex ring of bone surrounding the foramen magnum; forms posterior wall of braincase and bears the occipital condyles.

ORBIT—the cavity in the skull in which the eye and associated muscles are situated; the eye socket.

PALATE—the bony region forming the roof of the mouth; composed of parts of the maxillary, premaxillary, and palatine bones.

PALATINE FORAMEN (ANTERIOR)—paired openings in the palate located near the suture of the premaxillary and maxillary bones; also called the incisive foramina.

PALATINE FORAMEN (POSTERIOR)—small foramina in the palate lying in the maxillary and palatine bones.

PALATINE SPINE (ANTERIOR)—a thin, bony projection extending forward between the palatine foramina.

PALATINE SPINE (POSTERIOR)—a pointed median projection on the free posterior border of the palate.

PALMATED—referring to antlers that are more or less flattened and expanded.

PARAOCCIPITAL PROCESS—a process projecting ventrally from the sides of the occipital bone.

PARIETAL—large paired bone that adjoins the frontal anteriorly, the temporal laterally, and the interparietal and occipital bones posteriorly.

PATAGIUM—any of the several membranous expanses of skin used in gliding or flying, for example, propatagium, plagiopatagium, uropatagium,

extending, respectively, from shoulder to wrist, wrist to fingers and/or
ankle, and ankle to tail.

PLANTAR TUBERCLES—the enlarged frictional pads found on the feet of many
rodents.

PLANTIGRADE—a form of locomotion; flatfooted on digits and tarsal (and/or
carpal) bones.

PLUMED—feathery or fluffy.

POSTAURICULAR PATCH—a distinctively colored patch of hair behind the ear.

POSTORBITAL PROCESS—a term applied to either of two processes, one extending up from the zygomatic arch and the other extending down from
the top of the skull behind the orbit.

PREHENSILE—adapted for seizing and grasping.

PREMAXILLARY—of or referring to the premaxilla, a paired bone bearing the
incisor teeth of the upper jaw.

PREMOLAR—one of the teeth in front of the true molars and behind the canine or incisors; in the upper jaw, the premolars are rooted in the maxillary bone.

PRONGHORN—a type of horn in the genus *Antilocapra* with an unbranched
bony core covered by a horny deciduous sheath that bears a forward-
projecting spike below its tip.

REENTRANT ANGLE—the sharp, indented angles on the sides of some teeth.

ROSTRUM—that region of the skull located anterior to the orbits.

RUMP PATCH—on some artiodactyls, a contrastingly colored patch of hair
surrounding the anal area (including more than the area covered by
the tail).

SAGITTAL CREST—middorsal longitudinal ridge over the cranium.

SALTATORIAL—a form of locomotion in which the animal progresses by a series of bounds or leaps with the hind legs synchronously providing the
propulsive force.

SEPTUM—a thin, bony sheet dividing a region into two compartments.

SUTURE—an immovable line of union (not fusion) between the edges of two
adjoining bones.

TEMPORAL RIDGES—two anteroposterior ridges on the dorsal surface of the
braincase that may be separate or fused into one, forming a sagittal crest.

TYMPANIC BULLAE—paired swollen bulbs in the ventro-posterior region of
the skull which encase the underside of the tympanic cavity; in life
they are air-filled and contain the middle ear ossicles.

UNICUSPID TOOTH—a tooth having only a single cusp.

UROPATAGIUM—the patagium or tail membrane located between the hind
legs of a bat; the interfemoral membrane.

VACUITY—a space or opening formed by failure of adjoining bones to knit together to form a suture.

ZYGOMATIC ARCH—the bony arc on each side of the skull forming the lower border of the orbit and temporal fossa; it is composed of zygomatic processes of the maxillary and temporal bones, with the jugal spanning the space between; if the jugal is absent, the arch is incomplete (as in shrews); cheek bone.

ZYGOMATIC PLATE—in some rodents, the anterior portion of the zygomatic arch which is a broadened, nearly vertical part of the maxilla; serves for the attachment of the external masseter muscle.

Illustrated Identification Key

William Caire and Bryan P. Glass

This key is based upon a combination of external and cranial characters of adult individuals. The key is constructed so that contrasting traits are presented in a grouped pair of statements. Each statement of the pair must be read carefully, and it must be determined which better describes the specimen in question. The chosen statement will then lead either to the next couplet or to the final identification. Each couplet usually contains both cranial and external character traits, and all such traits should be examined for a positive identification. After an identification has been made, the individual species accounts should be consulted for additional descriptions and comparisons. The preceding glossary will assist readers unfamiliar with some of the technical terms.

All identification keys are limited somewhat by the amount of morphological variation that exists in natural populations. The characters selected for this key and the range of variations used should be reliable for the recognition of most of the mammals of Oklahoma. Species of suspected but unverified occurrence are included in the key.

Key to Orders of Oklahoma Mammals

1. Incisors 5/4 (Fig. 11); tail naked, scaly, and prehensile, basal 1/3 black, distal 2/3 white; hind foot with opposable big toe (Fig. 12); females with pouch (marsupium) on belly enclosing mammary area; males with scrotum suspended from abdomen in front of anus and penis, the latter being withdrawn into anterior border of anus . . . .
. . . . Marsupialia, p. 89
Incisors 3/3 or fewer; tail not as above, if scaly then neither prehensile nor bicolored; big toe not opposable; no pouch on belly of females; males with penis anterior to scrotum (if testes are scrotal) and not withdrawn into anus 2

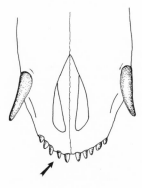
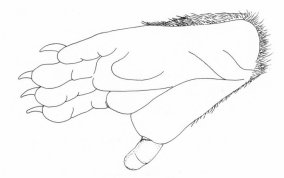

Fig. 11. Marsupial incisors (ventral view).

Fig. 12. Marsupial hind foot.

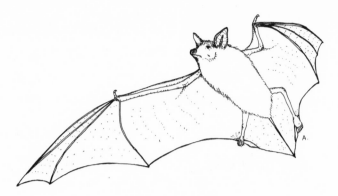

Fig. 13. Bat wing.

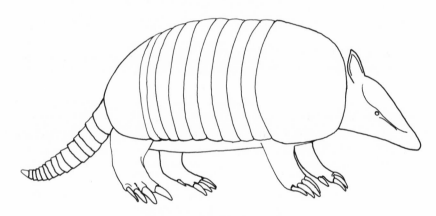

Fig. 14. Armadillo bony plates.

2. Forelimbs modified into wings (Fig. 13) .... Chiroptera, p. 105
   Forelimbs not modified into wings 3
3. Skin reinforced except on underside by dermal bones (bony plates)
   (Fig. 14); virtually hairless except on belly; limbs strong and feet heavily clawed; mouth opening very restricted; tongue long and protru-
   sible; teeth consisting of eight simple teeth in the side of each jaw
   .... Xenarthra, p. 153
   Skin not armored with bone; body covered with hair; limbs various;
   mouth normally gaping; tongue not exceptionally long and protru-
   sible; teeth differentiated, some occupying front of jaws 4

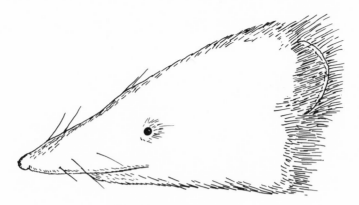

Fig. 15. Insectivore snout.

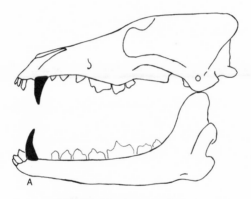

Fig. 16. Carnivore canines.

4. Fur lax and plushlike; external ears absent or hidden in fur; eyes inconspicuous or covered with skin; snout long and pointed (Fig. 15) .... Insectivora, p. 93
   Fur not lax or plushlike, lying against the body in normal fashion, directed posteriorly; eyes conspicuous; ears apparent (except in pocket gophers); snout not especially long and tapering 5

5. Incisors 3/3; large canine teeth present (Fig. 16) .... Carnivora, p. 276
   Incisors 2/1, 1/1, or 0/3; upper canines absent except in elk, lower canines absent, or if present, crowded foward and resembling incisors (incisiform), giving the appearance of 4 incisors 6

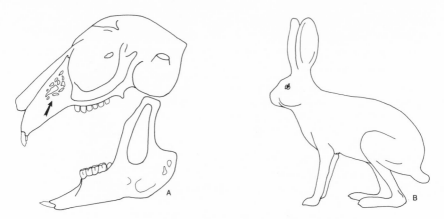

Fig. 17. (a) Fenestrated rostrum; (b) rabbitlike body form.

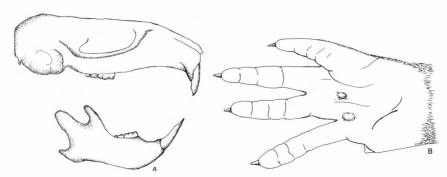

Fig. 18. (a) Rodent skull; (b) rodent foot.

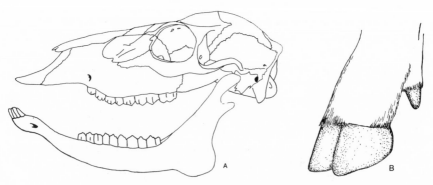

Fig. 19. (a) Artiodactyl skull; (b) artiodactyl hoof.

6. Incisors 2/1; sides of rostrum in front of orbit fenestrated (Fig. 17*a*); body form rabbitlike (Fig. 17*b*) .... Lagomorpha, p. 157

   Incisors not 2/1; sides of rostrum in front of orbit not fenestrated; body form not rabbitlike. 7

7. Incisors 1/1; no canines (Fig. 18*a*); feet with toe pads and claws (Fig. 18*b*) .... Rodentia, p. 169

   Incisors 0/3; lower canines present and incisiform (Fig. 19*a*); feet hooved (Fig. 19*b*) .... Artiodactyla, p. 350

Key to the Insectivora

1. Forepaws broad and heavily clawed for digging; eyes and external ears lacking; nostrils opening upward (Fig. 20); teeth white; zygomatic arch complete; tail short and naked ....
.... Talpidae—*Scalopus aquaticus* (Eastern Mole), p. 102
   Forepaws small and delicate; eyes small but apparent; external ears present but usually short and hidden in the fur; at least some teeth pigmented with red or brown; zygomatic arch incomplete (Fig. 21); tail short to medium in length, covered with short hairs; nostrils terminal 2
2. Tail short, much less than length of head and body; unicuspid teeth 3, 4, or 5 (Fig. 22*a*, *b*, *c*) 3
   Tail longer, at least approximately equal to head and body length; color grayish; unicuspid teeth 5 (Fig. 22*a*) 5
3. Size very small; color brown above, whitish below; unicuspids 4 (Fig. 22*b*); skull light and delicate ....
.... *Cryptotis parva* (Least Shrew), p. 97
   Size larger; color brownish or gray; unicuspids 3 or 5, not 4 (Fig. 22*a*, *c*) 4
4. Unicuspids 3 (Fig. 22*c*); color silvery gray; teeth mostly white, only 3 pair lightly touched with orange; tail approximately 40 percent of length of head and body ....
.... *Notiosorex crawfordi* (Desert Shrew), p. 99
   Unicuspids 5; most or all teeth heavily pigmented; tail either short (= hindfoot length) or long (= head and body length) 5
5. Size larger; color grayish to black, little difference in color between dorsum and venter; skull robust; unicuspids 5 (Fig. 22*a*); tail short

42

Fig. 20. Talpid nostrils and forefeet.

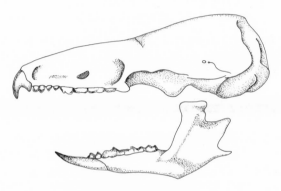

Fig. 21. Soricid skull.

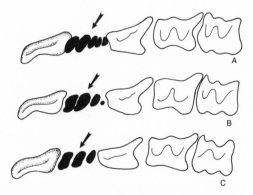

Fig. 22. Unicuspids: (*a*) *Blarina* or *Sorex* (upper occlusal view); (*b*) *Cryptotis* (upper occlusal view); (*c*) *Notiosorex* (upper occlusal view).

(= hindfoot length .... *Blarina* sp. (Shorttailed shrews), p. 95
Size smaller; color dark brown or reddish brown, whitish below; unicuspids 5, deeply pigmented with blackish orange (Fig. 22*a*); tail
longer (approaches head and body length) ....
.... *Sorex longirostris* (Southeastern Shrew), p. 94

Key to the Chiroptera

1. Terminal one-third portion of tail projecting conspicuously beyond the tail membrane (Fig. 23*a*); prominent notch in hard palate round in shape because of inwardly projecting incisors (Fig. 24*a*) . . . .
. . . . Molossidae, *Tadarida* . . . 2
Terminal one-third portion of tail included in the tail membrane for almost its entire length (Fig. 23*b*); notch in hard palate U-shaped (Fig. 24*b*) . . . . Vespertilionidae . . . 3

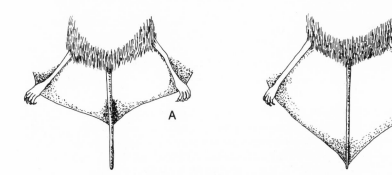

Fig. 23. Tails: (*a*) *Tadarida;* (*b*) Vespertilionid.

Fig. 24. Palates: (*a*) *Tadarida;* (*b*) Vespertilionid.

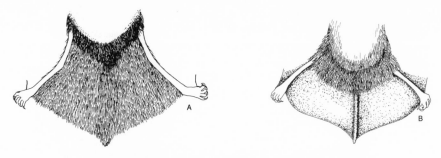

Fig. 25. Tail membranes: (*a*) *Lasiurus;* (*b*) *Lasionycteris.*

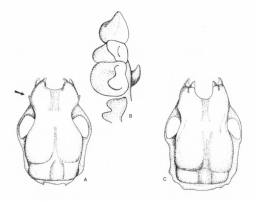

Fig. 26. Lacrimal ridges: (*a*) *Lasiurus borealis;* (*b*) *Lasiurus borealis,*
enlarged ventral view; (*c*) *Lasiurus seminolus.*

2. Length of forearm 42–50 mm; ears not joined across forehead; basal
    eighth of hair on body white; skull length usually less than 19 mm
    . . . . *Tadarida brasiliensis* (Brazilian Free-tailed Bat), p. 147
    Length of forearm 60–64 mm; ears joined across forehead; basal third of
    hair of back white; skull length usually more than 19 mm. . . . .
    . . . . *Tadarida macrotis* (Big Free-tailed Bat), p. 151
3. Ears low and rounded, close to the head; tail membrane with the upper
    side densely haired (Fig. 25*a*); dorsal hairs with four distinct color
    bands (from base to tip these are black, yellow, some shade of red or
    brown, and white, with the third band largely determining the overall
    coloration of the body); total teeth 32, with only one upper and three
    lower incisors . . . . *Lasiurus* . . . 4
    Ears erect, projecting conspicuously above the crown of the head; upper

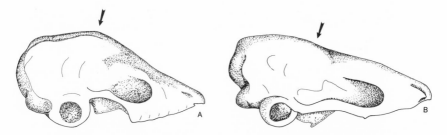

Fig. 27. (*a*) Rounded profile of bat skull; (*b*) flat profile of bat skull.

side of the tail membrane naked or sparsely clothed with hair on basal
half (Figs. 23*b* and 25*b*); dorsal hairs two- or three-banded or uni-
color; total teeth usually not 32, if 32 then having two upper and three
lower incisors 6
4. Color dark brown, frosted with white; size large, forearm exceeding
50 mm; length of skull usually more than 15.5 mm . . . .
. . . . *Lasiurus cinereus* (Hoary Bat), p. 133
Color reddish or mahogany; size smaller, forearm 38–43 mm; length of
skull usually less than 15.5 mm 5
5. Color red or maroon, yellow bands on the dorsal hairs conspicuous;
a pronounced lacrimal ridge present (Fig. 26*a*, *b*) . . . .
. . . . *Lasiurus borealis* (Red Bat), p. 131
Color dark mahogany, yellow bands on dorsal hairs narrow and incon-
spicuous; lacrimal ridge absent or indistinct (Fig. 26*c*) . . . .
. . . . *Lasiurus seminolus* (Seminole Bat), p. 135
6. Ears exceeding 25 mm in height from notch; total teeth 28 or 36; if 36
total teeth, then dorsal profile (lateral view) of skull rounded and not
straight (Fig. 27*a*) 7
Ears not exceeding 25 mm in height from notch; total teeth usually not as
above; if total teeth number 36, then dorsal profile (lateral view) of
skull straight (Fig. 27*b*) 9
7. Color of body yellowish brown above, white below; rostrum long, nostrils
encircled above by a horseshoe-shaped ridge (Fig. 28); tips of the ears
erect; size large, forearm 51–61 mm in length; total teeth 28; one pair
of upper incisors . . . . *Antrozous pallidus* (Pallid Bat), p. 144
Color of body grayish brown to blackish brown above and below; rostrum short, bearing an erect, fleshy, club-shaped lump on either side
(Fig. 29); tips of ears turned back and outwards; size medium, fore-
arm 40–45 mm in length . . . .
. . . . *Plecotus* . . . 8
8. Hairs dusky black, tipped with pale brown on the back, belly hairs with

Fig. 28. *Antrozous pallidus* rostrum.   Fig. 29. *Plecotus* rostrum.

Fig. 30. Upper incisors: (a) *Plecotus rafinesquei;* (b) *Plecotus townsendii.*

white tips; first upper incisor usually bifid (Fig. 30a) . . . .
. . . . *Plecotus rafinesquii* (Rafinesque's Big-eared Bat), p. 139
Hairs brownish, without appreciable color change from root to tip; first
upper incisor unicuspid (Fig. 30b) . . . .
. . . . *Plecotus townsendii* (Townsend's Big-eared Bat), p. 141
9. Tragus blunt and rounded (Fig. 31a), tip may be turned forward and
   is less than half as high as the ear (from notch); total teeth fewer than
   38 10
   Tragus erect, slender, and pointed (Fig. 31b), at least half as high as the
   ear (from notch); total teeth 38 . . . .
   . . . . *Myotis* . . . 14

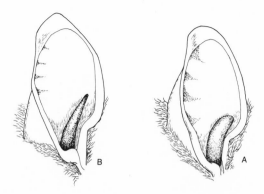

Fig. 31. (*a*) Rounded tragus; (*b*) pointed tragus.

Fig. 32. Skulls: (*a*) *Pipistrellus subflavus;* (*b*) *Pipistrellus hesperus.*

10. Forearm 35 mm or less in length; general color buffy brown to golden brown; total teeth 34 . . . .
. . . . *Pipistrellus* . . . 11
Forearm 35 mm or more in length; general color dark chestnut brown or blackish; total teeth fewer than 34 12
11. Hair tricolored; general color golden brown, ears pinkish brown; forearm approximately 31 mm in length; skull somewhat concave in dorsal profile (lateral view) (Fig. 32*a*); palate usually extending very little beyond molars . . . . . . *Pipistrellus subflavus* (Eastern Pipistrelle), p. 127
Hair bicolored; general color buffy brown; ears black; forearm 26–35 mm in length; skull nearly straight in profile (Fig. 32*b*); palate usually extending well beyond the molars . . . .
. . . . *Pipistrellus hesperus* (Western Pipistrelle), p. 125
12. Forearm 45–50 mm in length; total teeth 32; general color dark brown with black patagia; tail extends 2–3 mm beyond edge of tail membrane
. . . . *Eptesicus fuscus* (Big Brown Bat), p. 129
Forearm 35–43 mm in length; total teeth not 32 13

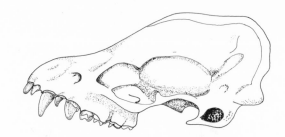

Fig. 33. Well-developed sagittal crest.

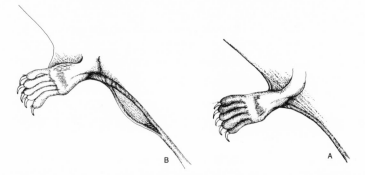

Fig. 34. Wing membrane attachments: (*a*) *Myotis grisescens;* (*b*) *Myotis velifer.*

13. Forearm 35–38 mm in length; color dark brown; patagia black; tail
    membrane not furred; total teeth 30 . . . .
    . . . . *Nycticeius humeralis* (Evening Bat), p. 137
    Forearm approximately 42 mm in length; color black, with many of the
    hairs tipped with white; tail membrane partly furred (Fig. 25*b*); total
    teeth 36 . . . . *Lasionycteris noctivagans* (Silver-haired Bat), p. 123
14. Forearm 40–45 mm in length; skull usually with a well developed and
    prominent sagittal crest (Fig. 33) 15
    Forearm 38 mm or less in length; skull with no or only slight sagittal
    crest absent or weakly developed (Fig. 32*a, b*) 16
15. Wing membrane attached to the ankle (Fig. 34*a*); hair unicolored, gray
    or brownish gray to the base; maxillary toothrow averages 5.9 mm
    in length; found only in eastern Oklahoma . . . .
    . . . . *Myotis grisescens* (Gray Myotis), p. 108
    Wing membrane attached to the base of the toes (Fig. 34*b*); hair bi-
    colored, slaty at the base, pale grayish brown distally; maxillary tooth-
    row averages 6.6 mm in length; found in the western third of the state
    . . . . *Myotis velifer* (Cave Myotis), p. 118

16. Ears long, 15–18 mm from notch, and when laid forward extending conspicuously beyond tip of nose; hair on back long (to 1 cm in length); condylobasal length averages 14 mm; found only in eastern Oklahoma
.... *Myotis keenii* (Keen's Myotis), p. 110
Ears shorter, 15 mm or less from notch, and when laid forward extend only to near tip of nose; hairs on back not conspicuously long (usually less than 1 cm in length) 17
17. Calcar keeled (Fig. 34*a*) 18
Calcar not keeled (Fig. 34*b*) 19
18. Forearm 31–36 mm in length; ears and facial mask jet black; color glossy brown; hair bicolored, slaty at base; condylobasal length averages 12.6 mm .... *Myotis leibii* (Small-footed Myotis), p. 112
Forearm 36–41 mm in length; ears and face dusky but not heavily pigmented and not jet black; hair grayish with pinkish cinnamon tips; condylobasal length averages 13.96 mm; found only in eastern Oklahoma .... *Myotis sodalis* (Indiana Myotis), p. 116
19. Fur thick and woolly, hair not bicolored, lead gray or bright buffy brown, sometimes with bright orange overwash on part or all of body; wing membrane attached at ankle; may have low sagittal crest on skull; found only in southeastern Oklahoma ....
.... *Myotis austroriparius* (Southeastern Myotis), p. 106
Fur thinner and not woolly, hair distinctly bicolored, some shade of brown over blackish; wing membrane attached at base of toes; no sagittal crest present 20
20. Forearm approximately 38 mm in length; color bronze brown with shiny tips to the hairs; greatest length of skull usually greater than 14 mm; found only in eastern Oklahoma ....
.... *Myotis lucifugus* (Little Brown Myotis), p. 114
Forearm 34–38 mm in length; color dull grayish brown; greatest length of skull usually less than 14 mm; found only in the panhandle area of Oklahoma .... *Myotis yumanensis* (Yuma Myotis), p. 121

Key to the Lagomorpha

1. Overall coloration gray or buffy gray; ears long, considerably longer than head, tipped with black; top of tail and adjacent rump black; interparietal indistinct and without obvious sutures (Fig. 35*a*) . . . .
. . . . *Lepus californicus* (Black-tailed Jack Rabbit), p. 166
Overall coloration brown; ears about as long as head, not conspicuously black tipped; top of tail same color as body, not black; interparietal distinct and with obvious sutures (Fig. 35 *b*) 2
2. Size larger, averaging 1.8–3 kg; nape patch small and indistinct; pelage with abundance of black guard hairs; postorbital processes usually fused to skull (Fig. 35*b*) . . . .
. . . . *Sylvilagus aquaticus* (Swamp Rabbit), p. 158

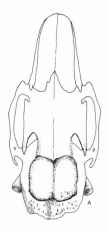 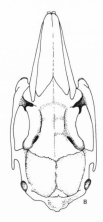

Fig. 35. Skulls (dorsal views): (*a*) *Lepus;* (*b*) *Sylvilagus.*

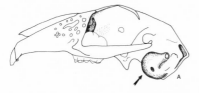

Fig. 36. Auditory bullae: (*a*) *Sylvilagus floridanus;* (*b*) *Sylvilagus audubonii.*

Size smaller, 1.8 kg or less; nape patch prominent behind ears; less black
   pelage; postorbital processes touching but not well fused to skull (as in
   Lepus, Fig. 35*a*) 3
3. Color reddish brown; nape patch bright rusty reddish; many individuals
   with white blaze on forehead; ears relatively shorter, 65–75 mm;
   auditory bullae of skull relatively small and very smooth (Fig. 36*a*)
   . . . . *Sylvilagus floridanus* (Eastern Cottontail), p. 163
   Color gray, washed with yellowish; nape patch pale reddish sandy, no
   white blaze on forehead; ears relatively longer, 75–100 mm; auditory
   bullae relatively larger, irregular, and rough-surfaced (Fig. 36*b*) . . . .
   . . . . *Sylvilagus audubonii* (Desert Cottontail), p. 160

Key to the Rodentia

1. Hind feet webbed; greatest length of skull usually more than 100 mm (except in muskrat, with skull less than 30 mm) 2
   Hind feet not webbed; greatest length of skull usually less than 100 mm, or if 100 mm, then infraorbital foramen very large (Fig. 37*a*) 3
2. Fur brown and fleecelike with guard hairs colored much like underfur; tail dorsoventrally flattened and scaly, without hair; second digit on hind foot with double "grooming claw" (Fig. 38); paraoccipital process not greatly elongate (Fig. 39*a*); infraorbital foramen small (Fig. 37*b*); cheek teeth more or less parallel rows ....
   .... *Castor canadensis* (Beaver), p. 210
   Fur dark smoky gray overlaid with long yellowish guard hairs; tail round, scaly, and sparsely haired; no grooming claw on hind foot; paraoccipital processes greatly elongated and curving slightly forward

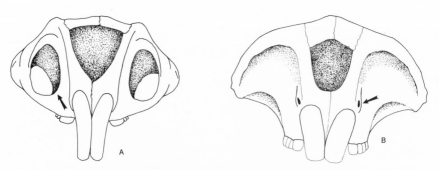

Fig. 37. (*a*) Large infraorbital foramen (frontal view); (*b*) small infraorbital foramen (frontal view).

54

Fig. 38. Castor grooming claw.

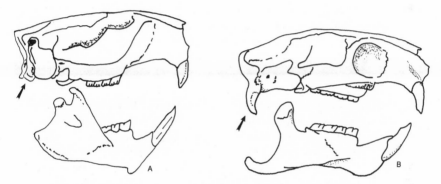

Fig. 39. Paraoccipital processes: (*a*) *Castor;* (*b*) *Myocastor.*

(Fig. 39*b*); infraorbital foramen large; cheek teeth convergent anteriorly and decreasing in size from front to back (Fig. 40) . . . .
. . . . *Myocastor coypus* (Nutria), p. 274
3. Back, sides, and tail covered with coarse black and yellow hair and
   quills, weight 4.5–9 kg; infraorbital foramen larger than foramen
   magnum; incisors not grooved . . . .
   . . . . *Erethizon dorsatum* (Porcupine), p. 272
   Body covered with fur, hair, or bristles but no quills, weight 4.5 kg or
   less, usually much less; infraorbital canal not as large as foramen magnum; if larger, then incisors grooved . . . .
   . . . . (*Zapus* only, see couplet 21) . . . 4

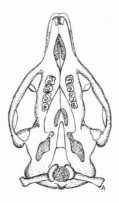

Fig. 40. Myocastor toothrows (ventral view).

4. Tail fully haired and bushy from base to tip (minimally so in prairie dogs); prominent postorbital processes present (Fig. 41*a, b*) 5
   Tail naked, close-haired, or bushy only on distal portion; postorbital processes lacking 14
5. Tail considerably shorter than head and body length 6
   Tail as long or longer than head and body length 9
6. Size large, body bulky, weight to 4.5 kg; face blackish, body grizzled brownish, legs and feet black; incisors white; skull with flat profile and postorbital processes projecting at right angles (Fig. 41*b*) ....
   .... *Marmota monax* (Woodchuck), p. 174
   Size medium to small, weight 1.4 kg or less; color not as above; incisor teeth pigmented; skull more arched in profile, postorbital processes projecting more posteriorly (Fig. 41*a*) 7
7. Color plain sandy yellowish, tail tipped with black; toothrows diverging anteriorly (Fig. 42) ....
   .... *Cynomys ludovicianus* (Black-tailed Prairie Dog), p. 182
   Color reddish brown to tan with spots or stripes on dorsum; toothrows more or less parallel 8
8. Color reddish brown with alternating rows of light stripes and dots extending from head to rump; auditory bullae not distinctly inflated (Fig. 43*a*); rostral and interorbital region comparatively narrower (Fig. 44*a*)..
   Spermophilus tridecemlineatus (Thirteen-lined Ground Squirrel), p. 178
   Color brownish tan with irregular squarish white spots on rump; auditory bullae somewhat inflated (Fig. 43*b*); rostral and interorbital region comparatively broader (Fig. 44*b*) ....
   .... *Spermophilus spilosoma* (Spotted Ground Squirrel), p. 176

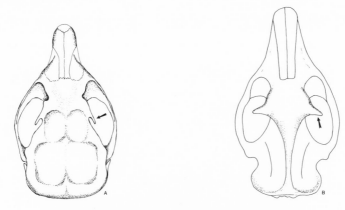

Fig. 41. (*a*) Sciurid postorbital process (dorsal view);
(*b*) *Marmota monax* skull (dorsal view).

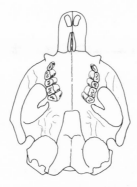

Fig. 42. Cynomys toothrows (ventral view).

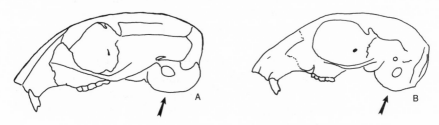

Fig. 43. Auditory bullae: (*a*) *Spermophilus tridecemlineatus;*
(*b*) *Spermophilus spilosoma.*

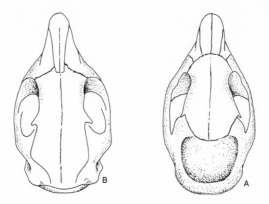

Fig. 44. Skulls (dorsal view): (a) *Spermophilus tridecemlineatus;*
(b) *Spermophilus spilosoma.*

Fig. 45. Skulls: (a) *Spermophilus variegatus;* (b) *Sciurus.*

9. Tail with most hairs erupting to the sides, making it appear flattened; gliding membrane extending from wrist to ankle; fur silky, grayish above, white below; interorbital region relatively narrow, with an obvious U- to V-shaped notch (Fig. 41a) . . . .
. . . . *Glaucomys volans* (Southern Flying Squirrel), p. 191
Tail round and bushy, no gliding membrane; if gray above and white below, then fur not silky; interorbital region relatively wide and lacking the U- or V-shaped notch 10
10. Entire body and tail grayish brown, appearing mottled; anterior margin of alveolar border steeply and abruptly joins diastema (Fig. 45a)
. . . . *Spermophilus variegatus* (Rock Squirrel), p. 180
Color not as above; anterior margin of alveolar border curves gradually to meet diastema (Fig. 45b) 11
11. Body and facial region striped; zygomatic plate present with an infraorbital foramen (Fig. 46a) 13

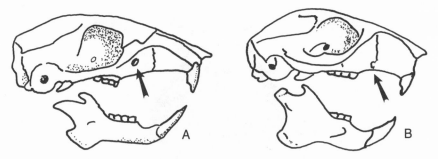

Fig. 46. Zygomatic plates: (*a*) *Tamias* and *Eutamias;* (*b*) *Sciurus.*

Body and face without stripes; zygomatic plate not pierced by a foramen, but an infraorbital canal located between plate and side of rostrum (Fig. 46*b*) 12

12. Color clear gray above, sometimes lightly washed with brown, white underneath; tail dark gray bordered with whitish; back of ears whitish; melanism common; five upper cheek teeth on a side (anteriormost one is small and peglike) ....
.... *Sciurus carolinensis* (Eastern Gray Squirrel), p. 185
Color dark gray flecked with rusty yellow, belly bright rust (color variants of white or black sometimes occur); tail bordered with rust; back of ears orangish only four upper cheek teeth on a side ....
.... *Sciurus niger* (Eastern Fox Squirrel), p. 188

13. Body marked dorsally with five black stripes which do not encroach upon the rump; two lateral interspaces between lateral dark stripes are white; only one upper and one lower premolar on a side ....
.... *Tamias striatus* (Eastern Chipmunk), p. 170
Body marked with five black stripes which do not encroach upon the rump; all four interspaces between dark stripes are white; two upper and one lower premolar on a side ....
.... *Eutamias quadrivittatus* (Colorado Chipmunk), p. 172

14. External fur-lined cheek pouch present on each side of head (Fig. 47); infraorbital canal opening on side of rostrum well in front of the zygomatic plate (Fig. 48) 15
No fur-lined cheek pouches; infraorbital foramen passing through or near the angle formed by the zygomatic plate and the rostrum (Fig. 46*a*) 21

15. Body cylindrical; hair close and glossy; external ears absent; forefeet with heavy claws (Fig. 49); tail short and essentially naked; skull heavy and

Fig. 47. External cheek pouches (ventral view).

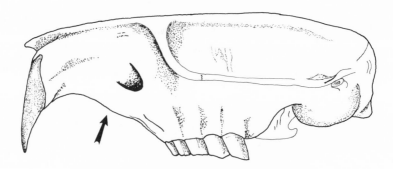

Fig. 48. Heteromyid or geomyid zygomatic plate.

Fig. 49. Gopher forefoot (ventral view).

Fig. 50. Dipodomys flank stripe.

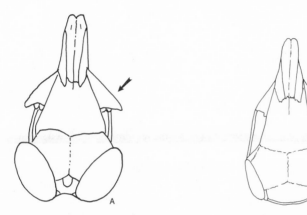

Fig. 51. Maxillae (dorsal views): (*a*) *Dipodomys* maxilla; (*b*) *Perognathus.*

robust, zygomatic breadth greater than mastoid breadth; incisors strong and chisellike 20

Form ratlike or mouselike; skull light and delicate; zygomatic breadth less than mastoid breadth; incisors relatively weak and less chisellike 16

16. Form saltatorial; hind legs long, much longer than forelegs; white diagonal stripe across flank (Fig. 50); tail long, distal half tufted with long hairs; hair soft; cheek teeth evergrowing; zygomatic arch greatly enlarged anteriorly; maxilla with laterally projecting flange (Fig. 51*a*) 17

Form ratlike, not saltatorial; no stripe across flank; tail not tufted, close-haired throughout; hair silky or bristly; cheek teeth not evergrowing; zygomatic arch not greatly enlarged anteriorly; maxilla lacking laterally projecting flange (Fig. 51*b*) 18

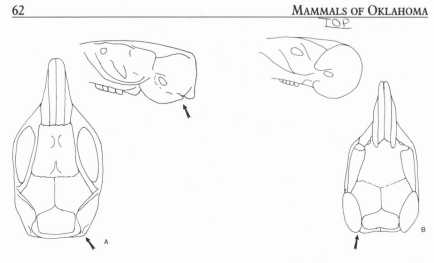

Fig. 52. Skulls (dorsal view): (*a*) *Perognathus (Chaetodipus)*; (*b*) *Perognathus*.

17. Tail about equal to head and body length, no white tuft at tip; five toes on
     hind foot . . . . *Dipodomys ordii* (Ord's Kangaroo Rat), p. 206
     Tail much longer than head and body length, and with conspicuous
     white terminal tuft; four toes on hind foot . . . .
     . . . . *Dipodomys elator* (Texas Kangaroo Rat), p. 204
18. Head and body approximately 85 mm in length; fur harsh and bristly,
     mixed orange and black with clear orange band on side, belly white;
     mastoids well developed but not projecting posteriorly beyond plane
     of occipital (Fig. 52*a*) . . . .
     . . . . *Perognathus hispidus* (Hispid Pocket Mouse), p. 201
     Head and body 85 mm or less in length; fur silky, mixed buffy and black,
     white beneath; mastoids well developed, projecting posteriorly beyond
     plane of occipital; bullae swollen and encroaching to midline of skull
     (Fig. 52*b*) 19
19. Yellowish white spot (postauricular patch) behind each ear (Fig. 53);
     total length usually less than 120 mm; length of skull usually less than
     21 mm . . . . *Perognathus flavus* (Silky Pocket Mouse), p. 199
     No yellowish white spot (postauricular patch) behind each ear; total
     length usually more than 120 mm; length of skull more than 21 mm
     . . . . *Perognathus flavescens* (Plains Pocket Mouse), p. 198
20. Incisors with two grooves on anterior face (Fig. 54*a*); claws on forefeet
     proportionately very large; color gray, brown, reddish, or reddish
     yellow . . . . *Geomys bursarius* (Plains Pocket Gopher), p. 193
     Incisors with one groove on anterior face (Fig. 54*b*); claws on forefeet

Fig. 53. Postauricular patch.

Fig. 54. Incisors: (*a*) *Geomys;* (*b*) *Pappogeomys.*

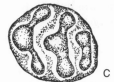

Fig. 55. (*a*) Loop and whorl molar cusp pattern (occlusal view); (*b*) triangulation of molar cusps (occlusal view); (*c*) cuspidate teeth (occlusal view).

proportionately smaller; color brownish yellow, yellowish on side of face .... *Pappogeomys castanops* (Yellowfaced Pocket Gopher), p. 196

21. Tail exceedingly long, much longer than head and body; color dusky on back, yellowish on sides, white beneath; hind legs saltatorial, proportionately very long; molars with complicated crown pattern of loops and whorls (Fig. 55*a*); upper incisors grooved ....
.... *Zapus hudsonius* (Meadow Jumping Mouse), p. 270
Tail shorter, never more than 1.3 times head and body length; color vari-

ous, rarely as above; hind legs not elongated for jumping; molars cuspidate or with a pattern of transverse loops or alternating triangles (Fig. 55b); upper incisors not grooved (except in *Reithrodontomys* and *Synaptomys*) 22

22. Snout pointed; whiskers long; eyes large; ears nearly naked and extending free of fur (scarcely so in *Sigmodon*); tail approximately as long as head and body (except in *Onychomys*); molar teeth cuspidate or with a crown pattern consisting of transverse enamel loops surrounding oval islands of dentine (Fig. 56) 23

Snout blunt; whiskers short; eyes small; ears hairy and nearly hidden in fur; tail much shorter than head and body (except in *Ondatra*); molar teeth with enamel surrounding alternating triangles of dentine ......
.... Microtinae . . . 46

23. Size large, weighing up to 227 g; feet white, body bicolored, gray, olive or buffy above, white or whitish below; tooth pattern of transverse loops (Fig. 56) .... Cricetidae (in part) . . . 27

Size smaller, if nearly 227 g in weight, then body not bicolored and tail naked and scaly; teeth cuspidate (Fig. 55c) 24

24. Tail scaly and nearly devoid of hair; upper molars with a crown pattern of three longitudinal rows of cusps (Fig. 57a) .... Muridae . . . 25

Tail with inconspicuous scales, covered with short hairs; upper molars bearing two rows of cusps (Fig. 57b) .... Cricetidae . . . 30

25. Mouse-sized; length of skull less than 20 mm; incisors notched (when viewed from the side) (Fig. 58a) ....
.... *Mus musculus* (House Mouse), p. 268

Rat-sized; length of skull more than 20 mm; incisors not notched (Fig. 58b) 26

26. Color grizzled brown; tail slightly shorter than head and body; braincase boxlike with nearly vertical sides and flat top; temporal ridges prominent (Fig. 59a) .... *Rattus norvegicus* (Norway Rat), p. 264

Color grizzled brown or black; tail considerably longer than head and body; braincase more rounded and without prominent temporal ridges (Fig. 59b) .... *Rattus rattus* (Black Rat), p. 266

27. Size large, usually 350 mm or more in total length; color olivaceous above because of a mixture of yellowish or black-tipped hairs, whitish below, belly hair often gray basally; septum between anterior palatine foramina complete; anterior palatine spine bifurcated (Fig. 60a)
.... *Neotoma floridana* (Eastern Woodrat), p. 248

Size smaller, usually less than 350 mm; septum between anterior palatine foramina complete or perforate; anterior palatine spine pointed (Fig. 60b) 28

28. Dorsal color clear gray, breast and belly gray with whitish tips; ventrally

Fig. 56. Enamel loops surrounding dentine (occlusal view).

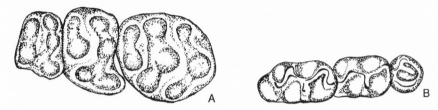

Fig. 57. Cusp patterns (occlusal view): (*a*) Muridae; (*b*) Cricetidae.

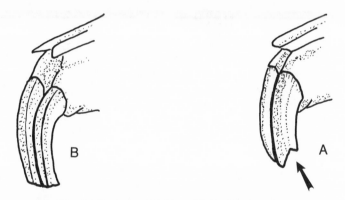

Fig. 58. Incisors: (*a*) *Mus;* (*b*) *Reithrodontomys.*

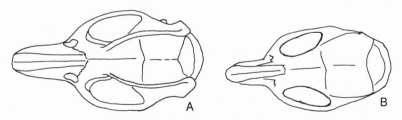

Fig. 59. Temporal ridges (dorsal view): (*a*) *Rattus norvegicus;* (*b*) *Rattus rattus.*

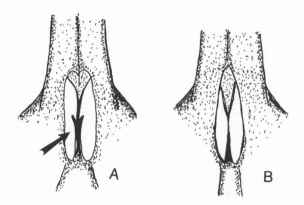

Fig. 60. Palates (ventral view): (*a*) *Neotoma floridana;* (*b*) other *Neotoma* species.

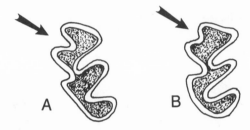

Fig. 61. Molar cusp patterns (occlusal view): (*a*) *Neotoma mexicana;*
(*b*) *Neotoma albigula.*

white with base of belly hair gray; nasal septum imperforate . . . .
. . . . *Neotoma micropus* (Southern Plains Woodrat), p. 252
Dorsal color not clear gray, ventrally white with gray belly or throat hair;
hairs olivaceous, gray, or buffy above, white or gray below; septum between anterior palatine foramina perforate 29
29. Dorsal color olivaceous; entire underside grayish with white tippings,
sometimes a little pure white on throat; lips dusky; antero-internal reentrant angle on molar extending at least halfway across anterior loop
(Fig. 61*a*) . . . . *Neotoma mexicana* (Mexican Woodrat), p. 251
Dorsal color gray washed with buff, throat and breast clear white, belly
hair gray basally; no dark lips; antero-internal reentrant angle on molar extending less than halfway across the anterior loop (Fig. 61*b*)
. . . . *Neotoma albigula* (White-throated Woodrat), p. 247
30. Body generally small and delicate; tail longer or shorter than head and

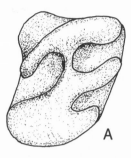
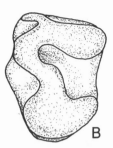

Fig. 62. Molar cusp patterns (occlusal view): (*a*) *Reithrodontomys fulvescens;* (*b*) other *Reithrodontomys.*

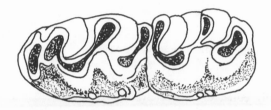

Fig. 63. Lower molars of *Reithrodontomys humulis* (occlusal view).

body; color varies but usually grayish brown to brownish or tawny; upper incisors grooved (Fig. 58*b*) 31

Upper incisors smooth; color and size variable 34

31. Tail obviously longer than head and body; last upper molar with worn cusps forming an E-shape (Fig. 62*a*).............................

.... *Reithrodontomys fulvescens* (Fulvous Harvest Mouse), p. 216

Tail shorter than (may be equal to) head and body length; last upper molar with worn cusps forming a C-shape (Fig. 62*b*) 32

32. Color grayish brown, underparts only slightly paler than back; tail not distinctly bicolored; first two lower molars with distinct labial ridge (Fig. 63)..

.... *Reithrodontomys humulis* (Eastern Harvest Mouse), p. 217

Color buffy to grayish brown, underparts whitish, tail somewhat bi-colored; first two lower molars without distinct labial ridge 33

33. Tail usually equal to (may be slightly longer than) head and body length; back and sides uniform in color; tail with an indistinct grayish dorsal tail stripe; rostrum comparatively shorter and broader ....

.... *Reithrodontomys megalotis* (Western Harvest Mouse), p. 219

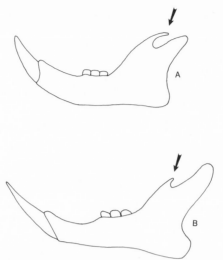

Fig. 64. Mandibles: (*a*) *Onychomys;* (*b*) *Baiomys.*

Tail usually equal to and often slightly shorter than head and body
length; back and sides contrast in color, back darker than sides; tail
with a distinct narrow blackish dorsal tail stripe; rostrum comparatively
longer and narrower . . . .
. . . . *Reithrodontomys montanus* (Plains Harvest Mouse), p. 220

34. Tail short and plump, approximately one-half of head and body length;
coronoid process relatively high and recurved (Fig. 64*a*) . . . .
. . . . . . *Onychomys leucogaster* (Northern Grasshopper Mouse), p. 242
Tail at least approximating head and body length; coronoid process
relatively low and not strongly recurved (Fig. 64*b*) (except *Baiomys*)
. . . . 35

35. Pelage very dark, black mixed with yellow, tail and feet colored like
body; nose blunt and ears small, overall appearance volelike, except
for long tail; crowns of cheek teeth with S-shaped looping cusps (Fig.
65) . . . . *Sigmodon hispidus* (Hispid Cotton Rat), p. 244
Pelage lighter, feet white or whitish; ears and nose not volelike; crowns
of cheek teeth without S-shaped loops 36

36. Tail sparsely haired, scaly and not distinctly bicolored; fur harsh, grayish
brown; underparts grayish white; molars with cusps in two rows di-
rectly opposite one another (Fig. 66*a*) . . . .
. . . . *Oryzomys palustris* (Marsh Rice Rat), p. 214
Tail close-haired, scales inconspicuous; fur soft; molars with cusps in two
rows alternating, not opposite (Fig. 66*b*) 37

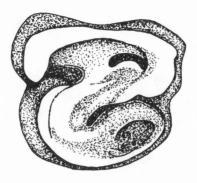

Fig. 65. Sigmodon hispidus molar cusp pattern (occlusal view).

Fig. 66. (*a*) *Oryzomys* cusp pattern (occlusal view); (*b*) molar cusp
pattern of alternating cusps (occlusal view).

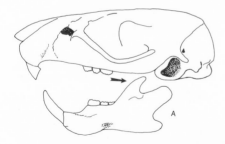
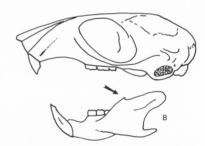

Fig. 67. (*a*) *Baiomys* skull and mandible; (*b*) obsolete coronoid process.

37. Size very small; dorsal coloration dark gray, undersides only slightly
    lighter; small lower jaw with stout recurved coronoid process (Fig.
    67*a*) . . . . *Baiomys taylori* (Northern Pigmy Mouse), p. 241
    Size larger; dorsal color grayish or brown, white or much lighter below;
    coronoid process of lower jaw obsolete, not as above (Fig. 67*b*) . . . 38
38. General color golden brown over head and body; posterior palatine for-

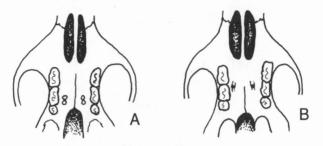

Fig. 68. Palates (ventral view): (*a*) *Ochrotomys;* (*b*) *Peromyscus.*

amina closer to posterior border of palate than to anterior palatine
foramina (Fig. 68*a*) ..... *Ochrotomys nuttalli* (Golden Mouse), p. 239
General color not golden all over; posterior palatine foramina midway between anterior palatine foramina and posterior palatal border (Fig.
68*b*) .... *Peromyscus* . . . 39
39. Ear 75 percent or more of hind foot length 40
    Ear less than 75 percent of hind foot length 41
40. Ear usually less than 22 mm; tail less than length of head and body; au-
    ditory bullae average, not greatly inflated (Fig. 69*a*) ....
    .... *Peromyscus difficilis* (Rock Mouse), p. 226
    Ear usually more than 22 mm; tail exceeding length of head and body;
    auditory bullae large and inflated (Fig. 69*b*) ....
    .... *Peromyscus truei* (Piñon Mouse), p. 237
41. Tail usually less than 91 mm, not tufted at tip (Fig. 70*a*) 42
    Tail usually more than 91 mm, tufted at tip (Fig. 70*b*) 44
42. Greatest length of skull more than 28 mm; body usually robust and 30 g
    or more .... *Peromyscus gossypinus* (Cotton Mouse), p. 229
    Greatest length of skull less than 28 mm; body smaller and usually less
    than 30 g 43
43. Tail 65 mm or less, sharply bicolored; skull usually less than 22 mm in
    length .... *Peromyscus maniculatus* (Deer Mouse), p. 233
    Tail more than 65 mm in length; not sharply bicolored; skull usually
    more than 22 mm ....
    .... *Peromyscus leucopus* (White-footed Mouse), p. 231
44. Entire foot and ankle white (Fig. 71*a*); toothrow usually less than 4 mm;
    interorbital breadth narrow ....
    .... *Peromyscus pectoralis* (White-ankled Mouse), p. 235
    Ankle gray, color encroaching on proximal part of upper surface of foot
    (Fig. 71*b*); toothrow usually more than 4 mm; interorbital breadth
    wider 45
45. Hind foot larger, more than 24 mm; cusps and lophs of upper and lower

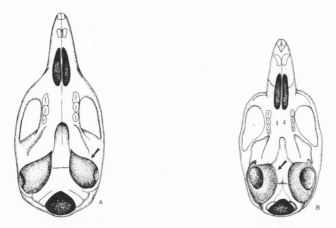

Fig. 69. Auditory bullae (ventral view): (*a*) *Peromyscus difficilis;* (*b*) *Peromyscus truei.*

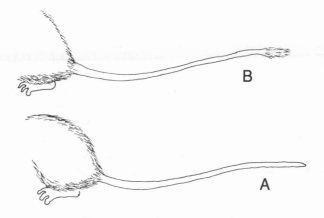

Fig. 70. Tails: (*a*) without tuft; (*b*) with tuft.

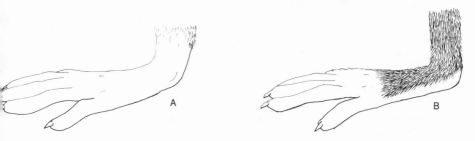

Fig. 71. (*a*) *Peromyscus pectoralis* with white ankle and foot;
(*b*) *Peromyscus* without white ankle and foot.

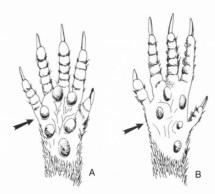

Fig. 72. (*a*) *Synaptomys* hind foot with six plantar tubercles;
(*b*) hind foot with five plantar tubercles.

molar teeth alike . . . .
. . . . *Peromyscus attwateri* (Texas Mouse), p. 223
Hind foot smaller, 23 mm or less; cusps of upper and lower molar teeth
different, uppers more complex . . . .
. . . . *Peromyscus boylei* (Brush Mouse), p. 225
46. Size large, head and body 250 mm or more; tail long, scaly, and vertically
compressed; hind feet webbed; greatest length of skull more than
30 mm . . . . *Ondatra zibethicus* (Muskrat), p. 259
Size much smaller, head and body 125 mm or less; tail short; greatest
length of skull less than 30 mm . . . . 47.
47. Upper incisors stout, grooved along lateral border; color brownish mixed
with gray, black and yellow; hind foot about the same length as tail; six
plantar tubercles on the hind foot (Fig. 72*a*) . . . .
. . . . *Synaptomys cooperi* (Southern Bog Lemming), p. 376
Upper incisors slender and smooth; color brownish gray or auburn to
reddish; hind foot longer than tail, or if approximately the same
length, then usually with only five plantar tubercles on the hind foot
(Fig. 72*b*) 48
48. Fur soft and silky, without longer guard hairs, auburn to reddish color in
adults, smoky gray in juveniles; interorbital width relatively broad,
often 4.5 mm or more; braincase as seen from rear wider than high
. . . . *Microtus pinetorum* (Woodland Vole), p. 257
Fur coarser, dark brownish gray with some fulvous-tipped hairs, longer
guard hairs present, belly hairs with tawny tips; juveniles much like
adults; interorbital width narrow, usually less than 4 mm; braincase as
seen from rear as high as wide . . . .
. . . . *Microtus ochrogaster* (Prairie Vole), p. 255

Key to the Carnivora

1. Bearlike, size very large; tail inconspicuous; 5 toes on each foot; gait plantigrade, hind foot naked-soled, with heel resting firmly on ground; jaws without carnassial teeth (Fig. 73*a*) .... Ursidae ... 2
   Not bearlike, size much smaller; tail conspicuous; toes 5-5 or 5-4; gait usually digitigrade (plantigrade with naked soles only in badgers, raccoons, and skunks); jaws with carnassial teeth (Fig. 73*b*) (poorly developed in raccoons) 3
2. Shoulder hump present (Fig. 74); longest claw on front foot greater than 50 mm; second upper molar broadest near anterior end ....
   .... *Ursus arctos* (Grizzly Bear), p. 304
   No distinct shoulder hump; longest claw on front foot less than 50 mm; second upper molar broadest near midpoint of tooth ....
   .... *Ursus americanus* (Black Bear), p. 300
3. Toes 5-4; limbs long; body form catlike or doglike; skull usually more

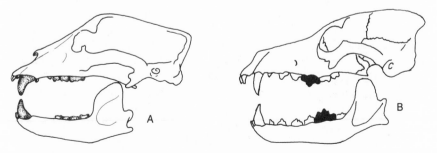

Fig. 73. (*a*) Ursid skull without carnassial pair; (*b*) carnivore with carnassial pair.

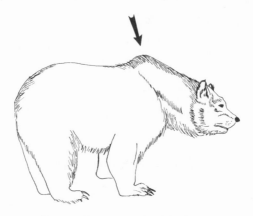

Fig. 74. Ursus arctos shoulder hump.

than 120 mm; distinct, well-developed carnassial teeth (Fig. 73*b*)
.... 13
Toes 5-5; limbs short; body form neither catlike nor doglike; skull
usually less than 120 mm; if greater, then carnassial pair not well developed 4

4. Anal scent glands absent; total teeth 40; tail ringed ....
.... Procyonidae . . . 12
Anal scent glands present; total teeth less than 40; tail not ringed
.... Mustelidae . . . 5

5. Feet plantigrade, soles of hind feet naked to heel; body relatively short
and heavy; no evident lordosis; posterior border of hard palate not extending appreciably beyond last molars, or if it does, then skull triangular and robust and the last upper molars are triangular in shape
(Fig. 75*a*) 6
Feet semiplantigrade or digitigrade; hind feet either webbed or with
hairy soles; body elongated and serpentine, lordosis prominent; posterior border of hard palate extending appreciably beyond molars
.... 9

6. Body heavy and broad; legs short, feet heavily clawed for digging; tail
short; legs and face dark brown or black; cheeks white, and medial
stripe from nose to nape white, stripe sometimes extending posteriorly
to shoulders or rump; braincase triangular (Fig. 75*b*); upper molar triangular in outline .... *Taxidea taxus* (Badger), p. 324
Body not broad and squat; feet more lightly clawed; tail long and plumed
with long hair; color black with contrasting white markings; braincase
elongate; first upper molar subrectangular in shape ... Skunks ... 7

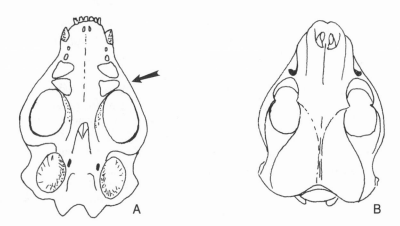

Fig. 75. *Taxidea:* (*a*) triangular first upper molar (ventral view);
(*b*) triangular braincase (dorsal view).

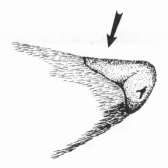

Fig. 76. *Conepatus* nose.

7. Nose flattened for rooting, naked on top for about 2 cm back from tip
(Fig. 76); top of head, entire back and tail completely white, not divided by any black; claws light-colored; fur short and harsh, tail not
greatly plumed; teeth 32 . . . .
. . . . *Conepatus mesoleucus* (Hog-nosed Skunk), p. 337
Nose normal, top of rostrum haired to tip; color variable, white coloration always divided to some extent by middorsal black area or broken
up into numerous white bars and spots; tail hairs very long, forming
plumelike tail; teeth 34 8
8. Color pattern consisting of a narrow frontal white stripe and a patch of
white on crown which extends backward as two dorsolateral white

stripes of variable width and length; tail hairs black with white bases; mastoid border concave when viewed from above; skull convex above (Fig. 77) .... *Mephitis mephitis* (Striped Skunk), p. 332

Color consisting of a variegated pattern of white stripes and spots on head, back, and sides; tail black with a few white hairs at tip (*S. putorius*, only a few terminal hairs white; *S. gracilis*, proximal 2/3 tail black, distal 1/3 white); mastoid border convex when viewed from above; skull nearly flat above (Fig. 78) .... *Spilogale* sp.

9. Hind feet enlarged and webbed; base of tail thick, faired into body contour in streamlined fashion; total teeth 36 ....
   .... *Lutra canadensis* (River Otter), p. 339

   Hind feet smaller and unwebbed; tail not faired into body; total teeth 34 .... *Mustela* . . . 10

10. Size larger, small females less than 300 mm in length, males larger; upper toothrow length more than 20 mm in males and 17.8 mm in females
    11

    Size smaller, larger males rarely exceeding 250 mm in length, females smaller; upper toothrow length less than 20 mm in males and 17.8 mm in females .... *Mustela frenata* (Long-tailed Weasel), p. 315

11. Overall color yellowish tan; legs, feet, and tip of tail black or dark brown, black mask on face; first lower molar with incipient metaconid .... *Mustela nigripes* (Black-footed Ferret), p. 318

    Overall color dark chocolate above and below, often with minor white markings on chin and throat; first lower molar with more distinct metaconid .... *Mustela vison* (Mink), p. 321

12. Body short and heavy; color dark grayish brown with glossy black guard hairs; tail ringed black and brown, shorter than head and body; face with black mask over eyes; hind feet plantigrade, soles naked; carnassial nature of teeth obsolete; greatest length of skull usually more than 95 mm; posterior border of palate extends beyond last molar .... *Procyon lotor* (Raccoon), p. 310

    Body long and slender; color buffy tan; tail ringed black and white, as long or longer than head and body; face with only black shadowing around eyes; hind feet digitigrade, soles hairy; carnassial teeth well-formed; greatest length of skull less than 95 mm; posterior border of palate even with last molar ..... *Bassariscus astutus* (Ringtail), p. 306

13. Form catlike; rostrum shortened; bulla divided internally by a bony septum; molars with shearing rather than grinding surfaces; only one upper and lower molar 14

    Form doglike; rostrum more elongate; bulla not divided by a bony septum; molars with both shearing and grinding surfaces; never only one upper and lower molar 15

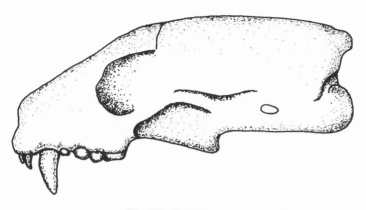

Fig. 77. Mephitis skull.

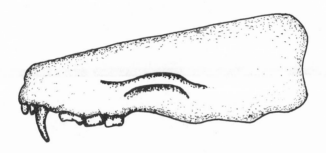

Fig. 78. Spilogale skull.

14. Size large, weight 36.4 kg or more; tail as long as head and body; color uniform tawny brown or gray, spotted in juveniles; total teeth 30 (P² present, two upper premolars between canine and carnassial) . . . . . .
. . . . *Felis concolor* (Mountain Lion), p. 342
Size medium, weight to 15.9 kg; tail short and stubby; color reddish or grayish, sparsely to profusely spotted; total teeth 28 (P² absent, one upper premolar between canine and carnassial) . . . .
. . . . *Felis rufus* (Bobcat), p. 346
15. Size larger, weight 9 kg or more; total length usually 1,000–2,050 mm; color variable from gray, grayish brown, black, to white; pupil of eye round; skull large and robust, usually more than 150 mm; postorbital processes thick and convex 16
Size smaller, weight usually not exceeding 7.3 kg; total length usually 700–1,200 mm; color gray to silvery, red or reddish, or buffy yellow;

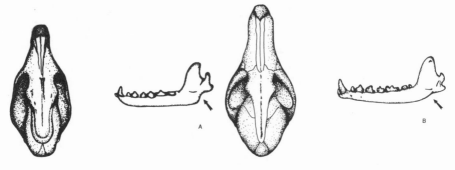

Fig. 79. Crania (dorsal view) and mandibles: (*a*) *Urocyon;* (*b*) *Vulpes.*

pupil of eye a vertical slit; skull smaller, usually less than 150 mm;
postorbital processes usually concave or depressed on top 18
16. Body more robust, total length usually greater than 1,400 mm; nose pad
usually more than 25 mm in diameter; heel pad greater than 31.8 mm
in width 17
Body smaller, total length usually less than 1,400 mm; nose pad usually
less than 25 mm in diameter; heel pad less than 31.8 mm in width
. . . . *Canis latrans* (Coyote), p. 277
17. Smaller and more slender in build; color varies from tawny to black; premolars more narrow; usually a conspicuous cingulum on outer edge of
first upper molar . . . . *Canis rufus* (Red Wolf), p. 284
Larger and more robust in build, color varies from black to white, often
shades of gray; premolars broader; usually first upper molar lacking a
conspicuous cingulum on outer edge . . . .
. . . . *Canis lupus* (Gray Wolf), p. 281
18. General color silvery gray bordered with rusty lower sides, back and tail
gray with mane of stiff, black-tipped hairs; lyre-shaped temporal
ridges on braincase (Fig. 79*a*); lower posterior margin of mandible
with prominent step (Fig. 79*a*) . . . .
. . . . *Urocyon cinereoargenteus* (Gray Fox), p. 296
General color red to reddish or pale buffy yellow, back and tail without
mane; V-shaped temporal ridges on braincase (Fig. 79*b*); lower posterior margin of mandible without prominent step (Fig. 79*b*) . . . .
. . . . 19
19. Size larger, 3.6–7.2 kg; color reddish yellow; tail red with white tip; feet
black . . . . *Vulpes vulpes* (Red Fox), p. 292
Size smaller, approximately 2.7 kg; color buffy yellow; tail with black
tip; feet not black . . . . *Vulpes velox* (Swift Fox), p. 288

Key to the Artiodactyla

1. Weight up to 910 kg; hump on shoulders; color dark brown; shaggy, especially on shoulder and forelimbs; bearded; head hung low; permanent hooked horns in both sexes, horn cores directed laterally from frontal region (Fig. 80), curl increasing with age ....
   .... *Bison bison* (Bison), p. 368
   Weight 454 kg or less, usually much less; no hump; not dark brown all over, pelage not shaggy, no beard; head more erect; head ornaments either confined to and deciduous in males or present in both sexes (small in females), with deciduous outer sheath 2

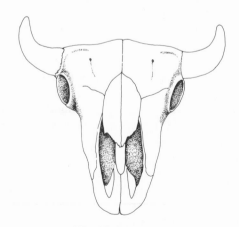

Fig. 80. Bison skull.

Fig. 81. Antilocapra head.

2. Both sexes with horns (Fig. 81), well developed in males, with forward-projecting prong and recurved tip, females bearing small spikes only; horny sheath shed each year, bony core permanent; dorsal color light fawn, ventrum and sides white, two white collars on throat (Fig. 81), tail evident, rump patch of brilliant white erectile hairs; no accessory hooves; erectile mane on back of neck . . . . *Antilocapra americana* (Pronghorn), p. 363
   Head of males only ornamented with deciduous bony antlers; color reddish, grayish fawn, or white; throat never with more than one white collar patch; tail various, but distinct; rump patch, if present, dull white and not erectile; no erectile mane on back of neck; four hooves on each foot; upper canine present or absent 3
3. Head and body white all over; antlers extending backward and upward, the tip palmated (Fig. 82); upper canine absent; ethmoid vacuity subrectangular . . . . *Cervus dama* (Fallow Deer), p. 373
   White areas confined to belly or rump; ethmoid vacuity triangular; canine present only in *Cervus elaphus*, otherwise absent; antlers not palmated at tip 4
4. Head and neck dark reddish brown, sides pale reddish, rump patch large and creamy white; tail short and inconspicuous; antlers with main beam directed backward, only brow tine extending forward over face (Fig. 83); posterior narial aperture not divided into two parts by vomer; upper canines present . . . . *Cervus elaphus* (Wapiti or Elk), p. 351
   Head and neck color not contrasting with rest of body; white on rump

Fig. 82. Cervus dama antlers.

Fig. 83. Cervus elaphus antlers.

confined to area around tail; tail long enough to be conspicuous; antlers with main portion bending forward over face; posterior narial aperture divided into two parts by vomer; upper canines absent
.... *Odocoileus* . . . 5

5. Ears relatively larger; tail shorter, close-haired or ropelike, black at tip,
the remainder white and surrounded by small whitish rump patch;
antlers usually with main beam forked into two more-or-less equal

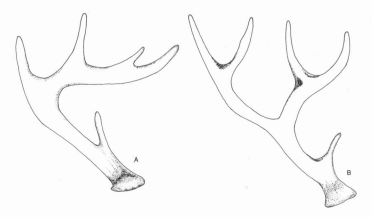

Fig. 84. Antlers: (*a*) *Odocoileus virginiana;* (*b*) *Odocoileus hemionus.*

branches, each of which divides again (Fig. 84*b*); preorbital pit deep; metatarsal gland usually longer than 100 mm .... *Odocoileus hemionus* (Mule Deer), p. 000

Ears relatively smaller; tail longer, bushy, brown on top, and brilliant white beneath, carried erect when running; antlers bending forward with a series of branches rising from main beam (Fig. 84*a*); preorbital pit shallow; metatarsal gland usually only about 25 mm long .... *Odocoileus virginianus* (White-tailed Deer), p. 358

Checklist of the Mammals of Oklahoma

Jack D. Tyler

Part Two

Species Accounts

Order Marsupialia

William Caire

The marsupials reach their greatest diversity in the Australian region. However, several species also occur in South and Central America. In North America only a single species—*Didelphis virginiana*—occurs, and this is the form in Oklahoma.

FAMILY DIDELPHIDAE   Opossum

Didelphis virginiana Kerr
Virginia Opossum
Didelphis virginiana Kerr, 1792:193

Didelphis virginiana is the only marsupial occurring in Oklahoma. It is a medium-sized mammal (approx. 2.7 kg = 6 lbs.) with a slender, pointed snout and a scaly, sparsely haired, prehensile tail. The tail is usually darker at the base than the tip. The leathery ears are short, black, and naked. Color varies from the more common gray to the rarer melanistic, white (with normally pigmented eyes and ears), and albino phases. Long black and white guard hairs on the sides and back extend out beyond the shorter, dense underfur. The hallux of the hind foot is opposable and clawless. Each foot has five toes that are whitish in color, and the soles of the feet are naked. The legs and feet are blackish.

Cranially, the opossum differs from other Oklahoma mammals in having a fenestrated palate, nasal bones which flare posteriorly, 50 teeth (5/4I 1/1C 3/3PM 4/4M), and a medially inflected angular process. Both sexes have epipubic bones. The male does not have a baculum.

Males and females may be distinguished at the age of two weeks. Males have a scrotum located anterior to the penis, and the female has a marsupium, where the young (which are born in an immature state) complete their development. On study skins, males are distinguished by black-pigmented skin in the genital region.

The Virginia opossum has been collected in most of the physiographic regions of Oklahoma, the only exceptions being the Black Mesa area and ex-

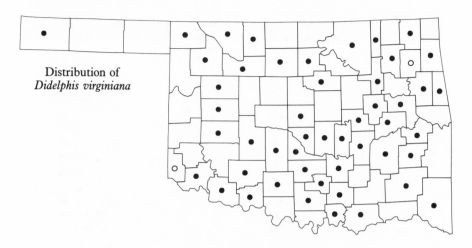

Distribution of
Didelphis virginiana

treme western portions of the Panhandle. In other western parts of the state opossums are usually confined to riparian habitats. The opossum is more common in the mesic eastern and southern portions of Oklahoma. Specific habitats include stream and river floodplains, woodlands, mesquite plains, tall-grass prairies, post oak–blackjack associations, mixed-grass uplands, mixed shrubs, shinnery oak areas, agricultural areas, and inside the limits of many cities and towns (Jackson and Warfel, 1933; Blair, 1939; Osborne and Kellogg, 1943; McCarley, 1952; Blair, 1954; Glass and Halloran, 1961; Ruffer, 1964a; Martin and Preston, 1970).

In Oklahoma, the breeding season probably extends from January to August. Gestation is short, about 12 days, after which the small (1/5 g = 1/100 oz.), immature, and partially developed young are born. The young (which may exceed 20 in number) instinctively crawl from the vagina to the pouch. Once in the marsupium, the young locate one of the 13 nipples, attach themselves to it, and begin nursing. If more than 13 young are born, those failing to locate a nipple will die. More commonly there are less than 13 pouch young; 8 to 10 seems to be about the usual range. The young are weaned in about three months. Two litters per year are possible in Oklahoma.

The opossum is nocturnal and solitary, denning during the day in logs, rocks, brush piles, thick weeds, and abandoned burrows of other animals. Occupied woodrat nests are sometimes used. Opossums are omnivorous and opportunistic scavengers. The diet consists of various small mammals, reptiles, amphibians, insects, crayfish, worms, snails, eggs, carrion, and a wide variety of plant material, including berries, persimmons, green corn, haws, and garden and orchard produce. Occasionally, the opossum will prey on domestic and game fowl, but these negative attributes are offset by the control

TABLE 2.   Number of opossum pelts purchased and average price paid by Oklahoma fur dealers, 1967–81. (Oklahoma Dept. Wildl. Conserv.)

Year	No. Pelts Bought	Avg. Price/Pelt	Total
1967–68	793	$0.37	$ 297.00
1968–69	990	0.55	553.05
1969–70	1,429	0.58	829.35
1970–71	323	0.37	119.85
1971–72	639	0.61	383.40
1972–73	1,518	0.89	1,349.45
1973–74	7,884	1.63	12,846.00
1974–75	23,393	1.53	35,831.73
1975–76	34,333	1.09	37,260.43
1976–77	35,282	1.56	55,013.68
1977–78	35,106	1.86	65,297.16
1978–79	52,910	3.18	168,253.80
1979–80	55,818	3.05	169,980.76
1980–81	40,533	1.43	57,962.19

exerted on many pests such as rats and mice. Because the opossum scavenges on road kills (insects, birds, mammals, etc.), it is often hit by cars.

Predators of opossums include foxes, bobcats, coyotes, and dogs. Young opossums are occasionally taken by hawks and owls. When threatened by danger, the opossum often "plays 'possum" (feigns death) in order to protect itself. The animal collapses on its side and partially flexes the body. The eyes remain open, saliva drools from the partly open mouth, and defecation occurs or foul-smelling fluids may be emitted from anal glands. The opossum is capable of defending itself by biting and scratching. A variety of sounds are emitted, including grunts, hisses, squeals, and clicks. Many opossums are killed each year by man for sport, food, and for the pelt. Table 2 reveals the number of animals taken during past years in Oklahoma. Gardner (1982) reviewed the literature concerning the immunity of opossums to snake venom and suggested that the North American opossum is immune to pit viper venom. This property allows it to prey on copperheads, water moccasins, and rattlesnakes. A good review of opossum biology and folklore can be found in Gardner (1982) and McManus (1974).

The subspecies occurring in Oklahoma is *D. v. virginiana* (Hall, 1981).

Order Insectivora

Shrews and Moles

William Caire

The insectivores occur over most parts of the world, the exceptions being Australia and southern South America. Two families composed of five species are known to occur in Oklahoma; these are Soricidae, the shrews and Talpidae, the moles.

FAMILY SORICIDAE

Blarina carolinensis (Bachman)
Southern Short-tailed Shrew
Sorex carolinensis Bachman, 1837:366
Blarina carolinensis: Genoways and Choate, 1972:114

Blarina carolinensis has a stocky body (total length usually 75–110 mm = 2.9–4.3 in.), a short tail (usually less than one-third the total length), a pointed nose, small external ears (mostly concealed in hair), velvety pelage (slate gray to brownish gray above; paler below), and pigmented teeth. The above characteristics separate it from *Cryptotis parva*, the least shrew, but not from the other short-tailed shrew in Oklahoma, *B. hylophaga*. The latter may be separated only by a specialist when a large series of specimens is present for comparison or through chromosome analysis. George *et al.* (1981) indicated that the diploid number (2N) of *B. hylophaga* is 52 and is 46, 39, 38, or 37 for *B. carolinensis*. In comparing the two, George *et al.* (1981) noted that in general the latter is significantly larger in both cranial and external measurements.

Few specimens of *B. carolinensis* are known from Oklahoma (George *et al.*, 1981), which precludes any detailed characterization of its range in the state. All specimens assigned to *B. carolinensis* are recorded from the extreme southeastern corner of the state in McCurtain County. However, there are numerous records of the southern short-tailed shrew from western Arkansas which are referred to as *B. carolinensis* (Sealander, 1979; George *et al.*, 1981). Until more specimens are available, further analysis of the systematics and distribution of *Blarina carolinensis* in Oklahoma cannot be made.

Preferred habitat is probably woodlands and moist swampy areas. In Arkansas, *B. carolinensis* breeds from February to October (Sealander, 1979). The gestation period is 21–22 days, after which five to seven young are born. Two to three litters may be raised each year. The young depart the nest after one month.

Distribution of
Blarina carolinensis

Food habits are probably similar to those listed in the account of *B. hylophaga*.

The subspecies occurring in Oklahoma is *B. carolinensis carolinensis* (Sealander, 1979).

Blarina hylophaga (Elliot)
Elliot's Short-tailed Shrew
Blarina brevicauda Elliot, 1899:287
Blarina hylophaga: George, Choate, and Genoways, 1981:493

Blarina hylophaga is difficult to distinguish from *B. carolinensis* without making comparisons of large series or examining a karyotype. Externally the two species are similar in being a slate gray to brownish gray above and paler

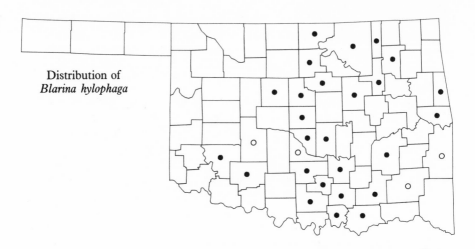

Distribution of
Blarina hylophaga

below. The ears are nearly concealed in the soft, velvety fur. *Blarina* has a long, pointed snout, small eyes, and a short tail (usually less than one-third the total length). The teeth are pigmented. George *et al.* (1981) distinguish *B. hylophaga* from *B. carolinensis* by the former's generally smaller cranial and external measurements. The diploid number (2N) of *B. hylophaga* is 52 and varies from 37 to 46 in *B. carolinensis*.

The systematics of short-tailed shrews in Oklahoma have been intensively studied in recent years. Jones and Glass (1960) considered all the short-tailed shrews in Oklahoma the same species, *B. brevicauda*. However, Genoways and Choate (1972) and Genoways *et al.* (1977) suggested that two species occurred on the Great Plains. *Blarina carolinensis* was described as occurring in the southern portions of the Great Plains (Oklahoma included), whereas *B. brevicauda* occurred only in the northern portions of the Great Plains. Karyotypic and multivariate morphological analyses led George *et al.* (1981) to conclude that *B. hylophaga* should be considered as a distinct western species. Therefore, the latter work recognizes two species of short-tailed shrews for Oklahoma. *Blarina hylophaga* is found in the eastern and central portions of the state, exclusive of the southeastern corner. Its western limits are roughly defined by a line extending north and south through Oklahoma City. *Blarina carolinensis* is known only from the extreme southeastern corner. To what extent the ranges of these two shrews may be sympatric in Oklahoma is unknown because of the paucity of specimens from eastern Oklahoma.

Blarina hylophaga has been collected in the following habitats: in mature parts of the oak-elm floodplain forest (Blair, 1939), in woody ravines (Hays, 1958), beneath decaying logs in wooded floodplain communities (Elliot, 1899b; McCarley, 1961); in grassy pastures adjacent to woody areas (Mc-

Carley, 1961), and in grassy areas strewn with rocks and boulders in the Wichita Mountains (Glass and Halloran, 1961).

Reproductive data for Oklahoma specimens are scant but are probably similar to those noted for Kansas (Hall, 1955). The gestation period is approximately 21 days, after which five to eight young are born. Several litters per year are common.

The diet includes insects, worms, millipedes, arachnids, and other invertebrates, as well as small vertebrates and some plant material. The saliva of short-tailed shrews is venomous and assists the individual in subduing larger prey (Pournelle, 1968). Owls are apparently one of the main predators of short-tailed shrews (as evidenced by remains in owl pellets). Other predators probably include coyotes, foxes, bobcats, hawks, and snakes. Domestic cats often will not eat shrews they kill but do deposit the prey on their owner's front steps.

The subspecies occurring in Oklahoma is *B. h. hylophaga* (George *et al.*, 1981).

Cryptotis parva (Say)
Least Shrew
Sorex parvus Say, 1823:163
Cryptotis parva: Miller, 1912:24

The least shrew, *Cryptotis parva,* is one of the smallest mammals in Oklahoma (about 4 g = 0.1 oz.). The snout is long and pointed. Ears and eyes are small and often concealed in the fur. The tail is short, usually less than twice as long as the hind foot. Least shrews are brownish above and paler below; a few gray specimens have been collected (Blair, 1939). From other shrews

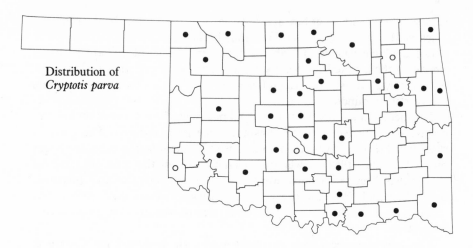

Distribution of
Cryptotis parva

(*Blarina* and *Notiosorex*) which occur in Oklahoma, *Cryptotis* differs in having four unicuspid teeth.

Least shrews occur over most of the state except for the extreme western part of the Panhandle (Cimarron County). This shrew is more common than the few recorded specimens indicate. Far greater numbers of specimens are recovered from owl pellets than from the traps of collectors. Grassy areas are the main habitat type. McCarley (1952) collected two specimens from the tall-grass habitat of Bryan County. Glass and Halloran (1961) collected the least shrew from the grassy areas bordering West Cache Creek in the Wichita Mountains.

Little has been recorded of the ecology of least shrews in Oklahoma. Diet is probably composed of insects, earthworms, and small mollusks. Owls, hawks, and snakes are its chief predators. McMurray (1945) found the remains of three *Cryptotis* in the stomach of a feral house cat.

The subspecies in Oklahoma is *C. p. parva* (Hall, 1981).

Notiosorex crawfordi (Coues)
Desert Shrew
Sorex (Notiosorex) crawfordi Coues, 1877:651
Notiosorex crawfordi: Merriam, 1895:32

Superficially, the desert shrew resembles several other species of shrews which occur in Oklahoma. However, it is easily distinguished by the presence of only three upper unicuspid teeth. The tips of the first incisor and first large molariform tooth have a touch of orange color, usually confined to a single cusp and very pale compared to the pigmentation of the teeth of other shrews. *Notiosorex* has conspicuous ears and a tail which is twice as long as the hind foot. Most desert shrews in Oklahoma are a dull plumbeous gray dorsally, tipped with brown. The venter is lighter gray with buff-tipped hairs.

The desert shrew is probably more common in Oklahoma than the few recorded specimens seem to suggest; Tyler and Gilliland (1979) and Preston and Martin (1963) summarized distributional records for the state. Almost all specimens have been recovered from owl pellets or from woodrat nests in the western half of Oklahoma. Specimens exist from the following physiognomic regions: Piñon-Juniper Mesas, Shortgrass High Plains, Mesquite-Grass Plains, and the western edge of the Post Oak-Blackjack Uplands. The easternmost specimen in Oklahoma is from near Nashoba in Pushmataha County (Clarke, 1953); however, *Notiosorex* has been collected in northwestern Arkansas (Sealander, 1952). The Nashoba and Arkansas specimens may represent Pleistocene relict populations.

Very little is known about the ecology of *Notiosorex*. Preston and Martin's (1963) account of collecting 20 individuals in Harmon County provides most of what is known ecologically about this species in Oklahoma. The shrews were collected by hand from the stick houses of the southern plains woodrat, *Neotoma micropus*, that were located in an area dominated by mesquite, mixed grasses, and prickly pear cactus. Erosion gullies and small mesas formed by

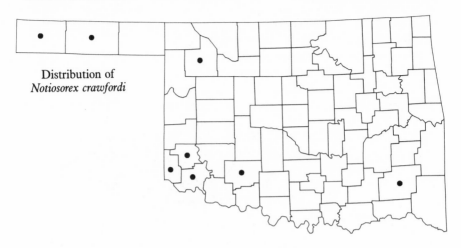

Distribution of
Notiosorex crawfordi

outcroppings of gypsum characterize the red Permian soils where most of the woodrat nests were located. In order to capture the shrews, the woodrats' nests were torn apart, then the burrow systems beneath were excavated. Only one shrew was captured in a given house, and sometimes 10–30 nests had to be examined before a shrew was located. Often another shrew or two would be taken from an adjacent nest as soon as one individual was located. This suggested a more clumped distribution for the shrews than was indicated by the woodrats' nests. Snap traps and live traps set in the same areas where shrews were hand-captured yielded no specimens. Preston and Martin (1963) estimated the density of *Notiosorex* to be one shrew per hectare (2.6 shrews per acre). Other species of mammals taken in the same area included *Reithrodontomys montanus*, *Perognathus hispidus*, *Peromyscus* spp., *Neotoma micropus*, *Onychomys leucogaster*, and *Sigmodon hispidus*.

Clarke (1953) live-trapped the Nashoba specimen near the summit of a ridge in a mesic ravine community in the Kiamichi Mountains. Other mammal species taken in this area were *Scalopus aquaticus*, *Tamias striatus*, *Peromyscus leucopus*, *P. gossypinus*, *P. attwateri*, *Neotoma floridana*, and *Microtus pinetorum*.

Preston and Martin (1963) found no pregnant females in December in southwestern Oklahoma, but did note that *Notiosorex* was reproducing in July and August. In July, one pregnant female had three embryos (8 mm, crown to rump length); three hairless suckling young were also found in July. Two females taken in August had enlarged nipples but were not pregnant. Baker and Spencer (1965) collected two pregnant females in November in Harmon County. One of these females was in a very early stage of pregnancy, while the other contained five embryos (12–13 mm = 0.5 in., crown to rump length). The five embryos weighed a total of 1.4 g (0.05 oz.), or about one-third of the mother's weight (5.7 g = 0.2 oz.).

Owls seem to be a common predator of *Notiosorex*. Glass (1953) and Glass and Halloran (1961) recovered partial specimens from barn owl pellets in Tesequite Canyon in Cimarron County and from northern Woodward County. Tyler and Gilliland (1979) also reported desert shrew remains from pellets of barn owls and burrowing owls, while Humphrey (1975) found *Notiosorex* remains in barn owl pellets in Woodward County. Armstrong and Jones (1972) comment on other aspects of the biology of *Notiosorex*.

The subspecies occurring in Oklahoma is *N. c. crawfordi* (Hall, 1981).

FAMILY TALPIDAE   MOLES

Scalopus aquaticus (Linnaeus)
Eastern Mole
(*Sorex*) *aquaticus* Linnaeus, 1758:53
Scalopus aquaticus: Oberholser, 1905:3

The distinguishing features of the eastern mole, *Scalopus aquaticus,* are its adaptations for a fossorial existence. The body is cylindrical and robust, and the snout distinctly pointed. A layer of skin covers the minute eyes, which can be observed only if dissected. The eyes are apparently used only to detect light (Slonaker, 1902). External pinnae are lacking; only a small perforation in the skin marks the entrance to the ear. The tail is short (about one-fourth the total length), round, and scantily haired. Broad, shovellike front feet aid in distinguishing moles from gophers and shrews. The palms of the forefeet are wider than long, and the long, stout claws extend beyond the pads. Both the forefeet and hind feet are webbed to the base of the claws. Color of the velvety fur varies from brown to gray and often has a silvery or golden metallic sheen. Blair (1939) suggested that color is correlated with soil type, paler individuals occurring in the west and darker forms in the east.

Moles occur over most of Oklahoma in areas where suitable soils allow extensive burrowing. Loamy and moist sandy soils are preferred. Rocky areas and habitats with very loose sand or compacted and heavy clay soils are usually avoided. Moles do not "swim" through the soil, but twist to one side and, with a lateral motion of the front feet, shove the loosened dirt back and up. They are rarely found above ground; however, their remains occur occasionally in owl pellets, attesting to at least some nocturnal surface activity. Martin and Preston (1970) collected road-killed moles in December and July from roads in the sandy shin-oak areas north of Hollis. Jackson and Warfel

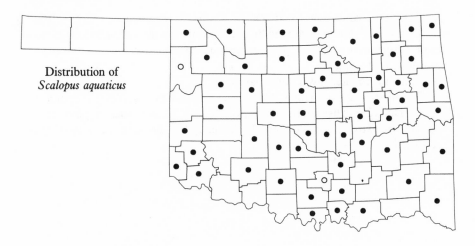

Distribution of
Scalopus aquaticus

(1933) noted mole runs (ridges of dirt pushed up during subsurface activity) near the salt flats and dry plains of the northwest. Blair (1954) found moles to be common in the following habitats of southern Oklahoma: sandy soils of the north bank of the Red River, sand-sage associations, three-awn–finger grass associations, plum-sage associations, and cottonwood associations. McCarley (1952) found mole runs in south central Oklahoma in flood plain forests and post oak–blackjack associations, but he did not see many of them in areas of dense, tall grass. Moles are common in the Wichita Mountains Wildlife Refuge (Glass and Halloran, 1961).

Moles are active all year, but daily activity is variable and sporadic, most of it seeming to occur diurnally. Two types of tunnels compose the burrow system. Surface tunnels, which produce the characteristic surface ridges, are used for food gathering and may be quite extensive. Deeper tunnels are employed as living quarters and as nest chambers. Random wanderings in search of food may increase gene flow to some extent and also possibly reduce inbreeding (Yates and Schmidly, 1978).

A large amount of animal matter, earthworms, beetles, and insects comprise the diet; however, vegetation is also taken. Yates and Schmidly (1978) reported that moles may be successfully maintained in the laboratory on canned dog food.

Moles are solitary, but males do seek out mates during the breeding season. Little is known about their reproduction. Apparently mating occurs in late winter or early spring (Yates and Schmidly, 1978), and after a gestation period of about 45 days (Jackson, 1961), two to five hairless young are born (Scheffer, 1949; Conaway, 1959). They are weaned several weeks later.

Moles are considered to be pests in most urban areas because their burrowing activities damage golf courses and lawns. In some agricultural settings moles may also damage crop seedlings. However, moles are beneficial to man as predators on many insect pests, in aerating the soil, and in reducing surface erosion by allowing water to drain into the ground. Chief predators of moles are badgers, coyotes, owls, and snakes.

The subspecies occurring in Oklahoma is *S. a. aereus* (Yates and Schmidly, 1978). Hall (1981) lists another subspecies, *S. a. machrinoides,* as possibly occurring in extreme northeastern Oklahoma, but no specimens have been recorded.

Order Chiroptera

Bats

Bryan P. Glass

The chiropterans are a diverse and widely distributed order, being absent from only a few oceanic islands and the polar regions. Over 850 species are known, and the greatest diversity of species is found in the tropical regions of the world. In Oklahoma, two families of bats are known: Vespertilionidae (the evening or common bats), represented by 19 species, and Molossidae (the free-tailed bats) represented by 2 species.

Myotis austroriparius (Rhoads)
Southeastern Myotis
Vespertilio lucifugus austroriparius Rhoads, 1897:227
Myotis austroriparius: Miller and G. M. Allen, 1928:144

The southeastern myotis is a small, buff-colored bat, with only a slight color contrast between the bases and tips of the hairs. Late summer specimens may be bright orange above and below, some normally colored, and others lead gray. Spring specimens are buffy. The wing membrane is attached to the ankle, a condition also found in *M. grisescens* but not in other North American *Myotis*. The forearm is approximately 37 mm (1.5 in.) in length.

The species occurs along the Gulf Coast from Louisiana to Florida and up the Mississippi Valley to extreme southern Illinois and Indiana. In Oklahoma it is known only from the Little River drainage basin in LeFlore, Pushmataha, and McCurtain counties.

The species has been taken only while in flight in Oklahoma; its daytime preferences for roosting sites are unknown. It flies low over the surface of rivers and streams, resembling *M. yumanensis* both in this respect and in its late emergence. Limited observations suggest that it appears when the afterglow of midsummer sunset is nearly faded. In Florida the species is principally a cave-dweller (Rice, 1957), but in Louisiana individuals have been found in buildings (Lowery, 1974).

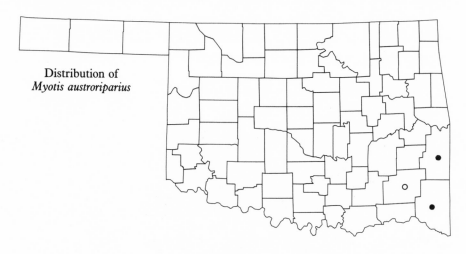

Distribution of
Myotis austroriparius

An adult female taken 7 June had enlarged, nonsecretory mammary glands and an empty uterus that was small and firm. On 8 June a juvenile was obtained that had broad cartilaginous segments in the wing phalangeal epiphyses and could not have been in flying condition for more than a few days. These meager data suggest a mid-May parturition, which is consistent with Rice's (1957) data from Florida.

Lowery (1943) named a new subspecies, *M. a. gatesi,* for his specimens from Louisiana that were in the orange phase of coloration. LaVal (1970) demonstrated that the coloration exhibited by this species over its range was not correlated with the geography of populations. It now appears that these color changes are cyclic for individuals and should not be accorded taxonomic recognition. Hall (1981) indicated no subspecific designations for this species.

Myotis grisescens Howell
Gray Myotis
Myotis grisescens Howell, 1909:46

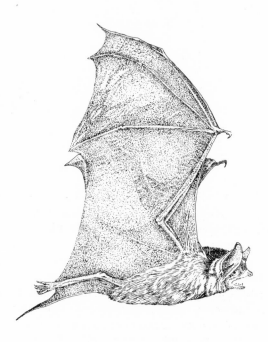

This species of *Myotis*, often called the gray bat, is fairly large, with hair either gray or brownish and of uniform color from root to tip. The young and newly molted adults are gray. Stains from glands or urine apparently affect coat color, so contact with other individuals during winter clustering in hibernation or in nurseries causes some discoloration of spring and summer pelts. The wing membrane attaches to the ankle, not at the base of the toes, a condition that distinguishes it from all other Oklahoma *Myotis* except *M. austroriparius*. The forearm is approximately 42 mm (1.7 in.) in length.

The gray myotis is found in the Ozark uplands west of the Mississippi River; in Kentucky, Tennessee, western Virginia, western North Carolina, southern Illinois and Indiana; and in northeastern Mississippi and eastern Alabama. In Oklahoma it is confined to the region of limestone hills east of the Grand (Neosho) River and north of the Arkansas River valley. It is strictly a cave-dwelling species in both summer and winter. Guthrie (1933) mentioned migrant members of this species, and other workers in Missouri have demonstrated that more caves in that state are used as nurseries than as hiber-

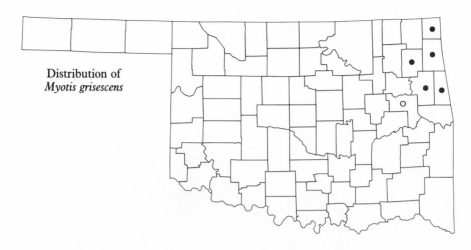

Distribution of
Myotis grisescens

nacula. In Adair Cave (see Glass and Ward, 1959; Grigsby and Puckette, 1982), the species is resident throughout the year, and Sealander (pers. comm.) has indicated that in Arkansas the species occupies the same caves in both winter and summer. Black (1936) indicated numerous caves in Arkansas, however, from which the species was absent in winter. In Oklahoma, only Adair Cave is known to have wintering gray bats. They hibernate in a dense cluster, below which a large pile of guano may accumulate. However, such piles also accumulate under nurseries, so in the absence of bats (as in spring or fall) one cannot positively identify the sites as nurseries or as hibernacula. Because of this, winter and summer checks are necessary. These facts are important, for the assumption that the gray bat hibernates in groups that are large in size but few in number in a few select locations is the principal reason it has been classified as endangered. Myers (1964), after banding and recovering many gray bats in Missouri, concluded that they gathered from many caves in the Missouri Ozark region to form large hibernating groups in only three large caves. Hall and Wilson (1966) reported one such cave in Kentucky, and Tuttle (1976) reported one in northern Alabama and two in Tennessee.

Young, one per female, are born during mid-June and are flying as early as 4 July. The skill with which these young bats pitch in and out among trees near their home cave suggests that they are adapted to forest foraging; they are rarely collected in the open or over streams.

The gray bat has never been divided into subspecies.

Myotis keenii (Merriam)
Keen's Myotis
Vespertilio subulatus keenii Merriam, 1895 : 860
Myotis keenii: Miller and G. M. Allen, 1928 : 104

Keen's myotis is similar in appearance to *M.lucifugus,* but with the tips of the hair less burnished. The dorsal hairs are very long. Its face and ears are blacker than those of *M. lucifugus,* and the ears are longer; when laid forward they extend beyond the nose. The wing membrane attaches at the base of the toes, and the calcar lacks a keel. The forearm is about 34 mm (1.3 in.) in length.

This species occurs as two disjunct populations, one in Washington, British Columbia, and southeastern Alaska, and another in the central, north central, and northeastern United States. In Oklahoma it has been taken from limestone caves in Adair and Delaware counties and was collected once from the space beneath a large sandstone slab on Kiamichi Mountain south of Muse in LeFlore County.

This is a secretive bat, and all individuals captured by hand in caves have been solitary. They sleep singly, tucked into small crevices, with the body as well as the feet in contact with the crevice wall. They have been caught in nets in the mouths of caves where they had not been detected by other means. They have never been found hibernating in Oklahoma, despite the fact that several caves where they are known to occur have been visited in winter.

Hamilton (1943) recorded pregnant females at full term in June and early July in New York, each bearing a single fetus. Caire *et al.* (1979) reported that in southeastern Missouri *M. keenii* hibernates from October to March. Parturition occurred in Missouri in late May or early June. In Oklahoma, lactat-

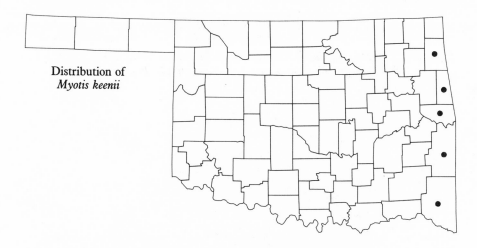

Distribution of
Myotis keenii

ing females have been taken on 20 June, and a specimen taken 30 June was already dry. These data suggest an earlier parturition date for Oklahoma, probably the first half of June. Several authors have reported nursery groups with sizes ranging from 2 to 30 adults.

The subspecies occurring in Oklahoma is *M. k. septentrionalis*. However, Barbour and Davis (1969), Van Zyll de Jong (1979, 1985) and Fitch and Shump (1979) indicate that the population in eastern North America may be a distinct species, in which case the proper designation should be *Myotis septentrionalis*.

Myotis leibii (Audubon and Bachman)
Small-footed Myotis
Vespertilio leibii Audubon and Bachman, 1842:284
Myotis leibii: Glass and Baker, 1968:257

The small-footed myotis is a glossy chestnut brown, and the ears and face are heavily pigmented with black. The calcar has a distinct keel, and the forearm is about 31 mm (1.2 in.) in length.

The range of *M. leibii* is divided. It is widespread from the Rocky Mountains westward, with one isolated population along the caprock east of the High Plains of Texas and another in the Wichita Mountains of Oklahoma. The eastern population lies mainly east of the Mississippi River, with a few specimens from Missouri (Davis and Lidicker, 1955; LaVal and LaVal, 1980), Kansas (Hall, 1981), and McCurtain County, Oklahoma (unpublished). In Oklahoma, besides the specimens mentioned from McCurtain County, the species occurs commonly in the Wichita Mountains, and it is also found in the Cimarron River canyons of Cimarron County. Blair (1939) first recorded the species (as *M. subulatus*) for the state.

Myotis leibii emerges in the evening while there is yet some light. In the Wichita Mountains, it emerges at the same time as the western pipistrel. No other bats emerge as early in Cimarron County. They fly about 4–5 m (15–

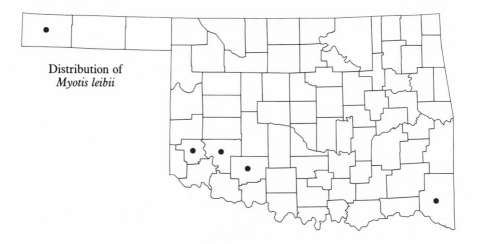

Distribution of
Myotis leibii

20 ft.) above ground and are easily seen against the sky at sunset. *Myotis yumanensis*, which also occurs in the same area in Cimarron County and emerges much later, is never seen against the sky.

Three females collected on 29 and 30 May and 6 June in the Wichita Mountains each bore a fetus (ranging in size from 9 to 12 mm [0.5 in.] crown–rump length) in the right uterine horn. It seems from these data that the period of birth probably is mid-June.

In the Wichita Mountains, the small-footed myotis is not as common as the western pipistrel, according to the comparative numbers of the two species collected at any one time and place. The only roosting small-footed myotis collected in the state was one found by W. C. Carter in a narrow rock crevice exposed to clear daylight only a few feet from the Mountain Fork River in McCurtain County. Several specimens from the Wichita Mountains have been collected in mist nets set in large caverns beneath boulders during daylight hours. All others have been taken during evening flights. Where it hibernates in Oklahoma, if at all, is not known.

For many years this species was named *M. subulatus*, a name that at different times has been used for four distinct species of *Myotis*. The nomenclatural history whereby *subulatus* was rejected and replaced by *leibii* may be found in a paper by Glass and Baker (1968), who also summarized the currently recognized subspecies. In their opinion the McCurtain County specimen represented *M. l. leibii*, while those from the rest of the state represented *M. l. melanorhinus*. However, Van Zyll de Jong (1984) has suggested that the western forms of this species represent a completely different species, *Myotis ciliolabrum*. The southern and eastern individuals are retained in *M. leibii* (Van Zyll de Jong, 1984).

Myotis lucifugus (Le Conte)
Little Brown Myotis
Vespertilio lucifugus Le Conte, 1831:431
Myotis lucifugus: Miller, 1897:59

The little brown bat is a small, brownish bat with long, glossy-tipped hair. The overall color is shiny olive brown that is slightly lighter on the underside because of the white-tipped hairs. There is no keel on the calcar of the foot. When laid forward, the tip of the ear barely reaches the end of the nose. The forearm is about 36 mm (1.4 in.) in adults.

This species occurs throughout North America from approximately the twenty-sixth parallel north to the limit of trees. Its occurrence in Oklahoma was not verified until 1954 (Glass and Ward, 1959), although its presence had been claimed or implied more than once previously. To date, it has been found only in Beaver's Bend State Park in McCurtain County. It has been recorded in eastern Kansas and central and northern Arkansas, and there is one record for Fort Smith, Arkansas, near the Oklahoma border; it is quite common in Missouri (Fenton and Barclay, 1980; Miller and Allen, 1928). Specimens also exist from northeastern New Mexico (Findley *et al.*, 1975), and eventually it may be found in extreme northwestern Oklahoma. The subspecies there is *M. l. carissima*.

The species exhibits an annual cycle of activity, hibernating in caves, but roosting primarily in man-made shelters during summer. Originally, the species probably used hollow trees during summer, but now it uses attics, gables, steeples, spaces behind shutters, and similar sites.

The sexes are segregated in summer, females clustering in nursery colonies where they bear and raise their young while the males occur elsewhere, either singly or in small groups. No nurseries have been found in Oklahoma, and all but one of the specimens from Beavers Bend were adult males. Since these

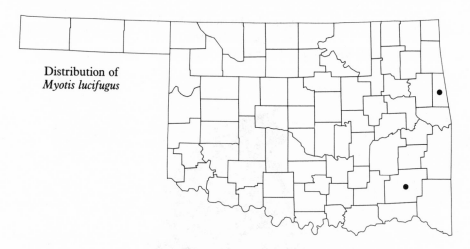

Distribution of
Myotis lucifugus

bats are known to move over distances of many miles from wintering caves to summer roosts (Davis and Hitchcock, 1965), the wintering sites for these bats may lie outside Oklahoma. The males were found in crevices behind the vertical corner boards on clapboard cabins in the old youth camp. The biology of the species has been reviewed by Humphrey and Cope (1976).

The subspecies *M. l. lucifugus* occupies all of the temperate parts of eastern North America.

Myotis sodalis Miller and G. M. Allen
Indiana Myotis
Myotis sodalis: Miller and G. M. Allen, 1928:130

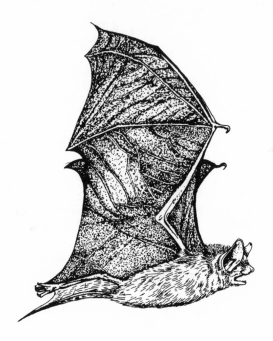

The Indiana myotis is about the size of *M. lucifugus,* but the lighter tips of the dark brown fur give it a faintly pinkish cast. The hairs are tricolored, having a narrow band of gray midway between the tip and the root. When laid forward, the ears reach the nose. A narrow but distinct keel is found on the calcar. The forearm of Oklahoma specimens averages about 38 mm (1.5 in.) in length.

The species ranges from eastern Oklahoma and Nebraska north and east to New England and south from Tennessee through eastern Alabama to north-western Florida. In Oklahoma, it has been collected only twice: once hibernating in a cluster of *M. grisescens* in a cave in Adair County, and once in a small fissure in sandstone in northeastern Pushmataha County. These collections were made on 24 October (reported as February in Glass and Ward, 1959) and 26 November, respectively. The nearest known permanent populations are in Missouri and Arkansas. There is very little information on the

Distribution of
Myotis sodalis

summer habits of *M. sodalis*. A defensible speculation is that all Oklahoma records are of waifs, lost from the main body of the species' population. Ecological information about maternity roosts, foraging behavior, and hibernation are in Humphrey *el al.* (1977) and La Val *et al.* (1977, 1980).

The Indiana myotis has never been divided into subspecies.

Myotis velifer (J. A. Allen)
Cave Myotis
Vespertilio velifer J. A. Allen, 1890:177
Myotis velifer: Miller, 1897:56

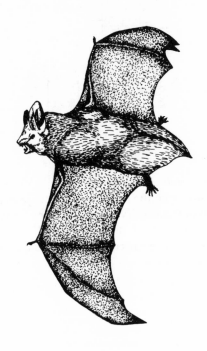

The cave myotis is the largest member of the genus (*sensu stricto*) in North America. Color above and below is grayish tan. In this species, the ears are not disproportionately long, and there is no keel on the calcar. The wing attaches to the base of the toes. Young have duller, grayish, more fluffy fur and are whitish behind the ears. Forearms of adults are approximately 44 mm (1.7 in.) long.

The species ranges widely in the arid southwestern states south through Mexico and Central America. In Oklahoma it is found throughout the western half of the state, excluding the Panhandle. It is primarily associated with gypsum caves, although in the Wichita Mountains it has been taken in caverns among granite boulders. Isolated records extend the known range eastward to Canadian, Garfield, Kay, and Payne counties.

Except for a few weeks in August, September, and October, the species occurs only in caves. Apparently, individuals show a strong preference for

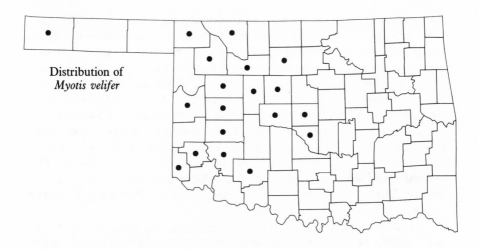

Distribution of
Myotis velifer

their home (natal?) cave, for of 2,930 banded individuals, 198 out of 201 were recovered at the same cave in which they were banded. A few bands have been recovered in the same cave as long as three years after banding. In a hibernaculum, Caire (pers. observ.) recovered bats which had been banded eleven years earlier. During late summer and early fall, these bats leave their caves and may occupy buildings such as barns and lumber sheds. These sites are usually (as far as banding has revealed) no more than 48 km (30 mi.) from their home cave. Kunz (1973) studied the movements of *M. velifer* in Kansas and Oklahoma and documented movements between the states. These bats are probably adults, and this summer scattering may be for the purpose of breeding. Thus, this otherwise sedentary species is provided the opportunity for genetic outcrossing among populations. One such aggregation in a granite cavern was observed on 24 August. One pair was observed mating, and several females that were examined gave evidence of having recently mated.

All pregnant females examined have been carrying a single young. Birth occurs during the fourth week in June. Flying young have been recorded as early as 17 July; however, newborn young also were seen on the same date, indicating a much more attenuated season of birth than is usual for bats that hibernate.

The cave myotis generally hibernates in large clusters, but it is not uncommon to see isolated individuals or pairs hibernating away from a large cluster. Caire (pers. observ.) monitored cluster size changes over the hibernation period and found that the size of the cluster is related to temperature; the colder it is, the larger the cluster.

This species is extremely sensitive to disturbance of its nurseries. Disturbance has been known to result in a nursery not being used the following year. One such nursery cave was not reoccupied for at least six years, but it was being used again twenty years later. This nursery was situated in a dome over a trail where conducted tours passed by several times daily. Nursery sites of these bats may be identified by the accumulation of guano on the cave floor; hibernating colonies do not produce such accumulations. The cave myotis prefers moist situations for hibernacula, and in the gypsum caves of western Oklahoma, such hibernacula are associated with underground streams that flow and wash away any guano that might accumulate. The species was studied extensively by Twente (1955), whose description of the microclimate during hibernation has shed much light on the behavior of this species. The osmolality and ion concentration in urine of hibernating *M. velifer* was examined by Caire *et al.* (1982). Normal blood values of hibernating *M. velifer* were reported by Caire *et al.* (1981).

Veal (1983) recorded more than 20 ectoparasite species occurring on *M. velifer* during hibernation in northwestern Oklahoma. Several recent studies (Caire and Ports, 1981; Caire and Hornuff, 1982, 1986: Caire *et al.*, 1985) have been made on the bat fly (*Trichobius major*), which is an ectoparasite of *M. velifer*.

Kunz (1974) studied the food habits and night roosting activity of this species. Caire *et al.* (1984) monitored the early foraging behavior of *M. velifer* at Alabaster Caverns and reported that it was an opportunistic forager, flying at a variety of heights in many habitats. Fitch *et al.* (1981) commented on other aspects of the biology of *M. velifer*.

The subspecies occurring in Oklahoma is *M. v. magnamolaris* (Choate and Hall, 1967).

Myotis yumanensis (H. Allen)
Yuma Myotis
Vespertilio yumanensis H. Allen, 1864:58
Myotis yumanensis: Miller, 1897:66

The Yuma myotis is a small, dusty gray bat with the tips of the hairs dull buff; the fur lacks luster. There is no keel on the calcar. The ears are short, when laid forward barely reaching the nose. The forearm is about 43 mm (1.7 in.) in adults.

The species occurs throughout much of western North America from southern British Columbia south to central Mexico. In Oklahoma it has been found only in the Cimarron drainage system in northwest Cimarron County, but its presence is suspected also along Currumpa (Corrumpa) and Cienquilla (Seneca) creeks, the principal sources of the North Canadian (Beaver) River. Oklahoma shares with the Rio Grande at Del Rio, Texas, the distinction of the easternmost records in the United States.

Distribution of
Myotis yumanensis

Yuma bats emerge from their roosts after dark and fly close to the ground. They are most easily detected where they fly over water. They regularly fly upstream or downstream along the Cimarron and its tributary creeks, but it is not known whether they forage above dry ground also. Dalquest (1947) reported that, in California, the species has become habituated to buildings, the sexes remain separate for much of the year, and females are gregarious whereas males are largely solitary. He gave numerous examples of females being found clustered in buildings; however, all dates given suggest the possibility that these were nursery aggregations. In Oklahoma, the Yuma bat is known to maintain at least one nursery, which is in a north-facing cave in Tesesquite Canyon. No roosting males have been found, but individuals of both sexes have been taken in a barn beside the Cimarron River northeast of Kenton, where they apparently were resting between nocturnal feeding sallies. The cave group has been seen as early as 29 May and as late as 18 August, which are the earliest and latest dates, respectively, that the cave has been examined. In every case the bats were clustered in the upper rear of the cave, and none were seen utilizing crevices.

All females examined from the nursery colony were pregnant during May and June, and all carried a single fetus. Fetuses measured on 30 May were 12 mm (0.5 in.) in crown-rump length, indicating mid-June as the probable peak time for births. However, a female taken on 8 August was still lactating although other females were dry. These data conform to the more extensive data given by Dalquest (1947) for California.

The species was first listed for the state by Glass and Ward (1959) but was reported earlier under the name *M. subulatus* by Glass (1951) and amended in Glass and Ward (1959).

Lasionycteris noctivagans (Le Conte)
Silver-haired Bat
Vespertilio noctivagans Le Conte, 1831:431
Lasionycteris noctivagans: H. Allen, 1894:1054

The silver-haired bat is a medium-sized bat with black hair and skin. Some of the hairs on both the back and belly are tipped with white, imparting a silvery or frosted appearance. Sparse black hair covers the basal half of the tail membrane. The ears are somewhat square-tipped, and the tragus is short and blunt. In adults, the forearm is about 40 mm (1.6 in.)

Lasionycteris noctivagans ranges throughout the cooler parts of North America. In the Appalachians and western mountains, it ranges farther south than in the midcontinent. In many northern states, it is the most abundant bat. It has been recorded as far south as Texas, Arizona, New Mexico, and Mexico. A few specimens exist from Arkansas. In Oklahoma specimens have been taken from Stillwater (Glass, 1961), Fort Sill (Tyler and Payne, 1982), and other parts of the state (Caire, 1985; Tyler *et al.*, in prep).

The silver-haired bat is a tree dweller and probably is nomadic, ranging widely, particularly during the nonbreeding season. It is very cold-tolerant and during winter in the northern states has been found sleeping in trees,

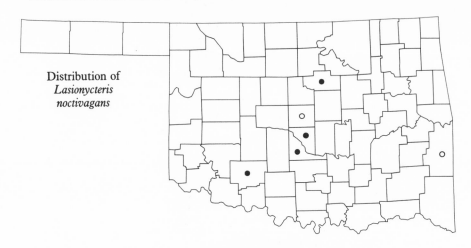

Distribution of
*Lasionycteris
noctivagans*

rock crevices, and buildings. Apparently it migrates to winter quarters in some parts of its range.

Little is known of reproduction in this species; two young seem to be the rule. The scant evidence available indicates the possibility that the sexes segregate in summer. Most records in southern regions are of males, whereas in summer most northern records are for females.

Most of the information on this species is anecdotal, and behavioral inferences should be made with caution. Finding a bat in an unusual situation is more noteworthy than is a more predictable observation, and the information available may therefore be biased toward the unusual. However, there is no doubt that, behaviorally, this is an unusual species. One was collected in a shed east of Juneau, Alaska, in November when there was a foot of snow outside and the winter freeze was commencing (Barbour and Davis, 1969); another was netted in New Mexico, flying at an air temperature of 2°C (28°F) (Jones, 1965). It apparently never associates with other species of bats.

No subspecies are recognized for the silver-haired bat.

Pipistrellus hesperus (H. Allen)
Western Pipistrel
Scotophilus hesperus H. Allen, 1864:43
Pipistrellus hesperus: Miller, 1897:88

The western pipistrel is among the smallest of North American bats. General coloration of adults is a reddish brown, with fur between the ears much lighter, often a golden yellow. The ears, face, and wing membranes are black. Many individuals resemble *Myotis leibii* so closely that it is only by the shape of the tragus (see key) that they may be identified with certainty. Juveniles are blackish olive in color. The forearm in adults measures about 31 mm (1.2 in.).

Pipistrellus hesperus ranges throughout the Southwest. It roosts in rocky places, usually in narrow crevices or under loose rocks. It is probably the commonest bat in the Wichita Mountains, occurring in all parts of the range, from Comanche to Greer counties. Because of the close proximity of specimens from northeastern New Mexico and southeastern Colorado, it is likely that this species occurs in the Panhandle of Oklahoma. It emerges well before dark and seems to need to drink water immediately. The pipistrel's fluttering

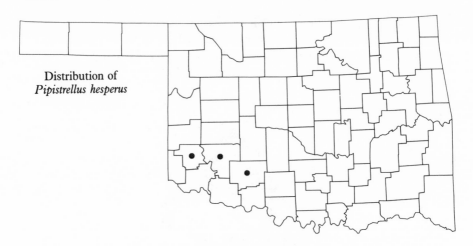

Distribution of
Pipistrellus hesperus

flight is quite characteristic, and when it comes in to drink (and while drinking), the wings are set at about a 45 degree angle to glide down to the water. Great numbers of these bats have been seen flying over a lake during the third week of March.

The species usually bears twins. In one female, the two embryos were of quite different sizes. This might indicate that ovulation was asynchronous between the two ovaries or that one embryo was being resorbed. Females having only one embryo have also been collected. Flying young have been collected as early as 16 July. Birth, therefore, seems to take place during middle to late June.

The western pipistrel was not known in Oklahoma until 1955 (Glass and Morse, 1959). Because of the larger size and darker coloration of the Oklahoma population, it was designated *P. h. oklahomae.* Later, Findley and Traut (1970) studied variation within the entire species and concluded that most differences were clinal, and only two subspecies should be recognized, *P. h. hesperus,* a tiny, straw-colored bat of western desert regions, and a larger, brownish form from eastern New Mexico, western Texas, and Oklahoma, the valid name of which is *P. h. santarosae* (Hatfield, 1936). However, Hall (1981) prefers to use *P. h. maximus.*

Pipistrellus subflavus (Cuvier)
Eastern Pipistrel
Vespertilio subflavus F. Cuvier, 1832 : 17
Pipistrellus subflavus: Miller, 1897 : 90

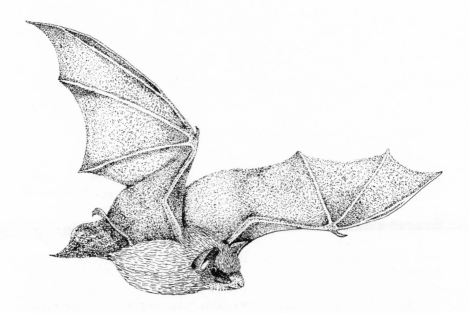

Pipistrellus subflavus is a small bat with an overall reddish golden color. The hairs are gray at the base, banded with light yellow in the middle, and have burnished brown tips. Pinkish brown ears are distinctive, and the tragus is blunt and short. The skin of the arm is also pinkish, but the flight membranes are black. The forearm length is about 33 mm (1.3 in.) in adults.

The eastern pipistrel is primarily a species of the forested parts of eastern North America, reaching its western limits in the Great Plains. It is very abundant in the eastern third of Oklahoma, but uncommon in central and western parts, where it is restricted to very specific habitat types. In the Arbuckle Mountains it is not uncommon, and these limestone hills appear to form the connecting link between the eastern and western areas where the species occurs. West of the Arbuckles this species occurs within the Wichita Mountains and in gypsum sinkhole caves in the Blaine Gypsum in the northwest parts of the state.

This bat hibernates in caves, where it hangs singly. It selects a hibernaculum with high humidity, and often it is covered with droplets of water

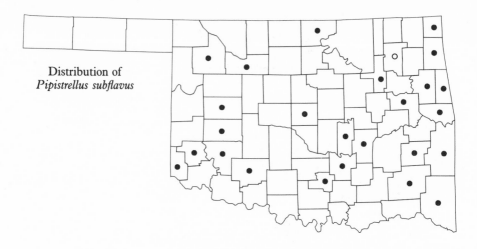

Distribution of
Pipistrellus subflavus

that have condensed on its fur. Throughout most of its range this bat abandons caves for the summer season and apparently lives in trees. Nets set in the entrances of caves reveal that it does use caves in summer as night roosts between feeding forays. However, the species is also very abundant in places hundreds of miles from the nearest cave, so it seems that caves are not a necessary component of the summer habitat. In western Oklahoma, eastern pipistrels are always found in caves having a high humidity. Since the summer air in that area is so dry, the bats may be forced to use caves for roosts throughout the year. Caire *et al.* (1984) netted eastern pipistrels exiting Alabaster Caverns to forage in Cedar Canyon. This species foraged in small, tight circles often above treetop level. Little is known of the summer ecology of this species anywhere (Humphrey *et al.*, 1977; Fujita and Kunz, 1984).

Two young are the rule in this species. In Oklahoma a female captured on 18 June was carrying two embryos, and one taken 25 June had just given birth. The uterus was large and empty, and the mammary glands were large but had not begun secreting milk. Since the bat was not carrying young, it seems that this species may sequester its young during feeding flights. Flying young of the year have been collected on 30 July. These bats mate in the fall. A female collected 16 October contained a large mass of sperm in the body of the uterus, and there were sperm in the oviducts and uterine horns as well.

The systematic status of the eastern pipistrel was reviewed by Davis (1959); *P. s. subflavus* is the subspecies in Oklahoma.

Eptesicus fuscus (Beauvois)
Big Brown Bat
Vespertilio fuscus Beauvois, 1796:18
Eptesicus fuscus: Mehely, 1900:206, 238

Eptesicus fuscus is a large, chestnut brown bat with black ears and flight membranes. Dorsal pelage is blackish at the base, glossy brown distally; the belly is somewhat paler. The tragus is short and blunt and the forearm averages 46 mm (1.8 in.) in adults.

This is one of the most widespread of North American bats, being found in all parts of the country except for parts of Texas and peninsular Florida. In Oklahoma it is widespread throughout the eastern half of the state, but in the west its distribution is discontinuous.

The big brown bat quite commonly roosts in houses. Apparently it must return to caves to hibernate, but buildings now seem to be the preferred site for nursery colonies. When hibernating, these bats secrete themselves singly in small crevices, where they are usually found with both back and belly

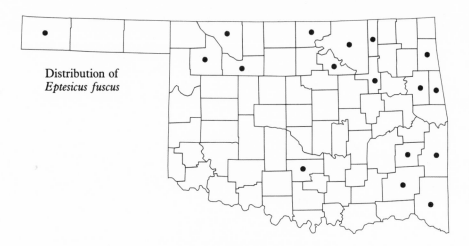

Distribution of
Eptesicus fuscus

touching the rock. Occasionally two or three individuals may be in proximity if the crevice is large enough. Most big brown bats are almost always found in the twilight region of caves. Nurseries may be placed in various sites, such as between studs in a wall, under the eaves of a roof, in a hollow gable of a lumber shed, under a sheetmetal roof (where the material was too hot to touch), or among the rafters of a bathhouse in a state park. Some large cities have buildings whose attics each year harbor a large colony of these bats. The species' apparent absence from the middle region of Oklahoma probably is a reflection of the scarcity of suitable hibernacula.

The breeding cycle of *E. fuscus* is similar to that of other hibernators. Mating takes place in the fall, but ovulation and fertilization do not occur until the animals emerge from hibernation. The females form nursery groups in May. Females taken during late April in McCurtain County were each carrying from two to five small embryos. The embryos in each uterine swelling were only about 4 mm across; most of them would probably be resorbed, as the species is reported to bear only one or two young. Barbour and Davis (1969) noted that the eastern form usually produces two young, but the one from the Rocky Mountains westward produces only one. They also reported that when the young are flying, males join the nursery groups to form large late-summer colonies. Caire *et al.* (1984) observed the early foraging behavior of *E. fuscus* near Alabaster Caverns and noted the big brown bat was a strong, fast flyer which foraged in large ovals at mid-canyon height.

Blair (1939) called bats from the western half of Oklahoma the Rocky Mountain form, *E. f. pallidus*, and those from eastern Oklahoma, *E. f.*

fuscus. The former is considered to be paler in color, but the difference is very slight, at least in Oklahoma specimens. Burnett (1983) has examined geographical and climatic correlates of morphological variation in *E. fuscus*. It would be interesting to know whether or not the bats of western Oklahoma bear only one young, as *E. f. pallidus* is reported to do.

Lasiurus borealis (Muller)
Red Bat
Vespertilio borealis Muller, 1776 : 20
Lasiurus borealis: Miller, 1897 : 105

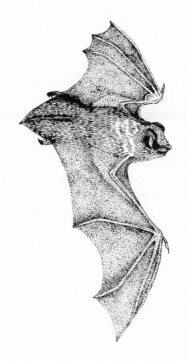

The red bat is considerably smaller than the hoary bat, *L. cinereus*, with which it shares the common characters of frosted hair, four nipples, and a densely furred interfemoral membrane. The hair on the back is four-banded, being dark gray at the base followed by a yellowish band, then one of red or maroon, with a white tip. These are the only North American bats that have a

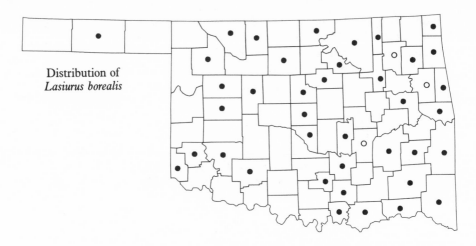

Distribution of
Lasiurus borealis

sexually dimorphic color. In males the subterminal band is carrot red, while in females it is maroon. Some females have the yellow band widened at the expense of the maroon band, making them appear almost yellow. The skin of the ears, face, and forearm is pinkish brown, the wing membranes are black, and the tufts of hair on the wrists are buffy. The forearm measures about 36 mm (1.4 in.) in adults.

The red bat is one of the most widespread bats in North America, being absent only from the Rocky Mountain and Great Basin regions. In Oklahoma it is uncommon in the western half, but is known from as far west as Texas County. This tree dweller is the most common summer bat in the central region of the state. It is not known to hibernate in Oklahoma, but there are a few records of torpid individuals being found in Illinois and in the Ohio River valley, areas where they may be seen on short foraging flights even in midwinter. There are records of these bats passing certain observation points in waves, and of multiple collisions with buildings, that suggest that at least part of the population performs long migrations. The species is occasionally recorded on Bermuda. Nonmigratory individuals hibernate in trees, probably under bark or in hollow branches. The species is so strongly tree-adapted that, should it enter a cave to sleep, it has no arousal mechanism; thus, cave roosting would be precluded.

These bats probably mate on the wing, for there are several records of such observations, and there is one record of a female collected in June which was apparently in the midst of parturition while flying (Glass, 1966). Mating in the red bat apparently takes place in late summer, at which time the males are in full breeding condition. This would argue in favor of hibernation, as fall mating and spring conception are phenomena associated with species that are known hibernators. This species is one of the few bats known to produce regularly more than two young (often four are born). Although this bat often carries its young when in flight, the frequency with which they drop to the ground when so burdened suggests that these may be attempts to move from one roost to another and are not feeding flights. The young are usually left behind when the mother is feeding. Glass once banded a female and two young and the next day saw the same female with two banded and one un-banded young. Moths seem to comprise the bulk of the diet. Shump and Shump (1982a) comment on other aspects of the biology of *L. borealis*.

The only subspecies occurring in Oklahoma is *L. b. borealis*.

Lasiurus cinereus (Beauvois)
Hoary Bat
Vespertilio cinereus Beauvois, 1796:18
Lasiurus cinereus: H. Allen, 18646:21

The hoary bat is the largest bat in Oklahoma. The hair of the back and tail membrane is chocolate brown, frosted with white; the underside is similar

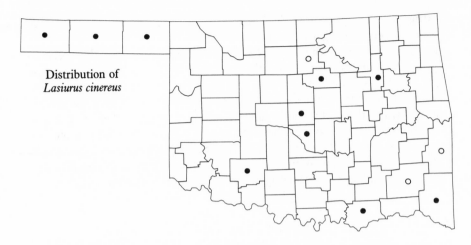

Distribution of
Lasiurus cinereus

but lighter. There is a bib of buffy yellow on the throat, which extends upwards on each side of the neck to behind the ears. A tuft of white hair covers the wrist. The ears are short and truncated, with the free edge rolled back. Its tail membrane is fully and densely haired, and the feet seem small for its body. The forearm is about 53 mm (2.1 in.) in adults.

The hoary bat is the most widely distributed bat in North America, being found in all states. Despite being so ubiquitous, the bat is not common in most localities. The few Oklahoma records indicate that it can be expected to occur anywhere in the state (Tyler and Scott, 1982; Caire *et al.*, 1986).

The species is a tree-dweller and is therefore highly nomadic. It migrates southward in the fall and northward in the spring (Findley and Jones, 1964). Those migrating through the western states in fall go south at least into Mexico. There are numerous records of waves of migrating hoary bats, but it is difficult to determine where they go. There are no records of band recoveries that might reveal how far south an individual will actually travel.

Although the hoary bat shares with its congeners the distinction of having four mammary glands (other bats have two), this species has never been recorded with more than two young. The few records of females with young indicate a birth date from the middle of May into early July. Such a protracted period suggests that mating may be in the spring, with conception not delayed as in hibernating bats. However, the red bat, *L. borealis*, breeds in late summer, even though there is some evidence that it too is migratory and may not go through prolonged winter torpor. The only records of bats being born in Oklahoma are of a female with two young from Enid and a juvenile male from Stillwater obtained 17 June. The latter was so young, judging from the condition of the wing knuckles, that it must have just commenced flying and could not have traveled very far from its place of birth. Other records indicate that these bats sometimes carry their young on feeding forays but may at times leave them hidden in a tree. Shump and Shump (1982*b*) commented on other aspects of the biology of *L. cinereus*.

Lasiurus cinereus cinereus occurs in North America. In South America and Hawaii other subspecific names are recognized (Hall, 1981).

Lasiurus seminolus (Rhoads)
Seminole Bat
Atalapha borealis seminola Rhoads, 1895 : 32
Lasiurus seminolus: Barkalow, 1948 : 415

Except for color and distribution, *Lasiurus seminolus* and *L. borealis* are identical; the seminole bat is a dark mahogany red, with a minimum of white tipping. The sexes are colored alike. The forearm averages about 40 mm (1.6 in.) in adults. Its range is from eastern Texas and southeastern Oklahoma east to southeastern Virginia. Occasional specimens are taken far beyond the stated range. It shares its range with the red bat, and the two species often forage together. Like *L. borealis*, it may have as many as four young. *Lasiurus*

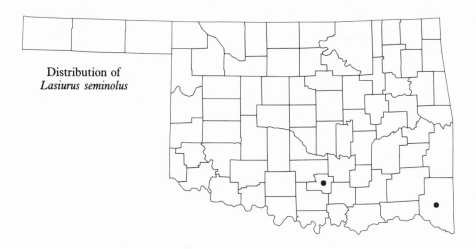

Distribution of
Lasiurus seminolus

seminolus is active throughout the year. Nothing is known about the timing of sexual activity in the male.

In Oklahoma, it has been taken twice, in McCurtain County about a quarter of a mile from the Arkansas border (Glass, 1958) and in Turner Falls Park in Murray County (Caire and Thies, 1987). The Seminole bat is monotypic (Hall, 1981).

Nycticeius humeralis Rafinesque
Evening Bat
Vespertilio humeralis Rafinesque, 1818:445
Nycticeius humeralis: Rafinesque, 1819:417

Externally, the evening bat appears to be a diminutive *Eptesicus fuscus*. Its ears, face, and flight membranes are black, and the body hair is deep chestnut brown dorsally, somewhat lighter on the belly. A short and blunt tragus and a calcar distinctly keeled characterize the species. Juveniles are much darker than adults because of the sooty basal color of the hair, extending almost to the hair tips. The forearm is about 35 mm (1.4 in.) in adults.

The evening bat is found over most of the eastern United States. In Oklahoma it is common throughout the eastern forested areas, with isolated representation from Payne, Oklahoma, and Murray counties. It is most abundant in the southeastern quarter of the state. Extensions of known range were reported by Glass and Humphrey (1971). The Oklahoma State University Museum has one specimen found dead on the pavement of Skirvin Plaza, Oklahoma City, in October, 1979.

Nycticeius humeralis is a tree-dwelling bat that has adapted to using buildings for nurseries. Throughout the southern states it is one of the commonest species. Despite this fact, its annual cycle is very poorly known. It disappears from its summer haunts, but there are no records of hibernation. The meager

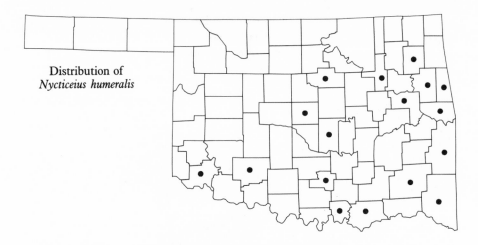

Distribution of
Nycticeius humeralis

data available indicate that the species mates in the fall, a characteristic of hibernators.

Females form nursery groups that in late spring may contain thousands of individuals. One such group has been reported from an abandoned house north of Valliant in McCurtain County (D. C. Carter and B. P. Glass, pers. comm.). The usual number of young is two, but there are records of females with up to four visible implantation sites. One female approaching full term had three fully developed embryos (with forearms 7 mm) (Jennings, 1958). One with four embryos was obtained on 12 May, but their sizes were unrecorded (Barkalow, 1948). The possibility of four embryos achieving full term seems remote. Oklahoma specimens collected 9 June had just given birth, as the uterine horns were large and empty and milk flow had not begun. In one of these bats, only the right horn was enlarged, in the other, only the left. Since neither was carrying its young in flight, these data corroborate observations of other observers that the species leaves its young behind while foraging. Recognizably immature bats, judging by color and condition of the wing knuckles, have been identified between 28 July and 18 August. On the latter date the knuckles were fully hardened and adult pelage was appearing.

The evening bat emerges early and is often seen in mixed feeding swarms with *Pipistrellus subflavus*. Its rather slow and steady flight contrasts sharply with that of the pipistrel, whose flight is faster and highly erratic. The general biology of *N. humeralis* has been reviewed by Watkins (1972), but no information specific to Oklahoma is listed.

Nycticeius humeralis is quite uniform in color and morphology throughout most of its range. The nominate subspecies, *N. h. humeralis*, occurs in Oklahoma (Hall, 1981).

Plecotus rafinesquii Lesson
Rafinesque's Big-eared Bat
Plecotus rafinesquii Lesson, 1827:96

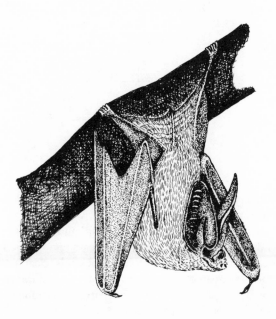

Rafinesque's bat and Townsend's big-eared bat are very similar species. The only other species known from Oklahoma which has ears an inch or more in length is the pallid bat, *Antrozous pallidus*, which in other respects only remotely resembles these two. Rafinesque's bat shares with all other members of the genus the ability to curl the ears back over the shoulders when at rest so that they resemble miniature ram's horns. Its fur is long and fluffy, dark gray for most of its length, and has light brown tips. On the underside, the hairs are tipped with white; young bats lack the brown tipping. The feet are covered with long hairs. In adults, the forearm is about 45 mm (1.8 in.).

This species has been taken only twice in Oklahoma, once at Houston, a locality now submerged beneath Wister Lake in LeFlore County, and once from a well 4 km (2.5 mi.) west of Smithville in McCurtain County (Blair, 1939). From southeastern Oklahoma it ranges eastward to the Ohio River valley and southward throughout most of the southeastern states.

There are no data recorded concerning reproduction of this species in Oklahoma. Elsewhere it seems to have begun using houses for roosting places, although occasionally it is found in caves in the northern part of its

Distribution of
Plecotus rafinesquii

range. Small nursery colonies are usually formed in dilapidated buildings. The species bears only a single young.

Plecotus rafinesquii emerges late in the evening, and its presence in an area usually goes undetected. The extremely large ears and erratic flight suggest that it is adapted to feeding in dense foliage, possibly gleaning insects from leaves, as do other large-eared bats. Jones (1977) reviewed the general biology of this species and indicated that, in some parts of its range (for example, Oklahoma), local distributional patterns and ecology are imperfectly known.

For many years, Rafinesque's bat was known by the species name *Corynorhinus macrotis* (Le Conte), and the Townsend's bat was known as *C. rafinesquii* (Lesson). Handley (1959) reviewed the New World big-eared bats and determined that the name *rafinesquii* had been misapplied to the more westerly and northerly species and was in reality the valid name for the southeastern form. He also determined that there were two valid races of Rafinesque's bat, and that *P. r. macrotis* Le Conte is the valid designation for the form occurring in Oklahoma.

Plecotus townsendii Cooper
Townsend's Big-eared Bat
Plecotus townsendii Cooper, 1837:73

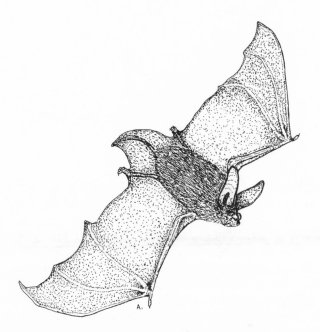

Townsend's big-eared bat is of the same form as Rafinesque's bat, differing mainly in color. Its hair is long and brown from base to tip on both upper and lower sides; there is little luster to the fur. The feet lack the long hairs characteristic of *P. macrotis*. The forearm is about 43 mm (1.7 in.). Like its conspecifics elsewhere, this species is a cave-dweller.

Townsend's big-eared bat occurs in those parts of western Oklahoma where there are gypsum caves, or where there are caverns under granite boulders in the Wichita Mountains. Its choice of roosting habitat parallels that of the eastern pipistrel in the western part of the state, and both species have been taken from the same caves on numerous occasions. *P. townsendii* is widespread throughout the western states, but east of the Great Plains it occurs only in the Ozark Mountains and in the central Appalachians.

Observations concerning reproduction in this species are in general agreement with the data obtained by Pearson *et al.* (1952). Mating takes place in the fall: all females examined in October have had sperm in the oviducts and

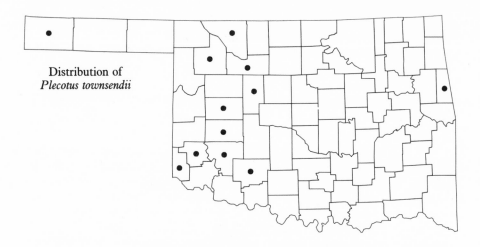

Distribution of
Plecotus townsendii

uterus. Only one young is born per year. On 31 May, a female was found bearing a 16 mm (0.6 in.) fetus in the right uterine horn. Young barely able to fly have been seen as early as 4 July and were still clustering with their mothers. Clustering females, a sign of gestation, have been seen in early May. Females still lactating have been seen on 21 July and 14 August, and females having large mammary glands and nipples (but lacking milk) have been seen on 13 August. These observations indicate a rather prolonged period for parturition, which may be correlated with the fact that these bats hibernate singly rather than in clusters and that awakening is therefore an individual phenomenon, not a synchronous one, as is common in species that cluster during their winter sleep. Individual awakenings would result in less synchronous ovulation.

The western subspecies seems to prefer cool, damp sites for hibernation. In Icebox Cave in northern Woodward County these bats have been found hibernating among fallen blocks of gypsum rock, only two or three feet above the cave floor and in proximity to the trickle of flowing water. All were hibernating individually, a phenomenon that has also been observed in many other caves in western Oklahoma. The eastern race of this species may have somewhat different habits, as Hamilton (1943) mentioned an aggregation of males observed in a cave in West Virginia. Humphrey and Kunz (1976) also noted mostly solitary individuals during hibernation. However, sizeable clusters did occur in some caves, and the frequency of clustering varied seasonally, beginning in December and ending in March. The life history strategies of *Plecotus* are also discussed by Humphrey and Kunz (1976). Caire *et al.* (1984) observed the early foraging behavior of *Plecotus* from Alabaster Caverns and noted that much of the foraging occurs close to the ground.

The involved nomenclatural history of this species has been resolved by Handley (1959), who also reviewed the distribution of the genus worldwide. All American *Plecotus* have a fleshy protuberance on each side of the rostrum, for which reason they have often been called "lump-nosed" bats, while none of the Old World forms are so ornamented. This character was the sole basis for placing the American forms in the genus *Corynorhinus*, which Handley relegated to subgeneric status. Much of the taxonomy of *P. townsendii* has been summarized by Kunz and Martin (1982).

Two subspecies occur in Oklahoma: a smaller, paler form, *P. t. pallescens*, in the western part and a larger, darker form, *P. t. ingens*, in the extreme northeast. The larger form, having a forearm averaging about 45 mm (1.8 in.) in adults, is restricted to the Ozark region of Oklahoma, Arkansas, and Missouri and is listed in the official list of rare and endangered species as endangered. The subspecies is considered to be endangered because of its vulnerability to human disturbance, extremely limited distribution, and small population size. Maternity and hibernation sites still exist in Oklahoma (Grigsby and Puckette, 1982).

Antrozous pallidus (Le Conte)
Pallid Bat
Antrozous pallidus Le Conte, 1856:437
Antrozous pallidus H. Allen, 1864:68

Antrozous pallidus is a large, light-colored bat with grayish flight membranes. Except at the tips, which are drab brown, the hair on the back is creamy white. The underside is white. Its very long ears are yellowish gray, and the fleshy parts of its face are faintly tinged with orange. The long rostrum is fairly broad and is truncated. A low ridge passing in a semicircle from the outer border of one nostril across the tip of the nose pad to the border of the opposite nostril imparts a vaguely piglike aspect to the snout. The forearm is approximately 54 mm (2.1 in.) in adults.

The species occurs in the canyons of northwestern Cimarron County and in the Blaine Gypsum and Wichita Mountains. The two populations are separated by the High Plains. Beyond Oklahoma the species ranges widely throughout western North America.

The circadian habits of this bat are unusual. During daylight hours it resorts to crevices in cliffs, where it may aggregate in groups of a few to perhaps

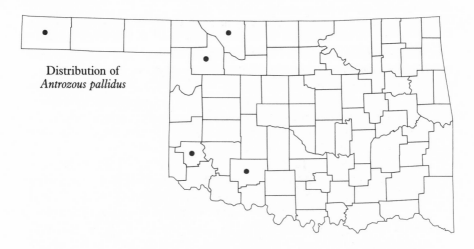

Distribution of
Antrozous pallidus

several dozen. Emergence is fairly late, when there is little light. In Oklahoma, its only night roosts of record are caves, although elsewhere it uses old buildings, rock overhangs, and other more exposed locations. Night roosts are used for the purpose of consuming large prey as well as for resting between feeding bouts; the inedible portions of their food (most frequently consisting of grasshoppers and crickets, sometimes including wingless forms) can be found under such places. This implies that they forage on or near the ground. In fact there are records of their having been caught in mouse traps set for small rodents, where they were probably preying on orthopteran baitrobbers. Pallid bats prefer narrow crevices in caves as hibernation sites. Twente (1955) described a hibernaculum in a gypsum cave in Kansas less than a mile north of the Oklahoma border. It was a ceiling crevice about 3 m (12 ft.) above the cave floor and within the zone of dim light. The bats were wedged into a crack in such a way that both their backs and bellies were in contact with the rock. To date, no hibernacula have been discovered in Oklahoma. Unfortunately, the one referred to above was torched by vandals about ten years after Twente's study and has not been in use since, but another hibernaculum nearby has been used. Orr (1954) reported extensively on the biology of this species in California, and the data available for the species in Oklahoma conform to his.

Reproduction follows the general pattern for bats that hibernate. The males begin spermatogenesis in August, and the function is complete by mid-September, by which time the epididymes are fully enlarged, remaining so until March. The accessory glands are fully developed by November and perhaps a few weeks earlier. Evidently mating can be accomplished from mid-autumn until spring. When winters are prolonged and severe, fall breeding is probably the rule. Of 17 females examined in late May and early June, 11 were carrying twins, which in one case were of remarkably different sizes. Of the remaining six, five carried only one young, and one was barren—it may have been a young of the previous year. Specimens in the U.S. National Museum collected by E. A. Mearns near Fort Hancock, Texas, on 23, 26, and 27 June were young with so much cartilage in the wing knuckles (epiphyses) that they surely were scarcely able to fly. Bats in northern Oklahoma, where spring is later than in that Texas vicinity (El Paso), probably do not have young that are able to fly until about the middle of July.

Antrozous pallidus was first reported from Oklahoma by Blair (1939), who obtained one in Cimarron County. He called it *A. bunkeri* Hibbard, a species name based on a series collected in Kansas near Aetna, not far from where Twente studied the hibernation site referred to above. *Antrozous bunkeri* continued to be recognized as a full species until a study by Morse and Glass (1960) reduced it to subspecific status. They assigned Blair's specimen from Cimarron County to *A. p. pallidus*. Martin and Schmidly (1982) provide a detailed taxonomic review of the pallid bat. Hermanson and O'Shea (1983) comment on other aspects of the biology of *A. pallidus*.

Tadarida brasiliensis (I. Geof. St. Hilaire)
Brazilian Free-tailed Bat
Nyctinomus brasiliensis I. Geoffroy St. Hilaire, 1824:343
Tadarida brasiliensis: Thomas, 1920:222

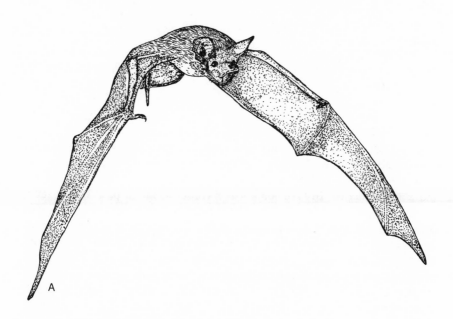

A

This bat is known by many different common names. The most widely used is "Mexican free-tailed bat," an inappropriate name since the species ranges from Argentina and Chile to North America; nor is the epithet "Brazilian free-tailed bat" appropriate for the same reason. "Guano bat" may be a better name. *Tadarida brasiliensis* is a small bat with long, narrow wings and a tail that projects for half its length beyond the border of the tail membrane. Its ears are truncated, point forward, and are not joined across the crown. The hair is white basally for about one-eighth its length, but the rest of the hair is slaty gray, appears velvety, and feels slightly greasy to the touch. The hair is shed once a year, in late August; bats appear reddish at that time because of the action of the dense ammonia fumes of their nursery caves. By contrast, newly fledged young have a pelage that is fresh and gray, so until the first molt is complete, young and adults can be recognized, even though both can fly. It is not uncommon to see these bats with varying amounts of white spot-

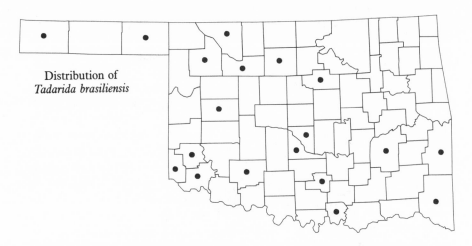

Distribution of
Tadarida brasiliensis

ting, and a few true albinos have been seen in Oklahoma caves. The forearm averages about 43 mm (1.7 in.) in adults.

As stated above, the Brazilian free-tailed bat has a vast range in both North and South America. In Oklahoma it is recorded from all parts of the state, but those records from east of the Blaine Gypsum are mostly of individuals, not of large colonies. Large nursery colonies in Oklahoma all occur in gypsum caves, of which there are five known in Greer, Major, Woods, and Woodward counties. Alabaster Caverns formerly also housed a large nursery, but it was abandoned many years ago when the cave was illuminated and opened to the public. Only a small colony of approximately a thousand individuals still uses the cavern.

The subspecies that occurs over most of Oklahoma is migratory, coming north each spring to nursery caves in Texas, New Mexico (this is the famous bat of Carlsbad Caverns), and Oklahoma. Glass (1982) has reported on the results of banding 170,000 of these bats between 1953 and 1968, from which most of this information is derived. When the young are capable of prolonged flight, the bats leave, beginning in late August, and during the next three months return to their winter range, which lies from the southern edge of the Edwards Plateau in Texas south nearly to the latitude of Mexico City. These bats pass through areas where other nurseries occur and intermingle with bats from those nurseries during the winter and during migration, but a high percentage return to their natal caves. Some bats have been recovered from one to eight years later in the same cave where they were banded as newborn. Adults in nursery caves are almost 100 percent females. Some males come north in spring and form small, predominantly male groups. These usually occupy smaller, nonnursery caves and sometimes take up residence in buildings, as do many of both sexes during their migratory passages. There is evidence, however, that many of the males remain on their winter range throughout the year.

As the Brazilian free-tailed bat is migratory and does not hibernate, its reproductive cycle is radically different from that of other Oklahoma bats. The males become sexually active in February, while the bats are on their winter range, and breeding takes place over several weeks, probably beginning in late February and lasting until early April. There is no delay between mating and conception, and it is during and immediately following the protracted breeding season that the females begin moving north. Some have been seen in Oklahoma as early as 3 April, but the greatest influx occurs in May, when the population builds rapidly. Females taken in May are always pregnant, but the size of embryos varies greatly, reflecting the protracted nature of the breeding period. The crown–rump length of embryos collected on 2 May, for example, varied from two to ten mm. Several females have been found to be pregnant after completion of their first migratory cycle and thus give birth at approximately one year of age.

Newborn have been seen from 5 June until the third week in July, but the peak of births seems to be the first week in July. These data strongly suggest a three-month gestation period. Only one young per female is the rule. One out-of-season pregnant female has been seen in early October.

Newborn young are pink but become gray in about a week before any hair becomes apparent. The females leave them behind when they fly out to feed. On returning, they seem to land at random and suckle the first infant that attaches itself. The "dairy syndrome" may be the cause, or the result, of these bats forming such large nursery aggregations. However, McCracken (1984), using genetic markers, has provided evidence that females in Texas maternity roosts nurse only closely related, if not actually their own, offspring. At any rate, if a nursery falls below an estimated 20,000 females, it is usually abandoned, and the bats presumably merge with other larger groups.

Flying young have been seen as early as 17 July, and many are able to fly by the first week in August. When compared to the peak season of births, these data indicate that young fly at approximately six weeks of age. Studies of marked newborn bats confirm this.

When the young are able to fly, the nursery colonies are at maximum size, and the evening flights are spectacular. Where caves harbor late-summer populations numbering in the millions, the bats begin emerging long before dusk. They emerge in a steady stream which may be continuous for many miles—the cloud of bats emerging has been described as looking like a plume of smoke. Eventually the column breaks up into smaller units, but groups of a few thousand evidently maintain audible contact during their entire foraging period; they may range as far as 80 km (50 mi.) from the cave to feed.

Caire *et al.* (1984) observed the exit flights of a small colony at Alabaster Caverns and noted that the individuals departed toward the east, possibly to avoid competition with individuals from another larger colony to the west. When they return, they come in groups, diving into the cave from a height of over 300 m (1,000 ft.) and sounding like a gale of wind. Some groups do not return until after daylight. Numerous predators feed on *Tadarida*. Owls and hawks capture individual bats at cave entrances during exit and re-entry flights (Caire and Ports, 1981). Skunks and racoons feed on bats in the roost.

During the northward migration in spring, several bats banded in northwestern Oklahoma have turned up in places far to the east of their regular southbound route. These records are usually from buildings and are from eastern Texas, northwestern Louisiana, eastern Oklahoma, eastern Kansas, and east central Nebraska. There is one record of a free-tail being found during April in Menno, South Dakota, and another from southwestern Iowa in September.

The current view on the taxonomy of the Brazilian free-tailed bat is given in Schwartz (1955), who listed all the known subspecies. The Oklahoma subspecies is *T. b. mexicana*, although *T. b. cynocephala* probably also occurs in southeastern Oklahoma (Hardisty *et al.*, 1987).

Tadarida macrotis (Gray)
Big Free-tailed Bat
Nyctinomus macrotis Gray, 1839:5
Tadarida macrotis: Shamel, 1931:15

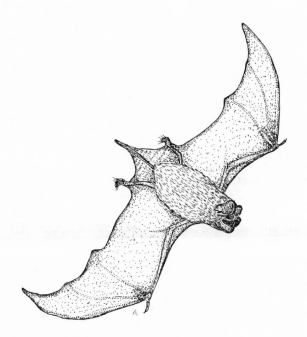

Tadarida macrotis is a large free-tailed bat, with the ears joined together across the top of the head. The overall color of the hair is dull, darkish brown above and below. The basal third of the dorsal hair is white. Length of the forearm is about 62 mm (2.4 in.) in adults.

This is primarily a species of the southwestern deserts of the United States and Mexico. Its nurseries are known from the Big Bend region of Texas, and one is known from north central New Mexico near Abiquiu (Constantine, 1961); the latter is the northernmost extent of the breeding range. After the young are grown, the species becomes a wanderer, as isolated records are known from eastern Iowa and Vancouver, British Columbia, far from its predictable range. There are three known records for Oklahoma: two from Texas County (one from Guymon has not been reported previously) and one from Oklahoma County (Cockrum, 1952; Pyle and Caire, 1979). A record

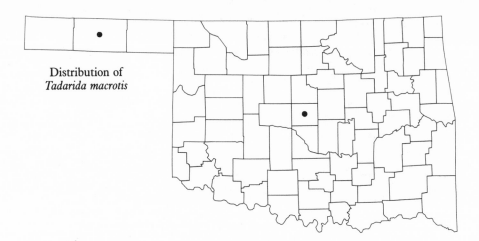

Distribution of
Tadarida macrotis

from Pittsburg, in southeast Kansas (Hays and Ireland, 1967), suggests that this large bat may occur sporadically anywhere in the state. This species is not divided into subspecies. Freeman (1981) reviewed the taxonomy of the family Molossidae and has suggested the genus name *Nyctinomops* instead of *Tadarida*.

Order Xenarthra (Edentata)

Anteaters, Sloths, Armadillos

Bryan P. Glass

The xenarthrans are found only in North and South America. Of the three different forms, anteaters, sloths, and armadillos, only the last presently occurs in the United States. The armadillo, *Dasypus novemcinctus*, is the only xenarthran in Oklahoma.

FAMILY DASYPODIDAE   Armadillo

Dasypus novemcinctus Linnaeus
Nine-banded Armadillo
Dasypus novemcinctus Linnaeus, 1758:50

This species is the only representative of its order, the Xenarthra, that occurs naturally in the United States. Its family, the Dasypodidae, includes all of the living members of the order with armored skin. The armor consists of bony plates embedded in the dermis. The epidermis over the scutes is cornified into keratinous scales. This flexible armor covers the frontal region of the head, the scapular and thoracic body region, the rump and flanks, and the tail. At midbody there are 7–11 (usually 8) transverse ossified bands. The leathery interspaces between these bands and separating them from the scapular and pelvic shields comprise the bands for which the species is recognized. The belly, neck, lower jaw, and limbs are covered with skin that bears sparse, coarse, whitish hairs. There are scales on the feet and legs. The very narrow gape of the mouth can be opened only slightly more than enough to permit extrusion of the long, densely papillated tongue. The simple peglike teeth are confined to the sides of the jaws; all are essentially alike, lack enamel, and are open-rooted. One commonly used ordinal name is Edentata, "toothless", which is certainly not the case. Unlike other armadillos, members of this genus have four claws on the forefeet rather than five.

Strecker (1926) recorded the spread of the armadillo through Texas in the late nineteenth and early twentieth centuries. He stated that before the "late seventies" it was largely confined to the Rio Grande valley of extreme south-

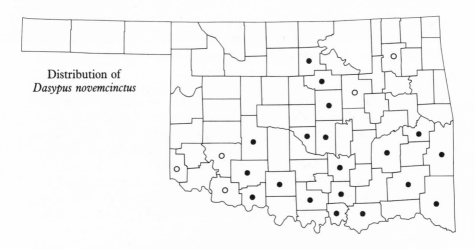

Distribution of
Dasypus novemcinctus

ern Texas, and as late as 1926 he regarded its occurrence as confined to Texas and western Louisiana. Blair (1936, 1939) mentioned specimens from Rogers County, Oklahoma, and from the Arkansas River valley in Creek County. He noted that it was known to have been extending its range in Texas and expressed belief that it was spreading into Oklahoma. The number of road kills encountered in the southern half of Oklahoma since at least the early post– World War II years attest to the abundance of armadillos there over the last thirty-five to forty years. Its numbers have increased in the northern half of the state during the last twenty years to the point that road kills are a common sight now over most of the state, excepting only the northwestern counties and the Panhandle. Marginal records for the species now are occasionally reported for Kansas (Humphrey, 1974). The species is well established in Payne County, and the population was able to survive the extremely cold and snowy winters of 1978, 1979, and 1980. Following these years the numbers were temporarily greatly reduced, suggesting that for practical purposes the species may have reached its northern limit and that from now on its range may expand and contract depending on climatic cycles.

The armadillo is primarily nocturnal but does some diurnal foraging on cloudy days. Armadillos den in holes which they dig themselves. Since an animal may have several "escape" burrows within its home territory, holes are a poor index to numbers except in a general sense. Their food consists primarily of invertebrates which are scratched out of the ground (Kalmbach, 1943; Fitch *et al.*, 1952; Zimmerman, 1982), but there are reports of their feeding on carrion (Newman and Baker, 1942; Clark, 1951) and persimmons (Hamilton, 1946).

Armadillos breed during the summer months after they are about one year of age. At this time the animals form pairs, occupying a single den. Apparently the pairs separate following female receptivity. Upon conception, the egg divides several times as it descends to the uterus, where, as a vesicular blastocyst, it goes into a resting state which lasts for several months. Implantation occurs in November, and as development continues, four embryos form from the single early blastocyst. Thus, four young of identical sex and genetic parentage are born, usually in April after approximately five months of true gestation. Litters of two, three, and five have been recorded, but in all cases the offspring were of the same sex, suggesting that multiple ovulations were not involved. For additional information on reproduction and an extensive bibliography, see McBee and Baker (1982).

These animals have a low metabolic rate, with a body temperature somewhat lower than is usual among mammals, and can undergo torpor during which the level of bodily functions is greatly reduced. This may explain their ability to survive, at least in mild winters, on the northern fringe of their range. It might also explain why, of all nonhuman mammals, only the armadillo is capable of harboring the causative organism of leprosy (a bacterium). It is thought to contract the disease spontaneously (Storrs, 1971, 1973). The leprosy bacillus incubates best at temperatures below those considered normal for most mammals.

Armadillos have few natural enemies. Their behavior in response to a perceived threat is to crouch motionless and then to spring upward with great strength when attack is imminent. This reaction is known to repel dogs successfully, but it is counterproductive on highways, where the reaction occurs just as a fast-moving automobile passes over the animal (Storrs and Labadies, 1982).

The species was known to Linnaeus when he published the tenth edition of *Systema Naturae*. His nomenclature stands, although there is an extensive synonymy. Current practice recognizes the North American form as *D. novemcinctus mexicanus* Peters, 1864, with *D. n. texanum* Bailey, 1905 as a synonym (McBee and Baker, 1982). Glass (1986) has summarized the history of the classification and nomenclature in Xenarthra.

Order Lagomorpha

Rabbits, Hares, and Pikas

William Caire

The order Lagomorpha is a small order; however, it is widely distributed, being native to all continents except Australia. In North America, two families are represented: Ochotonidae (the pika) and Leporidae (rabbits and hares). Only the latter is common to Oklahoma, and four species are known.

Sylvilagus aquaticus (Bachman)
Swamp Rabbit
Lepus aquaticus Bachman, 1837:319
Sylvilagus aquaticus: Nelson, 1909:270

Sylvilagus aquaticus is the largest cottontail rabbit (total length 490–540 mm
= 19.3–21.3 in.; weight 1.3–2.7 kg = 2.9–5.9 lbs.) occurring in Oklahoma.
The larger size of the swamp rabbit should distinguish it from the other
cottontails. Swamp rabbits also have denser, shorter, and coarser hair than
eastern cottontails. The dorsal surface of the front and hind legs of the swamp
rabbit is a rich rufous brown. Overall coloration is usually cinnamon to
brown washed with black, and the underside is whitish. Although the tail is
white like that of the other cottontails, it is longer and less "cottony." Tracks
of swamp rabbits made in mud are often easy to recognize because of definite
toe impressions.

The range of *S. aquaticus* is diminishing rapidly in Oklahoma, primarily as
a result of destruction of habitat. Swamp rabbits prefer low, wet areas near
rivers, streams, lakes, or ponds. The draining of swampy areas, the clearing
of floodplains, and the damming of rivers often result in the removal of prime
swamp rabbit habitat. Formerly, the species occurred widely over the eastern
half of the state (Blair, 1939), but it is now abundant only in the extreme

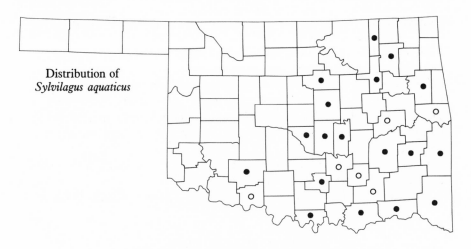

Distribution of
Sylvilagus aquaticus

southeastern corner. Other areas in eastern Oklahoma also support swamp rabbits, but not in abundance. Records of occurrence exist from southeastern Kansas (Hall, 1955), southwestern Missouri (Schwartz and Schwartz, 1981), northwestern Arkansas (Black, 1936) and northeastern Texas (Davis, 1974). Populations of swamp rabbits are still common along the following rivers, creeks, and associated tributaries: Little River; Deep Fork River in McIntosh County; Boggy Creek in Pontotoc, Coal, and Atoka counties; and Lee's Creek in Sequoyah County (Bond, 1964). Blair (1939) noted that the woody and brushy floodplains along creeks and rivers allowed the range of *S. aquaticus* to be extended in fingerlike projections toward the west. Elliot (1899a) reported swamp rabbits in dense thickets and bottomlands of the Washita River near Dougherty. He indicated that the species was common but very wary and remained in the nearly impenetrable thickets of grapevines and briers near the river. McCarley (1952) noted that sightings were made in Bryan County near Colbert only in a floodplain association which consisted of an herbaceous ground cover, shrubby understory, and deciduous trees, particularly pecans, cottonwoods, oaks, and elms.

Little information is available on the ecology and reproduction of swamp rabbits in Oklahoma. The following material is based on accounts summarizing the biology of swamp rabbits from other portions of its range (Hall, 1955; Chapman and Feldhammer, 1981; Chapman et al., 1982). Swamp rabbits probably have two litters (four to six young) per year. The breeding season is from January to September, peaking in February and March. Gestation lasts approximately 40 days. The altricial, furred young are born in a nest of leaves that is often placed in a hollow log, in a hole along a bank, or in thick vegetation. The nest is lined with fur pulled from the doe.

Although little is known about the food habits of swamp rabbits, grass and sedges apparently compose a large part of the diet (Terrel, 1972). Coprophagy (reingestion of fecal pellets) occurs, as in other lagomorphs.

Swamp rabbits readily take to water and swim well. The dense, short fur helps to insulate the animal. Evasion of predators is often effected by swimming and hiding in the water with only the nose and eyes exposed. Major predators include coyotes, foxes, bobcats, snakes, hawks, owls, and, in southeastern Oklahoma, possibly alligators. Man has avidly hunted swamp rabbits for sport and meat. Floods may kill them or force them into less suitable habitats.

Ward (1934) reported on the parasitic cestodes, nematodes, trematodes, and ticks found on swamp rabbits in Oklahoma.

The subspecies occurring in Oklahoma is *S. a. aquaticus* (Hall, 1981).

Sylvilagus audubonii (Baird)
Desert Cottontail
Lepus audubonii Baird, 1858:608
Sylvilagus audubonii: Nelson, 1909:214

The desert cottontail, *Sylvilagus audubonii*, may be difficult to distinguish from the eastern cottontail, *S. floridanus*, in western Oklahoma where these two species are sympatric. Desert cottontails generally have longer ears (59–69 mm = 2.3–2.7 in., usually more than 60 percent of the length of the hind

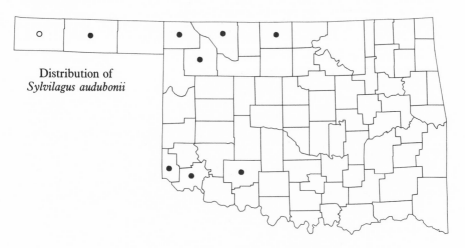

Distribution of
Sylvilagus audubonii

foot) and longer hind legs (82–93 mm = 3.2–3.7 in.) than eastern cotton-tails. Rough, inflated auditory bullae distinguish the skull of *S. audubonii* from that of *S. floridanus*, which has less inflated and smoother bullae. Most desert cottontails are light brown in color over most of the dorsum. The ven-ter is white, as is the short tail. The nape patch is pallid buff, and no white has been reported on the forehead.

Desert cottontails occur in the Oklahoma Panhandle and the western one-third of the main part of the state. Records of occurrence exist from the fol-lowing physiognomic regions: Piñon-Juniper Mesas, Shortgrass High Plains, Mixed-grass Plains, Mesquite-Grass Plains, and Post Oak–Blackjack Up-lands. Specific habitat is varied but usually includes arid grassland, brushy, or rocky areas (Blair, 1939). Martin and Preston (1970) suggested that in Har-mon County desert cottontails were more common on the mesquite plains than in the brushy riparian habitats, where *S. floridanus* was more abundant. Desert cottontails also were commonly seen in active prairie dog towns and sought refuge in the burrows when threatened (Martin and Preston, 1970; Tyler, 1970). Glass (1951) indicated that desert cottontails were most com-mon on the valley floors and mesa slopes of the Black Mesa region. In the Wichita Mountains, *S. audubonii* was found in the grassy valleys (Glass and Halloran, 1961).

Blair (1954) suggested that, in areas supporting both *S. audubonii* and *S. floridanus*, an ecological separation exists. Near Olustee, *S.audubonii* fre-quented rocky slopes dominated by *Juniperus*, whereas *S. floridanus* pre-ferred the riparian areas. However, both species were found together on the rocky slopes on several occasions.

Desert cottontails are crepuscular, active in early mornings and evenings,

TABLE 3.   Rabbit hunting season harvest in
Oklahoma, 1967–80. (Oklahoma Dept.
Wildl. Conserv.)

Year	Average Kill/Hunter	Total Kill
1967	8.8	379,817
1968	9.0	385,866
1969	8.5	524,782
1970	8.1	405,413
1971	10.0	463,300
1972	9.7	567,796
1973	7.5	329,912
1974	7.1	326,450
1975	9.4	363,968
1976	9.3	536,796
1977	8.7	496,813
1978	10.0	755,401
1979	8.3	658,171
1980	9.5	502,912

spending the majority of their time foraging. The diet consists primarily of grasses and forbs. Resting periods are spent in shallow burrows, crude forms (slight depressions in the ground surrounded by vegetation), or thick clumps of vegetation. When startled, desert cottontails either "freeze" or flee in a zigzag fashion toward protective cover. The white tail is usually flashed (held erect) while the rabbit runs, but once cover is reached, the tail is dropped, allowing the animal to blend into its surroundings. Desert cottontails can swim and occasionally will climb low trees. When captured or wounded, a high-pitched squeal is often emitted.

This species is not gregarious except during the breeding season, when several males may chase a female. As with most rabbits, desert cottontails are prolific breeders and may breed all year in Oklahoma. The gestation period is approximately 28 days, after which a litter of two to three young is born. The altricial young (eyes closed, hairless body, little movement) are born in a nest or burrow lined with grass, weeds, and hair pulled from the female's body. After three to four weeks the young rabbits depart the nest area.

Predators include coyotes, foxes, bobcats, snakes, hawks, owls, and domestic dogs and cats. Man also hunts desert cottontails for sport as well as for the meat and pelt (Table 3).

Cestodes isolated from desert cottontails in Oklahoma are described by

Buscher (1975) and Buscher and Tyler (1975). The desert cottontail may also harbor tularemia.

Most of what is known about the ecology of desert cottontails in North America is summarized by Chapman and Willner (1978).

The subspecies occurring in Oklahoma is *S. a. neomexicanus* (Hall, 1981).

Sylvilagus floridanus (J. A. Allen)
Eastern Cottontail
Lepus sylvaticus floridanus J. A. Allen, 1890 : 160
Sylvilagus floridanus: Lyon, 1904 : 322

Sylvilagus floridanus is the most common cottontail rabbit in Oklahoma. Among the other cottontails in Oklahoma (*S. aquaticus, S. audubonii*), the eastern cottontail may be most easily confused with *S. audubonii*. It is distinguished from the latter by shorter ears (50–65 mm = 2–2.6 in.; usually less than 60 percent of hind foot length) and shorter hind feet (80–115 mm = 3.1–4.5 in.). Cranially, *S. floridanus* usually differs in having less inflated and smoother auditory bullae than *S. audubonii*. From *S. aquaticus* the eastern cottontail may be distinguished by a smaller head and larger overall size (338–454 mm = 13.3–17.9 in. total length). Dorsal coloration is a rusty brown or a deep ochraceous buff washed with black. The sides are paler,

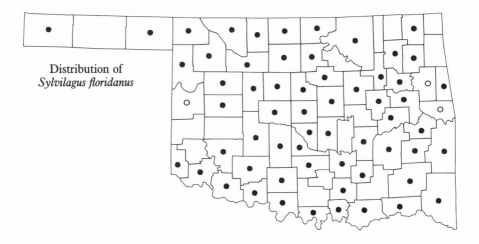

Distribution of
Sylvilagus floridanus

often slightly grayish, and the venter is white. There is always a reddish nape, and usually a white spot or streak on the forehead.

The eastern cottontail has the widest distribution in the state and occupies the greatest variety of habitats of any cottontail in Oklahoma. It occurs across the entire main part of the state and across the Panhandle. This species is found most commonly associated with stream valleys, grassy fencerows, forested areas, and brushy sites in riparian situations (Blair, 1939; Bigham, 1966). However, it also occurs in sand dune communities (Blair, 1939; Elliot, 1899a). Osborne and Kellogg (1943) indicated that this rabbit was seen in the following communities in Roger Mills and Custer counties: tall-grass bottomlands, forest bottomlands, mixed-grass uplands, sagebrush areas, mixed shrub, and shinnery oak areas. In Bryan County, McCarley (1952) recorded numerous sight records in all plant associations but most commonly in the tall-grass prairie. Along the Salt Fork River, eastern cottontails were abundant among willow brush, high grass, and prairie flats as well as in canyon bottoms and creek areas (Elliot, 1899a). Jackson and Warfel (1933) indicated that eastern cottontails inhabited the salt flat areas of northwestern Oklahoma but were not as plentiful as jack rabbits. Ruffer (1964a) often sighted these cottontails in floodplain forests in Cleveland County. Glass and Halloran (1961) indicated that *S. floridanus* was very common at lower levels in post oak–blackjack forest and along streams in good grass cover in the Wichita Mountains. In extreme western Oklahoma, where *S. floridanus* and *S. audubonii* are sympatric, some ecological separation may occur. In Harmon County, Martin and Preston (1970) found *S. floridanus* most often in the brushy, riparian situations and *S. audubonii* on the mesquite plains. Blair

(1954) suggested that *S. floridanus* prefers more mesic riparian situations than *S. audubonii*. He noted that the latter frequently occupied the arid uplands and *S. floridanus* the stream valleys. However, he did find both species together on the rocky, cedar-covered slopes near the Red River at Olustee. Dalquest (1968) suggested that *S. floridanus* was becoming more common than *S. audubonii* in north central Texas.

The remains of eastern cottontails have been found associated with prehistoric man in a dig (600–800 years before present) on the Washita River in Garvin County (Ahshapanek and Burns, 1960).

Bigham (1966) examined the reproductive biology of the eastern cottontail in north central Oklahoma. The breeding season may vary in different years, but most often it occurred from mid-February to early September. Males are apparently ready to breed earlier than females, with gonads reaching maximum development in March. Activity in the testes declined slowly until June, then rather rapidly between June and July, and reached a minimum in October (the only month when spermatozoa were absent) and November. A slow increase in testis size began in December. Bigham also suggested that the presence or absence of the testes in the scrotum is not a reliable indicator of sexual activity. The time of gestation ranges between 25 and 35 days, after which three to four altricial young are usually born. A single female may bear three or four litters during the year. The nest, usually constructed in thick vegetation or in a shallow, slanted burrow, is often lined with hair pulled from the female's own body.

Cottontails feed on a variety of herbaceous and woody plants. Grasses, forbs, and other weedy vegetation comprise most of the summer and spring diets. In the winter, stems of woody plants (sumac, plum, and willow) are eaten. Most feeding and other activity is crepuscular, although on occasion cottontails may be seen foraging late into the night. Coprophagy is also practiced by the eastern cottontail (Hamilton, 1955). Two types of fecal pellets are excreted: hard brown fecal pellets and soft greenish food pellets (Chapman *et al.*, 1980). The digestive processes have extracted all usable nutrients from the hard pellets, whereas the soft pellets (produced in the caecum) are reingested for additional nutrient extraction. Bird (1930) reported that *S. floridanus* could easily open the cocoons and eat the pupae of the large silk moth (*Samia cecropia*).

Numerous parasites have been isolated from cottontail rabbits. Ticks, fleas, botflies, mites, cestodes, and trematodes are commonly found (Chapman *et al.*, 1980). Cottontails may also transmit tularemia; therefore, sick animals should be avoided. Predators of cottontails include coyotes, foxes, bobcats, raccoons, feral dogs, hawks, owls, and man. The cottontail is an important game animal that is hunted for sport as well as meat. Table 3 reveals the total number of cottontails (all three species, *S. audubonii*, *S. floridanus*, and *S. aquaticus*) taken in Oklahoma during past years. Chapman *et al.* (1980) summarized the pertinent literature and ecology of *S. floridanus* over the entire range of the species.

The subspecies occurring in Oklahoma are *S. f. llanensis* and *S. f. alacer* (Chapman *et al.*, 1980).

Lepus californicus Gray
Black-tailed Jack Rabbit
Lepus californicus Gray, 1837:586

Lepus californicus is the only jack rabbit occurring in Oklahoma. From the cottontail rabbits (*Sylvilagus aquaticus*, *S. audubonii*, and *S. floridanus*) jack rabbits may be distinguished easily by larger size (total length 510–582 mm = 20.1–22.9 in.; 1.4–2.3 kg = 3.1–5.1 lbs.), enormous, black-tipped ears that are as long as the hind foot, long legs, and a black dorsal stripe extending from the tail onto the grayish rump. Dorsally, jack rabbits are usually an

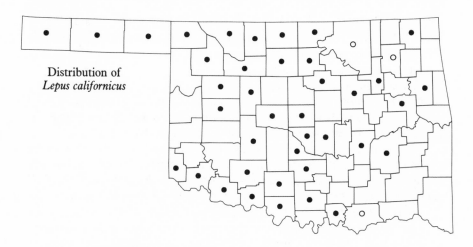

Distribution of
Lepus californicus

ochraceous buff washed with black, and the sides are grayish buff. Both the venter and hind feet are pure white. The lack of an interparietal bone easily distinguishes the skull of *Lepus* from that of *Sylvilagus*.

Jack rabbits are not rabbits, but hares. Hares differ from rabbits in having precocial rather than altricial young and in using forms (slight depressions in the ground, usually in taller vegetation) rather than nests for giving birth.

Black-tailed jack rabbits have been reported from most portions of the state but are more characteristically and abundantly found in the arid western one-half of Oklahoma. Very few specimens have been reported from the east and none from the extreme southeastern parts of the state even though records exist for jack rabbits from southeastern Kansas (Hall, 1955), western Arkansas (Black, 1936; Sealander, 1979), southwestern Missouri (Schwartz and Schwartz, 1981), and northeastern Texas (Davis, 1974). Preferred habitat is open country with scattered thickets or shrub patches. Phillips (1936) indicated that jack rabbits were very abundant in moderately overgrazed pastures. Dense forested areas are usually avoided. Individuals may be seen on occasion in the piñon-juniper woodlands of the Black Mesa region but are more common in grassland-prairie areas there (Glass, 1951; Geluso, 1970). Jackson and Warfel (1933) reported jack rabbits as being common in the salt plains of northwestern Oklahoma. They observed the jack rabbits running across the salt flats from one grassy island to another. Martin and Preston (1970) reported that *L. californicus* was widely distributed in Harmon County but was most common in the mesquite plains southwest of Hollis. Tyler (1970) observed *Lepus* resting in the shade of *Cirsium* in prairie dog towns in southwestern Oklahoma. Jack rabbits have also been seen in the following habitats: sagebrush, scattered tall-grass bottomlands, mixed-grass uplands, shinnery oak areas, and mixed shrub communities (Jackson and Warfel, 1933; Blair, 1939; Osborne and Kellogg, 1943). McCarley (1952) noted that jack rabbits were not common in Bryan County, but the few seen were in tall-grass prairie and cleared areas within post oak–blackjack associations. In the Wichita Mountains, Glass and Halloran (1961) suggested that jack rabbits were fairly common in the grass meadows, as evidenced by numerous road kills. In eastern Oklahoma, jack rabbits are found in the prairie peninsula; the clearing of forest there may be a factor in range extensions.

Jack rabbits are crepuscular but often feed well into the night. During the day most of the time is spent resting in a form. Occasionally jack rabbits will rest in the open, lying on their sides. If threatened, jack rabbits will "freeze," slowly creep into thicker vegetation, or bolt and flee at speeds of up to 60 kph (35 mph). When at top speed, their leaps may cover several meters.

Lepus californicus is tolerant of conspecifics and often gathers in large groups to feed. However, during the breeding season, chases and "boxing" matches may occur. In favorable years in Oklahoma jack rabbits may breed throughout the year; however, the principal reproductive periods are in spring and summer. The gestation period varies from 41–47 days, after which two to four precocial young are born. The eyes are open at birth and the well-haired young are capable of running soon thereafter.

The diet includes grasses, herbs, sagebrush, and forbs. Smith (1940b) suggested that jack rabbit populations increase with overgrazing because food plants preferred are more common in overgrazed pastures. Large fluctuations in jack rabbit population sizes are not easy to explain and warrant closer examination.

Predators of jack rabbits include coyotes, foxes, bobcats, owls, hawks, badgers, and domestic dogs. Man has long hunted jack rabbits for sport and food in Oklahoma. When populations became very large, "rabbit drives" were used to collect hundreds and, in some cases, thousands of rabbits into a fenced area where they were killed. Many of these rabbits were used in the dog food industry (Bond, 1964). In Kansas during the winter of 1894–95 approximately 20,000 rabbits were shipped to meat markets (Hall, 1955).

Jack rabbits, like other lagomorphs, harbor numerous parasites, including fleas and ticks (Ellis, 1955; Ward, 1934), several of which may transmit to man serious diseases such as tularemia and bubonic plague.

The subspecies occurring in Oklahoma is *L. c. melanotis* (Hall, 1981).

Order Rodentia

Rodents

William Caire

Rodentia is the largest order of mammals, with more than 1,700 species described. This order is distributed world-wide, being absent only from extreme polar regions. Nine families and at least 49 species have occurred in recent times in Oklahoma. These nine families are Sciuridae (squirrels, woodchucks, and chipmunks); Geomyidae (gophers); Heteromyidae (pocket mice and kangaroo rats); Castoridae (beaver); Cricetidae (New World rats and mice); Muridae (Old World rats and mice); Zapodidae (jumping mice); Erethizontidae (porcupine); Capromyidae (nutria).

FAMILY SCIURIDAE   Squirrels, Woodchucks, Chipmunks

Tamias striatus (Linnaeus)
Eastern Chipmunk
[*Sciurus*] *striatus* Linnaeus, 1758:64
Tamias striatus: Baird, 1857:55

This alert and active chipmunk, *Tamias striatus*, is easily recognized by its typical chipmunk coloration and behavior. Alternating dark brown, blackish, grayish, or tan and whitish stripes cover the dorsum, extend back, and terminate in a bright reddish to orangish rump. Two facial stripes on either side are buff-colored, and the venter is a buffy white. The tail is blackish brown above and below, with white-tipped rufous hairs along the sides. Late spring and summer coats are normally brighter than the winter coats, which appear to be somewhat faded.

In Oklahoma the eastern chipmunk is distributed across the eastern one-half of the state. Specimens have been reported from the following physiognomic regions: Oak-Hickory Ozark Plateau, Tall-grass Prairie Hills, Oak-Hickory-Pine Ouachita Highlands, and the Post Oak-Blackjack Uplands. Characteristically, chipmunks live on rocky, forested slopes and in mesic ravines (Blair, 1939). They are also known to occur in blackjack–post oak stands, in wooded rocky ravines, and near buildings. Westward extensions of riparian forest and vegetation types from the east provide avenues of dispersal and colonization into areas of central Oklahoma which would not otherwise be inhabited. The

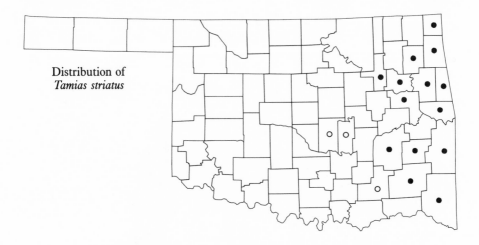

Distribution of
Tamias striatus

westernmost counties occupied are Pottawatomie and Seminole (Black *et al.*, 1977).

Eastern chipmunks are not colonial and (except for family groups) it is unusual to see more than one or two together. This species apparently does not hibernate in Oklahoma (McCarley, 1961) but may remain below ground in burrows for extended periods during winter. Burrows are often placed under the edge of rocks or boulders, near the base of trees, or under the edge of buildings. During times of favorable weather, the major activity appears to be the gathering and storage of food in subterranean chambers. Even in areas where winters are cold and chipmunks undergo deep torpor, they store food as well. Evidently they cannot maintain full torpor without intermittent feeding and are best described as quasi-hibernators. Food is usually gathered with the forefeet and carried in cheek pouches. Principal food items are acorns, nuts, berries, wild seeds, and some insects and mushrooms.

The gestation period is approximately 31 days. Three to five young are born during spring or early summer. Predators are the same as those for most rodents and include hawks, owls, snakes, foxes, and other carnivores. Snyder (1982) comments on other aspects of the biology of *T. striatus*.

The subspecies occurring in Oklahoma is *T. s. venustus* (Hall, 1981).

Eutamias quadrivittatus (Say)
Colorado Chipmunk
Sciurus quadrivittatus Say, 1823:45
Eutamius quadrivittatus: Miller and Rehn, 1901:43

In Oklahoma, *Eutamias quadrivittatus* is confined to the Black Mesa region and is the only chipmunk that occurs there. The white eye stripes and five dark bands alternating with four white interspaces dorsally easily distinguish the Colorado chipmunk from ground squirrels and other diurnal rodents in this part of the state. *Tamias striatus*, the eastern chipmunk, occurs only in the eastern half of Oklahoma.

These small chipmunks appear to be much more common in Colorado and New Mexico than in Oklahoma (Armstrong, 1972; Findley *et al.*, 1975; Tate and Nice, 1928). However, in those counties contiguous with Oklahoma in Colorado and New Mexico the Colorado chipmunk is less common than it is in the Rocky Mountains proper.

This chipmunk inhabits dry, rocky, piñon-juniper canyons. It has also been observed in rocky ravines and on mesa and talus slopes (Blair, 1939). Geluso (1970) indicated that the Colorado chipmunk is a common member of the piñon-juniper community in the Black Mesa region and is most often col-

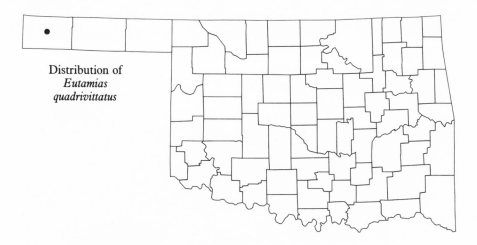

Distribution of
Eutamias
quadrivittatus

lected with the piñon mouse (*Peromyscus truei*). Less frequently taken mammals in this habitat are the white-throated woodrat (*Neotoma albigula*) and the rock squirrel (*Spermophilus variegatus*) (Geluso, 1970). Warren (1909) captured several Colorado chipmunks in similar habitats in nearby Baca and Las Animas counties, southeastern Colorado.

Oklahoma specimens are currently assigned to the subspecies *E. q. quadrivittatus* (Hall, 1981). Armstrong (1972) noted that a few specimens from southeastern Colorado are distinctively colored compared to those specimens from western regions of Colorado. The Oklahoma specimens closely resemble those of southeast Colorado. Patterson (1984) examined the geographic variation and taxonomy of Colorado and Hopi chipmunks and included some specimens from Oklahoma. A thorough analysis of the geographic variation of *E. quadrivittatus* may reveal that these southeastern Colorado, northeastern New Mexico, and far western Oklahoma populations represent a distinct subspecies. The subspecies name available for the Oklahoma animals thus would be *E. q. animosus*, proposed by Warren (1909). Strong evidence is presented by Levenson *et al.* (1985) for *Tamias* to be the generic name for all chipmunks.

Marmota monax (Linnaeus)
Woodchuck
(*Mus*) *monax* Linnaeus, 1758:60
(*Marmota*) *monax:* Trouessart, 1904:344

The large size (2.7–4.5 kg = 6–10 lbs.) of *Marmota* easily distinguishes it from other rodents, particularly the squirrels. Its pelage is grayish brown in color and has a yellowish or reddish cast. Varying amounts of buffy white adorn the head and facial region.

The woodchuck is limited in distribution to the eastern portions of Oklahoma. Few records exist for the woodchuck in Oklahoma, making difficult the characterization of its range in the state. Blair (1939) recorded sightings of woodchucks near Scraper in Cherokee County and at Locust Grove in Mayes County. The first Oklahoma specimen preserved was obtained in Ottawa County in 1960 (Long, 1961). Previously, the specimen records nearest to Oklahoma were from Fayetteville, in Washington County, Arkansas (Sealander, 1956); from McDonald County, Missouri (Black, 1936); and from Hamilton in Greenwood County and Fontana in Linn County, Kansas (Cockrum, 1952). However, local residents of Ottawa County indicated to Long (1961) that the woodchuck was a fairly common inhabitant there. Since Long's specimen, woodchucks have been reported as far south as Red Oak in Latimer County (McCarley and Free, 1962). The Oklahoma State University Museum contains specimens from Stillwater and near Glencoe, both previously unreported. The Museum at Northern Oklahoma College in Tonkawa contains a mounted specimen from southeast Kay County.

Specific habitat for woodchucks in Oklahoma appears to be hilly and rocky areas in open woodlands having fields or meadows adjacent (Long, 1961; McCarley and Free, 1962).

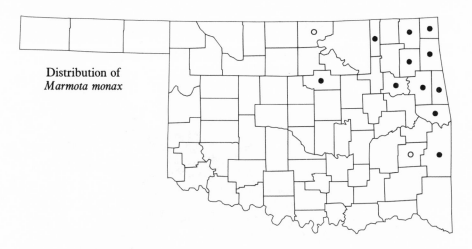

Distribution of
Marmota monax

There is little information on reproduction of woodchucks in Oklahoma. However, a lactating female was shot in April in Ottawa County (Long, 1961). No other data exist describing the ecology of the woodchuck in Oklahoma. Since no winter specimens have been taken in the state, it is assumed that the woodchuck hibernates here as it does in other portions of its range. An extensive review of the biology of all North American marmots is given by Lee and Fundenburg (1982).

The subspecies occurring in Oklahoma is *M. m. monax* (Long, 1961).

Spermophilus spilosoma Bennett
Spotted Ground Squirrel
Spermophilus spilosoma Bennett, 1833:40

Spermophilus spilosoma is easily distinguished from the other ground squirrels and chipmunks occurring in Oklahoma by the lack of a bushy tail and by an indistinct dorsal pattern of irregularly placed squarish light spots that may be faint in some specimens and quite distinct in others. Upper parts vary in color from fawn to light drab or grayish. The ears are rather inconspicuous, and the tail is short (about one-third the total length).

This species occurs in the more westerly sections of Oklahoma. It has been taken in the following physiognomic regions: Piñon-Juniper Mesas, Shortgrass High Plains, Mixed-grass Plains, Mesquite-Grass Plains, and the western edge of the Post Oak–Blackjack Uplands. The easternmost specimens in Oklahoma are recorded from the intermontane valleys of the Wichita Mountains (Glass and Halloran, 1961). Two of the three specimens taken there came from a prairie dog town which is now abandoned. The other specimens came from a meadow east of Comanche Lake. Elsewhere in Oklahoma, the spotted ground squirrel has been taken primarily in sandy areas. Martin and Preston (1970) found small groups of them on both the sandy and tight soils of the mesquite-covered plains in Harmon County. Sandy areas in Harmon County supported only *S. spilosoma*, whereas *S. tridecemlineatus* was taken on other soil types. Several Harmon County specimens were collected in the winter (December), and this supports Howell's (1938) contention that the species is not a continuous hibernator in some southern portions of its range. However, McMurray (1947), in 16,210 trap nights during three winter seasons, collected only a single juvenile specimen on the Southern Great

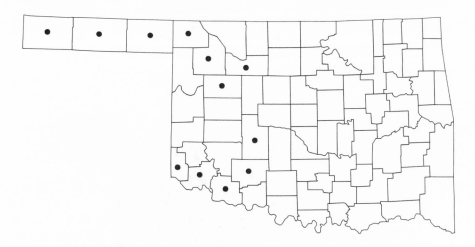

Plains Experimental Range north of Fort Supply. Summer trapping in the same area revealed a density of 0.4–1.3 animals per hectare (1–3 per acre). The extent to which *S. spilosoma* hibernates in Oklahoma is not completely understood. Streubel and Fitzgerald (1978) summarized information on *S. spilosoma,* while Tomich (1982) reviewed information on North America ground squirrels.

The subspecies occurring in Oklahoma is *S. s. marginatus* (Hall, 1981).

Spermophilus tridecemlineatus (Mitchill)
Thirteen-lined Ground Squirrel
Sciurus tridecem-lineatus Mitchill, 1821:248
Spermonhilus tridecemlineatus: J. A. Allen, 1895:337

This diurnal ground squirrel, *Spermophilus tridecemlineatus,* may be distinguished from all other Oklahoma mammals by the light buffy and dark brown stripes running lengthwise down the body. There are rows of squarish white spots in each of the dark stripes. The ears are small and the tail slightly bushy. Overall color of these ground squirrels is correlated with soil color. Distinctly reddish individuals occur on the Permian red soils, whereas paler-colored ones occur on light-colored soils (Blair, 1939). Thirteen-lined ground squirrels have well-developed internal cheek pouches.

Specimens have been either seen or collected in the following physiognomic regions: Piñon-Juniper Mesas, Shortgrass High Plains, Mixed-grass Plains, Mesquite-Grass Plains, Post Oak–Blackjack Uplands, and the Tallgrass Prairie Rolling Hills. Throughout most of its range in Oklahoma, *S. tridecemlineatus* is found most frequently in grassy habitats. Small colonies are often seen along roadsides, on golf courses, in cemeteries, on dirt or grass airfields, and in park areas. Osborn and Kellogg (1943) reported thirteen-lined ground squirrels common in the tall-grass bottomlands, in the mixed-grass uplands, in sagebrush areas, in mixed shrublands, and in shinnery lands of Roger Mills and Custer counties. Clark and Skryja (1969) and Geluso (1970) reported several in the grassland habitats and high plains of the Black Mesa region. These ground squirrels were considered to be uncommon inhabitants of the intermontane valleys of the Wichita Mountains (Glass and

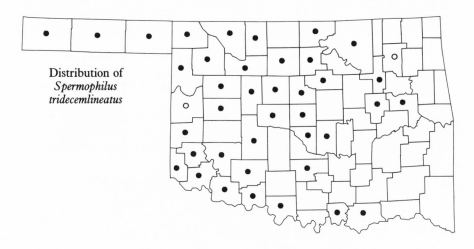

Distribution of
*Spermophilus
tridecemlineatus*

Halloran, 1961). Jackson and Warfel (1933) found *S. tridecemlineatus* in dry, sandy portions of open prairies surrounding the salt plains of northwestern Oklahoma. Martin and Preston (1970) observed and collected several specimens in the mesquite plains of southwestern Oklahoma and found them to be more abundant on tighter soils than in sandy areas. Occasionally this species will utilize tall-grass habitats in pastures and along fencerows.

Thirteen-lined ground squirrels appear to be rather solitary, but often occur in small colonies or groups because of similar habitat requirements (McCarley, 1966; Wistrand, 1974). Several different burrows are constructed; these are used for hiding, nesting, and hibernation (Desha, 1966). In southern Oklahoma the same burrow may be used for both nesting and hibernation (Desha, 1966), because the winter frost depth is not deep (< 15 cm [6 in.]). Murray and Vestal (1979) and Desha (1966) described the various burrow systems. Grubitz (1963) described various aspects of the social behavior of thirteen-lined ground squirrels.

The gestation period is about 27 days, with emergence of the young from the burrow in 32 days, or approximately five weeks after birth (Bridgewater, 1966). Bridgewater (1966) suggested that breeding is most common during the third week of April, with births occurring during May (average litter size 8.6). McCarley (1966) reported that mating occurs aboveground during the day from April to June, with males actively seeking out estrous females. He also suggested that young female squirrels bear smaller litters ($\bar{x}$ = 4.9 young) than older females ($\bar{x}$ = 7.0 young).

Spermophilus tridecemlineatus is a true hibernator that has been studied extensively in the laboratory. McCarley (1966) reported that older males precede older females into hibernation beginning in July. Juveniles are the last to enter hibernation and may be active as late as August and October. The average length of hibernation is about 240 days, and emergence occurs in early March.

Grass, herbs, seeds, and insects compose the bulk of the diet. However, thirteen-lined ground squirrels have been known to kill and consume young cottontail rabbits (*Sylvilagus*), mice, young birds, and lizards (Bridgewater and Penny, 1966).

Streubel and Fitzgerald (1978) summarized the information in the literature concerning the biology of *S. tridecemlineatus*. One of the better accounts of the seasonal activities of this species is given by Scheck and Fleharty (1979). A good review of all ground squirrels in North America was given by Tomich (1982). Cothran (1983) discusses the morphologic relationships of hybridizing *S. tridecemlineatus* and *S. mexicanus*.

Two subspecies are reported in Oklahoma, *S. t. arenicola* in the northwest and *S. t. texensis* throughout the remainder of the state (Hall, 1981).

Spermophilus variegatus (Erxleben)
Rock Squirrel
(*Sciurus*) *variegatus* Erxleben, 1777:421
Spermophilus variegatus: Nelson, 1889:898

A variegated pattern of black and white on the upper parts that extends into the rather bushy tail gives this largest of Oklahoma ground squirrels a

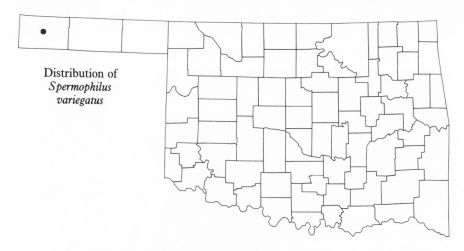

Distribution of
Spermophilus
variegatus

grizzled, mottled appearance. This mottled coloration distinguishes the rock squirrel from tree squirrels (*Sciurus niger* and *S. carolinensis*), which are somewhat smaller.

In Oklahoma, *S. variegatus* is known only from the Panhandle area. One of us (Glass) is of the opinion that this specimen (OKSU 254), listed as occurring in Beaver County, dates from the prestatehood period of Oklahoma history (1890–1907), when the Panhandle was Beaver County, and that the true range of this species is, and always has been, confined to the canyons of the Cimarron River in the northwest corner of the Panhandle. There is no rock habitat in the Panhandle except in the above-mentioned area. Habitat similar to that in the Panhandle is found in Woodward and Major counties, but no records of rock squirrels exist from these areas. Blair (1939) suggested that this saxicolous species has dispersed into Oklahoma from the Rocky Mountains via the rock outcrops along the North Canadian and Cimarron rivers. Geluso (1970) recorded two rock squirrels from the rock cliff community of the Black Mesa region and four from the piñon-juniper community. Other mammal associates in the Black Mesa area were the Colorado chipmunk (*Eutamias quadrivittatus*), the piñon mouse (*Peromyscus truei*), and the white-throated woodrat (*Neotoma albigula*) (Geluso, 1970).

Reproductive and ecological data for this species in Oklahoma are scant; one female taken in May near Kenton contained five embryos. Tomich (1982) reviewed the biology of North American ground squirrels.

The subspecies in Oklahoma is *S. v. grammurus* (Hall, 1981).

Cynomys ludovicianus (Ord)
Black-tailed Prairie Dog
Arctorys ludoviciana Ord, 1815:292
Cynomys ludovicianus: Baird, 1858:331

The black-tailed prairie dog, *Cynomys ludovicianus,* is a stocky, diurnal, ground-dwelling squirrel. The general coloration of the short, coarse pelage is pinkish cinnamon buff. The tail is short (72–115 mm = 2.8–4.5 in.) and black-tipped. The legs are short and the feet are large with well-developed claws; larger claws are found on the forefeet than on the hind feet. The ears are well-haired, rounded, and short. Cheek pouches are rudimentary.

Most black-tailed prairie dogs are inhabitants of shortgrass prairies. Tyler (1968) summarized the distributional status of *Cynomys* in Oklahoma. Specimens exist from the following physiognomic regions: Piñon-Juniper Mesas, Shortgrass High Plains, Mixed-grass Plains, Mesquite-Grass Plains, and in the western edge of the Post Oak–Blackjack Uplands. Osborn (1943) noted the occurrence of prairie dogs in shinnery oak savanna in Roger Mills County.

In the 1800s, black-tailed prairie dogs covered a vast portion of Oklahoma—apparently millions of acres of dog towns were present (Lewis and Hassien, 1974). Now only a few scattered disjunct populations exist in the

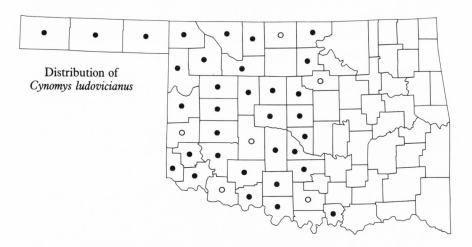

Distribution of
Cynomys ludovicianus

state. This decline in numbers is a direct result of control programs introduced to rid the land of the rodents and clear the way for ranching and farming industries. In 1967, only 280 active dog towns (totaling 9,522 acres) were known in Oklahoma, and 42 percent of this acreage occurred in the three Panhandle counties, Cimarron, Beaver, and Texas (Tyler, 1968). Lewis and Hassien (1974) noted an increase in acres (15,000) seven years later. Some areas of the state still have declining numbers, while in others they have increased or remained about the same. The black-tailed prairie dog is in need of protection as a part of Oklahoma's heritage. In 1972, the Department of Wildlife placed a moratorium on the control of prairie dogs, but it was short-lived and presently any landowner may obtain a permit from a local game ranger to poison dog towns on his land with strychnine-treated grain or with carbon disulfide gas. Lewis *et al.* (1979) discussed the techniques which may be used to reestablish and limit prairie dog towns.

The general public is not aware of the ecological consequences of the removal of a prairie dog town. Complete removal may result in the undesirable spread of brush. Many other animals are dependent to a certain degree upon the existence of the towns. Wilcomb (1954) reported on the numerous arthropods which inhabit prairie dog burrow systems. Tyler (1968) reported seven species of amphibians, ten species of reptiles, and 56 species of birds using the dog towns. He found the following 18 mammalian species in dog towns: eastern mole (*Scalopus aquaticus*), desert cottontail (*Sylvilagus audubonii*), black-tailed jack rabbit (*Lepus californicus*), thirteen-lined ground squirrel (*Spermophilus tridecemlineatus*), spotted ground squirrel (*S. spilosoma*), plains pocket gopher (*Geomys bursarius*), Ord's kangaroo rat (*Dipodomys ordii*), various species of deer mice (*Peromyscus* spp.), the southern plains woodrat (*Neo-*

toma micropus), northern grasshopper mouse (*Onychomys leucogaster*), coyotes (*Canis latrans*), foxes (*Vulpes* sp.), raccoon (*Procyon lotor*), badger (*Taxidea taxus*), striped skunk (*Mephitis mephitis*), bobcat (*Felis rufus*), white-tailed deer (*Odocoileus virginianus*), and bison (*Bison bison*). O'Meilia (1980) noted that pastures with prairie dogs had a higher diversity of small mammals and significantly fewer insects. Two of the vertebrates that are most dependent upon prairie dogs are the burrowing owl (*Athene cunicularia*) (Butts, 1973, 1976, 1982) and the black-footed ferret (*Mustela nigripes*). Because of the poisoning programs, the black-footed ferret is now probably extinct in Oklahoma, and the burrowing owls are greatly reduced in numbers.

Restorations of black-tailed prairie dog towns have been accomplished in the Wichita Mountains National Wildlife Refuge, in the Canton Public Hunting Area, at the Darlington Game Farms (which has a colony of very light-colored individuals) near El Reno, and at other locations. Prairie dogs are not easy to trap; however, Carpenter and Martin (1969) designed a simple, inexpensive pressurized water technique to capture and transplant prairie dogs.

Prairie dogs are very social animals and live in large groups referred to as colonies or towns. These towns are further subdivided into wards and coteries. A complete discussion of the behavior of the animals in these social groups is given by King (1955) and Smith (1967). Koford (1958), in a study of the biology of *Cynomys*, commented on the populations in Comanche County. The smallest, most functional of these social groups, the coterie, usually consists of a male, several females, and the young. Each small group lives in an extensive burrow system 4–6 m (15–20 ft.) deep. Surrounding the main entrance is a conical mound of dirt 30–60 cm (1–2 ft.) high. These mounds are spaced about 7–22 m (25–75 ft.) apart. The mounds serve to keep water from the burrow system, as lookout posts, and as a means of ventilating the tunnel system. One mound to each burrow system is usually higher than the others, helping to create a venturi system that helps the burrow system "breathe" as the wind blows across the openings. When a predator or other threat to the town is noted by an individual animal, a warning call or "bark" is given. This "bark" is responsible for the common name, "prairie dog."

The breeding season is in late winter or early spring, and the first young are born in April (Anthony and Foreman, 1951; Glass and Halloran, 1961; Tyler, 1968). Testicular activity begins in October; ovarian activity starts in December (Anthony and Foreman, 1951). The gestation period is 30–35 days. The average litter size is 4.6 (range, 2–10) (Tyler, 1968). The young are altricial, and their eyes open in about five weeks. At six to seven weeks of age, the young begin to venture forth from the burrows. By the time they reach one year of age they are ready to mate. The older adult animals usually move from the area and establish new burrow systems, leaving the old systems to the now mature young.

The diet of black-tailed prairie dogs is primarily grass, but many forbs and other annuals are consumed as they become available. Smith (1967) gives a fairly detailed account of prairie dog food habits in Kansas. Their grazing habits allow the tall vegetation within a town no chance to grow, and this is advantageous in at least two ways: it allows an unobstructed view for detecting predators, and it encourages forbs and weedy seed-producing plants to grow inside the town to supplement the diet. Buscher and Tyler (1975) examined and reported on the parasites occurring on the vertebrates in prairie dog towns.

The subspecies occurring in Oklahoma is *C. l. ludovicianus* (Hall, 1981).

Sciurus carolinensis Gmelin
Gray Squirrel
(*Sciurus*) *carolinensis* Gmelin, 1788:148

The gray squirrel, *Sciurus carolinensis*, is seasonally variable in color. In the summer, the dorsum may be reddish brown rather than the normal gray color. The venter is white. Occasionally, melanistic or albino individuals may

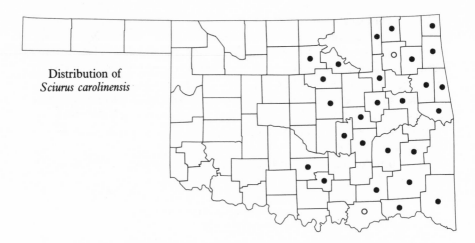

Distribution of
Sciurus carolinensis

occur. From the fox squirrel (*S. niger*), the gray squirrel is distinguished by smaller size (total length usually less than 475 mm = 18.7 in.) and white-tipped (not rusty orange) tail hairs. Tan or brown patches of hair occur on the cheeks, the middorsum, the forelegs, and the ears. Cranially, the gray squirrel differs from the fox squirrel in having five upper cheek teeth instead of four.

Gray squirrels occur in the timbered eastern half of Oklahoma. Specific habitat is primarily oak-hickory forest but also includes bottomland and lowland woods, swampy areas, and mature woodlands with thick tangles of secondary growth. Gray squirrels prefer stands of vegetation that are more dense than those favored by fox squirrels. Gray squirrels are also common in many city parks, zoos, and golf courses.

Tree cavities and leaf nests constructed of a mass of loosely woven twigs and leaves are used as resting sites and dens. Gray squirrels spend considerably more time in trees than do fox squirrels, and when threatened, gray squirrels prefer to escape through the canopy. These squirrels do not hibernate but will remain in their nests during inclement weather. Vocalizations consist of chucks, raspy barks, chirps, whines, and teeth chattering. Gray squirrels are active earlier in the day than fox squirrels.

Diet items vary seasonally and ordinarily include hickory nuts, pecans, acorns, walnuts, mulberries, corn, buds, seeds, and flowers. Food is cached for winter use, and usually a single item is cached per hole. Each cache seems to be relocated by smell. When food supplies in an area are depleted, local migrations of many squirrels to other areas may occur.

Reproduction is similar to that of the fox squirrel. Mating occurs in the winter (December to January) and occasionally again in early summer. After

TABLE 4. Squirrel hunting season harvest
in Oklahoma, 1967–80. (Oklahoma
Dept. Wildl. Conserv.)

Year	Average Kill/Hunter	Total Kill
1967	13.5	869,414
1968	17.2	1,067,070
1969	11.7	842,728
1970	11.4	818,338
1971	13.0	841,776
1972	14.5	966,207
1973	12.5	730,912
1974	13.3	798,812
1975	9.3	531,141
1976	13.0	861,978
1977	11.6	642,257
1978	13.3	1,032,053
1979	15.3	1,500,463
1980	15.1	1,010,537

a 45-day gestation period, the young are born naked with their eyes and ears closed; litters average three to four. Hair develops after three weeks, the eyes open in about five weeks, and weaning occurs at about ten weeks of age. Adult squirrels may survive for five years or longer in the wild.

Predators of squirrels include foxes, hawks, owls, snakes, bobcats, and feral dogs and cats. A variety of parasites are associated with gray squirrels: protozoans, nematodes, fleas, ticks, mites, tapeworms, and bot flies. Man-made alterations of habitat for farmlands and lumber reduce suitable squirrel habitat. As with the fox squirrel, gray squirrels are extensively hunted. Table 4 lists the number of squirrels (both fox and gray combined) taken by hunters over the last several years. A good review of the biology of the gray squirrel was given by Flyger and Gates (1982).

The subspecies in Oklahoma is *S. c. carolinensis* (Hall, 1981).

Sciurus niger Linnaeus
Fox Squirrel
(*Sciurus*) *niger* Linnaeus, 1758:64

Sciurus niger is the largest tree squirrel in Oklahoma. Adults vary between 450 and 698 mm (17.7–27.5 in.) in total length and have an average weight of 800 g (1.8 lbs.). In eastern Oklahoma, the fox squirrel occurs sympatrically with the gray squirrel, *S. carolinensis*, and the flying squirrel, *Glaucomys volans*. From *S. carolinensis* it may be distinguished by larger size and coloration. The dorsum is a brownish grizzled color, and the venter is rusty, reddish brown, or orange. The tail and ears also differ: the fox squirrel has a bushier, rusty to orange-colored tail and shorter, more rounded ears, whereas the gray squirrel has a white-tipped tail and ears that are more tapered. Occasionally melanistic or albinistic individuals may be seen, but these are more common in other parts of the United States. From *G. volans*, *S. niger* may be distinguished by its diurnal rather than nocturnal habits, by its much larger size and lack of patagia, and by an orange (rather than white) venter. Flyger and Levin (1977) have demonstrated that fox squirrel skulls are unique in having accumulations of uroporphyin which fluoresces a bright red under

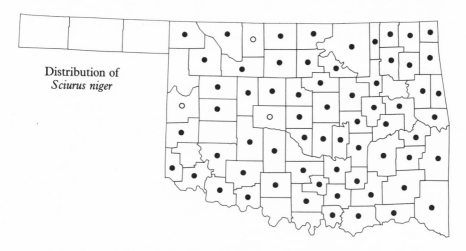

Distribution of
Sciurus niger

long-wave ultraviolet light. Fox squirrels have four upper cheek teeth instead of five as in the gray squirrel.

The fox squirrel has the most extensive distribution in Oklahoma of all the tree squirrels, occurring not only in the eastern part of the state but also over the western half along river systems and windbreaks. Introduced animals are occasionally seen in towns and tree-lined areas of the Panhandle. Preferred habitat usually consists of open stands of mixed hardwood forest (Blair, 1939; Glass and Halloran, 1961). In the east, upland forests are preferred over bottomland forest, but further west fox squirrels are restricted to the forested creek and river bottoms (Jackson and Warfel, 1933; Blair, 1939; Osborn and Kellogg, 1943; McCarley, 1952; Martin and Preston, 1970). City parks, golf courses, orchards, and other urban areas usually support substantial populations of fox squirrels. Populations reach greatest densities in the transition region between the prairies and oak areas in the central portions of the state.

Hollow trees and nests of loosely woven twigs and leaves (25–60 cm = 9.8–23.6 in. in diameter) are used as den sites. Leaf nests are more easily seen in the fall and winter months when trees are bare. Winter leaf nests are usually more densely woven than summer ones.

Early fall is the season of greatest activity for fox squirrels. They do not hibernate but may remain inside the nest for several days during inclement weather. Compared to gray squirrels, fox squirrels are less active and are active later in the day, usually from midday to late afternoon. When frightened, the fox squirrel may attempt to hide behind a tree trunk and, if pressed, will often attempt to escape across the ground to another tree. Vocalization is less frequent than in the gray squirrel and consists of a series of "chucks," teeth clattering, or crisp "barks."

The diet varies seasonally but commonly includes such things as pecans, walnuts, beechnuts, acorns, osage orange fruits, seeds, insects, mushrooms, leaves, bulbs, flowers, bird eggs, tubers, berries, plums, and twigs. Food items are individually cached in holes dug in the ground, in tree cavities, or among rocks. Caches which are not harvested may germinate and aid in plant dispersal and revegetation.

Fox squirrels usually mate during December or January, and a second mating season may occur in early summer. After a 45-day gestation period, a litter averaging four young is produced. The young are hairless, and both their eyes and ears are closed. Within three weeks hair develops, and in about four to six weeks the eyes and ears open. Weaning occurs after about 8–10 weeks, and the family group may remain intact in the nest until the female is ready to mate again. The average life span in the wild of a fox squirrel is about five to six years.

Home range size varies depending on a variety of environmental factors such as type of habitat, population density and composition, and food availability. Chesemore (1975) determined that male fox squirrels had an average home range of 2.87 ha (7.1 acres) and females 0.44 ha (1.1 acres).

Predators of fox squirrels include owls, hawks, snakes, foxes, bobcats, and feral house cats. Parasites of fox squirrels include nematodes, protozoans, tapeworms, fleas, ticks, mites, and bot flies. Destruction of squirrel habitat by fire, lumbering practices, urban development, overgrazing, and drought may increase predation because of loss of cover. Both the fox squirrel and the gray squirrel are extensively hunted in Oklahoma. Table 4 records the number (both species combined) of squirrels taken each year and the average kill per hunter. The data suggest that squirrels are the most preferred game species in the state.

The subspecies in Oklahoma is *S. n. rufiventer* (Hall, 1981).

Glaucomys volans (Linnaeus)
Southern Flying Squirrel
[*Mus*] *volans* Linnaeus, 1758:63
Glaucomys volans: A. H. Howell, 1915:110

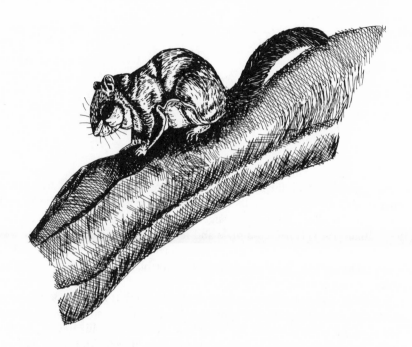

Because of their nocturnal habits, southern flying squirrels are seldom seen. *Glaucomys* is a small tree squirrel that seldom ventures down to the ground. It has large eyes, a flattened bushy tail (hairs grow out to the sides), and loose folds of skin along the sides. These folds of skin (patagia) stretch between the front and hind legs; when the legs are extended the folds serve as a "parachute" to allow the animal to glide from one tree to another. Color is drab brownish tan on the upper parts and creamy white on the venter.

Southern flying squirrels occur primarily in the wooded eastern half of the main part of Oklahoma. The species has been recorded from the following physiognomic regions: Oak-Hickory Ozark Plateau, Oak-Hickory-Pine Ouachita Highlands, Tall-grass Rolling Plains, and Post Oak–Blackjack Uplands. The principal habitat is mature deciduous forest; however, riparian habitats have provided avenues of dispersal into the central Oklahoma grasslands. Woodpecker holes are frequently used for nests. Often, more than one

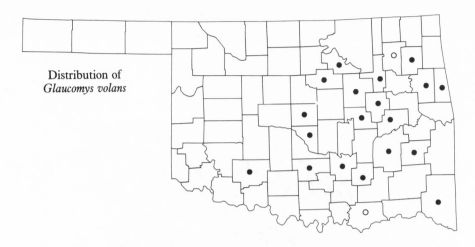

Distribution of
Glaucomys volans

flying squirrel may be flushed from a single tree. Glass and Halloran (1961) reported that a pair of squirrels was obtained from a building on the Wichita Mountains Wildlife Refuge and suggested that *Glaucomys* was uncommon there. Blair (1938) collected a male and female in a large oak tree in an oak-elm association in August along Bird Creek in Tulsa County. McCarley (1952) found *Glaucomys* in the floodplain forest and blackjack–post oak forest of Bryan County.

Very little is known of this squirrel in Oklahoma, but its habits and ecology are probably similar to these reported from Arkansas and Texas. Diet consists of seeds, insects, buds, nuts, acorns, berries, and bird eggs. Food is cached for the winter. Chief predators are owls, snakes, and man, who frequently destroys the large, dead hollow trees of the forest where dens are often located. Typical parasites include fleas, ticks, mites, lice, and nematodes.

Blair (1938) collected a pregnant female in September which contained four embryos. Gestation is about 40 days. Two breeding seasons probably exist, February–March and July. Dolan and Carter (1977) commented on other aspects of the biology of *G. volans*.

The subspecies occurring in Oklahoma is *G. v. saturatus* (Black, 1936; Blair, 1939; Hall, 1981).

FAMILY GEOMYIDAE   Gophers

Geomys bursarius (Shaw)
Plains Pocket Gopher
Mus bursarius Shaw, 1800:227
Geomys bursarius: Richardson, 1829:203

The fossorial plains pocket gopher, *Geomys bursarius*, is a medium-sized, stocky, short-legged rodent that varies in color from light ochre to dark brown. Individuals with white patches of hair, and some that are nearly all white or grizzled, have been collected (McCarley, 1951). The common name "pocket gopher," is derived from the two large, external, fur-lined cheek pouches which open just to the sides of the mouth. These pouches are used to transport roots, tubers, rhizomes, stems, and other portions of plants that make up the diet. The touch-sensitive tail is nearly naked and short (usually less than one-half the body length). The front feet have three well-developed claws, while the thumb is merely a knob with a small nail. The ears are short and nearly concealed in the pelage. Two upper and two lower orange-colored incisors protrude through the lips, allowing the lips to be shut behind the teeth, which are used in digging. This adaptation prevents dirt from entering the mouth. The only other genus of gopher which occurs in Oklahoma is *Pappogeomys castanops;* it is distinct from *Geomys* in having only a single longitudinal groove on the outer face of each incisor. *Geomys* has two distinct grooves, one near the center of the tooth and a much finer one near the inner margin. Gophers can also be easily differentiated from moles, since the latter

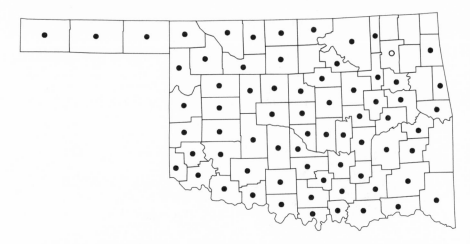

lack cheek pouches, external ears, prominent eyes, and grooved incisors. Moles also have broader, more flattened front feet, each with five claws.

The plains pocket gopher is common in all the physiognomic regions of Oklahoma (Glass, 1951) except the Oak-Hickory Ozark Uplands in the extreme northeastern part of the state. Throughout their range in Oklahoma these gophers most frequently inhabit sandy or moist alluvial soils. Burrow systems are relatively easy to construct in this type of soil, and they are usually located 150–300 mm (6–12 in.) below the surface of the ground. Since most gopher activity is subterranean, they are seldom seen. Except for the mounds of loose dirt excavated from the burrows that they deposit on the surface, one might not be aware of their presence. The dirt mounds are about six inches high and two feet in diameter. Mounds are often seen in pastures, old fields, and roadside right-of-ways near railroads; along creeks and streams; on golf courses; and in sand dune areas. Watts (1970) reported on some of the burrowing habits of gophers in north central and northwestern Oklahoma.

Downhower and Hall (1966) provided a good discussion of the pocket gopher in Kansas, and that information is probably applicable to Oklahoma gophers as well. These authors indicated that pocket gophers do not hibernate and do not require water to drink (they obtain enough from their food plants). Apparently only one litter is produced per year, and the size of the litter varies from one to six, with the average number being four. Gophers are solitary animals except during the breeding season, which is in the spring. Males locate females by a keen sense of smell. When the young are ready to be weaned, they are forcibly ejected from the mother's burrow system and often may be caught in snap traps above ground during this period. Sudman *et al.* (1986) also discuss gestation and postnatal development in the plains pocket gopher.

Natural enemies consist of owls, skunks, coyotes, bobcats, snakes, and badgers. Burnham (1953) examined 121 pocket gophers and found 65 individuals to be parasitized by one or more species of worm. Both cestodes (*Hymenolepis, Monoecoestus, Cittotaenia*) and nematodes (*Mastophorus, Litomosa, Ostertagia*) were found in the gophers. Other parasites such as ticks, fleas, and mites are common on gophers (Downhower and Hall, 1966). Timm and Price (1980) discussed the taxonomy of *Geomydoecus*, a louse from *Geomys*. Chase *et al.* (1982) review the biology of plains pocket gophers.

The systematics of gophers in Oklahoma is unclear and difficult to resolve because of their low vagility and small, local, parapatric populations (Honeycutt and Schmidly, 1979). Hart (1978), in examining the karyology and evolution of *G. bursarius,* suggested that several chromosomal types existed in Oklahoma and that reproductive compatibility between them may be seriously questioned. Baker and Glass (1951) were the first to unite the species *G. bursarius* and *G. breviceps* into a single taxon. Later Glass (unpublished) indicated that the subspecies of the High Plains was *G. b. jugosicularis* Hooper. *G. b. major* (Davis) was recognized for the reddish form occupying western Oklahoma and *G. b. dutcheri* for the form on Mississippian, Pennsylvanian, and older soils of the eastern half of Oklahoma. Honeycutt and Schmidly (1979) recognized at least two subspecies in Oklahoma: *G. b. sagittalis* in eastern Oklahoma and *G. b. major* in western areas. Penny and Zimmerman (1976) examined the genetic divergence and local differentiation in populations of pocket gophers. Considerable evidence has been presented by Bohlin and Zimmerman (1982) and Cothran and Zimmerman (1985) for the recognition of *G. breviceps* of central and southeastern areas of Oklahoma at the species level. Other studies which evaluate the complex systematics of pocket gophers of the Great Plains include those of Heaney and Timm (1983) and Burns *et al.* (1985).

Pappogeomys castanops (Baird)
Yellow-faced Pocket Gopher
Pseudostoma castanops Baird, 1852:313
Pappogeomys castanops: Russell, 1968:635

Pappogeomys castanops, the yellow-faced pocket gopher, can be distinguished from the plains pocket gopher, *Geomys bursarius*, by the presence of a single deep groove on the anterior face of the upper incisors. *Geomys* has two grooves. In addition, the feet of *Pappogeomys* are blackish compared to the whitish feet of *Geomys,* and the claws are proportionally much smaller. The upper parts are a dull yellowish brown.

Records for this gopher in Oklahoma exist only from the Panhandle counties (Cimarron, Texas, and Beaver). *Pappogeomys* prefers deep, sandy soils or open plains mantled with sandy soils (Miller, 1964; Russell, 1968; Birney *et al.*, 1970). In Kansas, this gopher was collected almost exclusively from the deep upland soils of the High Plains and in roadside ditches having loamy soils and calcareous deposits (Birney *et al.*, 1970). Moulton *et al.* (1983) discussed the biogeographic relationships of pocket gophers in southeastern Colorado. Blair (1954) indicated that *Pappogeomys* is found in the mesquite-shortgrass plains areas of the Texas Panhandle. Oklahoma specimens have been taken in sandy alfalfa fields along North Carrizo Creek in Cimarron County, and mounds were also seen at the edge of a prairie dog town east of Kenton (Glass, 1951). Specimens were taken in Beaver and Texas counties on the Potter Mansher and Richfield-Dalhart-Portales soil series, respectively (nomenclature follows USDA county soil survey maps). These soils are de-

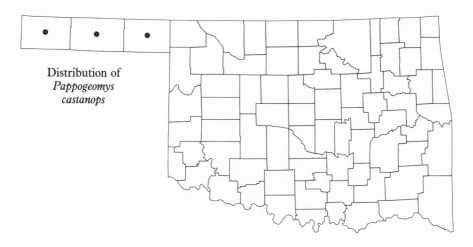

Distribution of
*Pappogeomys
castanops*

scribed as dark-colored loams and clay loams with caliche deposits. Cimarron County specimens are from the Travessilla-Berthud series, which is a brown loamy soil associated with basalt mesas and breaks.

Pappogeomys has been collected near Hooker in Texas County, but recent attempts to collect this species there have produced only *Geomys* (Birney *et al.*, 1970). This may represent a recent competitive exclusion by *Geomys*. *Geomys* apparently is a superior competitor and excludes *Pappogeomys* in friable soils (Blair, 1954; Miller, 1964; Birney *et al.*, 1970). Moulton *et al.* (1983) discuss the relationship of these two species in Colorado. Chase *et al.* (1982) review the biology of *Pappogeomys*.

Russell (1968) reviewed the systematic status of *Pappogeomys* and referred Oklahoma specimens to the subspecies *P. c. castanops*. Honeycutt and Williams (1982) suggest a return to the use of *Cratogeomys* as the generic name for the yellow-faced pocket gopher.

Perognathus flavescens Merriam
Plains Pocket Mouse
Perognathus fasciatus Merriam, 1889 : 11
Perognathus flavescens: Osgood, 1900 : 20

Perognathus flavescens, the plains pocket mouse, is a small mouse that is usually less than 150 mm (6 in.) in total length. Its fur is silky and yellowish buff in color. External fur-lined cheek pouches are present. This species differs from the silky pocket mouse, *P. flavus,* in being larger (more than 125 mm = 4.9 in. in total length) and in usually having faint, instead of bright, postauricular patches.

Only a few specimens have been recorded from Oklahoma, all from the western and Panhandle portions of the state. It has been taken in the following physiognomic regions: Piñon-Juniper Mesas, Shortgrass High Plains, Mixed-grass Plains, and Mesquite-Grass Plains. Martin and Preston (1970) collected the southwesternmost specimen in Oklahoma in a sandy shin oak–dominated field in Harmon County. Blair (1939) indicated that in extreme northwestern Oklahoma this species was found on the rocky, brushy ravine slopes in association with *Peromyscus maniculatus* and *P. leucopus.* In Woods County, three specimens were taken in sand dune areas south of Waynoka (Blair, 1939). The ecology and reproductive biology of *P. flavescens* is essentially unknown in Oklahoma.

Williams (1978) synonomized *Perognathus apache* and *P. flavescens* after confirming a zone of intergradation in southern New Mexico. Apparently

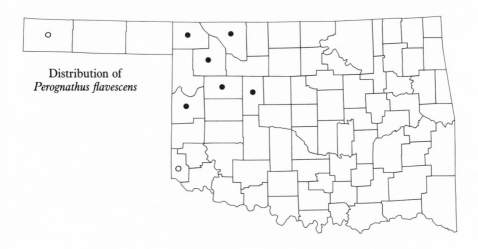

Distribution of
Perognathus flavescens

three subspecies occur in Oklahoma; *P. f. copei, P. f. cockrumi,* and *P. f. flavescens* (Hall, 1981). Western Oklahoma may well be the region of intergradation of these three forms (Reed and Choate, 1986).

Perognathus flavus Baird
Silky Pocket Mouse
Perognatus [sic] *flavus* Baird, 1855:332

Perognathus flavus is a small (usually less than 125 mm = 4.9 in. in total length) mouse with external fur-lined cheek pouches. It has upper parts that

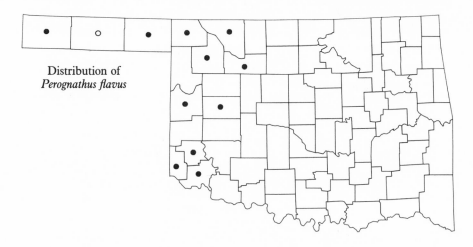

Distribution of
Perognathus flavus

are ochraceous buff (yellowish brown) and a white venter. The fur is soft and silky to the touch. A buff-colored but conspicuous postauricular patch of fur is located behind each ear, a trait that helps to separate this species from *P. flavescens*. The plains pocket mouse (*P. flavescens*) is also slightly larger (usually more than 135 mm = 5.3 in. in total length).

Perognathus flavus occurs in the western one-third of the main portion of Oklahoma and in the Panhandle region. Specimens have been taken in the following physiognomic regions: Piñon-Juniper Mesas, Shortgrass High Plains, Mixed-grass Plains, and the Mesquite-Grass Plains. Martin and Preston (1970) live-trapped numerous individuals during July and August (27 percent of all individuals captured), but during the winter months very few were trapped. This indicates either reduced activity and possible hibernation in the winter or hesitation of this species to enter the cold metal live trap. Jackson and Warfel (1933) collected only four specimens on open ground on the Edith Salt Plains in Woodward County but suggested that this species was more abundant there than the few specimens indicated. Glass (1951) and Geluso (1970) found *P. flavus* to be common on the valley floor prairie associations in the Black Mesa region. Specimens collected in Major County have been taken in live traps set on exposed areas of the rough gypsum outcrops. This species is difficult to trap with snap traps and only moderately easier with live traps. The simplest way to collect specimens of the silky pocket mouse is at night, using a hand net and a lantern.

Burrows are often located under the edge of rocks, in crevices, or under the edge of a bush and are often plugged during the day. Martin and Preston (1970) estimated the home range of a female in Harmon County to be 0.032 ha (0.08 acres), with a maximum distance of travel of 57.9 m (190 ft.).

The systematic status of *P. flavus* was examined by Wilson (1973), who found *P. flavus* and *P. merriami* to be conspecific with intergradation occurring in southeastern New Mexico. Davis (1974) continued to regard these as distinct species, and certain cranial features can still be used to separate the two. Based upon geographic location, the two subspecies in Oklahoma are *P. f bunkeri* and *P. f. merriami*. Interpretation of which subspecies are represented in Oklahoma is difficult, as with *P. flavescens;* western Oklahoma may be a region where several forms (*P. f. flavus, P. f. gilvus, P. f. merriami,* and *P. f. bunkeri*) are in contact.

Perognathus hispidus
Hispid Pocket Mouse
Perognathus hispidus Baird, 1858:421

Perognathus hispidus, the hispid pocket mouse, is the largest member of this genus occurring in Oklahoma. The upper parts are olive buff, and a distinct orchraceous (yellow orange) lateral stripe separates the upper parts from the white underparts. The bicolored tail is neither bushy nor well haired and is shorter than the head and body length combined. The common name "his-

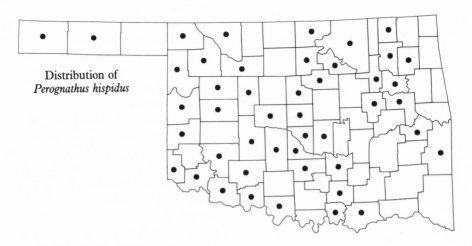

Distribution of
Perognathus hispidus

pid" derives from the coarse hair, which contrasts with the silky soft pelage of *P. flavus* and *P. flavescens*. Like other members of this family, *P. hispidus* has external fur-lined cheek pouches.

The hispid pocket mouse occurs over all of Oklahoma except the extreme northeastern and southeastern corners; it may ultimately be found in these areas too, but its distribution would probably be very local. There are records of occurrence from the following physiognomic regions: Piñon-Juniper Mesas, Shortgrass High Plains, Mixed-grass Plains, Mesquite-Grass Plains, Tall-grass Prairie Rolling Hills, and Post Oak–Blackjack Uplands. Within these regions, *P. hispidus* has been taken in a variety of habitat types, but nearly always in grassland associations. Glass (1949) found *P. hispidus* uncommon on the valley floors along dry irrigation ditches, fence rows, and roads and in plowed fields in the Black Mesa region. Martin and Preston (1970) reported that it was most common in Harmon County in areas which usually had good grass cover, even though a few were taken in other vegetative associations. This species composed 13 percent of the individuals of all species collected by Martin and Preston (1970) during a live-trap study in July and August, but only 5 percent in the winter months. The decrease in winter activity could have been because of hibernation or simply reduced winter activity. Elliot (1899a) found this species to be common both on the High Plains and in the bottomlands near Alva in Woods County. Blair (1954) collected *P. hispidus* in plum-sage associations on deep sandy soils near the Red River in the Mesquite-Grass Plains region. Very few specimens have been collected in the Wichita Mountains, although the species is apparently quite abundant there because of the numerous occurrences of skeletal remains in owl pellets from that region (Glass and Halloran, 1961). Jackson and Warfel

(1933) noted that *P. hispidus* was collected more commonly near water in the salt plains areas of western Oklahoma than was its smaller congener, *P. flavus*. They also found *P. hispidus* to be common in canyons, whereas *P. flavus* was usually on the tops or sides of the ridges. In central Oklahoma, Hays (1958) suggested that *P. hispidus* occurred predominantly in grasslands along terraces in grazed pastures and was never taken in the adjacent woodlands. However, McCarley (1952) suggested that an occasional *P. hispidus* can be collected in Bryan County along the edge of the Post oak–Blackjack Uplands. Blair (1938) found this species to be abundant in the sumac-grama and the grama–beard grass associations of eastern Oklahoma, but not in areas where continuous grass cover occurred. Many of the specimens Blair (1938) collected came from along ridges where limestone slabs were common; burrows were found under the edge of the limestone slabs.

The wide distribution of the hispid pocket mouse results in its association with many other species of Oklahoma mammals. Some of the more common rodent species include *Perognathus flavus, Peromyscus maniculatus, Peromyscus leucopus, Neotoma floridana, Sigmodon hispidus,* and *Spermophilus tridecemlineatus.*

Thompson and Barrett (1969) examined a complex of four *P. hispidus* nests in Cotton County; these nests were located in a grassy field but were not near rocks. The burrows were built at a rather steep angle (45°) and ended in a deeply placed (.3 m = about 1 ft.) nest. Both Hill (1942) and Elliot (1899*a*) described openings of *P. hispidus* burrows as circular, extending perpendicularly into the ground. Thompson and Barrett (1969) found the nest in the burrow to be composed of grass strips (25–75 mm = 1–3 in. long) placed in a 50-mm-diameter (2-in.) chamber at the end of the burrow. Associated with the nests were several invertebrates: phalangids, millipedes, fungus gnats, mites, and worms. Blair (1937) suggested that the burrows became more complicated with time; however, Thompson and Barrett (1969) suggested that this species generally dug new burrows rather than enlarging old ones. Blair (1937) found burrows to be plugged during the day, while Thompson and Barrett (1969) found no burrows plugged. Several side tunnels in the burrow complex may be used to avoid a pursuing predator. Parasites include fleas, lice, cestodes, and nematodes.

Glass (1947) studied geographic variation in this species and listed two subspecies as occurring in Oklahoma: *P. h. paradoxus* and *P. h. spilotus*. The former occurs in the Panhandle and western one-third of Oklahoma, while the latter is found in the eastern three-fourths of the state. Intergradation of these two subspecies occurs along a line drawn from the eastern edge of Dewey County north through the middle of Woods County; the southern part of the line extends south across the Red River and turns eastward.

Hafner and Hafner (1983) have suggested that the spiny-rumped pocket mice should all be referred to as *Chaetodipus* instead of Perognathus. In Oklahoma this would affect only *P. hispidus.*

Dipodomys elator Merriam
Texas Kangaroo Rat
Dipodomys elator Merriam, 1894:109

The Texas kangaroo rat, *Dipodomys elator,* is distinguished from Ord's kangaroo rat, *D. ordii,* by having four instead of five toes on the hind foot and by the conspicuous white "banner" tuft on the tip of the tail. *Dipodomys ordii* rarely has a white-tipped tail. Texas kangaroo rats are also larger than Ord's kangaroo rats, averaging more than 300 mm (11.8 in.) in total length. The underparts are whitish, while the dorsum is buffy and washed with blackish hairs.

It has been more than seventy-five years since the Texas kangaroo rat was last recorded in Oklahoma. Bailey (1905) listed the occurrence of this species in a kafir (*Sorghum*) field near Chattanooga in Comanche County. This species has a very limited geographic range occurring in only a few north central Texas counties (Archer, Baylor, Clay, Ford, Hardeman, Motley, Wichita, Wilbarger), and in only the single county in Oklahoma. *Dipodomys elator* still occurs in Texas, but recent attempts to locate it in Oklahoma have failed (Martin and Matocha, 1972). Possibly the Oklahoma portion of the former range is now unsuitable (Martin and Matocha, 1972). The clearing of native

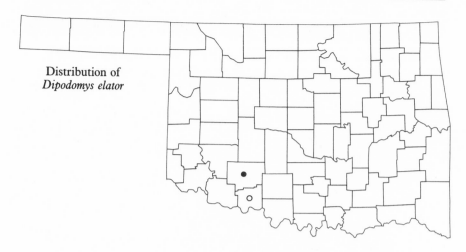

Distribution of
Dipodomys elator

vegetation to increase rangeland and other brush control projects, sometimes involving the use of 2, 4-D herbicide, may have adversely affected the habitat (Chapman, 1972).

Recently, a specimen of *D. elator* which was trapped in Oklahoma in 1969 was discovered in the University of Arizona Mammal Collection (#18299) (Baumgardner, 1987). The animal was obtained just north of a bridge crossing the Red River in Cotton County, Oklahoma. Though this does not substantiate a viable population existing in Oklahoma, it does suggest that an occasional individual may cross into Oklahoma from Texas.

The habitat preference of *D. elator* is unique for kangaroo rats. Most kangaroo rats (for example, *D. ordii*) prefer very sandy substrates; however, the Texas kangaroo rat has been collected in areas underlain by firm clay soils supporting shortgrass and scattered mesquite brushland (Dalquest and Collier, 1964; Roberts, 1969). *D. elator* does not make elaborate tunnels; each individual has a den, usually with only one opening that is oval, with the long axis vertical. In Texas, these kangaroo rats often were taken along fencerows adjacent to cultivated fields and roads (Martin and Matocha, 1972). The habitat of *D. elator* is also typically impoverished of other mammals. The few species that occur commonly within the same habitat are cotton rats (*Sigmodon hispidus*), white-footed mice (*Peromyscus*), cottontail rabbits (*Sylvilagus*) and hispid pocket mice (*Perognathus hispidus*) (Dalquest and Collier, 1964). The difference in habitat preference between the Texas kangaroo rat and Ord's kangaroo rat (clay versus sand) keeps these two species ecologically separated. Possibly the sandy regions of the Red River have prevented populations of *D. elator* in Texas from spreading into the southwestern portions of Oklahoma.

Additional notes on the biology and demography of the Texas kangaroo rat can be found in Carter *et al.* (1985) and Webster and Jones (1985).

The systematic status of *D. elator* has been much debated (Grinnell, 1921; Davis, 1942; Blair, 1954). Presently the Texas kangaroo rat is considered to be in the *merriami* group by Davis (1942; see Hall, 1981). This species is not divided into subspecies.

Dipodomys ordii Woodhouse
Ord's Kangaroo Rat
D. (ipodomys) ordii Woodhouse, 1853:224

Dipodomys ordii is the most common kangaroo rat in Oklahoma. It has five toes on the hind foot and a relatively long tail that is seldom white-tipped. Coat color of kangaroo rats is apparently correlated with soil color (Setzer, 1949). Specimens in western Oklahoma are dark cinnamon buff (reddish), while southeastern specimens are a paler vinaceous buff (grayish buff). Conspicuous white patches are present at the base of the ears and above the eyes. A white stripe crosses each flank. Size decreases from west to east in a clinal fashion. Kennedy *et al.* (1980) suggested that small size is an adaptation to an unpredictable habitat that occurs in small patches and is subject to destruction by periodic flooding. *Dipodomys elator,* the only other kangaroo rat occurring in Oklahoma, has not been collected in the state for over seventy-five years. It would be distinguished from Ord's kangaroo rat by having four

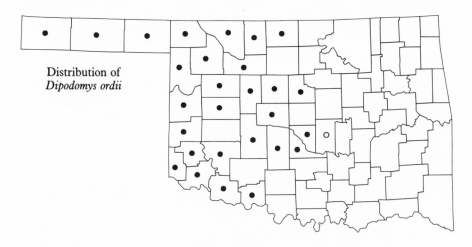

Distribution of
Dipodomys ordii

instead of five hind toes and a banner tail (that is, one with a white tip on the end).

In general, kangaroo rats occur in the western half of Oklahoma, west of a line drawn from Wichita, Kansas, southward through Love County, Oklahoma. The easternmost portion of their range extends along the floodplains of the South Canadian River to Pottawatomie County and along the South Fork of the Arkansas in Grant County (see Blair, 1939) near Lamont. This species is essentially limited to sandy areas along the low-lying floodplains of rivers and creeks. It usually is not found on clay or in areas of coarse soil. Glass (1951) noted that these rodents were common on the plains west of Boise City. Along most drainage systems, *D. ordii* is more common on the small active sand dunes or in blowout areas of the more stabilized dunes (Trowbridge and Whitaker, 1940; Kennedy *et al.*, 1980). Hays (1958) reported that kangaroo rats were numerous only in the sparsely vegetated sandy areas along the South Canadian River. Flooding, wind flattening, and stabilization by vegetation cause the loose sandy areas to become unavailable for use by kangaroo rats (Trowbridge and Whitaker, 1940). This loss of habitat forces *D. ordii* to move and colonize newly formed sandy areas; therefore, it may be referred to as a true pioneer species. Kennedy *et al.* (1980) suggested that periodic flooding provides a method of introducing new genetic material into eastern populations from those located farther west; they trapped larger reddish specimens of *D. ordii* in the same habitat with the paler smaller eastern forms only after substantial flooding. These darker individuals eventually disappeared from the area, probably being differentially eliminated by predators because they were no longer protectively colored in the lighter downstream soils. Baccus (1971) also implied that river systems and their associated sandy soils provided a similar dispersal route for kangaroo rats in Texas. These rodents constantly rework their burrows. Kangaroo rats are notoriously intolerant of others of their own species, and each burrow, however complex, is the home of a single adult. A well-established burrow of *D. ordii* will have many openings, and nearly every morning at least one of the entrances will show signs of digging (damp sand, foot tracks, tail whisk marks in the sand). Openings are usually circular or wider than high. This burrow system contrasts sharply with those of *D. elator*.

Trowbridge and Whitaker (1940) indicated that few plants occurred in the sandy areas where these kangaroo rats are found. The most common plant was cocklebur (*Xanthium* spp.); trails 61 m (200 ft.) in length were seen leading to cocklebur patches in the winter. Cheek pouches examined by Trowbridge and Whitaker (1940) contained seeds of the following plant types: wildbean (*Strophostyles helvola*), lesser ragweed (*Ambrosia artemisiifolia*), spurge (*Euphorbia* spp.), purple sandgrass (*Triplasis purpurea*), and switch grass (*Panicum virgatum*). Best and Hoditschek (1982) examined the cheek pouch contents of 423 kangaroo rats collected in Cleveland County. They never found any animal food in the cheek pouches. The following seeds and items were found in the cheek pouches: *Aristida* spp. (three-awn), *Populus deltoides* (cottonwood), *Cycloloma atriplicifolium* (winged pigweed), *Corispermum hyssopifolium* (bug seed), *Cassia fasiculata* (partridge pea), *Trifolium* spp. (clover), *Strophostyles helvola* (wild bean), *Helianthus* spp. (sunflower), plant segments (roots and stems), unidentified leaves, plant debris, and sand.

McCulloch and Inglis (1961) summarized several years of breeding records for a population of kangaroo rats located in a sand-sagebrush grassland near Fort Supply in Woodward County. They found that this species seldom bred from April to July; breeding usually began in August and continued to November, ceasing completely in March. The rate of reproduction was apparently influenced by the amount of precipitation, available food supply, and density of kangaroo rats and other rodent species. The population they were monitoring declined after a severe drought in 1956 but increased in the next year after a favorable growing season. Many of the females had two litters during favorable years, and females born early in the season produced a litter before the end of the same season. The breeding age was estimated to be two months, gestation time 30 days, and the nestling period three or four weeks. Kennedy *et al.* (1980) implied that eastern populations had larger average litter sizes than western forms. However, McCulloch and Inglis (1961) found that litter size is seasonally variable and fluctuates under the influence of the environmental variables mentioned above. Hoditschek and Best (1983) also discuss the reproductive biology of *D. ordii* in Oklahoma. LeVick (1982) evaluated maternal response to neonate vocalizations.

Morphological variation of kangaroo rats in Oklahoma has been examined by Davis (1942), Setzer (1949), Thompson (1969), Best and Schnell (1974), Hartman (1980), McCullock (1961), and Kennedy *et al.* (1980). Sexual dimorphism in various traits has been demonstrated for this species (Desha, 1967; Shaver, 1973; Kennedy and Schnell, 1978) and probably varies geographically (Schmidly, 1971; Kennedy *et al.* 1980). Chromosome and electrophoretic studies involving Oklahoma populations have been conducted by Johnson and Selander (1971) and Stock (1974).

Two subspecies of *D. ordii* are reported in Oklahoma. The small, pale individuals from the floodplains of the South Canadian River in Canadian and Cleveland counties are referred to as *D. o. oklahomae:* the other populations in Oklahoma are referred to as *D. o. richardsoni.* Trowbridge and Whitaker (1940) first described *D. o. oklahomae* as a distinct species. Later studies by Davis (1942), Setzer (1949), and Kennedy *et al.* (1980) demonstrated that intergradation does occur between these two subspecies along the South Canadian River. Glass (1971) clarified the type locality of *D. o. richardsoni* as being in Cimarron County.

Castor canadensis Kuhl
Beaver
Castor canadensis Kuhl, 1820:64

The beaver, *Castor canadensis,* is the largest rodent in Oklahoma. Adults usually weigh between 16 and 31.5 kg (35–69 lbs.). The largest beaver reported in Oklahoma weighed 83 lbs. (37.5 kg) and was run over by a car near McCloud. Modern beavers are small in comparison to the large extinct forms that existed in the Pleistocene period and weighed nearly 182 kg (400 lbs.).

Many of the distinguishing features of the beaver are adaptations for an aquatic existence. The broad, paddlelike tail is dark brown, nearly hairless, and covered with uncornified scales. It is used as a prop when sitting, as a community warning device when slapped against the water, for steering, and for swimming. Most forward propulsion is generated by the large webbed hind feet. The forelegs are short, and the hands are adept at manipulating objects and digging. The second digit on the hind foot has a split nail which curves in toward the body and is used as a grooming claw (also called a combing claw or louse catching claw). These claws comb oil from the "castor gland," located near the base of the tail. The nostrils and ears are both valvular and capable of being sealed during dives. A nictitating membrane covers the eye when the animal is under water. The pelage is glossy. Beavers

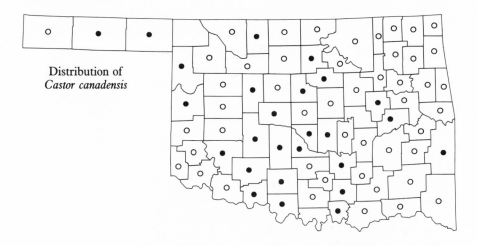

Distribution of
Castor canadensis

vary in color from a dark chocolate to lighter hues of brown. The underparts are tawny. Larger, coarser guard hairs extend beyond the underfur, which is very fine, soft, and often one inch thick. This fine underhair is valued by the fur industry. The large incisors (5 mm = 0.2 in. wide) are orange on the anterior surface. These large teeth provide the means for felling trees as well as a defense against some predators. The lips close behind the incisors, allowing use of those teeth underwater. In both sexes, reproductive organs are internal and lie anterior to a cloacal region into which they open. An os penis is present in the male.

Beavers were at one time widespread in Oklahoma, especially during the early eighteenth century, when beaver populations across North America were at a zenith (Seton, 1929). Extensive trapping during the late 1800s drastically reduced their numbers to the point that Blair (1939) could not reference a single specimen from Oklahoma preserved in a museum. Cross (1917) and Blair (1939) suggested that the beaver was nearly extinct in Oklahoma in the 1900s. Remnant populations evidently survived in parts of the Red and North Canadian river systems, and the restocking of many streams both in western and eastern Oklahoma was done with animals from Oklahoma (Jones, 1952). Jones (1952) reported on the status of Oklahoma beavers, listing nine river systems where they were known to occur and a minimum estimate of 485 individuals in 40 colonies. Since that time, restocking and control of trapping have allowed numbers to increase. Today beavers are once again present statewide, especially along many creeks and streams which are part of the following watersheds: Arkansas, Cimarron, Deep Fork, Beaver–North Canadian, Canadian, Washita, North Fork of Red River, Red River, and Kiamichi (Reynolds, 1977). Ponds and lakes in the watersheds also have beavers.

TABLE 5.   Number of beaver pelts purchased and
average price paid by Oklahoma fur dealers, 1967–81.
(Oklahoma Dept. Wildl. Conserv.)

Year	No. Pelts Bought	Avg. Price/Pelt	Total
1967–68	581	$ 5.92	$ 3,539.52
1968–69	319	6.82	2,175.50
1969–70	289	5.63	1,627.40
1970–71	89	6.04	537.50
1971–72	82	6.25	528.90
1972–73	661	8.66	5,724.19
1973–74	705	7.18	5,064.25
1974–75	1,941	8.50	16,490.32
1975–76	1,003	5.13	5,147.28
1976–77	3,090	8.07	24,941.50
1977–78	1,904	6.21	11,823.84
1978–79	1,592	6.39	10,172.88
1979–80	2,894	12.05	34,881.50
1980–81	2,686	7.78	20,897.08

Beaver pelts are still of value to the fur industry. Table 5 reflects the number of pelts taken and corresponding values over the last few years.

In Oklahoma, beavers usually construct burrows into stream or river banks and very rarely build larger dome-shaped lodges in open water. A few small mud and stick lodges may occasionally be seen near the bank burrows. Large lodges can occasionally be seen in eastern Oklahoma. Caire (pers. observ.) has seen them in southeastern Oklahoma in McCurtain County. Usually a pile of logs and twigs is stacked over the burrow entrance, and an underwater entrance to the burrow is necessary. When dams are built, small ponds result from the restricted water flow. Mud slides over the dam and on the stream banks reflect the routes used by beavers in nocturnal wanderings.

Food items frequently include the inner bark or cambium layer as well as the twigs of a variety of deciduous trees found near the watercourses: willows, cottonwoods, elms, and hackberry. Vegetative materials such as Johnson grass, water lilies, duckweed, reeds, algae, and fungi also compose part of the diet. Trees as large as one to two feet in diameter are felled in order to obtain the twigs and leaves. Most trees are cut down while the beaver is in a sitting position. The direction of fall of the tree is not controlled, and a beaver may occasionally be trapped under a falling tree. Stockpiles of twigs and branches may be deposited in the bottom of ponds near the burrows and intermittently used as food throughout the winter. Canals leading away from the main water source are often constructed and used as routes to feeding areas. Beaver cuttings several hundred feet inland from the water are not uncommon. The extensive cutting of trees near human habitations or recreational areas sometimes causes the beaver to be considered a pest rather than a natural part of the ecosystem. A large family group of beavers can do extensive damage to trees in a city park. Relocation of the groups, rather than extermination, is probably the most intelligent solution to this problem. Reynolds and Lewis (1978) evaluated various structures for preventing beavers from plugging impoundment outlets.

Beavers in Oklahoma breed in midwinter, and one to six kits are born in April or May. Young are born in the burrow system and are fully furred at birth. Weaning requires about six weeks. The family group remains together in the same general vicinity for two generations depending upon the resources of the area. When the kits are two years old (approaching sexual maturity), they are driven from the family group area prior to the birth of a third litter to the adult pair. Overland migration is commonly used both in searching for a mate and for locating a new unoccupied water source. Beavers are long-lived, possibly reaching ages of ten to fifteen years. The length of time a colony site will remain occupied depends upon whether or not accessible supplies of food are sufficient to replace those eaten by beavers.

Because of its size and aquatic habits, the beaver has few predators. The young may be taken by coyotes, bobcats, foxes, and, formerly, by bears and mountain lions. Jenkins and Busher (1979) comment on other aspects of the biology of *C. canadensis*.

The taxonomic status of beavers in Oklahoma was reviewed by Glass (1960). Specimens from the Red River drainage are *C. c. texensis*, and those of the Arkansas River drainage are *C. c. missouriensis*. Transportation of beavers from western Oklahoma into the eastern part of the state without regard for provenance probably has, or will, blur the distinctions between these two subspecies.

Oryzomys palustris (Harlan)
Marsh Rice Rat
Mus palustris Harlan, 1837:385
Oryzomys palustris: Baird, 1858:459

The marsh rice rat, *Oryzomys palustris*, the hispid cotton rat, *Sigmodon hispidus*, and the black and Norway rats (*Rattus rattus* and *R. norvegicus*) are all rather similar in appearance, having a brownish overall coloration. *Oryzomys* may be distinguished by its whitish feet, faintly bicolored tail, and smooth pelage.

Oryzomys occurs primarily in moist areas of Oklahoma in spotty, disjunct populations. The first marsh rice rats collected in Oklahoma were taken in August 1934 on a river-bottom flat covered with cane (*Arundinaria gigantea*) near the Mountain Fork River in McCurtain County (Whitaker, 1937). McCarley (1952) later captured a male rice rat north of Colbert, Bryan County, in a tall-grass prairie consisting primarily of little bluestem (*Schizachyrium scoparium*), beard grass (*Setaria geniculata*), and side-oats grama (*Bouteloua curtipendula*). This capture in xeric habitat suggests that tallgrass prairies may not necessarily be barriers to dispersal from one moist habitat patch to another (McCarley, 1960). Two adult males and one adult female were captured in Marshall County in July, near three man-made stock ponds (McCarley, 1960). Below these ponds a semiaquatic community had developed which contained spike rushes (*Eleocharis* spp.), sedges (*Fuirena simplex*), rushes (*Juncus torryeyi*), and cattails (*Typha* spp.). The sedges and rushes had formed a tangled mat that contained numerous rodent runways. Several other species, including hispid cotton rats (*Sigmodon hispidus*), white-footed mice

Distribution of
Oryzomys palustris

(*Peromyscus leucopus*), and house mice (*Mus musculus*), were also common in this habitat.

The most recent records for marsh rice rats in Oklahoma were from Push-mataha and Pittsburg counties in 1959 (McCarley, 1961). In both counties, the habitat was similar, consisting of wet boggy areas dominated by various species of berry vines and tall grasses (*Andropogon* and *Smilax*) (McCarley, 1961). The occurrence of this species in more northern locales of eastern Oklahoma should not be discounted, because specimens exist for extreme northwestern Arkansas (Sealander, 1979).

The only reproductive data available for Oklahoma consist of reports of male and female marsh rice rats in nonbreeding condition in July (McCarley, 1960) and a juvenile captured in August (Whitaker, 1937). Wolfe (1982) com-mented on the biology of *O. palustris* across its entire range.

The subspecies occurring in Oklahoma is *O. p. texensis* (Hall, 1981).

Reithrodontomys fulvescens J. A. Allen
Fulvous Harvest Mouse
Reithrodontomys mexicanus J. A. Allen, 1894:319
Reithrodontomys fulvescens: J. A. Allen, 1895:138

Reithrodontomys fulvescens can be distinguished from other Oklahoma harvest mice by its longer tail (noticeably longer than head and body length) and its bright fulvous sides. The underparts are a pale buff or white. As in all members of this genus, the incisors are grooved.

The fulvous harvest mouse occurs throughout eastern and southern sections of the main body of Oklahoma. Specimens have been collected in the following physiognomic regions: Mixed-grass Plains, Post Oak–Blackjack Uplands, Tall-grass Rolling Plains, Oak-Hickory Ozark Plateau, Oak-Hickory-Pine Ouachita Highlands, and Cypress-Oak Floodplains. This species prefers brushy grasslands, prairies, and forest-grassland ecotones. Jones and Anderson (1959) collected this species from a grassy field that bordered riparian woods in Latimer County. Blair (1939) recorded a series collected from a lowland thicket in eastern Oklahoma, and Elliot (1899*a*) found this species to be rather common along the edges of cotton fields among dense growths of vines and bushes. Goertz (1962) determined that, in Payne County, the fulvous harvest mouse was more commonly associated with areas where the grassy ground cover (*Sorghum halapense, Sorghastrum nutans, Andropogon* spp., and *Schizachyrium scoparium*) amounted to 59 percent or more, and the vegetative height was at least 137 mm (5.4 in.). Goertz (1962) and others (Elliot, 1899*a;* Glass and Halloran, 1961) suggested that this species is rather uncommon. In Payne County, only 34 were collected in 73,864 trap nights (Goertz, 1962).

Reproductive information is scarce for this species. Goertz (1962) collected 11 females during April and May; 2 of these were juveniles, and 3 were pregnant with either three or four embryos. Two females had uterine scars and four females collected in October were lactating. Thirteen males had scrotal testes varying from 7 mm to 10 mm (1/4–1/2 in.) in April, May, and June.

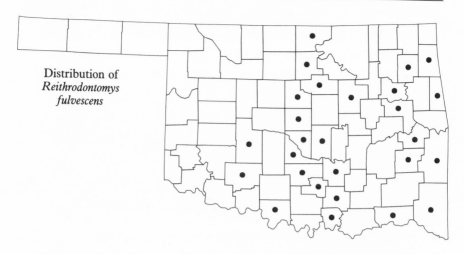

Distribution of
Reithrodontomys
fulvescens

During the winter months (October to March) two males had abdominal testes and two had scrotal testes. Spencer and Cameron (1982) commented on other aspects of the biology of *R. fulvescens* across its entire range.

The two subspecies occurring in Oklahoma, *R. f. aurantius* and *R. f. laceyi*, have been discussed by Howell (1914), McMurray (1945), Russell (1953), and Glass and Halloran (1961).

Reithrodontomys humulis (Audubon and Bachman)
Eastern Harvest Mouse
Mus humulis Audubon and Bachman, 1841:97
Reithrodontomys humulis: Osgood, 1907:49

The eastern harvest mouse is a small (total length 134 mm = 5.3 in.) brownish gray mouse with a blackish middorsal region. The bicolored tail is about as

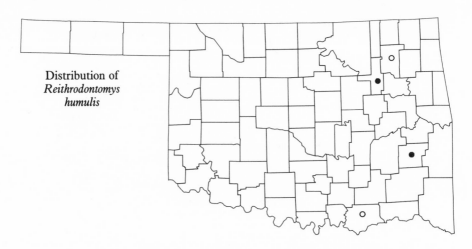

Distribution of
*Reithrodontomys
humulis*

long as the head and body length, and each ear is black from base to tip. *Reithrodontomys humulis* differs from *R. fulvescens* in being smaller and having a shorter tail; *R. fulvescens* has a tail which is longer than head and body length. From *R. megalotis* and *R. montanus, R. humulis* differs in having dark (instead of pale) flesh-colored or yellowish ears and in being more grayish than yellowish brown. The incisors of all *Reithrodontomys* are grooved.

Only a few specimens of *R. humulis* from Oklahoma have been reported in the literature. One was obtained by Jones and Anderson (1959) in Robbers' Cave State Park in Latimer County. They trapped the specimen on the edge of a grassy clearing of a wooded area near Fourche Maline Creek. Other species taken in the same area included *R. fulvescens, Peromyscus leucopus, Sigmodon hispidus, Neotoma floridana,* and *Microtus pinetorum.* We have examined another specimen from Latimer County and a third from Rogers County. Three or four of these small mice were captured during the environmental impact study of the proposed Black Fox nuclear reactor site near Inola, Rogers County. These specimens were last known to be in the possession of Ecological Associates of Fort Collins, Colorado. Smith (1964) recorded the eastern harvest mouse from Bryan County. The distribution of the eastern harvest mouse in Oklahoma is confined to the eastern portions of the state in the following physiognomic regions: Oak-Hickory Ozark Plateau, Oak-Hickory-Pine Ouachita Highlands, and Cypress-Oak Floodplains. Because so few specimens of *R. humulis* have been taken in Oklahoma, essentially nothing is known of its ecology or reproductive biology.

The subspecies occurring in Oklahoma is probably *R. h. humulis* (Jones and Anderson, 1959).

Reithrodontomys megalotis (Baird)
Western Harvest Mouse
Reithrodon megalotis Baird, 1858:451
Reithrodontomys megalotis: J. A. Allen, 1893:79

Reithrodontomys megalotis is a medium-sized harvest mouse. The total length usually measures less than 200 mm (7.9 in.). The bicolored tail is as long as the head and body length. The upper parts are a brownish buff and the venter is white. In most specimens, the middorsal region is darker than the sides. The incisors are grooved. *Reithrodontomys megalotis* is easily distinguished from *R. fulvescens* by its shorter tail, which is not noticeably longer than the head and body (the tail of *R. fulvescens* is longer than the head-body length). The separation of specimens of *R. megalotis* and *R. montanus* is often very difficult for inexperienced persons. Some useful distinguishing traits include the length of the tail, which is usually less than head and body length in *R. montanus;* tail more distinctly bicolored in *R. montanus*. The ranges of *R. humulis* and *R. megalotis* do not overlap in Oklahoma.

Based on the few specimens of *R. megalotis* in collections, the distribution of this species seems to be confined to the western one-half of Oklahoma. Urban and Wimmer (1959) reported *R. megalotis* from Texas and Cimarron counties. It has been taken in the following physiognomic regions: Mixed-grass Plains, Shortgrass High Plains, and Piñon-Juniper Mesas. Near Kenton in Cimarron County, specimens were collected in alfalfa fields (Clark and Skryja, 1969). Elliot (1899a) found *R. megalotis* to be common in the flat bottomlands along the Salt Fork River near Alva, but uncommon on the upland prairies. He collected this species in the winter, even during blizzards. Packard and Anderson (Urban and Wimmer, 1959) collected eight specimens in ungrazed grass along the right-of-way of U.S. Highway 54 about 120 m (200 yds.) north of the Beaver River in Texas County.

Little ecological information exists for this species in Oklahoma. Webster

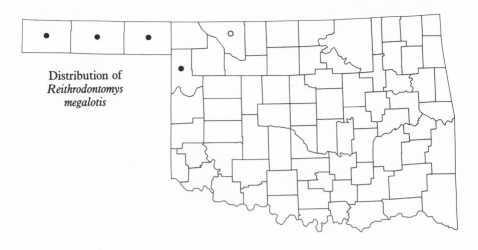

Distribution of
Reithrodontomys
megalotis

and Jones (1982) commented on aspects of the biology of *R. megalotis* in other parts of its range.

There are apparently two subspecies in Oklahoma: *R. m. aztecus* in the Panhandle and *R. m. dychei* in the main portion of Oklahoma (Hall, 1981).

Reithrodontomys montanus (Baird)
Plains Harvest Mouse
Reithrodon montanus Baird, 1855:335
Reithrodontomys montanus: J. A. Allen, 1893:80

The plains harvest mouse is small (usually less than 130 mm = 5.1 in.) and has a tail that is shorter than the head and body length. This species is grayer

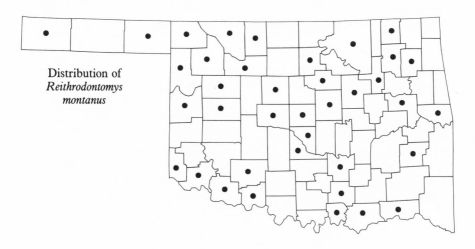

Distribution of
*Reithrodontomys
montanus*

overall with less tawny (or brownish) upper parts than those of *R. megalotis*, with which it is most easily confused. Most specimens of these two species require a specialist for correct identification. Traits which may help in distinguishing the two are listed in the species account for *R. megalotis*. Of these, the best external characteristics seem to be the distinctive dark middorsal stripe and the distinct narrow and dark dorsal tail stripe present in most specimens of *R. montanus*. The short tail of *R. montanus* easily distinguishes it from *R. fulvescens*, which has a tail noticeably longer than its head and body length. The separation of specimens of *R. humulis* and *R. montanus* may also be difficult; however, the brownish gray underparts of *R. humulis*, versus the white underparts of *R. montanus*, should provide a means of separating these two species.

The distribution of *R. montanus* in Oklahoma is statewide, with specimens known from all physiognomic regions. Even though it has been found in the eastern forested regions of Oklahoma, this species is more commonly found in prairie areas. In the mesic areas of eastern Oklahoma, Blair (1938) collected several specimens in the sumac-grama and grama-beardgrass associations on the Garnett Prairies in Tulsa County. He located one nest (38 mm = 1 1/2 in. in diameter and made of cotton) beneath a limestone slab. In the more xeric areas of western Oklahoma, Martin and Preston (1970) found *R. montanus* to be common (12.5 percent of all individuals collected in a live-trap study) on the mesquite plains in Harmon County. Other workers have suggested that *R. montanus* is not commonly taken in traps but is found frequently in owl pellets in the same areas (Jackson and Warfel, 1933; Hays, 1958; Glass and Halloran, 1961). Other habitats from which *R. montanus* has also been collected include the edges of grain fields and from intermontane meadows in the Wichita Mountains (Hays, 1958; Glass and Halloran, 1961).

Goertz (1963) provided the most extensive biological notes about *R. montanus* in Oklahoma. He found *R. montanus* to be rather uncommon (97 collected in 74,206 trap nights) during a two-year live- and snap-trap study in Payne County. Many specimens were collected in the winter months, and this could reflect either an increase in the actual size of the population or an increase in trapping success because of other food resources being reduced. Goertz's analysis suggested that *R. montanus* was more common on three study sites which had 62.5, 63.1, and 64 percent vegetative ground cover, respectively; the height of the vegetative cover was 254, 236, and 181 mm, (10, 9.3., and 7.1 in.). *Reithrodontomys fulvescens* and *Sigmodon hispidus* were also taken during this study but always in areas which had more ground cover and taller vegetation. The two species commonly taken in the same habitat with *R. montanus* were *Perognathus hispidus* and *Peromyscus maniculatus*. The live-trap studies indicated that males had an average home range of 0.17 ha (0.42 acres), whereas females occupied 0.2 ha (0.51 acres). Male *R. montanus* traveled on the average 59.7 m (196 ft.) in 46 days whereas females moved an average of 67.7 m (222 ft.) in 35 days. Goertz's study also suggested that *R. montanus* reproduces throughout the year in Oklahoma, since males and females in various reproductive states were taken in almost every month. Seven pregnant females (each containing three or four embryos) were collected in February, May, June, July, and November, and lactating females were captured during nearly every month. Males with scrotal testes varying in size from 3 mm to 6 mm were collected nearly every month.

The subspecies occurring over most of Oklahoma is *R. m. griseus* (Hall, 1981), but specimens from the Black Mesa region are paler than typical *R. m. griseus* and may be referrable to the race *R. m. montanus* (Blair, 1939). Additional specimens from the northern and western areas of Oklahoma are needed to clarify the status of the *montanus* and *albescens* races within the state.

Peromyscus attwateri J. A. Allen
Texas Mouse
Peromyscus attwateri J. A. Allen, 1895:330

The Texas mouse, *Peromyscus attwateri*, has a cinnamon brown dorsum which is separated from the nearly pure white venter by an ochraceous (yellow orange) lateral line. The tail is tufted, bicolored, and slightly longer than the head and body. Four other species of *Peromyscus* occur sympatrically with *P. attwateri* in Oklahoma, and all are similar in general appearance. Three of these species, *P. maniculatus*, *P. leucopus*, and *P. gossypinus*, are easily separable by the absence of an ochraceous lateral line. However, specimens of *P. pectoralis*, the white-ankled mouse, may be difficult to separate from those of *P. attwateri*. In overall size and color, these two species are very similar. Close examination will reveal that *P. attwateri* differs in having a dusky-colored tarsal-joint region rather than a white one as in *P. pectoralis*.

The distribution of the Texas mouse is discontinuous in Oklahoma and adjacent states because of its preference for rocky situations, which are also discontinuous in distribution (Schmidly, 1974). The Texas mouse occurs in all but the northwestern parts of the state north of the Washita River and west of north-south line drawn through the center of the state. Almost all specimens have been taken in the vicinity of limestone outcrops or large rocks. Glass and Halloran (1961) found *P. attwateri* abundant in all rocky areas of the Wichita Mountains. Taylor (1964) collected *P. attwateri* in Johnston County only from

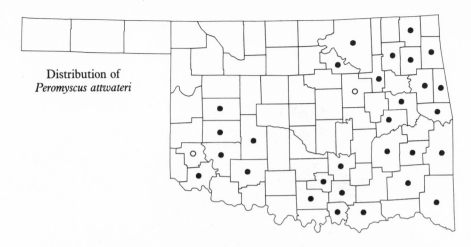

Distribution of
Peromyscus attwateri

rocky limestone prominences. In northeastern Oklahoma, Blair (1938) noted that this species was quite common in steep-walled limestone ravines which supported an oak (*Quercus* spp.), hickory (*Carya* spp.), and elm (*Ulmus* spp.) forest. These northeastern Oklahoma populations may represent the source of origin of the Kansas populations (Choate *et al.*, 1966). Schmidly (1974) reviewed what is known about the biology of *P. attwateri* in the United States, but little is known of its ecology.

Schmidly (1973) examined the geographical variation in several morphological features of *P. attwateri*, but deemed it insufficient to recognize subspecies. However, northern populations in Oklahoma, Kansas, Arkansas, and Missouri are darker than the southern populations in Texas.

Peromyscus boylii (Baird)
Brush Mouse
Hesperomys boylii Baird, 1855:335
Peromyscus boylii: Mearns, 1896:139

Peromyscus boylii is a medium-sized mouse (total length of 176–248 mm = 6.9–9.8 in.), and it has a sparsely haired, penicillated (tufted) tail which is slightly bicolored. The tail is slightly longer than the head and body length. The upper parts are a cinnamon buff, and a distinct ochraceous (yellow orange) lateral line separates the darker dorsal pelage from the white underparts. In Oklahoma, *P. boylii* is sympatric with four other species of *Peromyscus*. Two of these species, *P. maniculatus* and *P. leucopus*, do not have an ochraceous lateral line and are easy to separate from *P. boylii*. The piñon mouse, *P. truei*, has noticeably larger ears (usually greater than 25 mm = 1 in.) than *P. boylii* (ears usually 20 mm = 0.8 in. or less). The most difficult species to distinguish from *P. boylii* is the rockmouse, *P. difficilis*. Geluso (1970) found that the ease with which the tail sheath is removed can be used to separate fresh specimens of these two species. The tail sheath of *P. boylii* is relatively tough and not easily removed, while that of *P. difficilis* slips off with little difficulty. In addition, the rock mouse has slightly larger ears (21–24 mm = 0.8–0.9 in.) than *P. boylii* (20 mm = 0.8 in. or less).

The brush mouse has been recorded only from the extreme northwestern portions of the Panhandle in the Black Mesa country. Formerly, the distribution of this species was said to include the eastern portions of Oklahoma. However, Schmidly (1973) returned the subspecies *attwateri* to its original status as a full species based on chromosomal and morphological differences. The ranges of these two are allopatric in Oklahoma.

Distribution of
Peromyscus boylii

Geluso (1970) found the brush mouse one of the most abundant mice in the Black Mesa region. The preferred habitat was dense, shrubby vegetation or rocky areas with many crevices, ledges, and holes. He collected 56 percent of his specimens on the rock-strewn slopes which were covered with thick brush; the remaining specimens were taken in rocky areas, including lava rimrock, sandstone cliffs, and piñon-juniper stands. The principal mammalian associate taken with *P. boylii* was *Neotoma albigula*, the white-throated woodrat.

The subspecies occurring in Oklahoma is *P. b. rowleyi* (Schmidly, 1973).

Peromyscus difficilis (J. A. Allen)
Rock Mouse
Vesperimus nasutus J. A. Allen, 1891:299
Peromyscus difficilis: Hoffmeister and de la Torre, 1961:7

Peromyscus difficilis is a large, pale gray mouse with a penicillated tail that is as long as or longer than the head and body length. An ochraceous (yellow

Distribution of
Peromyscus difficilis

orange) band separates the darker dorsal pelage from the white underparts. In Oklahoma, the rock mouse will most likely be confused with the brush mouse (*P. boylii*) or the piñon mouse (*P. truei*), as all three species are sympatric in extreme northwestern Oklahoma.

The piñon mouse can be distinguished by its larger ears (usually more than 19.7 mm = 0.78 in. from the notch) and a tail which is shorter than the head and body. The greatest difficulty lies in separating *P. difficilis* and *P. boylii*. The ease with which the tail sheath (the terminal portion of skin and hair) detaches in fresh specimens differs in these latter two species: in *P. boylii*, the tail sheath slips off more easily than does that of *P. difficilis*. In addition, the ear length of *P. difficilis* (17.0–19.6 mm = 0.7–0.8 in.) is longer than in *P. boylii* (usually less than 16.9 mm = 0.7 in.). Geluso (1970) developed skin and skull keys for the identification of the five species of *Peromyscus* occurring in the Black Mesa region and suggested the use of comparative series as the best method for positive identifications.

Peromyscus difficilis occurs only in the Black Mesa region of northwestern Oklahoma (Blair, 1939; Geluso, 1970, where it is contiguous with populations farther west in New Mexico and to the north in Colorado (Armstrong, 1972; Findley *et al.*, 1975).

Geluso (1970, 1971) discussed the ecological distribution of the rock mouse in Oklahoma. His study revealed that *P. difficilis* is found primarily in rocky areas; 68 percent of his captures occurred at higher elevations on rock cliffs where vegetation was often lacking. Wilson (1968) demonstrated a similar habitat preference for *P. difficilis* in New Mexico. In the Black Mesa area, Geluso (1970) found also that *P. difficilis* seldom inhabited brushy rock slopes or rocky areas in piñon-juniper stands. Mammal associates taken in the same habitat preferred by the rock mouse included the Colorado chipmunk, *Eu-*

tamias quadrivittatus; the rock squirrel, *Spermophilus variegatus;* the white-throated woodrat, *Neotoma albigula;* the Mexican woodrat, *Neotoma mexicana;* and the spotted skunk, *Spilogale putorius.*

Little reproductive data exists for *P. difficilis* in Oklahoma. Males had enlarged testes in March (4–11 mm), April (5–7 mm), May (14 mm), and June (10–15 mm). Pregnant females have been collected in late May (four embryos, 17 mm) and early June (four embryos, 11 mm). These data coincide with the period of peak reproductive activity reported for Colorado specimens (Cinq-Mars and Brown, 1969).

The systematic status of *P. difficilis* is not clear. It was first described as a distinct species under the name *nasutus* by Allen (1891), but Hoffmeister and de la Torre (1961) considered *nasutus* to be a subspecies of *difficilis.* Recent chromosome and protein studies by Zimmerman *et al.* (1975) suggest that the Mexican populations of *P. difficilis* are specifically distinct from those in New Mexico, Colorado, and Oklahoma. If this is the case, then all Oklahoma specimens should be referred to *P. nasutus nasutus.* However, this is uncertain at present.

Peromyscus gossypinus (LeConte)
Cotton Mouse
Hesp(eromys) gossypinus LeConte, 1853:411
Peromyscus gossypinus: Rhodes, 1896:189

Within its distributional range and habitat in southeastern Oklahoma, *Peromyscus gossypinus* can be confused only with *P. leucopus*, the white-footed mouse. These two species are very similar in general appearance, both having upper parts that are a tawny yellowish brown and underparts that are white. McCarley (1954) suggested that hybridization between these two species was possible, making the identification of some specimens very difficult. However, Engstrom *et al.* (1982) contend that most supposed hybrids are separable into one species or the other. The cotton mouse is generally larger than the white-footed mouse in most traits, averaging more than 30 g (1.1 oz.) in weight and over 28 mm (1.1 in.) in greatest skull length.

Peromyscus gossypinus occurs primarily in the Cyprus-Oak Floodplains and Oak-Hickory-Pine Ouachita Highlands physiognomic regions of Oklahoma. Its distribution is seemingly limited to the more mesic forested areas typical of adjacent states where this species occurs (McCarley, 1952; Davis, 1974; Sealander, 1979). Habits and specific habitats are not well known for this

Distribution of
Peromyscus gossypinus

species in Oklahoma (Dice, 1937, 1940; McCarley, 1954, 1959; Taylor and McCarley, 1963). Blair (1939) recorded the cotton mouse as being common in the mesic hardwood forest of frequently flooded terraces formed by the Glover River. Taylor (1964) captured the westernmost recorded specimens of *P. gossypinus* in Bryan County from a relatively high limestone ledge. Other mammals taken in the same trap line included *P. attwateri* and *P. leucopus*.

Wolf and Linzey (1977) reviewed the biology of *P. gossypinus* over its entire range in the United States. Robbins *et al.* (1985) reviewed some of the biochemical polymorphism as it relates to chromosomal and morphological variation in *P. gossypinus*.

The subspecies occurring in Oklahoma is *P. g. megacephalus* (Hall, 1981).

Peromyscus leucopus (Rafinesque)
White-footed Mouse
Musculus leucopus Rafinesque, 1818:446
Peromyscus leucopus: Thomas, 1895:192

Peromyscus leucopus is one of the most common small rodents occurring in Oklahoma. It can be distinguished from other *Peromyscus* in Oklahoma, except *P. maniculatus* and *P. gossypinus*, by its short tail and lack of an ochraceous (yellow orange) lateral line. *Peromyscus leucopus* differs from *P. maniculatus* in having a tail that is less distinctly bicolored and longer (more than 65 mm = 2.6 in.). In addition, *P. leucopus* adults generally average larger in most cranial features (for example, greatest length of skull usually more than 26 mm = 1 in.). *Peromyscus leucopus* differs from *P. gossypinus* in that it is smaller and not so darkly colored. Occasionally, *Ochrotomys nuttalli* is mistaken for *P. leucopus*. However, *Ochrotomys* should easily be recognized by its brighter, more golden color and the lack of a well-defined line separating the dark upper parts from the whitish venter. In *O. nuttalli* the venter is buffy or cream-colored, while in *P. leucopus* it is almost pure white. In Oklahoma, the upper parts of *P. leucopus* vary from a dull grayish brown to reddish brown.

The white-footed mouse occurs in all the physiognomic regions of Oklahoma. Whereas *P. maniculatus* is most commonly taken in grass associations, *P. leucopus* is more commonly found in brushy or wooded associations. Vegetative associations from which *P. leucopus* have been taken include ravine for-

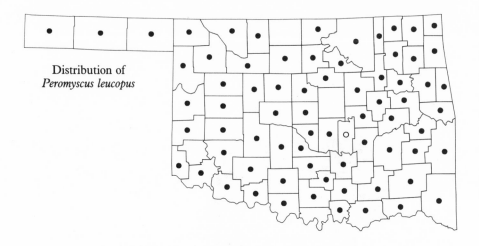

Distribution of
Peromyscus leucopus

est near limestone rocks, oak-hickory forest around logs, oak-elm forest next to brush piles, post oak–blackjack woodlands, flood plain forest, cottonwood groves, wooded areas near streams in the Wichita Mountains and in Boiling Springs State Park, plum-sage associations, sumac-grama associations, mesquite-grama associations, rocky and brushy slopes with juniper trees, and dune areas in Woods County,woody ravines in central Oklahoma, and mesa tops and valley floors of the Black Mesa region (Jackson and Warfel, 1933; Glass, 1951; Blair, 1938, 1954; Hays, 1958; Glass and Halloran, 1961; Clark, 1966; Geluso, 1970). Because of its wide geographic and ecologic distribution in Oklahoma, the white-footed mouse has been taken in association with almost all other mammal species that occur in Oklahoma.

Reproduction is probably year-round, with litters of four to five young. Food includes seeds and insects. Parasites include cestodes, nematodes, lice, fleas, and ticks. Warbles also occur on *P. leucopus*. Grau (1982) noted that individuals of *P. leucopus* were capable of recognizing close kin without a previous encounter.

Baker *et al.* (1983) and Stangl (1986) discussed chromosomal variation in *P. leucopus* and how it relates to the systematics of the species. Three subspecies of *P. leucopus* intergrade in Oklahoma: *P. l. tornillo, P. l. noveboracensis,* and *P. l. leucopus* (Hall, 1981).

Peromyscus maniculatus (Wagner)
Deer Mouse
Hesperomys maniculatus Wagner, 1845:148
Peromyscus maniculatus: Bangs, 1898:496

The deer mouse, *Peromyscus maniculatus*, is a small (total length usually less than 160 mm = 6.3 in.) white-footed mouse with a sharply bicolored (distinct, narrow, dark dorsal stripe) short tail. The tail is always shorter than the head and body length and averages about 50–60 mm (2–2.4 in.) in length. The short tail distinguishes the deer mouse from all other *Peromyscus* in Oklahoma except *P. leucopus*. A series of specimens often is required to identify some individuals of these two species. Part of the difficulty is that during summer months, *P. leucopus* may sometimes have a bicolored tail; however, its tail is nearly always longer than 65 mm. Chromosomally, *P. leucopus* has a larger number of acrocentric pairs than does *P. maniculatus* (Hsu and Arrighi, 1968). In addition, adult *P. leucopus* averages larger in most cranial characters (Caire, in prep.).

The deer mouse may be found throughout Oklahoma in all of the physiognomic regions except the Cypress-Oak Floodplains in the extreme southeastern corner of the state. Specific habitats within which specimens have been taken vary considerably, but most appear to have been taken in grass or prairie associations. The habitats recorded include grasslands, mesquite-buffalo grass associations, three-awn–finger grass areas, mixed-grass areas, bluejoint–switch grass associations, cleared fields in post oak–blackjack areas, sand plum thickets, tall-grass prairies, upland meadows in the Wichita Mountains, shinnery oak associations, salt cedar–groundsel tree associations, and sand sage associations (Blair, 1938, 1939, 1954: Glass, 1951; McCarley, 1952; Hays, 1958; Glass and Halloran, 1961; Geluso, 1970: Martin and

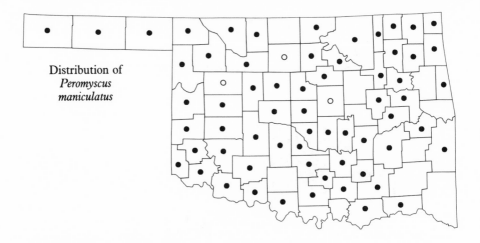

Distribution of
Peromyscus
maniculatus

Preston, 1970). Wyman and Schaefer (1972), in a study of the ectoparasites of *P. maniculatus* in Texas County, found the following parasites: *Orchopaeus leucopus, Monopsyllus wagneri, Epitedia wenmanni, Meringis parkeri, Peromyscopsylla hesperomys, Hoplopleura hesperomydis,* and *Dermacentor parumapterus*. Reproduction is probably year-round, with litters averaging four to five young. Deer mice feed primarily on seeds and, to a lesser extent, on insects.

Presently five subspecies—*bairdii, luteus, nebrascensis, pallescens,* and *ozarkiarum*—are recorded from Oklahoma. Three of these five, *pallescens, bairdii,* and *nebrascensis,* barely occur in the state. Bryan County is the only recorded locality for *pallescens* in Oklahoma. Caire and Zimmeran (1975) examined specimens from the region of contact of *P. m. ozarkiarum* and *P. m. pallescens* in Texas and Oklahoma and found that these two subspecies apparently do not interbreed. However, gene flow between them occurs via a third subspecies, *P. m. luteus,* in western Oklahoma. A zone of intergradation among *nebrascensis, luteus,* and *rufinus* (in eastern Colorado and New Mexico) probably occurs in the Oklahoma Panhandle. In addition, an intergradation zone probably exists in northeastern Oklahoma, where *bairdii, ozarkiarum,* and *luteus* converge. These zones of intergradation increase the difficulty of allocating specimens to the proper subspecies as well as increase the complexity of geographic variation within this species in Oklahoma.

Peromyscus pectoralis Osgood
White-ankled Mouse
Peromyscus attwateri pectoralis Osgood, 1904:59
Peromyscus pectoralis: V. Bailey, 1906:57

The white-ankled mouse, Peromyscus pectoralis, is a medium-sized mouse with a tail that is usually longer than its head and body. The tail is hairy, bicolored, and coarsely annulated. Throughout much of its geographic range, P. pectoralis occurs sympatrically with other species of the boylii species group, especially P. boylii and P. attwateri. Because of the wide specific overlap in most characters of these species, comparison of large series will aid in identification. Externally, P. pectoralis differs from P. attwateri and P. boylii in having white instead of dusky ankles (the dark color of the shank does not extend over the tarsal joint). Chromosomally, P. pectoralis has eight large biarmed autosomes, whereas P. attwateri has six and P. boylii two. The baculum has a long, attenuate, cartilaginous tip instead of being short and rounded as in P. attwateri and P. boylii.

Peromyscus pectoralis occurs in small disjunct populations from Mexico across the Trans-Pecos and Edwards Plateau regions of Texas into southern Oklahoma. It has, however, been collected from only one locality in Oklahoma; eight specimens were taken along limestone outcrops along a deep ravine at Rock Creek, 4 mi. west of Marietta, in Love County (Kilpatrick and Caire, 1973). Peromyscus pectoralis may eventually be found to occur at other similar limestone outcrops farther north in the state.

Little ecological information is available for P. pectoralis in Oklahoma. The only two species of mammals taken with P. pectoralis near Marietta were Neotoma floridana and P. leucopus. The dominant vegetation at the Marietta site consisted of post oak (Quercus stellata) and Smilax. In Texas, and possibly in Oklahoma, P. pectoralis is seemingly microallopatric with P. boylii and P. attwateri (Kilpatrick and Caire, 1973).

Distribution of
Peromyscus pectoralis

Schmidly (1972) discussed geographic variation in several body and cranial characters of *P. pectoralis* and listed *P. p. laceianus* as the subspecies in north central Texas; Oklahoma specimens apparently are of the same subspecies. Kilpatrick and Zimmerman (1976) discussed the genetic structure of populations of *P. pectoralis* throughout its range. Their data suggest the possibility that *P. pectoralis* has spread into Oklahoma from a Pleistocene refugium on the Edwards Plateau.

Peromyscus truei (Schufeldt)
Piñon Mouse
Hesperomys truei Schufeldt, 1885:407
P. (eromyscus) truei: Thomas, 1894:365

The piñon mouse, *Peromyscus truei,* has exceptionally large ears; they are longer than the hind foot. An ochraceous (yellow orange) line separates the dark upper parts from the white venter. The tail is usually shorter than head and body length. *Peromyscus boylii* and *P. difficilis* may be confused with *P. truei.* In most cases the short tail and long ears will help distinguish the piñon mouse from other species. Both *P. difficilis* and *P. boylii* have tails that are longer than the head and body and ears that are shorter than the hind foot.

Little information is available on the ecology or behavior of this species in Oklahoma. Hoffmeister (1981) commented on the biology in other portions of *P. truei* range. The piñon mouse is a common inhabitant of the piñon-juniper zone of the southwestern United States and Mexico (Hoffmeister, 1951; Wilson, 1968; Geluso, 1971). This species is known in Oklahoma only from the Black Mesa region (Blair, 1939; Chase, 1939; Glass, 1949; Geluso, 1970). Geluso (1970) reported that 65 percent of all *P. truei* collected in the Black Mesa region were trapped in rocky areas under either Piñon (*Pinus edulus*) or juniper trees (*Juniperus monosperma*). The piñon mouse also showed

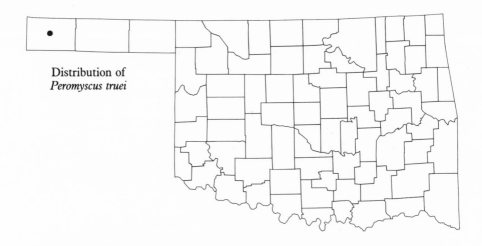

Distribution of
Peromyscus truei

a preference for the more widely spaced piñon-juniper stands and on a few occasions was collected in prairie communities (Geluso, 1970). Other mammals taken with the piñon mouse included the Colorado chipmunk (*Eutamias quadrivittatus*), rock squirrel (*Spermophilus variegatus*), brush mouse (*Peromyscus boylii*), white-footed mouse (*P. leucopus*), and rock mouse (*P. difficilis*).

The subspecies occurring in Oklahoma is *P. t. truei* (Hoffmeister, 1951).

Ochrotomys nuttalli (Harlan)
Golden Mouse
Arvicola nuttalli Harlan, 1832:446
Ochrotomys nuttalli: Hooper, 1958:23

The golden mouse is appropriately named, having upper parts which are a rich golden brown color. The venter is usually white or washed with a pale pinkish cinnamon color. The tail, which is prehensile (Packard and Garner, 1964*a*), is faintly bicolored. Except for its bright color, *O. nuttalli* superficially resembles a *Peromyscus*. Distinctive cranial and bacular traits support its recognition as a separate monotypic genus (Blair, 1942; Hooper, 1958).

Ochrotomys reaches its northwestern distributional limits in Oklahoma. Only a few specimens have been collected and preserved from Oklahoma, making it difficult to characterize its distribution within the state. Based upon the ecological data collected for this species in other states (Black, 1936: McCarley, 1954; Goodpaster and Hoffmeister, 1954; Packard and Garner, 1964*a*), the golden mouse is probably limited to the eastern timbered regions of Oklahoma. Sealander (1956) reported this species from 6 mi. west of Mena in Polk County, Fourche la Fave in Scott County, and Fayetteville in Washington County, Arkansas, all of which adjoin the eastern border of Oklahoma. Its preferred habitat is probably the brushy valleys and hillsides covered with dense stands of oaks (*Quercus* spp.) and hickory (*Carya* spp.) and tangles of vegetation such as honeysuckle (*Lonicera* sp.), greenbrier (*Smilax* sp.), and grapevines (*Vitis* spp.). *Ochrotomys* builds nests and feeding plat-

Distribution of
Ochrotomys nuttalli

forms 2.5–4.5 m (8–15 ft.) above ground in this intertwining understory (Goodpaster and Hoffmeister, 1954: Packard and Garner, 1964*a*). Little else is known about the natural history of this mouse in Oklahoma. Linzey and Packard (1977) reviewed the biology of *O. nuttalli* in the United States.

The last systematic revision of the species (Packard, 1969) concluded that the Oklahoma race was *O. n. flammeus.*

Baiomys taylori (Thomas)
Northern Pygmy Mouse
Hesperomys (*Vesperimus*) *taylori* Thomas, 1887:66
Baiomys taylori: Mearns, 1907:381

The only specimen of *Baiomys taylori* recorded from Oklahoma was taken in Cotton County (Stangl and Dalquest, 1985). This species has been taken

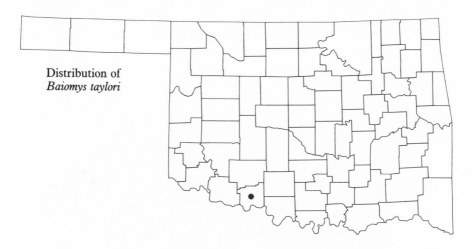

Distribution of
Baiomys taylori

more often in several north central Texas counties (Baccus, 1968, 1971; Hart, 1972). *Baiomys* is very small in size, the total length averaging near 100 mm (3.9 in.), and can be recognized by its grizzled upper parts. The tail is shorter than the head and body combined. The house mouse (*Mus musculus*) and harvest mice (*Reithrodontomys*) may be mistaken for the pygmy mouse. The house mouse has a longer tail, usually as long or longer than the head and body, and has notched upper incisors. Harvest mice are more brightly colored with brownish above and whitish below and have grooved upper incisors.

The Oklahoma specimen was taken in sandy rolling hills dominated by bluestem (*Schizachyrium*). In Texas, pygmy mice are found in weedy and low grassy places as well as habitats containing bluestem grass (Davis, 1974). Baccus (1971) captured *Baiomys* in a mesquite savanna association in Baylor County, Texas, composed of mesquite (*Prosopis glandulosa*), several types of grass (*Bouteloua, Aristida, Andropogon, Triodia*), and scattered forbs and cacti. Similar areas exist in south central Oklahoma and may support disjunct populations of pygmy mice. However, Packard (1960) quoted W. B. Davis as being of the opinion that *B. taylori* has extended its range northward from the Coastal Prairie within recent times. If so, its rarity in Oklahoma may indicate its inability as yet to easily negotiate a crossing of the Red River. Cotton rats (*Sigmodon hispidus*), harvest mice (*Reithrodontomys*), kangaroo rats (*Dipodomys ordii*), and deer mice (*Peromyscus maniculatus*) have been taken with *Baiomys* (Davis, 1974; Stangl and Dalquest, 1985). Pygmy mice either make their own tiny runways or use those of cotton rats or other mammals (Davis, 1974). Stangl and Dalquest (1985) suggest that *Baiomys* may only be an intermittent component of the fauna of Oklahoma because of spells of severe weather which periodically eliminate resident populations.

The subspecies occurring in Oklahoma is *B. t. subater* (Hall, 1981).

Onychomys leucogaster (Wied-Neuwied)
Northern Grasshopper Mouse
Hypudaeus leucogaster Wied-Neuwied, 1841:99
Onychomys leucogaster: Baird, 1858:459

The northern grasshopper mouse, *Onychomys leucogaster,* is a stout, robust mouse with a short, thick tail. It is distinguishable from species of *Peromyscus* by its larger, more heavily clawed front feet, a shorter, thicker tail (ranging from 29 mm to 62 mm = 1.1–2.4 in.), and more hypsodont molars. The coronoid process is robust and strongly curved posteriorly. *Onychomys* is an attractive mouse with distinctly bicolored fur. Age variations in pelage colors do occur, and the molt patterns have been described by Engstrom and Choate (1979). The color of the sparse juvenile coat on the dorsum varies from pale to dark gray, but the venter is always white. At about 60 days of age, the juveniles molt into subadult fur, which is grayish brown to brown (Ruffer, 1965). The molting period is usually from June until December. Subadults molt into adult pelage sometime between August and February. The color of the adult pelage is pinkish cinnamon or a darker cinnamon.

Specimens of the northern grasshopper mouse have been recorded from the following physiognomic regions: Piñon-Juniper Mesas, Shortgrass High Plains, Mixed-grass Plains, and Mesquite-Grass Plains. These mice are seldom very abundant but are most often found in association with sandy soils, semistabilized dunes, shortgrass gypsum soils, overgrazed pastures, and weedy roadside ditches. The sandy habitats may be an edaphic requirement permitting frequent sand baths (Egoscue, 1960). Grasshopper mice apparently are nomadic within large, well-defined, and actively defended territories (Ruffer, 1964b). Blair (1953) estimated the average home range to be 2.3 ha (5.8 acres).

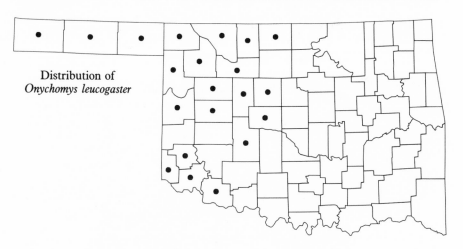

Distribution of
Onychomys leucogaster

Ruffer (1965, 1968) has studied the behavior of *Onychomys leucogaster* in Oklahoma, including development of young, mating, hoarding of food, vocalization, and inter- and intraspecific interactions. The unusual vocalization consists of various high-pitched whistles or peeps. One frequent cry is emitted with the mouth open and the nose raised and pointing up, in a manner similar to coyotes or wolves. This has been responsible in part for the colloquial name "wolf mouse." The calls are easy to detect in the wild once the sound is pointed out by someone already familiar with it. The cries are probably used in territorial and social behavior. Jahoda (1973) demonstrated a daily and lunar periodicity in *Onychomys*.

Grasshopper mice are more carnivorous than most small rodents. The chief food items vary from predominantly insects, scorpions, various small mammals, and seeds in the spring, summer, and early fall to a diet of plants and an occasional small mammal in the winter. Harriman (1973) showed that, under some conditions, grasshopper mice from Harper County exhibited dietary selectivity depending upon individual physiological needs. In the laboratory, grasshopper mice have been observed easily overpowering and killing *Reithrodontomys*, *Peromyscus*, *Perognathus*, and *Mus*.

Females are seasonally polyestrous from January to July. Litter sizes range from 1 to 6, averaging 3.8 (Ruffer, 1964b): gestation is about 32–38 days. There may be six litters per year for up to three years.

McCarty (1978) has summarized much of what is known of the biology of *O. leucogaster* throughout its entire range. Engstrom and Choate (1979) and Riddle and Choate (1986) examined the geographic variation, systematics, and biogeography of *O. leucogaster*. Only a single subspecies, *O. l. arcticeps*, is presently described as occurring in Oklahoma. The other subspecies, *O. l.*

breviauritus, was considered by Engstrom and Choate (1979) to be a subjective junior synonym.

Sigmodon hispidus Say and Ord
Hispid Cotton Rat
S. [igmodon] hispidus Say and Ord, 1825:354

Hispid cotton rats have rough, coarse body fur. The dorsal coloration is variegated, an effect produced by mixing several shades of brown, tan, and black, instead of uniform as in most other rodents. The venter is dull grayish. These stocky, rather robust rodents have a sparsely haired tail which is shorter than the head and body length. The ears are blackish, hairy, and almost concealed by the body hair. A distinctive dental trait of the genus is the S-shaped cusp pattern of the molars.

The northward range extension of *Sigmodon* from Texas and Mexico through Oklahoma and Kansas to Nebraska in recent times has been well documented (Cockrum, 1948; Jones, 1960; Genoways and Schlitter, 1966). At present, cotton rats occur in every physiognomic region of Oklahoma. The species is limited to those habitats providing dense overhead cover for the runways; dense stands of grass, forbs or low-growing woody vegetation (Goertz, 1964; Martin and Preston, 1970). Hispid cotton rats have been

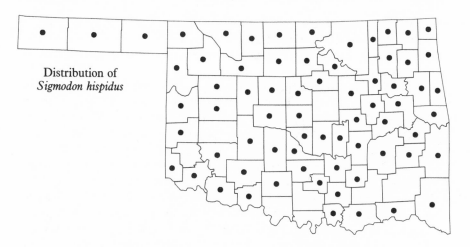

Distribution of
Sigmodon hispidus

collected from upland meadows (Osborn and Kellogg, 1943; Glass and Halloran, 1961), tall-grass prairies (Phillips, 1936; Frank, 1950; Smith, 1940a; McCarley, 1952), abandoned fields with scrub post oak and weeds (McCarley, 1952), grassy areas near irrigation ditches (Clark and Skryja, 1969), grassy clearings near streams and stream banks (Elliot, 1899a; Jackson and Warfel, 1933; Jones and Anderson, 1959), open grassy areas (Ruffer, 1964a), brush piles (Elliot, 1899a), grassy and weedy fence rows (Hays, 1958), mixed grass and forb areas (Schendel, 1940), and sedge marsh associations (Blair, 1938). Localities with dense tree stands having canopies thick enough to shade out the ground cover are usually avoided by *Sigmodon* (Goertz, 1964).

Extreme fluctuations in population sizes do occur. In years having mild winters and summers, large populations are maintained, but cold, severe winters and hot, dry summers often result in very small populations (Smith, 1940; Goertz, 1964). Goertz (1964) and Hays (1958) noted that the largest populations of *Sigmodon* usually occurred in summer and early fall, while declines were frequent during the cold months of winter. A similar pattern was found in Kansas near Hays (Fleharty *et al.*, 1972). Exceedingly large populations seem to follow breaks in periods of prolonged drouth (for example, 1939, 1958), when cotton rats may reach plague proportions. In southwestern Oklahoma, Martin and Preston (1970) collected larger percentages of cotton rats compared to other rodent species during December. When populations reach large numbers, individuals are often forced into marginal habitats (Goertz, 1964). Individual cotton rats do not survive long in the wild. Goertz (1964) noted that 50 percent of all marked individuals disappeared from his study area within two months; 98 percent did not survive past the sixth month. Seemingly the entire population turnover rate varies from five to twelve months (Goertz, 1964; Fleharty *et al.*, 1972).

Home range size varies inversely with population densities (Goertz, 1964), being larger with low densities. That of males varied from 0.2 to 4.0 ha (0.55–9.90 acres) during periods of low densities and from 0.1 to 2.9 ha (0.31–7.2 acres) when populations were high. Comparable figures for females were 0.3–1.3 ha (0.80–3.30 acres) and 0.1–0.5 ha (0.30–1.20 acres).

Sigmodon are seemingly capable of breeding throughout the year in Oklahoma; however, severe cold weather often curtails breeding in the winter (Goertz, 1965). Litter sizes range from 1 to 11 young, with older females having the largest litters (Goertz, 1965). Glass has seen *in utero* litters of 12 to 14. The average litter size is 5.9 young per female (Goertz, 1965), with a gestation period of about 27 days and irruptions at any time of year. Green (1964) suggested that *Sigmodon* in Payne County ceased breeding in early fall when population densities were high. Kirkpatrick (1965) reported on litter size and age determination in this species.

Since cotton rats are active at all hours of the day (Phillips, 1936; Smith, 1940*a*; Hays, 1958; Goertz, 1964), they become the prey of numerous predators, such as coyotes, foxes, badgers, hawks, and owls (for example, see Tyler and Jensen, 1981). Several channel catfish (*Ictalurus punctatus*) stomach contents have also been reported to contain cotton rats (Heard, 1959). The diamond-back water snake (*Natrix rhombifera*) and other snakes are predators of *Sigmodon* (Sisk and McCoy, 1964). Wind-blown prairie fires which sweep rapidly across the grassy areas are potentially dangerous because the burrow systems are shallow and nests may be above ground (Glass and Halloran, 1961). The remains of cotton rats have also been found in association with prehistoric man in Oklahoma, suggesting the possibility that this species may have been a food item for early man (Ahshapanek and Burns, 1960). Cotton rats are parasitized by a wide variety of fleas, ticks, nematodes, and cestodes (Smith, 1954). Coggins and McDaniel (1975) reported on seasonal variations of cestode and nematode parasites. They also noted heavier infestations in males. Goertz (1966) reported on bot fly warbles in *Sigmodon*. Cameron and Spencer (1981) summarized the literature concerning *Sigmodon*.

One subspecies of *Sigmodon hispidus*—*S. h. texianus*—is reported from Oklahoma; however *S. h. alfredi* occurs in extreme southeastern Colorado and may also be found to occur in northwestern Oklahoma (Hall, 1981; Armstrong, 1972).

Neotoma albigula Hartley
White-throated Woodrat
Neotoma albigula Hartley, 1894:157

The white-throated woodrat is generally brown, with throat and chest hairs that are white from tip to base. Two other woodrats, *N. mexicana* and *N. micropus*, are sympatric with *N. albigula* in Oklahoma, but differ in that the former has throat hairs that are gray at the base while those of the latter are steel gray.

All Oklahoma specimens of *N. albigula* are from the Piñon-Juniper Mesas physiognomic region in extreme northwestern Oklahoma. However, there are specimens from Hardeman and Childress counties in Texas (Davis, 1974), suggesting the possibility that the species might also occur in extreme southwestern Oklahoma. Specific areas inhabited by *N. albigula* in the Black Mesa region are rock canyons and brushy slopes (Blair, 1939; Glass, 1949). Geluso (1970) collected specimens of *N. albigula* in rock cliff areas, on brushy slopes, and in piñon-juniper associations. This woodrat has been obtained with most of the species of rodents which occur in northwestern Oklahoma, including *N. micropus*, *N. albigula*, *Peromyscus boylii*, *P. difficilis*, *P. leucopus*, *Reithrodontomys* spp., *Spermophilus variegatus*, *Eutamias quadrivittatus*, and *Perognathus* spp. Little information exists on the ecology of white-throated woodrats in Oklahoma.

The subspecies in northwestern Oklahoma is *N. a. warreni* (Hall, 1981). If

Distribution of
Neotoma albigula

it is found to occur in southwestern Oklahoma, then the subspecies there
would be *N. a. albigula* (Hall, 1981).

Neotoma floridana (Ord)
Eastern Woodrat
Mus floridanus Ord, 1818:184
N [*eotoma*]. *floridana:* Say and Ord, 1825:346

Eastern woodrats, *Neotoma floridana,* are medium-sized rodents with a total
length of approximately 350 mm (13.8 in.) and a bicolored, hairy tail that is

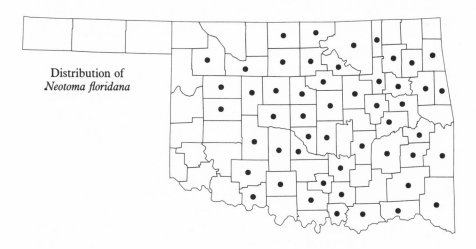

Distribution of
Neotoma floridana

slightly shorter than the head-body length. The ears are large and nearly naked. Dorsal coloration varies from brownish gray to olivaceous or dusky gray, while the venter is white or grayish white. In northwestern Oklahoma near Seiling and Cleo Springs in Major County, the ranges of *N. floridana* and *N. micropus* meet along the north side of the Cimarron River (Spencer, 1968; Birney, 1973), and it is often difficult to relegate individuals to either species with certainty: one-fourth appear to be *N. floridana*, one-fourth *N. micropus*, and one-half have intermediate traits.

Usually, *N. micropus* is easily distinguished from *N. floridana* by the steel gray dorsal color of the former. Over most of western Oklahoma, the two species are allopatric. Two other woodrats, *N. mexicana* and *N. albigula*, also occur in Oklahoma but only in the Black Mesa region of the Panhandle in Cimarron County; thus, they are allopatric with *N. floridana*.

The eastern woodrat occurs in the eastern two-thirds of Oklahoma. Records are known from several physiognomic regions, including; Oak-Hickory Ozark Plateau, Oak-Hickory-Pine Ouachita Highlands, Cypress-Oak Floodplains, Post Oak–Blackjack Uplands, Tall-grass Rolling Plains, and Mixed-grass Plains. Specific habitats are most often in woody areas (Jones and Anderson, 1957; Glass and Halloran, 1961; Ruffer, 1964a), ravines, post oak–blackjack areas (McCarley, 1952), fringe-forest ravines, upland oak woods, upland locust-planted areas (McCarley, 1952), rocky bluffs in wooded ravines (Blair, 1939; Hays, 1958), and oak-elm floodplain forest (Blair, 1939; McCarley, 1952). Goertz (1970), in a study of eastern woodrats in Payne County, noted that the order of preference of plant associations (from greatest to least) was upland woods, riparian woods and savanna edges, and grass-forb associations.

Stick houses 0.3–1.2 m (1–4 ft.) high are frequently built in brush piles, under fallen trees, at the bases of trees, or in tangles of vegetation. In rocky areas, smaller stick houses are built in crevices or along rock ledges. A third type of house, rarely constructed, may be placed in the lower branches of juniper trees. These aerial nests are built of juniper twigs, oak leaves, and other branches and twigs (Murphy, 1952). Terrestrial nests are usually composed of combinations of twigs; leaves; bark; stones; cactus joints; dung of cattle, horses, and other animals; and other loose material. Several "middens" or toilet areas are usually located at the periphery of the nest. These sites contain fecal droppings, seed parts, and other food items. Ancient woodrat middens have proved to be a useful tool for reflecting the changing vegetation of the southwestern United States during periods of climatic fluctuations caused by glacial activity during various ice ages (Van Devender, 1977). The stick houses of woodrats afford protection from predators and from climatic extremes. In addition, they provide refuge for many other organisms, such as spiders, ants, sow bugs, millipedes, beetles, bumblebees, lizards, snakes, various rodents, shrews, skunks, opossums, and several other species (Murphy, 1952).

Foods of eastern woodrats are quite varied and include both animal and plant material. Acorns, nuts, dogwood tree parts, poison ivy, sumac, Kentucky coffee beans, juniper berries, leaves, twigs, various fruits and berries, mushrooms, snails, grasshoppers, and scorpions have all been shown to be food items of woodrats (Blair, 1939; Murphy, 1952). Food is cached in galleries inside the stick house.

Goertz (1970) examined reproduction, growth, and movements of eastern woodrats in Payne County. Both sexes are capable of breeding throughout the year during favorable weather; however, reproduction is probably curtailed during most winters. Litter sizes varied from 2–7 per female, with the average being 3.2. Sex ratios were equal. Males had larger home ranges (0.26 ha = 0.64 acres) than females (0.17 ha = 0.41 acres). Nearly all (95 percent) of the individuals marked by Goertz (1970) disappeared from his study area within a year. Blair (1939) and Murphy (1952) noted that eastern woodrats are active all year long except during severe winters. Most adults are solitary except during mating periods, or while the female raises her litter.

Murphy (1952) listed the following parasites of woodrats: *Cuterebra* larvae, various mites and ticks (*Ixodes* and *Eutrombicula*), fleas (*Dolichopsyllidae*), and helminths (*Longistriata, Bohmiella, Trichuris, Andrya, Taenia*). Wiley (1980) commented on the biology of *N. floridana*.

The subspecies recorded for Oklahoma is *N. f. osagensis* (Hall, 1981).

Neotoma mexicana Baird
Mexican Woodrat
Neotoma mexicana Baird, 1855 : 333

Neotoma mexicana is sympatric with two other woodrats in northwestern
Oklahoma, N. albigula and N. micropus. It differs from N. albigula, the
white-throated woodrat, in having a patch of hair located in the throat region that is composed of hairs that are white at the tips and gray at the base.
The upper parts are grayish buff, but not as distinctly steel gray as those of

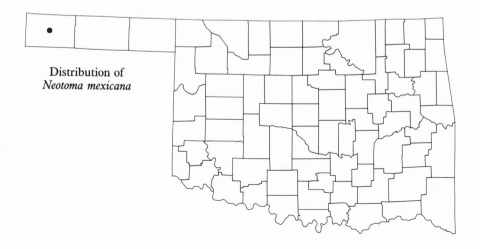

Distribution of
Neotoma mexicana

N. micropus. The Mexican woodrat is a medium-sized rat averaging about 300 mm (11.4 in.) total length.

The first specimens of *N. mexicana* were collected in 1938 in Tesequite Canyon in Cimarron County (Chase and Barclay, 1939); since then, no specimens have been recorded from outside that general area in the Piñon-Juniper Mesas physiognomic region. It is a saxicolous (rock-dwelling) species occurring in rock canyons of the Black Mesa area. Geluso (1970) trapped one on a high sandstone ledge in association with *Peromyscus difficilis,* the rock mouse. Glass (1949) collected specimens of it in the Black Mesa region with *N. micropus* and *N. albigula* and noted no obvious ecological separation among the three species. Practically nothing is known of the ecology of this species in Oklahoma.

The subspecies occurring in Oklahoma is *N. m. fallax* (Hall, 1981).

Neotoma micropus Baird
Southern Plains Woodrat
Neotoma micropus Baird, 1855:333

Neotoma micropus, the southern plains woodrat, is steel gray in color with a venter that is usually white but that may be buffy or tinted gray. The tail is faintly bicolored and sparsely haired. From *N. albigula* (the white-throated woodrat) and *N. mexicana* (the Mexican woodrat), it differs in having a gray rather than brownish dorsal coloration. However, *N. floridana,* the eastern

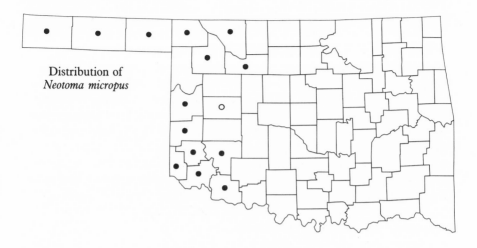

Distribution of
Neotoma micropus

woodrat, may be very difficult to distinguish from *N. micropus* in certain areas of Oklahoma. Secondary intergradation between these two species may be occurring in two very localized areas of northwestern Oklahoma (Spencer, 1968; Birney, 1973). One area of sympatry is located north of the North Canadian River between Chester and Seiling in Major and Dewey counties. The second area of sympatry is along the north side of the Cimarron River east and west of Cleo Springs in Woods and Major counties. It is very difficult to allocate specimens from these localities to either species. Outside these regions of hybridization, *N. floridana* and *N. micropus* are distinguishable by differences in dorsal coloration. *Neotoma floridana* is usually pale cinnamon to olivaceous gray with white underparts. Cranial characteristics are also useful in separating *N. micropus* from other woodrats (see key).

In general, *N. micropus* occurs in the more xeric regions of western Oklahoma. It has been recorded from the following physiognomic regions: Piñon-Juniper Mesas, Shortgrass High Plains, Mixed-grass Plains, and Mesquite-Grass Plains. Blair (1939) indicated the preferred habitats of the southern plains woodrat as rock canyons and open grasslands. Similar habitats are listed by Blair (1954), Glass (1949), and Geluso (1970). Jackson and Warfel (1933) noted that these woodrats were common on rocky hillsides and along ledges or on bluffs in the Glass Mountains in Major County. In areas of sympatry between *N. floridana* and *N. micropus*, habitats are bottomland forest and stabilized sand dunes. These types of edaphic and vegetative associations are found principally along river and creek systems of northwest Oklahoma. The watercourses provide avenues of dispersal along which eastern mesic species may extend their range into the more xeric portions of Oklahoma. The habitat adjacent to the rivers and creeks is a prairie-forest ecotone (Blair,

1939; Penfound, 1962) allowing both woodrat species to intermingle. Outside these areas the habitats are quite dissimilar and may account for the allopatry over most of the rest of their ranges.

Neotoma micropus constructs a "stick nest" or "stick house." These structures are built using a variety of different materials: sticks, bones, cactus joints, cattle droppings, etc. Usually located below the structure is a burrow system which contains one or more food caches, nests, and fecal depositories. In Harmon County, Martin and Preston (1970) noted that *N. micropus* often constructed a dome-shaped "house" in *Opuntia* patches. In August these houses had numerous mesquite beans, while in November and December large quantities of prickly pear cactus and ragweed were present. The size, shape, and location of nest and houses are probably a function of the supporting substrate; the availability of building materials may account in part for the particular distributions of woodrats (Finley, 1958).

Spencer (1968) recorded the following reproductive data for *N. micropus* in Oklahoma. The breeding season is from late January through May, with a quiescent period during June, July, and August. In the fall, reproductive activity commences again. Usually each female will bear three litters per year, with an average of three young per litter. A postpartum heat often follows the first litter. Spencer (1968) noted no observable differences between the mating behaviors of *N. floridana* or *N. micropus* in the laboratory. He was able to cross these two species and produce F_1 hybrids which were fertile. In general he concluded that the gestation periods, litter sizes, birth weights, stage of development at birth and development following birth were the same for each species as well as for the hybrids. Martin and Preston (1970) located dens in Harmon County in July and August that contained females which usually had two young (rarely one or three). Males were not found with these females: however, a few subadult males were sometimes in the same nest as a female with nursing young.

Two subspecies occur in western Oklahoma, *N. m. micropus* and *N. m. canescens* (Hall, 1981).

Microtus ochrogaster (Wagner)
Prairie Vole
Hypudaeus ochrogaster Wagner, 1842:592
Microtus (Pedomys) ochrogaster: J. A. Allen, 1898:459

This dark, blackish brown mouse has long, lax fur that practically conceals the ears. On the venter, the hairs are tipped with buffy brown. The short tail is usually less than twice the length of the hind foot. The woodland vole, *Microtus pinetorum*, is similar to the prairie vole but can be distinguished by the traits listed in the species account of *M. pinetorum*.

The distribution of the prairie vole in Oklahoma is difficult to characterize because of the paucity of recorded specimens. Most records are from north central counties and represent populations of the prairie vole near the southern terminus of its range in North America. Findley *et al.* (1975) reported specimens from Colfax County in northeastern New Mexico, several hundred miles west of the westernmost records in Oklahoma.* They indicate that the New Mexico population may be a relict from a more southwesterly distribution in the past. Similarly, Armstrong (1972) recorded a relict population in central Colorado, northwest of the Oklahoma records. However, in southwestern Kansas, *M. ochrogaster* occurs rather frequently, and the populations are not relicts (Hall, 1955). Dice (1922) found that *M. ochrogaster* taken in Illinois would succumb at temperatures greater than 37°C (98°F). This may be a physiological factor that limits this species from establishing populations in the xeric sections of western Oklahoma, southwestern Kansas, and adja-

*After the completion of this book, Reed and Choate (Southwest. Nat. 1988. 33: 495–496) reported a specimen from north of Hardesty in Texas County.

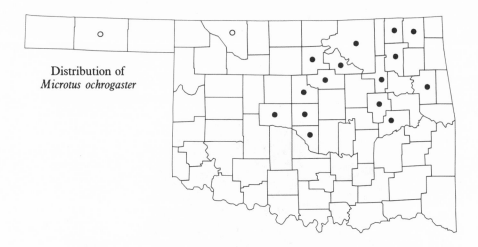

Distribution of
Microtus ochrogaster

cent regions of Colorado and New Mexico. Moreover, the destruction of natural grasslands for agricultural purposes by the early settlers has greatly reduced the extent of habitat suitable for this species (Blair, 1938; Hibbard and Rinker, 1943).

In Oklahoma, *M. ochrogaster* has been taken primarily in grass associations. Blair (1938) collected a specimen in the bluestem (*Andropogon* spp.) and switch grass (*Panicum* spp.) areas near Garnett in Tulsa County in April. Elliot (1899*a*) collected thirteen specimens near Alva in Woods County in river-bottom habitat and on the High Plains where numerous runways were seen. Drabek (1977) collected ten specimens in a prairie association in Oklahoma County that consisted of little bluestem (*Schizachyrium scoparium*), big bluestem (*Andropogon saccharoides*), switch grass (*Panicum virgatum*), sumac (*Rhus* spp.), and scattered blackjack oak (*Quercus marilandica*). Birney *et al.* (1976) captured numerous prairie voles in Osage County in a tall-grass prairie association on uncultivated upland pastures. The dominant vegetation consisted of big bluestem (*A. saccharoides*), little bluestem (*S. scoparium*) and switch grass (*P. virgatum*).

Other mammals commonly taken in association with prairie voles include cotton rats (*Sigmodon hispidus*), deer mice (*Peromyscus maniculatus* and *P. leucopus*), shrews (*Blarina hylophaga* and *Cryptotis parva*), harvest mice (*Reithrodontomys fulvescens* and *R. montanus*), thirteen-lined ground squirrels (*Spermophilus tridecemlineatus*), plains pocket gophers (*Geomys bursarius*), and house mice (*Mus musculus*).

Birney *et al.* (1976) suggested that Oklahoma populations of the prairie vole may cycle every two years and that the cycles are correlated with the amount of cover present in the habitat. Heavy grazing by cattle decreases the grass cover and dampens the multiyear cycles of the voles. The populations monitored by Birney *et al.* (1976) varied from 42.7 individuals per hectare (17.3 per acre) in May, 1970, to a low of 0 per hectare in May of 1971, with a subsequent increase to 75.9 per hectare (30.7 per acre) in May of 1972.

. Based on geographical distribution, three subspecies of *M. ochrogaster* may occur in Oklahoma (Hall, 1981). To date, all specimens recorded from Oklahoma appear to be referable to the subspecies *M. o. haydeni;* however, the probable occurrence of *M. o. taylori* and *M. o. ochrogaster* cannot be completely discounted. Choate and Williams (1978) suggest that the only subspecies occurring in the south central Great Plains, including Oklahoma, is *M. o. haydeni.*

Microtus pinetorum (LeConte)
Woodland Vole
Psammomys pinetorum LeConte, 1830:133
Microtus pinetorum: Miller, 1896:9

This small mouse has a dense, silky, chestnut-colored fur. The underparts are slightly paler than the dorsum. The tail is conspicuously short, slightly longer than the hind foot. Juveniles and subadults lack the reddish color component and are a dark bluish gray. In Oklahoma, the woodland vole may be confused with the prairie vole, *Microtus ochrogaster,* from which it differs in having a shorter tail, four instead of six mammae, and silkier fur.

Woodland voles are found predominantly in the eastern one-half of Oklahoma. The westernmost record in the state is from the Wichita Mountains Wildlife Refuge in Comanche County (Glass and Halloran, 1961). Very few specimens have been collected in the refuge; however, signs have been seen

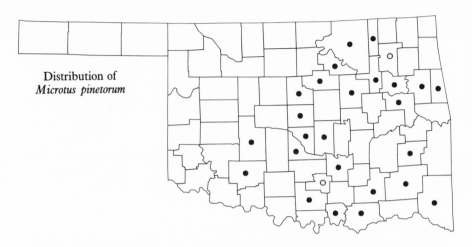

Distribution of
Microtus pinetorum

on many of the high peaks where the spaces between the larger rocks are filled with lush vegetation.

The habitats from which woodland voles have been taken vary considerably. Goertz (1971) studied various aspects of the ecology of woodland voles in Payne County and noted that favored plant associations, in order of preference, were savanna edge, upland woods, grass-forbs, and bottomland woods. Blair (1939) reported that *M. pinetorum* was confined to the mesic floor of oak-elm associations in Tulsa County. This woodland habitat is similar to that reported for voles in northwestern Arkansas (Black, 1936) and is probably typical for the woodland vole in many areas of eastern Oklahoma. Toward the western limits of its range this species is taken more frequently in upland grassy areas associated with blackjack oak and post oak (McCarley, 1952; Goertz, 1971). Voles have also been taken in high open grassland along fencerows (Hays, 1958), in dense tangles of vines and weeds bordering a railroad (Glass, 1949), in open runways in river bottoms (Elliott, 1899), and in grassy areas containing blackjacks and post oaks (McCarley, 1952). Ruffer (1964*a*) captured a vole in the forested section of the Oliver Wildlife Preserve in Cleveland County.

Goertz (1971) suggested that woodland voles may be in competition with cotton rats (*Sigmodon hispidus*) for certain habitats. Where cotton rats are very common, woodland voles are seldom captured, having apparently been forced into habitats not preferred by the cotton rats. When cotton rat populations decline, the voles spread back into the area formerly occupied by the rats. The home range diameters for female and male voles have been estimated to be 68 m (74 yds.) and 87 m (95 yds.), respectively (Goertz, 1971). Nests composed of grass, leaves, and shredded bark have been found under rotten and crumbling logs in Tulsa County (Blair, 1939).

This vole apparently reproduces in all months of the year, but the peak period of reproduction occurs from October to May (Blair, 1939; Glass, 1949; Goertz, 1971). Each female may have from one to four litters per year, averaging 2.6 young per litter (a range of 1–5) (Goertz, 1971). Individuals over 20 g (0.7 oz.) were considered by Goertz (1971) to be adults, which averaged 27.2 g (0.96 oz.).

Climatic variations as well as population fluctuations of associated mammal species probably account for high populations during some years and low populations in others (Goertz, 1971). There is a rapid turnover of individuals within a population. Goertz (1971) found that the "average" vole disappeared from his study plots in 2.3 months; the longest survival time recorded was 14 months. The sex ratio of the populations studied by Goertz (1971) was 47 percent male to 53 percent female. He suggested that there is some degree of selective mortality of males associated with their reproductive ambitions and greater travel rates. Smolen (1981) reviewed the literature of *M. pinetorum* in the United States.

Bailey (1898) described the subspecies which occurs in Oklahoma, *M. p. nemoralis*, from specimens obtained from Stilwell in Adair County, Oklahoma.

Ondatra zibethicus (Linnaeus)
Muskrat
[*Castor*] *zibethicus* Linnaeus, 1766:79
[*Ondatra*] *zibethicus:* Link, 1795:76

The muskrat, *Ondatra zibethicus*, is the largest (total length 409–620 mm = 16.1–24.4 in.) volelike rodent in Oklahoma. A small nutria, *Myocaster coypu*, might be mistaken for a muskrat; however, the laterally compressed (rather

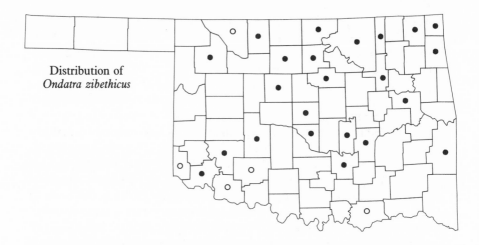

Distribution of
Ondatra zibethicus

than round) tail and smaller body size of *Ondatra* easily distinguish the two. Many of the muskrat's distinguishing external traits are adaptations for an aquatic existence. The naked, scaly, laterally flattened tail is used as a rudder and for propulsion during swimming, and possibly it also serves as a thermo-regulating heat sink at higher ambient temperatures (Johansen, 1962). Broad, partially webbed hind feet (the toes are fringed with stiff hairs) are used for propulsion during swimming. The front feet are small and are used for ma-nipulating objects during feeding and nest building. Short, rounded ears barely protrude above the fur on the blunt head. Dorsal coloration is cin-namon brown, and the venter is lighter, often nearly gray. The soft underfur that is interspersed with coarser guard hairs is most dense in winter (January and February) and is waterproof (Errington, 1963). Air trapped in the fur aids in insulating the animal and also increases buoyancy. Molting takes place during the summer. Muskrats have large, unrooted incisors, and the mouth closes behind the teeth, allowing them to gnaw while under water.

The muskrat is found over most of Oklahoma (Blair, 1939) but is most abundant in the northeastern corner of the state. Abundance declines toward the southeast and the more arid west. Prior to the construction of numerous lakes and impoundments in Oklahoma by man, muskrats were primarily stream dwellers and bank burrowers (Glass, 1952). Jackson and Warfel (1933) noted that muskrats were widely distributed along streams and creeks in the regions adjacent to the salt plains of northwestern Oklahoma. Martin and Preston (1970) found muskrats in the larger ponds and lakes of extreme southwestern Oklahoma (Harmon County). Many of these ponds were in sand-sage brush associations. Martin and Preston (1970) were not able to determine if these muskrats were recent introductions or had descended from original stock. However, Blair (1954) and Hollister (1911) reported native populations of muskrats in north central Texas (near Harmon County, Oklahoma) along Bugbee Creek, and also in the Canadian River. Glass and Halloran (1961), in a survey of the mammals of the Wichita Mountains Wildlife Refuge, did not indicate whether or not muskrats occurred there. McCarley (1961) suggested that muskrats have been common in the state fish hatcheries north of Durant in Bryan County for over 20 years.

Although water is a requisite for muskrats, not all aquatic habitats are suitable. Large artificial impoundments are often unsuitable because the fluctuating water levels fail to provide a constant source of aquatic plants needed for food and nest construction. Large, swift-moving creeks and rivers are avoided. The most commonly used habitats in Oklahoma are marshy areas, farm ponds, fish hatching ponds, strip mine pits, small creeks and streams, slow-moving sections of rivers, and areas of large reservoirs where the water level is stable. Small ponds and lakes support larger populations than do large lakes because the former have a higher ratio of shoreline to open water (Glass, 1952).

Dens are built in the banks adjacent to preferred aquatic habitats. Usually a steep bank is burrowed into from under water and the burrow angles up toward the surface. A nest chamber is constructed above water level and is partially lined with herbaceous material. Tunnels that radiate away from the nest chamber often will collapse and thus open to the surface. Runways through the vegetation are evidence of muskrat activities above ground. In ponds and other areas where the vegetation is dense, conical houses composed of mud and plant material may be constructed, but these are uncommon in Oklahoma. Several underwater entrances to the houses lead to a central nest chamber. Muskrats may be seen during the day, but late afternoon or early evening is the best time to observe activity around burrows and nests.

Food items taken consist primarily of herbaceous material such as roots, bulbs, and leaves (for example, cattails, water lily, sedges, willows). Occasionally some animal matter is also consumed, such as mussels, fish, small amphibians, crayfish, and turtles. Glass (1952) listed the following genera of plants eaten by muskrats: *Nelumbo, Najas, Cypernus, Jussiaea, Ceratophyllum, Eleocharis, Potamogeton, Polygonum, Dianthera, Juncus, Sagittaria, Heteranthera, Nymphaea.* Two exotic plants common in the diet of muskrats are Johnson grass (*Sorghum*) and Bermuda grass (*Cynodon*), from which the rhizomes are eaten (Glass, 1952).

Male and female muskrats are similar in the external appearance of their genitalia because of a prominent urinary papilla anterior to the female's vaginal orifice. However, it is not furred, as is the perineum of the male. Teats are absent in males. Paired musk glands near the base of the tail in both sexes secrete a "musk oil" which is used to mark nests, trails, and other objects

TABLE 6.   Number of muskrat pelts purchased and
average price paid by Oklahoma fur dealers, 1967–81.
(Oklahoma Dept. Wildl. Conserv.)

Year	No. Pelts Bought	Avg. Price/ Pelt	Total
1967–68	910	$0.56	$ 509.60
1968–69	684	0.73	499.80
1969–70	1,145	0.70	818.25
1970–71	45	0.67	30.25
1971–72	529	1.37	724.75
1972–73	926	1.57	1,454.80
1973–74	1,395	1.90	2,655.75
1974–75	3,235	1.89	6,126.31
1975–76	4,201	2.38	9,997.20
1976–77	5,291	3.68	19,477.75
1977–78	3,277	3.88	12,714.76
1978–79	2,414	3.76	9,076.64
1979–80	2,563	4.82	12,362.40
1980–81	3,182	4.47	14,223.54

during the breeding season (Errington, 1963). The glands are more active in males than in females. Stevens and Erickson (1942) determined the musk oil to consist of a mixture of cyclopentadecanol, cycloheptadecanol, and other odoriferous ketones.

Muskrats have a high reproductive capacity. Mating most often occurs in the water during the peak breeding seasons in spring and fall. During favorable years, reproduction may continue all year. Gestation is approximately 30 days, and the litter size is four to five young. The newborn "kits" are altricial (blind, hairless, and capable of only feeble movements). Their eyes open in about 14 days. Weaning occurs after about one month, and the young are fairly independent of the mother from that point. They usually depart the nest area only when the female is ready to bear another litter.

Muskrats are generally solitary animals but may be described as being semi-colonial because several individuals utilize the same general area. Males and females may cooperate in nest construction, and occasionally during winter several muskrats huddle together in a den for warmth. Territoriality is common in muskrats (Errington, 1943; Schwartz and Schwartz, 1981). Fighting does occur, and individuals are quite capable of defending themselves when cornered or isolated from water. They escape danger by swimming and submergence (up to 15 minutes).

Muskrats are normally silent: however, during the breeding season a high pitched "n-n-n-n" may be heard, and squeals and snarls during fighting are not uncommon. Tail slapping on the water may act as an alarm signal (Schwartz and Schwartz, 1981). Teeth rattling also is common.

Mink, coyotes, foxes, bobcats, hawks, owls, and man are some of the more common predators of muskrats near the water's edge. Snapping turtles and large fish may prey on young animals in the water. Large numbers of muskrats are harvested annually by man for the thick fur pelt (Table 6). Glass (1952) reviewed factors affecting survival of muskrats in Oklahoma.

Nutria, although not common in Oklahoma, do have similar habitat requirements as muskrats, and the two species may compete if populations of nutria increase. In Louisiana, where nutria and muskrats have coexisted for many years, biologists have reported only circumstantial evidence that muskrat populations decline as nutria populations increase (Perry, 1982). However, muskrat populations did increase when nutria populations declined.

Literature surveys and detailed descriptions of the ecology of muskrats throughout North America may be found in Willner *et al.* (1980) and Perry (1982).

The subspecies occurring in Oklahoma are *O. z. zibethicus* and *O. z. cinnamominus* (Willner *et al.*, 1980).

Rattus norvegicus (Berkenhout)
Norway Rat
Mus norvegicus Berkenhout, 1769:5
Rattus norvegicus: Hollister, 1916:126

The Norway rat, *Rattus norvegicus*, is similar in general appearance to *R. rattus* but differs in its more stocky, robust build and in having a tail that is shorter than its head and body length. It is brown above and grayish below. The tail is naked and scaly. The dental traits listed in the key and the naked, scaly tail separate *R. norvegicus* from other, similar-sized rodents in Oklahoma.

This rodent is an exotic species that was introduced into Oklahoma by white settlement. The original introduction into North America occurred about the time of the American Revolution if not before, and the species has subsequently spread over most of the North American continent. It can be found in and around almost all cities and towns in Oklahoma. This species is competitively superior to *R. rattus* and usually forces the latter species out of the buildings the two occupy together. Feral populations of *R. norvegicus* are not common. *Rattus norvegicus* is known from the Wichita Mountains Wildlife Refuge (Glass and Halloran, 1961), from Oliver Wildlife Preserve in Cleveland County (Ruffer, 1964*a*), and from Weatherford in Custer County (King, 1959). Other records are listed in the records of occurrence. More specimens need to be collected and preserved.

Only a single study of the ecology of *R. norvegicus* has been done in Oklahoma. Landreth (1972) studied a population of *R. norvegicus* on a deserted farm in Custer County, near Weatherford. He found that the population was

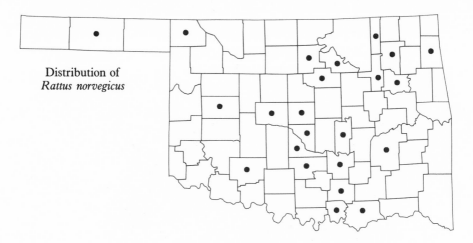

Distribution of
Rattus norvegicus

largest in September (19 animals) and declined to a low in February (3 animals) and March (4 animals). Marked male rats moved an average of 90 m (98.4 yards) between captures while females moved an average of 63.4 m (69.3 yards). A distinct movement from the fields to buildings was noted in the fall and may have been related to abundance of food and cover. Other species taken in the area included the hispid cotton rat (*Sigmodon hispidus*), eastern woodrat (*Neotoma floridana*), house mouse (*Mus musculus*), hispid pocket mouse (*Perognathus hispidus*), and the deer mouse (*Peromyscus leucopus*). Possible predators noted in the area were hawks, owls, bobcats, domestic cats, snakes, and skunks.

This species is a very prolific breeder and probably reproduces all year long in Oklahoma. It has economic importance, being a species that damages foodstuffs and other materials and is a potential vector of diseases which may be transmitted to man. Pratt and Good (1954) and Wilcomb *et al.* (1952) recorded several species of fleas and mites from *R. norvegicus* in Oklahoma. This is the same species that serves as the common, but very important, laboratory rat.

The subspecies in Oklahoma is probably *R. n. norvegicus*. Some workers consider this species to be monotypic and do not divide it into subspecies (Lowery, 1974).

Rattus rattus (Linnaeus)
Black Rat, Roof Rat
(*Mus*) *rattus* Linnaeus, 1758:61
Rattus rattus: Hollister, 1916:126

The common name, black rat, of *Rattus rattus* is somewhat misleading. While it is true that there are individuals that indeed are black, many specimens are brown. There are at least three subspecies of *R. rattus* in North America, and all vary in coloration (Hall, 1981). *Rattus rattus rattus* is a subspecies which is black, and the common name "black rat" has been used in the literature for this subspecies; the two other subspecies are more brown. One, *R. r. alexandrinus*, is grayish brown above with a gray venter, whereas the other, *R. r. frugivorus*, has a brownish dorsum and a white or yellowish white venter. Considerable mixing of these subspecies has occurred, making identification very difficult. The latter form can be confused with *R. norvegicus*, the Norway rat, but the relative length of the tail serves to separate the two species. *Rattus rattus* has a tail that is noticeably longer than its head and body length, whereas *R. norvegicus* has a tail that is less than or equal to the head and body length. Both species can be distinguished from other rat-sized rodents by their long, scaly tails and the dental traits listed in the key. When *R. rattus* and *R. norvegicus* occur together, the competitively superior *R. norvegicus* usually either forces out the former or displaces it to the higher lofts of the buildings they are cohabiting.

The distribution of *R. rattus* in Oklahoma is not known with certainty. Taylor (1964) collected specimens from 1.6 km (1 mi.) east of Colbert, Bryan County, in an old house used as a feed shed. He also collected specimens from several locales in barns in Marshall County. Taylor (1964) suggested that *R. rattus* has spread into Oklahoma via the Red River and perhaps the Arkansas

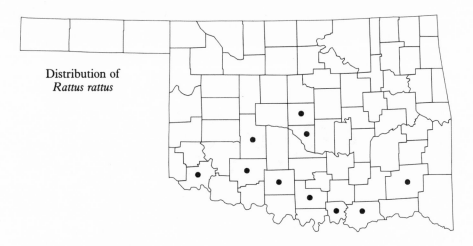

Distribution of
Rattus rattus

River from areas further east in the Mississippi River valley. Other populations of this species probably exist in Oklahoma, but because the animals are introduced, they are not usually prepared as museum study skins: few specimens have been saved or even trapped.

The black rat was introduced into North America about the time of the establishment of Jamestown in 1609. Specimens were probably introduced into South and Central America in the mid-1500s. The Norway rat, *R. norvegicus*, was introduced about the time of the American Revolution and has displaced *R. rattus* in many areas.

Economically, *R. rattus* is not a desirable species. It destroys much food material and is a dangerous vector of many diseases which are easily transmitted to man. Pratt and Good (1971) and Wilcomb *et al.* (1952) recorded several species of fleas, lice, and mites from *R. rattus* in Oklahoma.

The subspecies recorded in Oklahoma is *R. r. alexandrinus*. However, considerable inbreeding occurs between the subspecies in North America, and repeated introduction often makes identification of subspecies problematic.

Mus musculus Linnaeus
House Mouse
(*Mus*) *musculus* Linnaeus, 1758:62

The house mouse is a small (total length less than 200 mm = 7.9 in.), gray to brownish gray mouse with a tail as long as the head and body. The tail is scaly and nearly naked. The venter is usually somewhat lighter than (but about the same color as) the dorsum. A population of *Mus* having a white venter exists west of Edmond, Oklahoma County. The slender appearance of *Mus*, its rather pointed snout, a naked, scaly tail, and a uniform coloration separate it from *Peromyscus*. The species most easily confused with *Mus* are *Reithrodontomys fulvescens*, *R. megalotis*, and *R. montanus* and *Baiomys taylori*. However, all *Reithrodontomys* have grooved incisors and only two longitudinal rows of cusps on the upper molars compared to the nongrooved but uniquely notched incisors and three rows of cusps in *Mus*. *Baiomys* can be separated by features listed in that account.

Mus musculus is an introduced species which probably occurs in all parts of Oklahoma. Introduction into North America probably occurred during the early colonization period of the Americas. It has spread west with man and is most commonly found around human habitations. However, feral populations do occur, especially in weedy situations and cultivated fields of wheat,

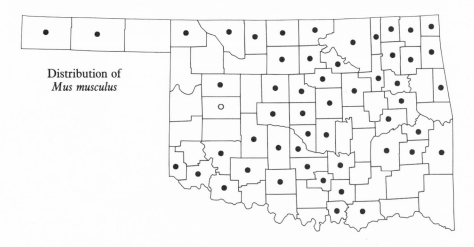

Distribution of
Mus musculus

corn, and sorghum. Plant associations from which *Mus* has been recorded include sumac-grama associations, lowland thickets, mesquite-grass plains, salt-cedar–groundsel–three-awn associations, and weedy roadside ditches (Blair, 1938, 1954; Martin and Preston, 1970). Glass (1951) reported the use of abandoned buildings by *Mus* in the Black Mesa region, and Glass and Halloran (1961) found it living in buildings on the Wichita Mountains Wildlife Refuge.

This species is capable of breeding year-round in Oklahoma and has a litter size ranging up to about ten, with as many as 10–13 litters per year. The laboratory mouse is a domestic derivative of this species.

The subspecies occurring in Oklahoma is not known with certainty.

FAMILY ZAPODIDAE   Jumping Mice

Zapus hudsonius (Zimmerman)
Meadow Jumping Mouse
Dipus hudsonius Zimmermann, 1780:358
Zapus hudsonius: Coues, 1876:253

The meadow jumping mouse is known in Oklahoma from only two specimens which were captured in Mohawk Park, Tulsa County, in 1938 (Blair,
1936). *Zapus* is a medium-sized mouse with an unusually long tail about
twice the head and body length. The underparts are white and the dorsum is
cinnamon buff, with the back having a greater admixture of dark-tipped hairs
forming a distinct broad dorsal band. The tail is bicolored and the feet are
white to grayish white.

Zapus is known to occur near Hamilton, Kansas, approximately 193 km
(120 mi.) north of the last recorded capture site in Oklahoma, and in other
areas of southeastern Kansas (Jones *et al.*, 1985). It may be that *Zapus* still
occurs in Oklahoma in isolated patches of suitable habitat. The only two
Oklahoma individuals were trapped by Blair (1938) in a lowland thicket association in Mohawk Park in Tulsa. An adult female was captured on 17 August, and four days later an adult male was taken 155 m (170 yds.) away in the
same plant association. This lowland association consisted of a very dense and
tangled thicket of young trees (spotted oak, *Quercus shumardii*; bitternut
hickory, *Carya illinoensis*; American elm, *Ulmus americana*; and persimmon,
Diospyros virginiana), shrubs (blackberry, *Rubus* spp.; and sumac, *Rhus*
spp.), vines (grape, *Vitis* spp.; greenbrier, *Smilax* spp.; trumpet creeper,
Campsis radicans; and wild potato vine, *Ipomoea* spp.), and weeds (tarweed,
Grindelia spp.; Jerusalem artichoke, *Helianthus* spp.; horsemint, *Monarda*
spp.; coneflower, *Rudbeckia* spp.; and ironweed, *Vernonia* spp.). Mammals

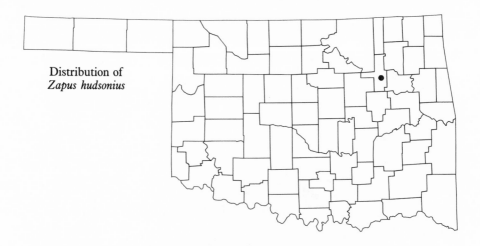

Distribution of
Zapus hudsonius

taken in the same association were *Mus musculus, Sigmodon hispidus, Pero-myscus leucopus, Sciurus niger, S. carolinensis, Sylvilagus floridanus, S. aquaticus,* and *Lasiurus borealis.*

Fossil records of *Zapus* from Oklahoma consist of several incisor and maxillary fragments collected in the Kingsdown Formation of the Doby Springs local fauna at Mrs. Dee's Ranch in Harper Co. (Klingener, 1963). These fragments are referred to the extinct subspecies *Z. h. transitionalis* and may represent a population of *hudsonius* which existed in Oklahoma during Illinoian glacial times (Klingener, 1963).

If *Zapus* still exists in northeast Oklahoma, it may hibernate during the winter, as it does in other portions of its range, and attempts to collect it should take place during the spring and summer months. Whitaker (1972) reviewed the literature related to *Z. hudsonius* in North America.

The two specimens from Mohawk Park were referred to the subspecies *Z. h. pallidus* by Krutzsch (1954).

FAMILY ERETHIZONTIDAE   Porcupines

Erethizon dorsatum (Linnaeus)
Porcupine
(*Hystrix*) *dorsata* Linnaeaus, 1758:57
(*Erethizon*) *dorsatum:* F. Cuvier, 1822:432

The porcupine is one of the more distinctive rodents in Oklahoma. Its large size (4.5–11.4 kg = 10–25 lbs.) and the presence of barbed spines (quills) on the back, sides, and tail make it a familiar mammal. Yellow-tipped guard hairs are dispersed among the quills, giving the animal a yellowish brown appearance.

Porcupines are not very common in Oklahoma. Hall (1981) and Woods (1973) used isolated reports to outline the extent of the range of the porcupine in Oklahoma from the Wichita Mountains to the Black Mesa. The number of recorded specimens is increasing. In the fifteen years following the first recorded occurrence of the porcupine in Oklahoma (Chase, 1939). Glass (1951) reported that the porcupine increased in numbers to the point of becoming a pest in alfalfa fields in Cimarron County. Records for other counties in Oklahoma are also increasing (McMurray, 1944; Halloran and Glass, 1964: Best and Kennedy, 1972). Since the sites of recent collections generally are not far from wooded valleys or streams, and seasonal movements are common for the porcupine (Woods, 1973), the increase in abundance in Oklahoma (Glass,

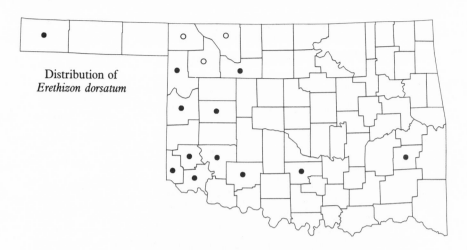

Distribution of
Erethizon dorsatum

1951; Halloran and Glass, 1964; Martin and Preston, 1970) may be primarily a result of more extensive seasonal wandering.

The specific habitat of the porcupine in Oklahoma is apparently dendritic. In the Black Mesa, Glass (1951) noted the porcupine was common in cliff and canyon habitats. Geluso (1970) reported two specimens from a prairie association, and one from a brushy slope in the Black Mesa. Caire (pers. observ.) observed a live porcupine in a sand-sage community adjacent to Trader Creek in Woodward County.

Little is known about the ecology and life history of the porcupine in Oklahoma. The subspecies occurring in the state is *E. d. bruneri* (Hall, 1981).

Myocastor coypus (Molina)
Nutria
Mus coypus Molina, 1782:287
Myocastor coypus: Kerr, 1792:225

This species was first introduced into the United States from South America more than eighty years ago (Ashbrook, 1948). *Myocastor*, in addition to being called the nutria, is also referred to as the swamp beaver, the coypu, and the South American beaver.

Nutria are similar in appearance to beavers (*Castor canadensis*) and muskrats (*Ondatra zibethicus*). However, nutria have a long, round, scaly tail instead of the dorso-ventrally flattened tail of the beaver or the laterally compressed tail of the muskrat. *Myocastor* is a relatively large rodent, with adults weighing between 6.8 kg and 9.1 kg (15–20 pounds). The upper parts are a dark umber brown overlaid with long, yellow guard hairs; the vibrissae (whiskers) are noticeably large, and the hind feet are webbed. The female's mammae are located along each side of the back rather than on the belly. The incisors are a bright orange. Domesticated strains of several colors have been bred, including all-black and all-white. In 1960 a nutria farm existed near Waukomis, in Garfield County, that had several color types as well as normal wild-colored animals.

Nutria have a very spotty distribution in Oklahoma, being reported from only a few southern locales. The nutria was introduced in Oklahoma as a po-

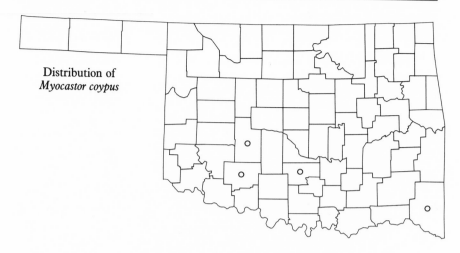

Distribution of
Myocastor coypus

tential commercial furbearer in the early 1950s near Hinton and Fort Sill (Kimsey, 1953). Glass and Halloran (1961) reported the capture of a male nutria in August, 1960, in a drain between Lake Elmer Thomas and Lake Lawtonka near the Wichita Mountains Wildlife Refuge. The origin of this animal was unknown. Possibly it was an individual from a feral population deriving from the early 1950s population at adjacent Fort Sill.

A nutria population exists southeast of Tom in Ward Lake in McCurtain County (Dolgos and Earls, 1973). This population apparently spread into Oklahoma from areas in northern Texas. Dolgos and Earls (1973) indicated that nutria breed several times during the year. The only information on reproduction in Oklahoma is a report of two females with litters near Tom in February. The nutria seen in February had constructed circular winter platforms 50.8–76.2 cm (20–30 in.) in diameter and 15.2–22.9 cm (6–9 in.) above the water. Very little burrowing was noted near Tom, in contrast to the extensive burrowing recorded for the population near Hinton (Kimsey, 1953). The nutria also were apparently coexisting with the beaver in Lake Ward, but no data exist clarifying any effect they might have had on muskrats there. In many areas the nutria reportedly cause a decline in muskrat populations (Davis, 1974).

Vegetation reported to be part of the diet of nutria in Oklahoma includes cattails (*Typha* spp.), southern wild rice (*Zizaniopsis* spp.), lizard's tail (*Saururus* spp.), water shield (*Brasenia* spp.), lotus lily (*Nelumbo* spp.), charas (*Chara* spp.), and bladderworts (*Utricularia* spp.) (Dolgos and Earls, 1973).

A recent summary of the biology of nutria in the United States by Willner (1982) also discusses some of the nomenclatural problems of this species in North America. The subspecies found in the United States may be *M. c. bonariensis* (Ashbrook, 1948).

Order Carnivora

Carnivores

Jack D. Tyler

The carnivores are a large order and have a worldwide distribution. In Oklahoma, five families represented by more than 20 species have occurred in recent times. The five families are Canidae (wolves, coyotes, foxes); Ursidae (bears); Procyonidae (ringtails, raccoons); Mustelidae (skunks, badgers, mink, weasels, etc.); and Felidae (cats).

FAMILY CANIDAE   Wolves, Coyotes, and Foxes

Canis latrans Say
Coyote
Canis latrans Say, 1823:168

Except for its narrower muzzle, shaggier coat and bushier tail, the coyote closely resembles a small, long-limbed German Shepherd. It differs from the gray and red wolves by its smaller proportions and narrower nose pad. From foxes, coyotes can be distinguished by their larger size, longer muzzles and buffier overall coloration. When in full stride, a coyote's tail is usually held down, a wolf's up, and a fox's straight out. Coat colors vary individually and according to geographic location, but are generally a light buff gray sprinkled with black-tipped hairs that give the pelt an uneven suffusion of black. The muzzle, ears, and lateral aspects of the legs are fulvous, the underparts are whitish, and the tail-tip is black. Halloran (1963*a*) described a melanistic coyote from Fort Sill, Comanche County. Adult coyotes generally weigh between 9.1 kg and 22.7 kg (20–50 lbs.), with males being slightly heavier. The average in Oklahoma is probably around 10.9–12.7 kg (24–28 lbs.). Seven males from the Wichita Mountains taken in 1917 averaged 13.9 kg (30.5 lbs.) (Crabb, 1925); 93 from northwest Oklahoma and 96 from the northeastern part of the state taken in 1947 averaged 11.4 and 12.3 kg (25 and 27 lbs.), respectively (Young and Jackson, 1951). The largest coyote on record was probably a male killed in Wyoming in 1937 that measured 1,600 mm (63 in.) in total length and weighed 34 kg (74.8 pounds) (Young and Jackson 1951).

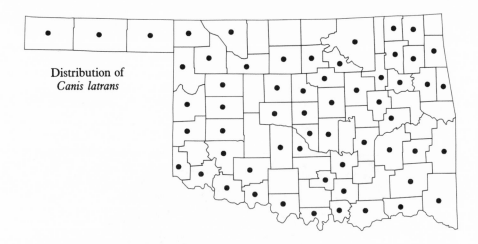

Distribution of
Canis latrans

The usual range in total length is from about 1,015 mm (40 in.) to 1,270 mm (50 in.).

Because in Oklahoma man has eliminated the grizzly, the gray wolf, and the red wolf, and has destroyed populations of the black bear and the mountain lion, *Canis latrans* is today the largest common wild carnivore in the state. Although coyotes have been shot, poisoned, trapped, chased with dogs, snared, and killed at the den-site, they still have remained numerous. Formerly an animal of plains and deserts, the coyote has even managed to expand its range into the eastern United States within recent years. It occurs statewide in Oklahoma.

The coyote is primarily a nocturnal and crepuscular hunter, and much of its prey is killed during the early morning or early evening. At times it does hunt during the day, but it usually spends most daylight hours resting.

Since coyotes are adaptive and opportunistic feeders, the relative economics of their food habits has been a subject of controversy for years, frequently provoking livestock and poultry owners to mount widespread eradication campaigns. Coyotes, also known as "prairie wolves," usually prefer to eat rabbits or small rodents, and they also devour considerable carrion (see Sperry, 1941; Tiemeir, 1955; Gier, 1968; Hamilton, 1974). Occasionally they kill fawns and may raid poultry houses or livestock enclosures. Deer (most often as carrion) and small birds are also preferred food items. Except in winter, coyotes often subsist on insects and fruits of native shrubs such as mesquite pods, juniper berries and prickly pear fruit (Meinzer *et al.*, 1975). Practically any small animal that a coyote can catch, it will eat. In 16 coyote stomachs from Cimarron County, Oklahoma, 91 percent of the contents by weight was rabbit and 8 percent cattle, probably carrion (Ellis and Schemnitz,

1958). Halloran and Glass (1959) tabulated the foods found in stomachs of 48 coyotes taken in the Wichita Mountains Wildlife Refuge in Comanche County between 1937 and 1940. Rabbits and invertebrates (mostly insects) led all other foods by a substantial margin, with rodents, carrion, and vegetable matter tied for third place. However, both Holle (1978) and Litvaitis (1978) found rodents to be the most important coyote food in the Wichitas, based on the contents of several hundred scats.

Best *et al.* (1981) analyzed 136 coyote stomachs from central Oklahoma and reported that, in descending order of importance, cattle (probably carrion), rodents, insects (grasshoppers and beetles), and rabbits appeared most often, and that 82 percent of the stomachs contained grass. In north central Oklahoma, Ellis (1959) found cotton rats and lagomorphs to be the most important foods. In eastern Oklahoma, poultry, persimmons, and insects probably play a greater role in the coyote's diet, as indicated by Gipson's (1974) study of 168 animals from Arkansas in which these items were the most important foods, in the order mentioned. During drought years, when rodent and rabbit populations are at a low ebb, coyotes will adapt to whichever foods are most obtainable. In many regions, particularly during the denning season in late spring and summer, high fawn predation or livestock depredation is the inevitable result. Bartush and Lewis (1981) reported that the 90 percent mortality of white-tailed deer fawns in the Wichita Mountains during 1976 and 1977 was attributable to coyote predation, and Stout (1982) contended that coyote reduction was in large part responsible for increased productivity in white-tailed deer at nearby Fort Sill.

Although a pair will sometimes remain together for several years, coyotes generally are not monogamous. Females can breed at one year of age. In Texas (Davis, 1974) the breeding season usually begins in January, peaks in late February or early March, and does not terminate until mid-May. The female usually appropriates and enlarges several old badger, rabbit, or fox burrows, one of which she chooses for the nursery den, but she may elect to dig one or several dens herself, usually near water. These may be located in canyons, arroyos, hillsides, or even on level ground. Sometimes the den is beneath a building, at others in a hollow log, thicket, or rock crevice. Coyotes often show fidelity to certain previously used denning locations and return to them in subsequent years. Gestation requires from 60 to 63 days (Young and Jackson, 1951), after which time up to nine (usually five or six) pups (or whelps) weighing approximately 225 g (0.5 lb.) are born—the number apparently varying with geographic location and nutrition. At 10 to 12 days their eyes open; at five weeks they can eat meat, and at eight to ten weeks of age they abandon the den. They learn from their parents how to hunt through the summer and by late fall are on their own.

Parasites have been studied in Oklahoma by Self and McKnight (1950) and

TABLE 7.   Number of coyote pelts purchased and average price paid by
Oklahoma fur dealers, 1967–81. (Oklahoma Dept. Wildl. Conserv.)

Year	No. Pelts Bought	Avg. Price/Pelt	Total
1967–68	9	$ 1.20	$ 10.80
1968–69	105	1.40	147.00
1969–70	438	2.50	1,093.00
1970–71	1,097	2.39	2,620.00
1971–72	959	3.61	3,462.00
1972–73	2,598	6.85	17,805.00
1973–74	6,935	11.97	82,998.68
1974–75	6,601	6.33	41,786.19
1975–76	8,514	8.79	74,804.60
1976–77	13,949	22.30	311,018.80
1977–78	11,366	18.48	209,230.98
1978–79	13,389	27.78	371,946.42
1979–80	5,426	24.02	130,328.51
1980–81	9,771	17.44	170,406.24

by Ellis (1955); Morrison and Gier (1979) found that certain nematode species infecting 181 coyotes collected from seven southwestern states were more
prevalent in the western Oklahoma–north Texas region than elsewhere.

Coyotes interbreed freely with domestic dogs, especially in the eastern
states (see Lawrence and Bossert, 1967; Severinghaus, 1974; Gipson et al.,
1974; and Elder and Hayden, 1977). The red wolf (Canis rufus), which formerly ranged through the eastern forests of Oklahoma, has interbred so
widely with Canis latrans that today probably fewer than one hundred full-
blood red wolves remain in Texas and Louisiana. As a result, coyotes from
eastern Oklahoma tend to be larger than those farther west, possibly reflecting the phenomenon of extinction through hybridization (see McCarley,
1962; Gipson et al., 1974; Goertz et al., 1975; Freeman and Shaw, 1979; and
red wolf account).

Coyotes are active throughout the winter. Murie (1940) watched for more
than an hour as two coyotes fed on a deer carcass when the temperature was
−30°F. They usually hunt singly, but occasionally in family groups or, for
brief periods, in pairs. Canis latrans seems to be loosely territorial. Home
ranges of coyotes in Arkansas were determined by Gipson and Sealander
(1972) to be 33.1 sq. km (12.8 sq. mi.) for adult males, 13.2 sq. km (5.1 sq.
mi.) for adult females, and 11.9 sq. km (4.6 sq. mi.) for female pups. Although various workers have reported sex ratios that favor one sex or the
other (most often the male), the sex ratio of 6,494 coyotes taken in Oklahoma
during all seasons between 1943 and 1947 (Young and Jackson, 1951) was
very near 1:1 (3,229 males, 3,265 females). The longevity record may be held

by a coyote that was held captive for eighteen and one-half years (Young and Jackson, 1951), but in the wild the average lifespan is probably only about three or four years (Adams, 1978). An idea of just how common coyotes are can be obtained from the following: between 1921 and 1950, 2,178 coyotes were taken from the Wichita Mountains Wildlife Refuge (Halloran and Glass, 1959), and during 1963, more than 6,300 were killed in New Mexico (Findley *et al.*, 1975). Coyotes are hunted for sport and for their pelts. Table 7 lists the number of pelts collected in recent years in Oklahoma. Additional comments about the ecology of coyotes is given in Bekoff (1977, 1978).

Coyotes are found throughout the state, there being two races: *C. l. frustor* throughout the eastern two-thirds and *C. l. latrans* in the west (Hall, 1981). The former is the largest race in North America, and the type specimen, a juvenile male, was collected by S. W. Woodhouse in 1850, probably near present-day Perkins in Payne County (Woodhouse, 1853).

Canis lupus Linnaeus
Gray Wolf
Canis lupus Linnaeus, 1758:39

About twice the size of a coyote, the gray wolf is heavier-bodied. Adult males usually weigh 30–45 kg (65–100 lbs.) and measure 1.35–1.52 m (4.5–5.5 ft.) in total length, averaging about 10 percent larger than females. Weights in excess of 45.5 kg (100 lbs.) are not uncommon. The limbs are proportionately longer than a coyote's and, overall, the gray wolf closely resembles a large gray German shepherd or husky. Its head, muzzle, and nosepad are considerably broader than a coyote's and its ears not so conspicuous and pointed. The fur is also longer and, although there is much individual variation,

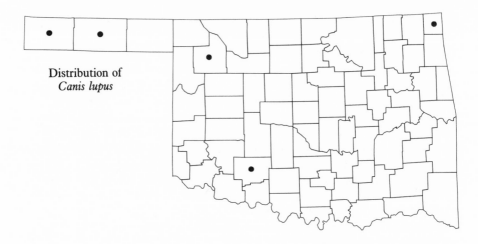

Distribution of
Canis lupus

wolves are usually a grizzled color suffused with black dorsally, shading to whitish or pale buff below. The ears and head are ochraceous or cinnamon, and the tip of the tail is usually black. The shoulders are higher than the rump, so that standing wolves may appear to be crouching. Females have ten mammae.

Because the greater part of Oklahoma was Indian land during most of the nineteenth century and was not opened to white settlement until 1889, the Indian Territory was bypassed as America moved westward. Primarily for this reason, there are few early historical accounts of the wolf in Oklahoma. One of the earliest was Lieutenant J. W. Abert's mention of a "large gray wolf" that his party observed in the fall of 1845 along the Canadian River in what is now Oklahoma (Abert, 1845–46). S. W. Woodhouse, who accompanied the Sitgreaves expedition in 1849, wrote that the "dusky wolf" was "very common throughout Indian Territory . . ." (Woodhouse, 1853). Captain Randolph B. Marcy (1854) listed the "large lobos wolf" as having been encountered "above [evidently west of] the Cross-Timbers" as his party traveled from the mouth of East Cache Creek westward along the Red River in 1852. With the demise of the great bison herds in the 1870s, however, the wolf's natural food base was gone. Cattle and sheep were steadily replacing the bison and were far easier prey. Cross (1917) wrote that the wolf was "never abundant enough to extend over any considerable portion of the State, but in bands of from four to eight they were able to kill deer and buffalo, and with the coming of cattle and sheep they were responsible for a destruction that aroused a widespread demand for their speedy extermination. The 'six-shooter', so characteristic of the western cowboy, was originally carried for the purpose of killing this wolf . . . [which] generally frequents the rough country and forages over definite ranges which he covers in cycles every seven days . . . [it] is now practically extinct in this State. . . ." In the University of Kansas are skulls of a female and two male gray wolves taken in "No Man's Land" (Oklahoma Panhandle) in November, 1888. Between 8 August and 10 December 1889, Jenness Richardson and J. Rowley, Jr., collected seven specimens, now in the American Museum of Natural History, along the Beaver (North Canadian) River and "Teepee Creek" in the "Neutral Strip" (northwestern part of main body of state). Teepee Creek empties into the Beaver River 19 km (11 mi.) west of Guymon in Texas County. Three of these specimens are represented by skulls and the other four (two males and two females) all were taken on 5 November. The skull of a specimen taken in December, 1889, at the "Head of Beaver River, Oklahoma," is now in the Los Angeles County Museum. Six skulls in the U.S. National Museum were collected in 1902 and are labeled "Afton," a town in Ottawa County, far northeastern Oklahoma. All are labeled "Bur. Amer. Ethnology," and two are juveniles. In the Wichita Mountains of southwestern Oklahoma, A. S. Wells obtained a male on 3 July 1906, and Vernon Bailey trapped a juvenile male and female on the following day. In March 1910, Frank Rush collected a very old female on Mount Tarbone in the Wichitas; on the skull tag is written, "Believed to be last in region." One that was killed in 1930 along Post Oak Creek, near the southwest corner of the Wichita National Forest, was seen and verified as a gray wolf by veteran forester Earl Drummond, and a 1935 report by Vernon Bailey stated that in 1933 Supervisor Harry French "shot one and wounded another but others who have been riding the range have not seen them for many years" (Halloran and Glass, 1959). The last Wichita Mountains Wildlife Refuge record was a report of two wolves observed by French in 1934 (Halloran, 1972). Blair (1939) examined specimens of *Canis lupus* from the Shortgrass Plains, the Mixedgrass Plains, and the Wichita Mountains biotic districts, which are in the Shortgrass High Plains and Mixed-grass Plains physiognomic regions.

Female wolves are sexually mature when two years of age, males at three. They are thought to mate for life. In Texas, Davis (1974) reported that the breeding season started in late December and continued through February. The den is usually high, most often in a hillside, rock crevice, cave, or a vertical dirt bank.

Gestation is complete after 60 to 63 days, and the usual litter size is 5 to 7, although as many as 13 pups have been reported. Their eyes open in about nine days and are gray-blue in color. Weaning takes place when the pups are approximately five weeks old, and both parents care for the young until they leave the den in late summer. It is during this time that losses of domestic animals usually reach their peak.

On the Great Plains, bison were the prey of choice, although pronghorn, elk, and deer were eaten as well (Young and Goldman, 1944). As free-ranging cattle began usurping the buffalo's grazing niche on the prairies, beef simultaneously replaced bison in the wolf's diet. Occasionally, sheep, goats, pigs, and horses also fell to the wolves. Rabbits, rodents, and small quantities of vegetable matter, such as fruits and berries, supplemented the diet.

The wolf ran in packs composed of one or more family groups, each consisting of from six to ten individuals, in which a dominance hierarchy was established. They accompanied the large bison herds, and when young or disabled animals were not available, the wolves preferred to select a young female bison as prey. After a bison had been isolated from the herd and surrounded, pack members alternately bit and slashed its head and rear quarters until the animal succumbed from exhaustion or injury. The wolves often began to devour their prey while it was still kicking (Young and Goldman, 1944). A general discussion of wolf ecology in North America is given by Mech (1970, 1974).

Black and Best (1972) described the right ramus of a wolf mandible several hundred years old that they recovered from a cave in Woodward County. Caire recently found another partial wolf skull in a Woodward County cave. The race that occurred in western Oklahoma historically was *Canis lupus nubilus* (Hall, 1981).

Canis rufus Audubon and Bachman
Red Wolf
Canis rufus Audubon and Bachman, 1851, 2:240

The red wolf is intermediate in size between the coyote and gray wolf, but its disproportionately longer legs make it appear "rangier" than either of these.

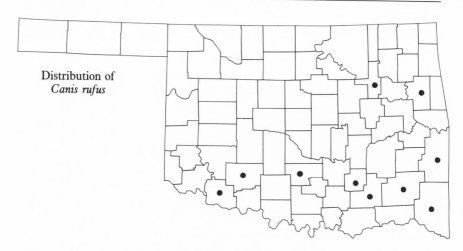

Distribution of
Canis rufus

Of 14 adult red wolves taken between 1968 and 1970 in Chambers County, Texas, males weighed 19–28 kg (42–62 lbs.), averaging 24 kg (52 lbs.), and females weighed 20–25 kg (45–54 lbs.), averaging 21 kg (47 lbs.) (Riley and McBride, 1972). By comparison, male coyotes seldom average more than about 14 kg (30 lbs.) and females 12.5 kg (27 lbs.). Male red wolves may weigh up to 35 kg (75–80 lbs.). Minimum lengths used in the U.S. Fish and Wildlife Service Red Wolf Recovery Program to separate red wolves from coyotes were 135 cm (53 in.) for males and 130 cm (51 in.) for females (Carley, 1979).

Distinguishing between red wolves, coyotes, and hybrids often requires an expert. Riley and McBride (1972) pointed out the following differences between full-blood coyotes and red wolves: in appearance, the wolf's broader head, muzzle, and nosepad, together with a habit of holding its longer ears more horizontally, impart a triangular (and less foxlike) face-on aspect. Overall, the wolf is more massive. Its legs are also longer and its feet larger than a coyote's. When displaying threat behavior, wolves do not ordinarily gape as does the coyote, but bare only the canine teeth, while erecting the hair on neck and shoulders; coyotes usually gape with back arched and tail held between the hind legs. Paradiso and Nowak (1972) compared greatest skull lengths of the two species. From presumed pre-hybrid red wolf populations, the range was 217.5–261.0 mm (8.6–10.3 in.) for males and 209.9–247.0 mm (8.3–9.7 in.) for females. Coyote measurements were 173.4–215.8 mm (6.9–8.5 in.) and 171.6–204.5 mm (6.8–8.0 in.) for males and females, respectively. Freeman and Shaw (1979) used discriminant function analysis to compare a series of measurements from wild canids in Oklahoma with those of gray wolves, red wolves, and coyotes. They concluded that only vestigial red wolf influence remained by the mid-1970s.

The dorsal color of the red wolf is usually a cinnamon buff or tawny, over-lain with a strong admixture of black hairs. However, coloration is extremely variable, especially considering the strong chance of coyote hybridization. The color variations are often expressed as brownish black, tawny gray, yel-lowish black, gray black, or yellowish. Time of year and habitat also influence coat color. Mead (1899) wrote that black wolves "were found in the eastern part of the Indian Territory, but not on the plains" in 1859, but the black phase is probably nonexistent now (Riley and McBride, 1972). Underparts range from whitish to "pinkish buff." The tail is black-tipped, and the muzzle, ears, and outer limb surfaces are tawny.

At one time the red wolf ranged throughout the entire southeastern United States, including the timbered eastern two-thirds of Oklahoma. It has been recorded from the Post Oak–Blackjack Uplands and Mixed-grass Plains physiognomic regions. If it still exists in the wild, *Canis rufus* is restricted to the coastal prairies and marshes of extreme southwestern Louisiana and adja-cent portions of southeastern Texas, though for all practical purposes it was projected to become extinct in the wild by 1980 (Carley, 1979). The species's extinction has been accelerated by several factors, none more important than direct interference by man. Relentless persecution by trapping and shooting greatly reduced populations (Russell and Shaw, 1971). However, the destruc-tion of woodlands, thick brush, and coastal prairies that composed prime red wolf habitat was a major factor leading toward extinction. The few remaining wolves not only were forced farther back into areas of marginal habitat, but a new threat emerged—the coyote. Clearing removed the ecological barrier that had generally prevented interbreeding between the two species and allowed coyotes to invade areas heretofore denied them. A hybrid that was capable of breeding with either species was the result, and *Canis rufus* was gradually eliminated from the wild through genetic "swamping" (McCarley, 1962). The red wolf was added to the federal list of endangered species in 1967, and several studies were undertaken in order to better understand the biology of this species (Lawrence and Bossert, 1967; Paradiso and Nowak, 1971; Russell and Shaw, 1971; Riley and McBride, 1972; Carley, 1979; McCarley and Carley, 1979). See also Gipson *et al.* (1974). Efforts are under way to establish populations on islands off the coast of the southeastern United States.

Reproductive biology is very similar to that of the gray wolf and the coyote. However, the red wolf's litter size (usually four) is generally smaller.

The red wolf is an opportunistic carnivore. Food habits have been studied by Stutzenbaker (1970), Russell and Shaw (1971), Riley and McBride (1972), and Shaw (1975) and summarized by Carley (1979). Historically, deer and wild hogs were eaten, as well as rabbits, rodents, birds, and other vertebrates. In the recent past, the wolves have depended primarily on nutria, swamp rabbits, cottontails, rice rats, cotton rats, muskrats and raccoons. They will also eat carrion. The major livestock damage is to poultry and pigs, although small calves or sheep may be taken occasionally. "The lack of a pack hunting structure and an abundance of smaller prey preclude the possibility of red wolves killing grown healthy cattle" (Carley, 1979:27).

The red wolf is predominantly nocturnal, systematically traveling over well-established, circuitous runways, some of which cover more than one hundred miles (Young, 1946*b*). Shaw (1975) reported an average home range size of 44 sq. km (17 sq. mi.), and Riley and McBride (1972) estimated home ranges to be 64.8–129.5 sq. km (25–50 sq. mi.), with males covering larger areas. The size fluctuates with changes in habitat, terrain, and availability of food. *Canis rufus* swims well when pursuing prey or when retreating from danger. The species seems to have little fear of man.

Red wolves are susceptible to several parasites, particularly sarcoptic mange, heartworms, and hookworms (Carley, 1979). Other ectoparasites which typically are found on canids probably also infested the red wolf. Paradiso and Nowak (1972) offer additional information on the ecology of red wolves.

Two subspecies are regarded as having formerly occurred in Oklahoma, *C. r. gregoryi* in far eastern Oklahoma and *C. r. rufus* in east and central sectors. In 1936, the Oklahoma Game and Fish Department reported that wolves had been taken in 24 Oklahoma counties during the year, but made no distinction between red wolves and gray (Blair, 1939). Most were probably red wolves or red wolf-coyote hybrids, since all but three of the counties were in the eastern, forested half of the state. McCarley (1962) was of the opinion that *C. r. rufus* was not a valid taxon, but represented wolf-coyote hybrids. In support of this contention, Hall (1981) wrote that R. M. Nowak, who recently examined a supposed specimen of *C. r. rufus* in the U.S. National Museum from the Wichita Mountains Wildlife Refuge and referred it to *C. latrans*. Nowak also assigned all specimens of this race from Arkansas to either *gregoryi* or considered them to be hybrids of *C. rufus* and *C. latrans*. It is therefore probable that the 14 other Oklahoma specimens of *C. r. rufus* in the National Museum are of the same taxonomic status. They are from the following counties: Tulsa, 7; Atoka, 3; Cherokee, 2; Comanche, 2; and Tillman, 1. All were collected between 25 January 1904, and 15 August 1940. There also are 64 skulls of *C. r. gregoryi* from these counties: McCurtain, 42; LeFlore, 15; Pushmataha, 6; and "Zafra," 1, all taken between 9 May 1919, and 11 December 1948. Of these, 29 were collected in McCurtain County and 11 in LeFlore County during 1919 alone. Numbers 232424–232432 (except 232430), all taken 15 mi. north of Broken Bow in McCurtain County by I. L. Ritchie on 22 May 1919, are juveniles. The tag on 232424 indicates that these all were "one family." Oddly, only one pup of the eight was a male. The parent wolves were apparently collected on 15 May (female, USNM 232422) and 16 May (male, 232423) at the same place. Also in the National Museum is a very large skull (USNM 8098)—labeled "*Canis rufus*" by E. A. Goldman—from "40 miles north of Ardmore" at "Cherokee Town Oklahoma," according to the tag. On the left parietal is written: "Black Wolf," "8098/9302," and "Cherokee Nation O." A black color phase in the red wolf was not uncommon, and Cherokee Town was near present-day Pauls Valley in Garvin County, well within the range of *C. r. rufus* (Morris *et al.*, 1976).

Vulpes velox (Say)
Swift Fox
Canis velox Say *in* Long, 1823:487
Vulpes velox: Audubon and Bachman, 1851:13

The little "prairie swift" or "kit fox" is about the size of a large house cat. Adults weigh 1.5–2.5 kg (3.5–5.5 lbs.). Males are slightly larger. The average weight of 19 adult males and of 14 females from Beaver County, Oklahoma, and the surrounding region in Texas, Kansas, and New Mexico, was 2.5 kg (5.37 lbs.) and 2.2 kg (4.95 lbs.), respectively (Kilgore, 1969). Average total lengths for 13 of the males was 800 mm (31 in.) and for 7 females, 788 mm (30.5 in.), with the tail contributing about one-third.

Like many other arid-land mammals, the swift fox has large ears and a pale-colored pelage. Its back, from front of eyes to base of tail, is buff brown basally, but the white subterminal band on each guard hair gives the pelt a "frosted" appearance. On the sides, legs, undersurface of the tail, and sides of the neck, warm ochraceous buff prevails. The dorsal portion of the bushy tail is sooty gray, but the tip is black. The venter is white. A black spot on either side of the snout, the black (instead of white) tail-tip, smaller size, and

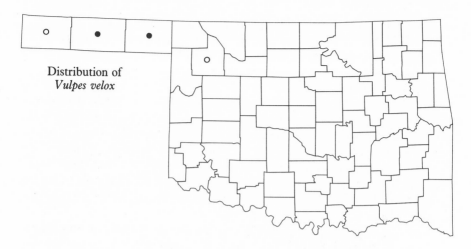

Distribution of
Vulpes velox

absence of black on the ears and legs of *Vulpes velox* readily distinguish it from the red fox, *V. vulpes*. The gray fox (*Urocyon cinereoargenteus*) is about twice as large as the swift fox and is grizzled above. It generally prefers woodlands and rough, broken country over the open prairie habitat of the swift fox. The closely related kit fox (*V. macrotis*) does not occur as far east as Oklahoma.

Mead (1899*b*) wrote that, on the plains of western Kansas in 1859, these foxes "lived in pairs; not more than two found together." Seton (1925–28) collected one at Clayton, New Mexico, only 12 mi. southwest of the Oklahoma Panhandle. The first specimen records (one male, two females) of *Vulpes velox* from Oklahoma were apparently taken in October, 1888, from the Neutral Strip, Indian Territory. Tihen and Sprague (1939) reported a specimen from Meade County, Kansas, about 15 mi. north of Beaver County, Oklahoma. Cockrum (1952) considered the species extinct in Kansas, but Martin and Sternberg (1955) discovered one in Gove County, the first from that state in more than fifty years. Since then, several records have been published for western Kansas (Anderson and Nelson, 1958; Andersen and Fleharty, 1964; Zumbaugh and Choate, 1985), for eastern New Mexico (Packard and Bowers, 1970; Best, 1971; Aday and Gennaro, 1973), and for the Texas Panhandle (Cutter, 1959; Packard and Garner, 1964*b*; Packard and Bowers, 1970). Two specimens in the U.S. National Museum were taken in eastern Las Animas County, Colorado (Long and Long, 1964), not far from Cimarron County, Oklahoma. There is a specimen in the Cameron University Museum from Cimarron County. In Oklahoma, Duck and Fletcher (1945) wrote that *Vulpes velox* occurred throughout the Panhandle and in the western counties, but was "very rare" and seldom seen or trapped, "although in earlier days it was frequently seen throughout this area." Cutter (1959) observed the swift fox in Texas County, Oklahoma, between 1951 and 1957. Glass (1959) reported it from Woodward, Beaver, and Texas counties. One of the most definitive studies available is that of Kilgore (1969), done in Beaver County, Oklahoma.

In 1966, federal trapper Robert McVicar stated that in several years of exterminating prairie dogs and coyotes, he had never seen or trapped swift foxes east of central Beaver County (*fide* J. D. Tyler). In 1964, Judge Hiner F. Dale fenced an acre of the Guymon City Park, then stocked it with about fifty prairie dogs. By the following spring, all had been killed by swift foxes, a pair of which reared a litter in the dog town (Tyler, 1968). Dale offered a five-dollar bounty on the foxes, and 17 were killed within a mile of Guymon (*fide* J. D. Tyler).

The largely nocturnal swift fox inhabits the shortgrass and semidesert country of the High Plains. These flat, arid reaches where small rodents and rabbits abound are typically covered with low vegetation, but much of the natural habitat has been altered for agriculture. This fox sometimes locates its den in abandoned prairie dog or badger holes, and there are usually several entrances. Kilgore (1969) felt that most dens were excavated by the foxes themselves. He found 16 of 35 dens in cultivated fields, and most were dug in flat, open areas. Six of them, however, were situated in the sides of wind-blown sand ridges near playa lakes. Most of the dens that Cutter (1958*a*) investigated in the Texas Panhandle were located in overgrazed pastureland. Although it uses the den as a refuge during winter, the swift fox does not hibernate.

Swift foxes are monoestrous, producing a single litter each year (Asdell, 1964). Kilgore (1969) suggested that the species probably pairs for life, but that males might sometimes be polygynous. In Texas, breeding is believed to begin in January or February (Davis, 1974), but Kilgore (1969) found that it commenced in late December or early January in the Oklahoma Panhandle. The time required for gestation is apparently unknown, but is probably similar to that of the red fox, 49–50 days (Asdell, 1964). The three to six (average: five) young kits are born in March or early April (Kilgore, 1969), and both parents care for them. Egoscue (1966) described a newborn kit fox that weighed 39.9 g (1.5 oz.). At 10–15 days, the eyes and ears of young swift foxes open, and they are weaned by the sixth or seventh week (Kilgore, 1969). Kit fox pups are at least a month old before appearing aboveground, and they begin to forage independently after four or five months. During the spring of 1964, Marvin Elliot watched a pair of foxes rear four pups in an active prairie dog town at Griggs, in Cimarron County (*fide* J. D. Tyler). Kilgore (1969) noted that swift fox families begin to break up in late August or early September, about the time that juveniles attain adult size. The maximum known age of a wild kit fox is seven years.

Studies of Kilgore (1969) in the Oklahoma Panhandle, Cutter (1958*b*) in the Texas Panhandle, and Zumbaugh *et al.* (1985) in western Kansas have shown that mammals of small to medium size—primarily rabbits—are the most important foods of *Vulpes velox* during most of the year. In a series of nonwinter scats and stomachs, Cutter (1958*b*) found that lagomorph remains (principally *Sylvilagus*) occurred almost as frequently as did all other species of vertebrates combined. In Oklahoma, *Sylvilagus* composed more than half the total food during early spring, but in autumn, nonlagomorph mammals made up 82 percent of total biomass in 488 scats (Kilgore, 1969). Many adult jack rabbits are probably eaten as carrion, since they are difficult for the little foxes to kill (Egoscue, 1962), and many other lagomorphs are immature individuals (Cutter, 1958*b*). Small rodents such as pocket mice, kangaroo rats, white-footed mice, harvest mice, ground squirrels, prairie dogs, and gophers are important foods, as are small ground-dwelling birds (horned larks, meadowlarks, lark buntings, etc.), various amphibians, and small reptiles. Many insects—primarily grasshoppers and beetles—are consumed. Rather than being selective, swift foxes normally take prey in proportion to its availability (Kilgore, 1969). Tyler (1968) found prairie dog and jack rabbit remains at fox burrows in active prairie dog towns in Texas County during November 1966 and in April 1967.

By nature, this species is less cunning than the red fox, seems to be more trustful toward man, and consequently often falls victim to traps and poisons set for coyotes. In addition, many are killed by automobiles or are deliberately shot. Fleas, ticks, cestodes, and nematodes heavily parasitized the adult foxes studied by Kilgore (1969), who listed all parasites known from *Vulpes velox*. The biology of swift foxes in North America is summarized by Samuel and Nelson (1982).

The race occurring in Oklahoma is *V. v. velox* (Hall, 1981). Thornton *et al.* (1971) and Rohwer and Kilgore (1973) have documented interbreeding between swift and kit foxes in western Texas and eastern New Mexico, where these two species are sympatric.

Vulpes vulpes Linnaeus
Red Fox
Vulpes vulpes Linnaeus, 1758:40

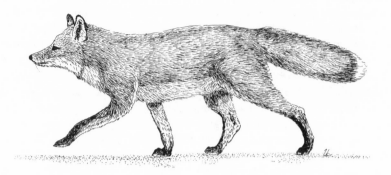

In appearance and size, the red fox is reminiscent of a miniature collie with a long, bushy tail and large, erect ears. Predominant coloration of the long, soft fur is golden red, darker toward the midline, with tawny orange on shoulders, neck, and muzzle. The flanks, rump, and tail are darker still, tending toward golden brown. The legs and backs of the ears are black. Underparts, as well as the throat, cheeks, insides of the ears, and tip of the tail, are white. The white-tipped tail distinguishes the red fox from the swift and gray foxes. There are several color phases (black, silver, and "cross"), all of which may occur in a single litter, but only the typical reddish color seems to have been reported in Oklahoma. The pupil, like that of other foxes, is vertically elliptical, and the iris is tawny. Males are slightly larger than females, usually weighing 3.6–5 kg (8–11 lbs.) and measuring approximately 1,016 mm (40 in.) in total length. Maximum weight is about 7 kg (15 lbs.). The female has eight mammae.

Marcy (1854), who found it in the "Red River Valley," was probably the first to report the red fox from Oklahoma. Cross (in Snider, 1917) listed the species as a part of Oklahoma's native fauna, but Bailey (1928) commented that "a few scattered records over Texas, Louisiana, Alabama, Arkansas, Oklahoma and Kansas are probably of wanderers, or the progeny of stock introduced for fox hunting." Its historical status was reviewed by Zumbaugh and Choate (1985). Probably the first museum specimen taken in Oklahoma was from twelve miles north of Tahlequah, in Cherokee County, and is housed at the University of Michigan (Blair, 1939). The Oklahoma Game and Fish Department (1952) reported that red foxes were confined largely to the eastern one-half of the state, especially the oak-hickory forest of the north-

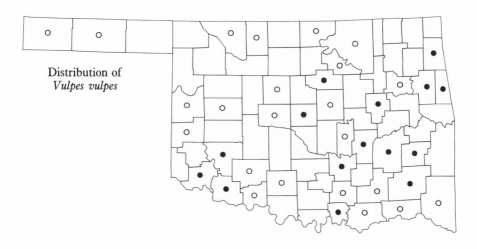

Distribution of
Vulpes vulpes

east, and that some specimens had also been taken along the Red River in southwestern Oklahoma. The first distributional study was done by Glass and Halloran (1960), who recorded specimens from seven Oklahoma counties and trapping records from 17 more, only 4 of which (Woods, Canadian, Stephens, and Comanche) were in the western half of the state. Martin and Preston (1970) and Tyler (1979) mentioned introductions in western Oklahoma, and the latter reported four museum specimens from southwestern Oklahoma and nine recent sight records in nine western counties. Hatcher (1975) reported specimens from several other counties in the main body of the state. A statewide survey in 1977 by Hatcher (1982) revealed that densities were highest in the oak-hickory forest of the Ozark uplands in the northeast and lowest in the northwest, the Panhandle, and the southwest corner, where shortgrass prairie predominates. He compiled 64 sightings and nine specimen records of foxes collected in the state since 1972 and concluded that populations were generally decreasing or stable in most sections.

Red foxes usually mate between late January and March and were thought to pair for life (Seton, 1925–28). However, both Palmer (1954) and Cahalane (1961) suggested this species is only seasonally monogamous. The female is monestrous and experiences a very short estrus lasting only two to four days (Asdell, 1964). The onset of breeding is usually announced by increased barking. Gestation lasts about 50–52 days, after which one to eight young, usually four to five (Asdell, 1964) are born. Weight at birth is about three and one half ounces. In northeastern Kansas, whelping takes place in March or April (Stanley, 1963). Both parents care for the kits; the eyes open at eight or nine days of age. The young are weaned when eight to ten weeks old, at which time they leave the den and learn to hunt with their parents (Davis,

1974). They acquire adult dentition at four or five months (Sheldon, 1949). In the fall, the family disbands and the pups are on their own. They continue to gain weight with age and are sexually mature by the following spring.

Dens are often located along well-wooded streams in friable soils near open areas and are used both for refuge and raising young. Sometimes a hole is dug into a hillside not far from water. Old woodchuck or badger burrows are sometimes used, as well as hollow logs, stumps, rock cavities, or even spaces under buildings. A pair of foxes will usually dig more than one den, each of which is furnished with several entrances. Den sites are sometimes used year after year.

The preferred food of red foxes is small rodents, particularly mice (Seton, 1925–28) and rabbits. Errington (1935) and Murie (1936) found that rabbits constituted 30–40 percent of foods eaten, mice 40–50 percent, and various birds, fruits, and insects the remainder. In Kansas, cottontails were the predominant food during fall and winter, but cotton rats, voles, mice, and wild birds also were frequently represented (Stanley, 1963). Fisher (1951) examined stomachs of 886 foxes from Missouri, with similar findings. The occasional fox-related loss of poultry, especially during the time of whelping, can usually be prevented through proper husbandry. Most of the poultry and small livestock remains in fox stomachs are probably carrion; Stanley (1963) found that these foxes even fed from garbage cans. Most game animals taken by red foxes are probably animals that have been crippled by hunters. Insects are most important in the warmer months, and vegetable matter (fruits, berries, and nuts) is often consumed in quantity.

The home range is usually 2–4 km (1–2 mi.) in diameter, but may be 8 km (5 mi.) or more if food is scarce, and twice that in winter (Sheldon, 1950). The same favored routes are usually followed when hunting, an activity often pursued by mated pairs. Red foxes are mostly nocturnal but may forage during the day. They are accomplished swimmers (Seton, 1909). Home ranges and individual movements also have been studied by Storm (1965) and Ables (1969).

Aging methods based on skull morphology were proposed by Churcher (1960) and Stanley (1963). Sullivan and Haugen (1956) developed a technique whereby X-rays of the forefeet were used, and several aging methods were reviewed by Reilly and Curren (1961).

Red foxes are subject to the same kinds of diseases as most other canids: coccidiosis, distemper, rabies, and mange. Stanley (1963) retrieved four different types of fleas, one tick, four species of nematodes, and a cestode from Kansas foxes, and reported that the helminth species were the same as those from Kansas coyotes (Gier, 1968). A key catalog of carnivoran parasites published by Stiles and Baker (1935) is still a reliable source of information, as is Erickson (1944).

TABLE 8. Number of red fox pelts purchased and
average price paid by Oklahoma fur dealers, 1972–76.
(Oklahoma Dept. Wildl. Conserv.)

Year	No. Pelts Bought	Avg. Price/Pelt	Total
1972–73	7	$ 8.86	$ 62.00
1973–74	59	13.42	792.00
1974–75	75	11.52	864.00
1975–76	90	30.26	2,723.50

A good discussion of the red fox's role in predation, its economic importance, and its management was given by Scott (1955). During the 1943–44
trapping season, 86 red fox pelts were sold to fur buyers at an average of
$5.00 each (Duck and Fletcher, 1945) as compared to an average price of
$2.00 apiece for gray fox skins. Data for red fox pelts sold in Oklahoma in the
period 1972–76 are given in Table 8. Additional information on the ecology
of red foxes throughout North America is summarized by Samuel and Nelson
(1982).

A question over which naturalists have long puzzled is whether or not the
red fox is native to North America. The European red fox, *Vulpes vulpes,* was
introduced more than once into the United States along the eastern seaboard
(including Virginia) about 1750 or before. Some evidence indicates, however,
that a native red fox inhabited America north of 40° or 45° north latitude,
though it was scarce in the unbroken forest (see Seton, 1925–28, and Zumbaugh and Choate, 1985). Did the two foxes widely interbreed? Was one supplanted by the other? Was there ever an indigenous form? It is known that a
red fox began to proliferate westward and southward, partially displacing the
gray fox (*Urocyon cinereoargenteus*) as the eastern forests were opened by
settlement. After studying specimens of both American and European foxes
from over their entire ranges, Churcher (1959) concluded that they were all
members of a single Holarctic species, *Vulpes vulpes.* Prior to this, the American red fox's scientific name had been *V. fulva* and comprised 12 races. Roest
(1979) proposed that the number of races be reduced to three; the subspecies
occurring in Oklahoma is *V. v. fulva.*

Urocyon cinereoargenteus (Schreber)
Gray Fox
Canis cinereo argenteus Schreber, 1775 : pl. 92
Urocyon cinereo-argenteus: Rhoads, 1894 : 524

The fur of the gray fox appears grayish at a distance, but when inspected closely, it is seen to be predominantly black. A narrow white band on each black guard hair creates the characteristic pepper-and-salt color on the upperparts and most of the tail. The cheeks, underside of the jaw, and a distinctive mid-dorsal tail stripe composed of stiff guard hairs are black. Rich rufous extends from behind the ears on either side ventrally across the upper chest. This rusty color also generously washes the limbs and outer thighs, the lower sides, and the underside of the tail. The venter, ear linings, lower muzzle, and throat are whitish. The tail is bushy, only about one-third the body length, roughly triangular in cross-section, and black-tipped.

The much smaller swift fox also has a black-tipped tail, but its overall coloration is pale buff yellow. The red fox has a white-tipped tail. Distinctive lyre-shaped temporal ridges on the gray fox's skull and a notch at the postero-ventral corner of the lower jaw make it easy to identify.

Adult gray foxes usually weigh between 3 kg and 5 kg (7–12 lbs.), to a maximum of about 7 kg (16 lbs.), and males average slightly larger. Total lengths normally vary from about 900 mm to 1,100 mm (35–42 in.). Average measurements are slightly smaller than those of the red fox (*Vulpes vulpes*), but ranges in weights of the two may overlap, particularly in the southern states. The swift fox, *Vulpes velox*, is considerably smaller.

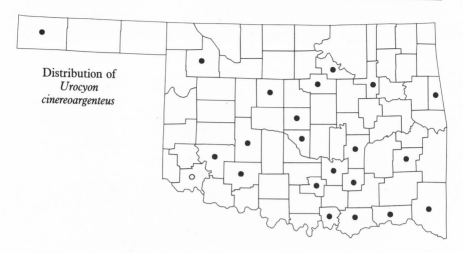

Distribution of
Urocyon
cinereoargenteus

The gray fox probably ranges throughout wooded sections of the entire state but is most abundant in the eastern oak-hickory forests. More than half of all pelts bought by fur buyers during the 1940–41 trapping season came from Cherokee and Adair counties (Duck and Fletcher, 1945). Gray foxes are now rather common in the Wichita Mountains and their outlying boulder-strewn hills after apparently having been quite rare between the latter half of the nineteenth century and the 1940s (Halloran and Glass, 1959). They seem to be uncommon to rare in the surrounding mixed-grass prairie, for example, in Harmon County (Martin and Preston, 1970). In 1940–41, pelts were mar-keted from as far west as Payne and Stephens counties (Duck and Fletcher, 1945). They often den in caves in the Blaine gypsum of western Oklahoma, and there are a few records of the species from the canyons of northwestern Cimarron County. Though it has been recorded in all the physiognomic re-gions in the state, treeless plains and shortgrass high plains in west central Oklahoma and through most of the Panhandle are effective distributional barriers.

Because of its unique ability to climb trees and its preference for woodlands, *Urocyon* is called by some the "timber fox." Whether mixed hardwoods, bot-tomland forest, piñon-juniper stands, mesquite savanna, or brushy areas, some type of woody cover is integral to its survival. Its propensity for rough, broken country, especially rocky regions, is well known. Whenever forests are opened up by man, the gray fox moves to thicker cover, often allowing the red fox—a species adapted to more open habitats—to invade these clearings. Dens are most often located in hollow logs or trees (occasionally well above ground), sometimes in brush piles or in rocky crevices, under a stump, or in some similar situation. Seldom do gray foxes dig their own dens, but they are

TABLE 9. Number of gray fox pelts purchased and
average price paid by Oklahoma fur dealers, 1972–81.
(Oklahoma Dept. Wildl. Conserv.)

Year	No. Pelts Bought	Avg. Price/Pelt	Total
1972–73	102	$ 4.50	$ 459.00
1973–74	442	12.29	5,431.50
1974–75	722	21.89	15,806.25
1975–76	1,839	20.67	38,012.65
1976–77	2,812	27.29	76,733.13
1977–78	1,619	25.98	42,061.62
1978–79	1,902	36.60	69,613.20
1979–80	1,631	37.70	61,493.20
1980–81	1,693	30.99	52,466.07

known to appropriate burrows abandoned by other mammals. The den, lined with grass, leaves, and shredded bark, is a warm refuge in winter even though this animal does not hibernate.

The gray fox is primarily a night wanderer, but often is active during the daytime. Occasionally it is found sunning well up in a tree. Normally a secretive animal, it is rather shy, but will fight when cornered. It seems to be not so cunning as the red fox, less wary, and when pursued by dogs, soon seeks trees or cover rather than running or employing the well-known craftiness of *Vulpes vulpes*.

Cottontails and small rodents are the mainstays of the gray fox's diet (Errington, 1935; Korschgen, 1957; Davis, 1974). Based on the contents of forty-two stomachs from Texas (Davis, 1974), cottontails and small rodents constituted 56 percent of winter foods, insects (mostly grasshoppers) 23 percent, and various birds 21 percent. In spring, small mammals made up 68 percent of the total, insects 25 percent, and small birds 17 percent. In late summer and fall, foxes turned to persimmons and acorns (30 percent) and insects (26 percent); small mammals were in third place (16 percent), followed closely by birds and crayfish (14 percent). Chicken and quail appeared only once each, doves twice. It is apparent that the food habits of *Urocyon* have little detrimental impact on man's economy. The stomachs of two foxes taken on the Wichita Mountains Wildlife Refuge in the 1930s contained rabbit fur, a deer mouse, and remains of insects, and in 1956 an adult turkey gobbler was killed and partially devoured on the refuge by a gray fox (Halloran and Glass, 1959).

The gray fox is probably monogamous, but may be polygynous to some degree (Seton, 1925–28; Sheldon, 1949). Mating occurs usually from February into March in Texas, and parturition is in April or May (Davis, 1974). The period of gestation is unknown, but is approximately two months, and the litter size varies from 2 to 7, but averages 3.8 (Fritzell and Haroldson, 1982). The female possesses six functional mammae (Sheldon, 1949). In approximately nine days the kit's eyes open (Jackson, 1961), and weaning takes place at eight to ten weeks, but full size is not attained until about 25 weeks (Sheldon, 1949).

Aging techniques are discussed by Wood (1958) and Schwartz and Schwartz (1981). Davis (1974) indicated a probable inverse relationship between coyote and gray fox populations in Texas. Parasites were reported by Jackson (1961) and Buechner (1944). Other aspects of gray foxes throughout their range in North America are summarized by Fritzell and Haroldson (1982). Longevity in the wild is probably less than six years, with a potential maximum of 14 (Jackson, 1961).

Gray foxes are trapped for their pelts. The fur is thin, coarse, and inferior to that of the red fox. An annual average of 1,010 gray fox pelts were sold during the four trapping seasons between 1940 and 1944 for an average $1.52 each, and only 303 were sold in 1951–52 (Oklahoma Game and Fish Department, 1952). Table 9 lists the number of pelts taken in Oklahoma in recent years.

U. c. ocythous occurs throughout the main body of the state, and *U. c. scottii* in the Black Mesa country (Hall, 1981).

Ursus americanus Pallas
Black bear
Ursus americanus Pallas, 1780:5

Like all bears, *Ursus americanus* is easily recognized by its hulky, virtually tailless form and broad head accented with short, rounded ears. Its long fur is commonly cinnamon to black, but bluish, white, blonde, and yellowish colors are not uncommon in some parts of the range (Hall, 1981). Each of the five toes on all four feet has a claw that is approximately 40 mm (1.6 in.) in length. Most adult black bears weigh between 90 kg and 205 kg (200–450 lbs.). Males are larger than females, but rarely weigh more than 225 kg (500 lbs.). Total lengths of adults usually vary from 1,300 mm to 1,800 mm (50–65 in.). Females have three pairs of mammary glands. See grizzly account for differences between these two species.

In the past, black bears probably occurred throughout Oklahoma. In 1824, A. P. Chouteau shipped skins of 300 females and 160 cubs from his trading post at the mouth of the Verdigris River near Muskogee in present-day Muskogee County, northeastern Oklahoma, to New Orleans (Foreman, 1926). These represented but one season's take from this virgin country of wild rivers and densely forested mountains. Gregg (1844) considered bears "very common" in the cross timbers of central Oklahoma and along the wooded tributaries of the Canadian and Red rivers between 1831 and 1839. Caucasian

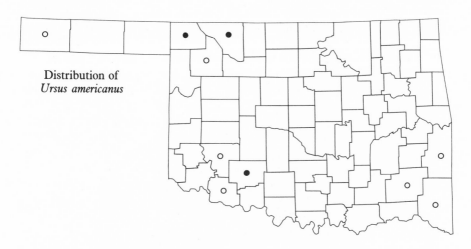

Distribution of
Ursus americanus

settlement followed swiftly, interrupted for only a brief period by the Civil War. The big carnivores were forced back into inaccessible regions by man until they were finally eliminated. Seton (1925–28) recorded that a black bear weighing 327 kg (720 lbs.) was killed in the "Keimeche" [*sic*] Mountains of Oklahoma on 16 November 1911, evidently by P. I. Dillingham of Smithville. The last bear known in the southeastern corner of the state was killed 19 April 1915, on Mount Pine, McCurtain County, by Johnie Beavers, and the skull is now in the Southeastern Oklahoma State University collection (McCarley, 1961). Another skull in the same collection bears only the apparent collector's name, "Mr. Goodman" (letter of 15 May 1979, from C. Taylor to M. Johnson, in CAMCO). Within the past 35 years or so, the state of Arkansas has transplanted bears into the Ozark Mountains until a breeding population has been reestablished there (Sealander, 1956). These bears occasionally wander into Oklahoma along one of the big river systems, as did the young male killed 6 mi. north of Spiro in LeFlore County on 22 April 1960 (McCarley, 1961), or the 250-pound black bear that was killed near Antlers in Pushmataha County in late May 1972 (*Lawton Constitution Press*, 1 June 1972). In early May 1981, a female black bear was captured a few miles west of Boise City in Cimarron County and released in the Black Mesa country after being tagged (*Outdoor Oklahoma* 1981, 37(5):55). Puckette (1976) reported on fossil remains of the closely-related Pleistocene short-nosed bear, *Arctodus simus*, found in an Adair County cave, indicating that *Ursus americanus* or its progenitors had inhabited this part of Oklahoma for thousands of years.

For the Wichita Mountains of southwestern Oklahoma there are several records of black bears, the earliest of which was given by Marcy (1854), who found them "throughout the (Red River) Valley." A Delaware Indian scout with his exploring party caught two cubs near Devil's Canyon in the Quartz Mountains (Kiowa County) on 1 June 1852, and brought one into camp. James H. Gaut collected an old sow and one of her three six-week-old cubs (male) on Mount Scott, 14 May 1904 (Halloran, 1963*b*). On West Cache Creek in the refuge headquarters area, a young black bear was photographed in 1909 (Halloran, 1956), and the following year one was killed by veteran forester Earl Drummond on Crater Creek immediately south of the refuge boundary (Halloran and Glass, 1959). Supervisor Frank Rush saw one in the area of Sunset Peak in 1915, and bears may have persisted a few more years as a 1935 report by Vernon Bailey stated: "The early settlers reported bear as common here many years ago and four were killed in 1934" (Halloran and Glass, 1959). Elsewhere in the state, Gregg (in Thwaites, 1905) noted the species in the "cross timbers." Only the right mandible remains in the U.S. National Museum of a skull (male) collected 2.9 m (9.5 ft.) below the bed of Eagle Chief Creek near Alva, Woods County, by L. F. Ward and T. W. Vaughan (no date). A skull (upper cranium) was recently found in a cave in Alabaster Caverns State Park, Woodward County (pers. comm. to Caire from Bill Robinson, park superintendent). Stangl and Dalquest (1986) reported a black bear mandible of pre-Columbian age from a small tributary of the Red River in Tillman County.

Black bears are fairly common in the mountains of New Mexico, and numbered approximately 3,000 in 1967 (Lee, 1967). A specimen from Bear Canyon in the northeast corner of Colfax County, about 75 mi. west of Cimarron County, Oklahoma, is in the National Museum (Lee, 1967). Glass (1951:28), who studied mammals in the Black Mesa country of Cimarron County, wrote that this animal "wanders into this portion of Oklahoma at times. One was reported at the time of our visit (August 1949) to have been seen about ten miles north of the state line in (Baca County) Colorado." Truman Tucker, who lives a few miles north of Kenton, related that Kindal Kohler (a local resident) observed a sow and two cubs in mid-March of 1982 in Sheep Pen Canyon, which is north of the Cimarron River and only about 12 or 15 mi. west of Kenton. Mr. Fred Daniel of rural Folsom, New Mexico, about 50 airline miles west of Oklahoma, reported that black bears were still fairly common in that area. His wife and boy watched a sow and her cub cross the road early one morning "a few years ago" near the village of Trinchera in southeastern Colorado, just north of the New Mexico state line. Occasionally, "blonde" bears are seen in that region (both accounts related to Tyler in 1982).

Although the bulk of the black bear's diet consists of vegetable matter, it is among the most omnivorous of mammals (Van Wormer, 1966). Grass, fruits, berries, seeds and nuts, acorns, the inner bark of trees, and succulent roots are taken when available. Animal material includes ants, bees (and honey), crickets, grasshoppers, fish, frogs, and any small mammal obtainable up to the size of a fawn. Carrion is eaten, though fresh meat is much preferred. Occasional individuals will kill young livestock, and bears frequently raid garbage dumps, both habits eventually placing them in direct contact with man.

Bears do not truly hibernate, but store up fat in late summer and fall that is drawn upon while they are torpid in the winter den—a cave, hollow log, rock crevice, or hole in the ground. Sometimes they emerge during warm spells in winter.

Mating normally takes place in June or July in Texas (Davis, 1974), but the fertilized ovum does not implant into the uterine wall for about four months. After a total gestation time of about seven months, the one to four young (usually two) are born in the winter den during January or February. They weigh 170–225 g (6–8 oz.) and are approximately 210 mm (8 in.) long. The cubs remain with their mother until the fall of their second year. Sexual maturity is attained in females at about three and one-half years of age. Additional information about black bear biology is summarized by Pelton (1982), and a comprehensive bibliography was published by Tigner and Gilbert (1960).

Ursus americanus amblyceps is the race occurring in the Oklahoma Panhandle, and *U. a. americanus* in the remainder of the state (Hall, 1981).

Ursus arctos Linnaeus
Grizzly
Ursus arctos Linnaeus, 1758:47

Differences between this species and the black bear are the grizzly's greater size, a pronounced "hump" above the shoulders, a somewhat concave facial profile, and front claws that are longer than 63 mm (2.5 in.). Most estimates of weight are probably exaggerated by at least half, for a large male specimen may only weigh about 227 kg (500 lbs.), even though there are authenticated weights approaching 454 kg (1,000 lbs.). A female would be exceptionally large if she weighed 182 kg (400 lbs.). In many specimens, especially in older individuals, the normally dark brown fur attains white tips, imparting a "frosted" or "grizzly" appearance.

The grizzly, though now extirpated from Oklahoma, probably at one time ranged into the western parts of the state along the major streams, and a few may have inhabited the Wichita Mountains and the Black Mesa region; information is scant. Available records indicate that the grizzly was exterminated in the adjoining states of Kansas, Colorado, New Mexico and Texas from fifty to one hundred years ago (James, 1823; Bailey, 1905; Cary, 1911; Cockrum, 1952; Lee, 1967; Dalquest, 1968; Findley *et al.*, 1975). Because of relentless persecution by man, only a few hundred grizzlies remain in the lower 48

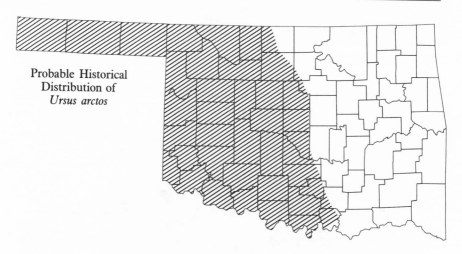

Probable Historical
Distribution of
Ursus arctos

states, primarily in Yellowstone and Glacier national parks and a few adjacent regions. Here their ranges are shrinking and numbers are steadily declining.

The grizzly is similar to the black bear in its catholic food habits and in many other aspects of its biology. Unlike the black bear, however, the grizzly cannot climb trees. It may cover a home range of up to 117 sq. km. (45 sq. mi.). Other ecological facts about the grizzly bear are summarized by Craighead and Mitchell (1982).

The subspecies that occurred in Oklahoma was *U. a. horribilis* (Rausch, 1963).

FAMILY PROCYONIDAE   Ringtails and Raccoons

Bassariscus astutus (Lichtenstein)
Ringtail
Bassaris astuta Lichtenstein, 1830:119
Bassariscus astutus: Coues, 1887:516

The ringtail resembles a squirrel-sized fox with short legs and an immense raccoon tail. This greatly elongated brush, encircled with vivid rings of black and white, easily sets the ringtail apart from other Oklahoma mammals. The foxlike appearance is primarily because of the large ears and pointed snout. Large, dark eyes are accented above and below with light patches. Whitish areas are prominent also on either side of the nosepad, the upper sides of the ears, as anterobasal ear spots, and throughout the undersides, leg linings, and throat. The soft dorsal pelage is yellowish gray, buff brown, or gray brown, with a profusion of black guard hairs throughout, darker near the midline. Lighter shades of the dorsal color extend onto the outer surfaces of the legs. The tail is black-tipped, a bit longer than the body, and alternately banded with six or eight black and pure white rings that merge into a white ventral stripe. The catlike tracks are tiny, and each of the five toes bears a short, semiretractile claw.

Adult weight varies from 0.9 kg to 1.4 kg (2–3 lbs.), females averaging slightly smaller. Two adult males from southwestern Oklahoma weighed 999.6 and 1,091 g (2.2 and 2.4 lbs.), respectively; total lengths were 812 and 870 mm (32 and 34 in.), and the tails measured 426 and 480 mm (16.8 and 18.9 in.). These measurements are near the upper limits for the species.

Probably the earliest mention of the species in Oklahoma was made by Marcy (1854), who included it in a list of mammals encountered by his party during the exploration of the Red River in 1852. He referred to it as "civet cat" and gave the location as "Cross Timbers." A specimen in the U.S. National Museum, labeled "Red River, Capt. Marcy," was entered into the museum catalog on 31 March 1853. Also on the label is "Red River, Ark."

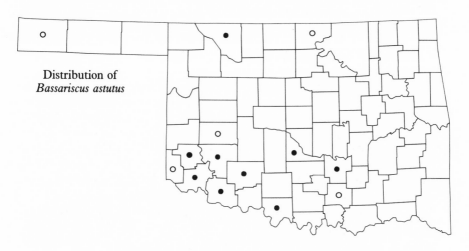

Distribution of
Bassariscus astutus

(Bailey, 1905). Hall's (1981) distribution map indicated a nearly statewide distribution except for the northwesternmost Panhandle and the northeastern corner of Oklahoma. However, Tyler (in prep.) mentions a reliable sight record for the Piñon-Juniper Mesas region in northwestern Cimarron County, and records are known for the southwestern corner of Kansas not far to the east (pers. comm., J. R. Choate to J. D. Tyler). Valid sight records or specimens are known for most of the southwestern counties; for Johnston, Pontotoc, and Cleveland in the south central area; and for Kay County in north central Oklahoma. Numerous sightings from the Wichita Mountain range of southwestern Oklahoma and limestone regions in south central Oklahoma indicate the presence of stable populations there within at least the past decade. Several animals have also been observed along major river systems or heavily wooded streams. In Colorado, R. E. Richards (1976) has recorded ringtails in Baca, Prowers, and Las Animas counties, all in southeastern Colorado only a few miles from Cimarron County, Oklahoma.

Because so few specimens are known from Oklahoma, very little ecological information is available for the ringtail in the state. However, its biology is probably similar to that described for animals in neighboring states. Ringtails frequent rocky or brushy places and rough, broken terrain, where they den in well-protected crevices or cavities near water and preferred food sources. Often the den is in a hollow tree or log; occasionally in a brush pile, an abandoned mine, or a skunk or armadillo burrow; or sometimes in an old building. It serves as both refuge and nursery but is seldom modified. In desert areas, the entrance is frequently protected by thorny vegetation. On the Edwards Plateau of southwest Texas, Toweill (1976) found that adult ringtails denned solitarily in rock openings, tree hollows, and brush piles 42 percent,

34 percent, and 24 percent of the time, respectively. Females usually occupied dens for longer periods than did males (2.25 vs. 1.58 days). This strictly nocturnal and reclusive carnivore sleeps in the den during the day, but at night forages nimbly over cliffs and through canyons and woodlands in search of rats and mice. Trapp (1972) discussed several specializations for climbing in this species. Despite the fact that it has been found as high as 9,300 ft. in Colorado (Richards, 1976), *Bassariscus* does not hibernate and usually lives at much lower elevations.

Toweill (1976) found a minimum annual average population density of 2.2 adults per sq. km (0.4 per sq. mi.) on the Edwards Plateau of Texas. Home range size averaged 43.4 ha (109 acres) for males and 20.3 ha (51 acres) for females. Male home ranges frequently overlapped those of females.

Nothing is known about the reproductive patterns of Oklahoma ringtails; however, breeding occurs in April or earlier in southwestern Texas (Taylor, 1954). In central Texas, females first experience estrus about 1 April (Davis, 1974). Most females are pregnant between 15 April and 18 May, but the actual time of gestation is unknown; it is thought to be about 45–50 days (Davis, 1974). The female reproductive tract has been described in detail by Snyder (1977). Females have six mammae, and the one to five (average three to four) young are born in May or June (Grinnell *et al.*, 1937). At birth, the kits average about 4 percent of adult weight, and their eyes and ear canals open in about a month (Toweill and Toweill, 1978). Not until three or four days after birth does the female show hostility toward her mate (Richardson, 1942). Deciduous tooth eruption commences on the 26th day and is completed by the 40th; permanent teeth begin to appear at 90 days, and all are present in another month (Toweill and Toweill, 1978). At eight weeks, the kits begin to accompany their parents on nocturnal hunting forays. Adult pelage has been attained by the 134th day (Richardson, 1942), and the kits are adult-sized by about the 160th (Toweill and Toweill, 1978). The young remain with the female until well into August, at which time weaning occurs and they leave the home den (Taylor, 1954). In Texas, juveniles denned within their mother's home range until they were approximately ten months old (Toweill, 1976).

No food habits data exist for Oklahoma ringtails. In choice of food, ringtails show a decided preference for small mammals, particularly packrats and white-footed mice, but they also consume insects, native fruits, passerine birds, other small mammals, and herptiles, depending on season and availability. Small mammals are apparently most important in spring and winter; arthropods (principally orthopterans) in summer, spring, and fall; and plant material (fruits and berries) throughout the year—particularly in fall (Taylor, 1954; Davis, 1974). Wood (1954) found that cotton rats, cottontails, and white-footed mice constituted 62 percent of the total food volume during winter in east Texas, but only 36 percent of total winter food volume in southwest Texas was mammalian—primarily leporids and cricetid rodents (Taylor, 1954). However, plant material constituted 74 percent, and mammals only 14 percent of the food in 182 scats from southwest Texas collected between October 1974 and April 1975 by Toweill and Teer (1977). Plants consumed most frequently were hackberry, prickly pear, juniper, and persimmon. Other plants preferred by ringtails include mistletoe, barberry, madrone, blackberry, buckthorn, condalia, yaupon, acorns, grapes and plums. Eggs, spiders, scorpions, centipedes, and occasionally lizards, frogs, snakes, and carrion also occur in the diet. Most food habits studies have been carried out in Texas (Taylor, 1954; Wood, 1954; Davis, 1974; Toweill and Teer, 1977) and investigations in Colorado (Lechleitner, 1969). Utah (Trapp, 1973), and California (Grinnell *et al.*, 1937) generally agree with the Texas findings.

Richards (1976) found that *Bassariscus* could achieve a higher urine concentration than any other carnivore. Vocalizations have been studied by Bailey (1974), Richards (1976), Toweill and Toweill (1978), and Willey and Richards (1981). Pence and Stone (1977) and Pence and Willis (1978) described helminth parasites, and Custer and Pence (1979) and Toweill and Price (1976) reported on the ectoparasites of ringtails. Behavioral notes were given by Bailey (1974) and Toweill and Toweill (1978). Grinnell *et al.* (1937) gave a comprehensive account of the biology of this species. The fur, which remains prime much longer than that of the raccoon, is of little importance except for the tail.

The subspecies in Oklahoma is *B. a. flavus* (Hall, 1981).

Procyon lotor (Linnaeus)
Raccoon
Ursus lotor Linnaeus, 1758:48
Procyon lotor: Illiger, 1815:70, 74

Even though nocturnal, the raccoon (*Procyon lotor*) is among the best known of Oklahoma mammals. The black facial mask and ringed bushy tail are diagnostic. Each of the five toes on the long, slender feet bears a nonretractile claw. The soles of the plantigrade hind feet are bare, leaving tracks that resemble a small child's. Color of the upper parts is a variegation of black, off-white, and gray, with suffusions of buff and light brown, with considerable individual variation. The dark underfur is dense, and the long guard hairs are coarse and sparsely distributed on the lighter venter. The face mask, the posterior bases of the short, pointed ears, and the five to seven rings on the tail are black.

Adult raccoons usually weigh between 4.5 and 14 kg (10–30 lbs.), males being larger than females (Stains, 1956). Of more than 400 raccoons live-trapped on the Wichita Mountains Wildlife Refuge between 1955 and 1957, the largest male weighed 12 kg (26.5 lbs.) and the heaviest female 8.6 kg (19 lbs.) (Halloran and Glass, 1959). Total length varies from about 700 mm (27.5 in.) to 960 mm (37.8 in.), the tail usually being slightly less than a third of this (Jackson, 1961). The largest raccoon on record weighed 28.4 kg (62 lbs., 6 oz.). It was a male killed in Buffalo County, Wisconsin, on 4 November 1950 (Scott, 1951).

Raccoons are found throughout the state in all physiognomic regions, but more commonly in the eastern deciduous woodlands, where they can find dens in large hollow trees. Wherever they live, it is seldom far from water,

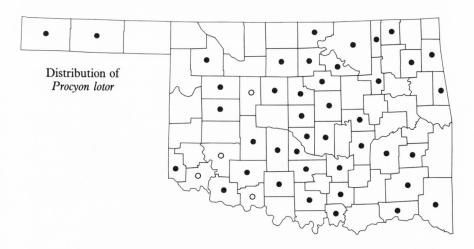

Distribution of
Procyon lotor

where they procure most of their food. In western Oklahoma, they are associated with riparian timber, but large den trees are scarce in this part of the state. Some additional habitat is provided by the woody vegetation around the numerous farm ponds and reservoirs built since World War II. Raccoons may also utilize caves, rock crevices, hollow logs, abandoned muskrat houses, hollows beneath tree roots, squirrel nests, haystacks, and similar refugia as den sites. Dens are used year-round as a home for the family and as a nursery. There are usually several dens within the home range of a raccoon. Temporary refuge may be furnished also by abandoned badger, coyote, woodchuck, or skunk burrows.

Scant information has been recorded about raccoon biology in Oklahoma; however, it is probably similar to that in neighboring states. A raccoon seldom prowls during nights of full moonlight, and usually travels alone except when accompanied by young. Nocturnal movements and behavior were described by Sharp and Sharp (1956). The species does not experience true hibernation in winter, and sleeps (sometimes communally) in the den only during periods of inclement weather. Most hunting is done leisurely along the edges of streams, ponds, or lakes, and always at night. On warm winter days, a raccoon will sometimes be outside the den on a limb, or in a squirrel or hawk's nest. Another factor that may influence nocturnal activity is temperature. Adults may enter a kind of torpid sleep when temperatures fall below −4.4° C (24° F), but cubs are often active during these colder nights.

Foraging distance varies with food availability, weather, sex, and age. Adult males usually have home ranges of up to 3.2 km (2 mi.) in diameter, depending on terrain, but this may be larger during the breeding season. Females cover less ground. When marked and released, raccoons are known to have traveled as far as 120 km (75 mi.) (Schwartz and Schwartz, 1981).

Not much is known concerning reproduction of Oklahoma raccoons, but the species has been studied elsewhere. Raccoons are promiscuous (males mate with more than one female each year), and breeding commences in February in Texas (Davis, 1974), lasting until about early March. Females can breed at ten months of age, but only about half conceive, ovulation being induced by coitus (Asdell, 1964). Males are not sexually mature until their second breeding season (Stuewer, 1943). The female bears six mammae. Only one litter, ranging from one to seven but averaging three or four, is produced annually. Gestation requires 63 days (Stuewer, 1943). Newborn raccoons weigh about 71 g (2.5 oz.). The eyes of the cubs do not open for 18 to 23 days. Weaning occurs at 10 to 12 weeks, at which time the young weigh about 1.4–1.8 kg (3 or 4 lbs.) and begin to forage outside the den. Apparently the female alone rears the young, and they remain with her through the following winter. They grow slowly, not attaining full adult size until at least the end of their second year (Stuewer, 1943). When a new litter is born in the spring, young of the previous year leave the den. Placental scars do not persist more than a year and, when present, are visible from outside the uterus (Sanderson, 1950).

Raccoons are omnivorous. Their flattened molar teeth are better adapted for crushing vegetable matter than for shearing flesh. Most foraging is done on or near the ground near water. Food is usually dunked before eating, presumably to heighten tactile acuity. To our knowledge, no food habits data exist for Oklahoma raccoons. Along the Neches River in east Texas, acorns and crayfish constituted more than half the yearly diet of raccoons during all seasons. Other foods of lesser importance there were grapes, persimmons, various other fruits, a few fish, birds, and snakes. Insects and miscellaneous invertebrates contributed substantially to the diet (Baker *et al.*, 1945). In the same region, Wood (1954) found that plants made up over 55 percent of the annual diet (primarily acorns, but also yaupon, holly, hackberry, and grapes), with insects second in importance (27 percent), followed by mammals (9 percent). Seton (1925–28) reported that frogs were a staple in summer, supplemented with insects and some mollusks, crayfish, fish, corn, turtle eggs, ducks, poultry, and mice. In Missouri, preferred plant foods were persimmons, grapes, plums, choke cherries, Osage oranges, greenbrier, blackberries, grasses, sedges, corn, acorns, and other nuts (Schwartz and Schwartz, 1981). Important animal prey in that state included crayfish, clams, fish, insects (particularly beetles and grasshoppers), spiders, earthworms, snails, and practically any small vertebrate or its eggs. In northeastern Colorado, Tester (1953) found that 73 percent of the fall diet was plant material, particularly corn, plums, cherries, and grapes, and that 23 percent was animal matter—crayfish, birds, small mammals, insects, and occasionally poultry.

Longevity in the wild is probably not over five or six years, but captives

TABLE 10. Number of raccoon pelts purchased and average price paid by Oklahoma fur dealers, 1967–81. (Oklahoma Dept. Wildl. Conserv.)

Year	No. Pelts Bought	Avg. Price/Pelt	Total
1967–68	2,144	$ 1.15	$ 2,459.00
1968–69	2,304	2.65	6,099.05
1969–70	4,716	1.77	8,354.50
1970–71	385	0.79	303.90
1971–72	882	1.95	1,719.90
1972–73	2,539	4.65	11,802.90
1973–74	12,834	7.09	91,037.88
1974–75	25,749	5.67	140,256.65
1975–76	43,499	8.59	373,489.30
1976–77	47,460	14.24	675,713.60
1977–78	39,165	14.24	557,709.60
1978–79	52,205	20.66	1,078,555.30
1979–80	52,288	18.21	952,119.41
1980–81	45,698	12.47	569,854.06

have lived to be fourteen (Jackson, 1961). Raccoons swim well and are expert climbers but amble about rather slowly on land. They are ferocious when faced with danger, often out-fighting or drowning several dogs before succumbing. They are very curious animals and are quick to "feel" strange objects with their dextrous, sensitive forefeet. Under various circumstances, they utter a "churring" sound, a growl, or a peculiar call, much like that of a screech owl. Schwartz and Schwartz (1981) listed the following diseases known from raccoons: rabies, distemper, tuberculosis, and fungal skin diseases. They also reported several parasites, including ticks, lice, fleas, botfly larvae, nematodes, flukes, and tapeworms. Ellis (1955) and Self and McKnight (1950) studied parasites of raccoons from the Wichita Mountains Wildlife Refuge. Several techniques for aging raccoons have been devised, and these were compared and summarized by Grau *et al.* (1970). Natural raccoon predators include coyotes or great horned owls that catch the young, but vehicles and men with dogs kill far more. Several man-induced changes have adversely affected raccoon populations, including excess cutting of large den trees, overhunting, pollution and silting of streams, inimical use of uplands (including clearing, plowing, and overgrazing), and lowering of the water table (Duck and Fletcher, 1945).

In Oklahoma, this animal provides both sport and furs for hunters and trappers. For example, between 1923 and 1934, 962 were trapped in the Wichita Mountains Wildlife Refuge, and from 1945 intermittently until 1964, 2,068 were taken alive there, 400 during the 1956–57 season alone (Halloran and Glass, 1959). An annual average of 3,136 pelts was sold to

Oklahoma fur dealers during the six seasons between 1938 and 1944, at an average price of about $1.90 per pelt (Duck and Fletcher, 1945). Table 10 reflects the number of raccoon pelts taken over the last few years. The long, durable fur is made into coats, collars, muffs, and trimmings. Young raccoons are purported to be savory when roasted. Near waterfowl nesting grounds in the north, some nest destruction occurs (Jackson, 1961); occasionally some poultry is killed; and in the Midwest, local corn damage may be a problem. But, on balance, the raccoon is beneficial to man because of its food habits and the sport and furs it provides. A good synopsis of the biology of the raccoon in the Southwest was given by Stains (1956).

The subspecies occurring in Oklahoma is *P. l. hirtus* (Nelson and Goldman, 1930).

FAMILY MUSTELIDAE   Skunks, Mink, Badger, Weasels and Allies

Mustela frenata Lichtenstein
Long-tailed weasel
Mustela frenata Lichtenstein, 1831:pl. 42

This is the only weasel that occurs in Oklahoma, and it is so secretive that little is known of its habits. Its low, elongate body, small head, and long, slender tail easily distinguish it from other mammals in the state. From the black-footed ferret, it is recognizable by its much smaller size and the usual absence of a black facial mask. Its low, rounded ears and shortened limbs are further adaptations for a weasel's singular specialization: pursuit of fossorial prey within their own burrows. The upper parts and tail are buff brown, darkening to black on the head and tail-tip. Ventral coloration, even onto the undersides of the legs, is buffy yellow shading to whitish on the chin (with a white bridle in the western Oklahoma races). The tail is usually about half the head and body length. Underfur is close, soft, and covered with long, glistening guard hairs. Adult males are usually about twice as heavy as females, averaging perhaps 220 g (7.75 oz.). Total lengths of adult males average about 400–450 mm (16–17.5 in.); of females, 350–400 mm (14–16 in.). In the parts of its range north of Oklahoma, this species's coat color changes from brown to white in winter ("ermine" refers to any weasel so colored).

Although weasels probably occur in all physiognomic regions of the state, very few specimens have been preserved in museums. The exact status of this species in Oklahoma is unknown. Hall (1951) described in detail the two specimens from the state listed by Blair (1939). One was from Norman, Cleveland County, and the other from 12.8 km (8 mi.) northwest of Still-

315

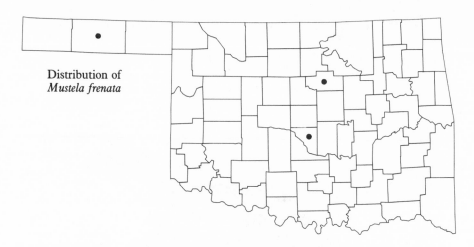

Distribution of
Mustela frenata

water, Payne County. Additional specimens have since been procured from near Guymon in Texas County and from Stillwater. Solitary wanderers that are active mostly at night, these secretive little carnivores are seldom encountered by man. Records show that fur dealers purchased only 167 weasel pelts between 1938 and 1943, as follows: 39 in 1938–39; 44 in 1939–40; 66 in 1940–41; 4 in 1941–42; and 14 in 1942–43. The average price paid for each pelt was about $0.50 (Duck and Fletcher, 1945). During the 1951–52 season, only 2 were bought (Oklahoma Fish and Game Department, 1952). Between 1967 and 1981, only 1 is reported in the annual Oklahoma fur harvest records of the Oklahoma Department of Wildlife Conservation. Even though trappers usually try to avoid taking them, it appears that the weasel population of Oklahoma may have suffered a severe decline over the years.

Little is known about the ecology of Oklahoma weasels. The following information is based on studies from nearby states. Weasels may have several dens. These are often in gopher or ground squirrel burrows, rock crevices, or brushpiles, or among tree roots. Within the confines of a home range of 160 ha (400 acres) or less, they have been known to wander in search of food up to 5.6 km (3.5 mi.) during a single night. They occasionally climb trees in search of small birds or eggs, and they can swim well. Like the mink, weasels rely on their keen sense of smell in tracking down their prey. They do not hibernate but sometimes spend one or two days holed up in their dens.

Food consists primarily of mice and other small rodents. In some areas, gophers or ground squirrels may contribute the bulk of the diet. Rabbits are sometimes taken, as are rats, moles, chipmunks, small birds, and, rarely, insects. On occasion, weasels catch frogs, small snakes and lizards, and tree squirrels. Many animals that are dragged to the den spoil before they can be eaten, for freshly killed prey is much preferred. Weasels will eat one-third their own weight every day, and proportionately more when very young. With their voracious appetite, they are a principal force in checking overpopulations of rodents, and they will even prey on each other. Frequently, they attack prey much larger than themselves. Several food habits studies have been published, including those of Hamilton (1933), Errington (1936), and Polderboer *et al.* (1941).

Weasels can be vicious and aggressive when cornered, often releasing a nauseating musky odor. Because of its diminutive size, the weasel itself is prey for bigger carnivores such as large snakes, hawks, owls, foxes, coyotes, bobcats, and house cats.

The species is promiscuous, and in Oklahoma mating probably occurs in July or August. Because of delayed implantation of the developing embryo, however, as few as 205 or as many as 337 days (average, 279) pass before the four to eight blind, helpless young are born in April or May. Each weighs about 2 g or less. They are furred by three weeks, teeth appear at four weeks, and their eyes open after five weeks of age, when weaning commences. By seven weeks, males are larger than their mother. They remain with her until nearly full-grown. Females reach sexual maturity in three or four months, males at about one year. Reproduction has been studied by Sanderson (1949) and Wright (1948).

The subspecies in Oklahoma are *M. f. primulina* in the eastern two-thirds, *M. f. neomexicana* in the Panhandle and western one-third, and *M. f. texensis* in southwestern Oklahoma (Hall, 1951). The eastern form, *M. f. primulina,* unlike the other two subspecies, lacks the white bridle over its face.

Mustela nigripes Miller
Black-footed Ferret
Putorius nigripes Audubon and Bachman, 1851:297
Mustela nigripes: Miller, 1912:102

The mink-sized body of *Mustela nigripes* is typically musteliform: elongate, small-headed, and short-limbed. Tail length is about one-fourth the combined length of head and body. Unlike the overall chocolate color of the mink's pelage, the dorsal coloration of the ferret's short fur is yellow buff and becomes lighter ventrally. The forehead, muzzle, and throat are whitish. Dark brown areas on the crown and middorsally are conspicuous. The face has a distinct black mask, and the legs, feet, and terminal one-fourth of the tail are black, contrasting with the lighter body color. The light phase of the European ferret or polecat (*Putorius putorius*) has been introduced as a pet species in North America and may escape into the wild. It is similar to *M. nigripes* in size and general coloration except that the guard hairs are longer and the fur is shaggier. The face mask and black on the legs of the polecat are not as prominent as in the black-footed ferret. Except for bridled weasels, weasels lack the face mask. Males usually weigh just over 1 kg (about 2 lbs.), females a bit less; total length of an adult male is approximately 510–560 mm (20–22 in.), and females are about 10 percent smaller (Henderson *et al.*, 1969; Hall, 1981). Females have three pairs of mammary glands.

This is one of the rarest mammals in North America. It is a secretive, nocturnal animal that spends most of its time underground and probably has

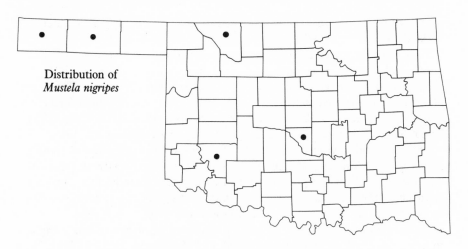

Distribution of
Mustela nigripes

never been numerous. After the original description by Audubon in 1851, it was not reported again for a quarter-century (Young, 1946*a*). Almost nothing is known about the biology of *M. nigripes* in Oklahoma or elsewhere. In the past, black-footed ferrets probably occurred throughout the Panhandle and western half of Oklahoma. Its range was congruent with that of its principal prey, the prairie dog. Intense poisoning campaigns this century, however, have nearly eradicated prairie dogs. Only five Oklahoma specimens of *M. nigripes* are known. One is the skin and damaged skull of a ferret collected one mile east of Norman, Cleveland County, on 25 July 1928, by Fred Barclay and now in the Oklahoma Museum of Natural History of the University of Oklahoma (Arvey and Glass, 1950). Another is a mounted specimen at Northwestern Oklahoma State University in Alva, Woods County, that was collected near Hopeton in the same county (letter to J. D. Tyler from W. Pitts dated 6 April 1967). The third specimen, another mount, was killed southeast of Adams, Texas County, in 1927 and donated to the Oklahoma State University Museum in 1972 by Glen Briles (Lewis, 1973). A skull collected in Cimarron County in 1923 and now in the National Museum constitutes the fourth record (Lewis and Hassien, 1974). Finally, James H. Gaut collected a skull from a prairie dog town near Mountain View, Kiowa County, in 1904; that skull subsequently could not be located in the National Museum (Halloran and Glass, 1964). Hibbard (1934) published a sight record for Texas County, 14 miles south of the Kansas border, in the winter of 1932. Lewis and Hassien (1974) frequently observed ferret signs in prairie dog towns in the Oklahoma and Texas panhandles and investigated 63 sight records that they considered valid. Six of these were of animals that had been killed by automobiles since 1967, but none were preserved. They concluded, as did Tyler (1968), that the black-footed ferret is probably now extinct in Oklahoma.

Four of the five records in Texas nearest Oklahoma were given by Bailey (1905) for Lipscomb, Childress, Baylor, and Cooke counties, and Davis (1974) mentioned an additional recent record from Dallam County. Choate *et al.* (1982) summarized the history and status of the black-footed ferret in Kansas and listed all specimens and sightings up to 1978. Armstrong (1972) listed three records from Baca County, southeastern Colorado.

Ferrets usually live in the burrows of black-tailed prairie dogs (*Cynomys ludovicianus*). Current evidence indicates that they rely heavily on these rodents as food. Recorded prey other than prairie dogs includes mice, ground squirrels, rabbits, gophers, snakes, ground-roosting birds, and occasional insects (Sheets and Linder, 1969; Henderson *et al.*, 1969).

Little is known of the black-footed ferret's reproductive habits. It is thought to breed in April or May in South Dakota (Henderson *et al.*, 1969). The closely related European ferret has a gestation period of 42 days, which means that birth would probably be in May or June. Comparable dates farther south would probably be somewhat earlier. From the limited information at hand, four young seems to be the normal litter size, and they are reared solely by the mother (Henderson *et al.*, 1969). Sheets *et al.* (1972) studied two litters in South Dakota.

Ferrets apparently do not hibernate, having been seen aboveground in temperatures well below freezing (Henderson *et al.*, 1969). Parasites were studied by Boddicker (1968). A comprehensive bibliography of the species was compiled by Harvey (1970), and life history and management aspects were summarized by Snow (1972).

No subspecies have ever been described for the black-footed ferret.

Mustela vison Schreber
Mink
Mustela vison Schreber, 1777: pl. 127b

A rich chocolate color prevails over the entire body of the mink, except for the white of the chin and occasional white splotches on the throat, chest, or belly. The dark brown color distinguishes the mink from weasels and ferrets, which are similar in size. Otters are much larger. The dense, soft underfur is overlaid with long, glossy guard hairs. Bodily proportions are characteristically weasellike: shortened limbs, small head, and elongated neck, trunk, and tail. The somewhat bushy tail is about one-third the body length. Small, rounded ears and short webs at the bases of the toes are adaptations for aquatic life. Adult males average a third heavier and about 10 percent longer than females, with median weights of around 1 kg (2.25 lbs.) and lengths of 610 mm (2 ft.). Females have three pairs of mammae.

Mink are found throughout the greater part of Oklahoma wherever permanent water is found. Thus, they are more abundant in the eastern two-thirds of the state. Crevices in rocks near water, holes under tree roots, hollow logs, muskrat houses, or mud bank burrows all may serve as dens.

Solitary except during the mating period (February to March), mink are promiscuous breeders (Marshall, 1936). Females bear three to six young

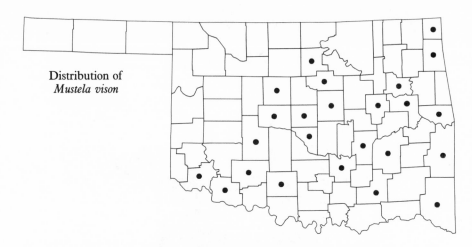

Distribution of
Mustela vison

(usually four) after a gestation period that averages 51 days but, because of delayed implantation of the blastocyst, may last from 40 to 75 days. The young minks are blind and helpless at birth and weigh only about six grams. They grow rapidly and their eyes open at about five weeks. After seven weeks or so, they first venture forth from the nest, and they are weaned at eight or nine weeks. The kits are as large as their parents when five months of age but do not attain sexual maturity until they are 10 months old.

As might be expected of a semiaquatic carnivore of its size and disposition, the mink's food consists of both terrestrial and aquatic prey. We know of no published food habit studies for Oklahoma mink. However, a study of 372 Missouri mink taken in the winters of 1951 through 1953 revealed that preferred foods (in descending order of importance) were frogs, mice and rats, fish, rabbits, crayfish, birds, and lesser amounts of other small vertebrates, arthropods, eggs, etc. (Korschgen, 1958).

The mink does not hibernate but may become inactive for a few days in its den during the colder parts of winter. It is occasionally observed during the daytime but is most active at night, and it frequently prowls about during dawn and dusk. Male mink are solitary wanderers during most of the year and may have a home range up to 8 km (5 mi.) in diameter. For their size, they can run swiftly (seven or eight miles per hour). They often rear up and stand on their hind limbs to look around. Although able to climb trees, they will, if possible, retreat from danger by taking to the water. They usually swim on the surface, but their underwater agility enables them to capture much of their food, including fish. To many people, mink musk is more repugnant and overpowering than that of skunks.

TABLE 11. Number of mink pelts purchased and
average price paid by Oklahoma fur dealers, 1967–81.
(Oklahoma Dept. Wildl. Conserv.)

Year	No. Pelts Bought	Avg. Price/Pelt	Total
1967–68	194	$ 5.62	$ 1,090.28
1968–69	251	7.35	1,843.50
1969–70	216	5.15	1,109.50
1970–71	8	2.00	16.00
1971–72	70	6.05	423.50
1972–73	140	8.00	1,120.50
1973–74	218	13.34	2,908.12
1974–75	356	6.18	2,198.62
1975–76	595	7.52	4,476.75
1976–77	860	13.07	11,238.75
1977–78	676	10.65	7,199.40
1978–79	727	13.54	9,843.58
1979–80	704	18.64	13,123.10
1980–81	1,025	17.08	17,507.00

Aging techniques have been studied by Elder (1951) and Lechleitner (1954). Hibbard (1957) and Birney andFleharty (1966) published their findings on age and sex ratios in mink. The lustrous brown fur of the mink has been valued by man for generations. In Oklahoma alone, an average 5,422 mink pelts annually were purchased from trappers between 1938 and 1952 at an average price of $15.00 each, with exceptional skins selling for $40.00 (Oklahoma Game and Fish Department, 1952). Table 11 lists the number of minks harvested and the average price per pelt for the last few years in Oklahoma.

Mustela vison letifera ranges through western Oklahoma and *M. v. mink* is the subspecies found in the east (Hall, 1981).

Taxidea taxus (Schreber)
Badger
Ursus taxus Schreber, 1778 : 520
Taxidea taxus: Rhoads, 1894 : 524

The badger is a squat, short-tailed, raccoon-sized carnivore with stout, elongated front claws. No other carnivore is so well suited for a fossorial life-style (Hall, 1955). The long dorsal guard hairs are banded, imparting a grizzled, blackish yellow color to the pelage. The tip of each hair is silvery, the midsection blackish, and the base, which blends into the dense underfur of the same color, is yellowish white, as is the belly fur. The unique black and white head pattern is a striking example of disruptive coloration. A conspicuous white stripe, originating on the nose and bordered with black on the head, extends posteriorly along the midline to shoulder level or beyond. Immediately behind the eyes, a vertical area of white juts up from the throat. Just back of this postocular white area and in front of each ear is a roughly triangular patch of black. The edges and backsides of the short, rounded ears are black. Males are larger than females, with total lengths of adults usually between 635–762 mm (25–30 in.), including the bushy tail, 127–152 mm (5–6 in.) long. Adult weights range upward from 4.5 kg to 11.4 kg (10–25 lbs.), but average about 6.4 kg (14 lbs.) (Davis, 1974). Females have four pairs of mammae. Long (1975) reported on molt in badgers.

There are a few reports of badgers from eastern Oklahoma (Taylor, 1965), but they apparently do not inhabit the southeast one-third of the state. The grasslands of western Oklahoma are the badger's preferred habitat, where it preys on ground squirrels and prairie dogs. Badgers prefer loamy, friable

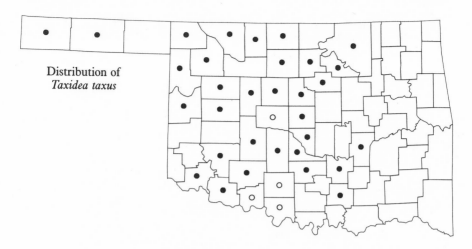

Distribution of
Taxidea taxus

soils where burrowing rodents commonly occur. There is usually a large pile of excavated dirt at the entrance to the badger's distinctively shaped (flat on bottom and domed above) burrow.

Little is known of badgers in Oklahoma, but studies in adjacent states are probably applicable. The badger is chiefly a nocturnal prowler. With its powerful, strongly clawed forelimbs, it quickly and efficiently digs out the holes of burrowing rodents, and it is particularly fond of ground squirrels, pocket gophers, kangaroo rats, and mice. A badger will often take up residence in a prairie dog colony, but when food is scarce, it becomes a wanderer (Bailey, 1905). Badgers also will feed on cottontail rabbits, lizards, birds, eggs, and carrion. Invertebrates, primarily grasshoppers, beetles, and scorpions, may supplement the diet (Errington, 1937; Snead and Hendrickson, 1942).

The mating period lasts through July and August, and females can breed at one year of age. As in many mustelids, the blastocyst does not implant until late winter or early spring of the following year. One to five young are born, "probably in late May or early June" (in Kansas; Hall, 1955), in the grass-lined nest burrow. The female raises the young (Davis, 1974), whose eyes open at four to six weeks of age. The reproductive cycle has been described by Wright (1966, 1969). Young badgers leave the family group in autumn, when they are nearly full grown.

Badgers do not hibernate in the true sense, but store up fat in the fall and subsist on it while sleeping underground, probably during only the most severe periods of winter (Davis, 1974). At other times they are active aboveground.

TABLE 12.   Number of badger pelts purchased and
average price paid by Oklahoma fur dealers, 1972–81.
(Oklahoma Dept. Wildl. Conserv.)

Year	No. Pelts Bought	Avg. Price/Pelt	Total
1972–73	35	$ 3.71	$ 129.96
1973–74	167	5.34	891.00
1974–75	183	5.77	1,055.50
1975–76	183	8.45	1,546.50
1976–77	486	12.36	6,007.00
1977–78	301	11.96	3,599.96
1978–79	470	17.30	8,163.90
1979–80	234	11.75	2,749.25
1980–81	345	7.49	2,584.05

Parasites of badgers have been described by Ellis (1955), Leiby *et al.* (1971), Wittrock and Wilson (1974), Wittrock and Ulmer (1974), and Pence and Dowler (1979).

The badger ordinarily is solitary and retiring unless it is cornered, at which time it can be a formidable antagonist. It prefers to dig itself out of sight quickly or to enter a burrow rather than face a potential opponent. Because of this shyness, and because of its secretive nocturnal habits, the badger is seldom observed. For example, although Tyler (1968) visited prairie dog towns almost daily for a year, he actually saw badgers on only two occasions even though their diggings were common in most of the colonies surveyed.

Economically, badgers are important in controlling injurious rodent populations. There is presently little demand for the pelts, which are of variable quality. Table 12 lists the number of pelts taken from Oklahoma over the last few years. As Bailey (1905) noted: "The rapid increase in the abundance of prairie dogs in certain parts of the State [Texas] and their constant extension of range is unquestionably due in great measure, if not mainly to the destruction of badgers." Badgers also eat large numbers of harmful insects. Poisoned prairie dogs and poisons set out for coyotes probably have killed many badgers each year. Badgers can swim well. A synopsis of the biology of this animal was published by Long (1973).

Two races of *T. taxus* occur in Oklahoma: *T. t. berlandieri* in Cimarron County and most of the main body of the state except the southeastern one-third, and *T. t. taxus* across the northern edge and in the remainder of the Panhandle (Hall, 1981).

Spilogale gracilis Merriam
Western Spotted Skunk
Spilogale gracilis Merriam, 1890:83

Externally, the western spotted skunk (*Spilogale gracilis*) differs from the eastern (*Spilogale putorius*) in its smaller size and overall color pattern. The most obvious differences are in the arrangement and quantity of white composing the stripes and spots. In *S. gracilis*, up to a third of the tail is white toward its tip, but the entire tail of *S. putorius interrupta*, the subspecies in Oklahoma, is black (except that there may be a few white hairs at the very end). The white dorsal stripes of *S. gracilis* are also broader and are not interrupted by black anterior to the lumbar region, whereas the subspecific name of *S. p. interrupta* derives from the fact that its narrower dorsal stripes are frequently broken. Another character that separates the two species is the white patch on the forehead, which is only slightly larger than the eye of *putorius*, but several times as big in *gracilis* (Van Gelder, 1959).

Except for reproductive differences noted in the eastern spotted skunk account, the biology of these two species appears to be quite similar.

Spilogale gracilis is considered by some authorities (for example, Van Gelder, 1959; Hall, 1981) to be conspecific with *S. putorius*, but Mead (1968) demonstrated that their reproductive biology is strikingly dissimilar. Furthermore, the two are isolated geographically and perhaps ecologically in the Black Mesa area of far western Oklahoma (see Van Gelder, 1959; Geluso,

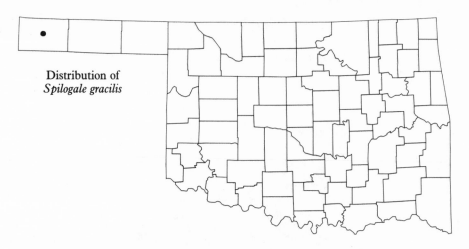

Distribution of
Spilogale gracilis

1972). Only a single specimen is known from the state, and it was taken on top of Black Mesa (Geluso, 1972).

The subspecies in Oklahoma is *S. g. tenuis* (Hall, 1981).

Spilogale putorius (Linnaeus)
Eastern Spotted Skunk
[*Viverra*] *putorius* Linnaeus, 1758:44
Spilogale putorius: Coues, 1875:12

The "civet cat," or eastern spotted skunk, is seldom observed because of its secretive nocturnal habits. *Spilogale* has a white patch on its forehead, in contrast to *Mephitis*, which has a thin white stripe extending from nose to forehead, and *Conepatus*, with its all-black forehead. *Spilogale* also has a unique body pattern, consisting of a white spot under each ear and four or more interrupted white "stripes" on the back and sides. The tip of the tail usually bears a few white hairs. *S. gracilis*, the western spotted skunk, can be separated by traits listed in that account. Weights of male spotted skunks average around 680 g (1.5 lbs.), females' about 450 g (1 lb.) (Davis, 1974). This is roughly about one-fifth the weight of *Mephitis*, and *Conepatus* weighs more than twice as much as *Spilogale*. Total length of both sexes (males are a bit larger) averages 500 mm (about 20 in.).

Spotted skunks are found in diverse habitats over the entire state in all physiognomic regions, but local populations apparently are small and fluctuate in size with changes in man's agricultural practices and other habitat alterations (Choate *et al.*, 1973). Tyler and Lodes (1980) published museum specimen records from the state and found no records from the northeast and southeast corners. Duck and Fletcher (1945) reported that this species "is

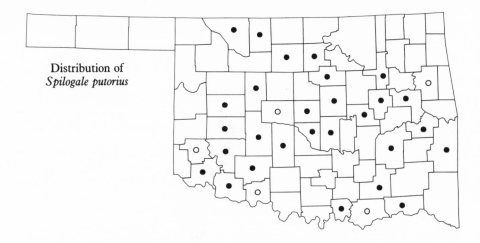

Distribution of
Spilogale putorius

taken in every county with the exception of the western panhandle counties where records are not available."

Little has been published on *Spilogale* from Oklahoma, but information from adjacent states is probably relevant. The skunks seem to prefer rocky canyons and outcrops in woodlands and prairies. They take advantage of the food and cover of farmyards, often making their den beneath a building (Davis, 1974). *Spilogale* is an excellent mouse catcher and will kill or drive off barn rats as well (Hall, 1955). Cracks and crevices among rocks, woodrat nests, hollow logs, and burrows under large rocks seem to be preferred densites. Unlike the striped skunk, *Spilogale* is adept at climbing and can utilize dens in standing hollow trees.

According to reports of fur dealers from the 1930s to the 1950s, the largest populations were in the central and northeastern parts of Oklahoma, and the smallest in southeastern and extreme western portions, particularly the Panhandle. The following numbers of pelts were bought by state fur dealers during the indicated seasons: 1938–39, 19,327; 1939–40, 15,641; 1940–41, 9,604; 1941–42, 7,836; 1942–43, 4,958; 1943–44, 6,234. The average price paid per skin ranged from $0.19 to $0.65 (Duck and Fletcher, 1945). During the 1951–52 trapping season, only 1,220 pelts were purchased (Oklahoma Game and Fish Department, 1952). In the Wichita Mountains Wildlife Refuge in Comanche County, 507 spotted skunks were trapped between 1923 and 1934 (Halloran and Glass, 1959). Table 13 reveals the number of pelts taken from 1967 until recently.

Eastern spotted skunks are omnivorous; they opportunistically prey on almost any invertebrate or small vertebrate and will even eat carrion. Their front claws are more than twice the length of their rear ones, enabling them to dig well. Davis (1974) reported that Texas skunks preferred insects but also

TABLE 13. Number of spotted skunk pelts purchased and average price paid by Oklahoma fur dealers, 1967–81. (Oklahoma Dept. Wildl. Conserv.)

Year	No. Pelts Bought	Avg. Price/Pelt	Total
1967–68	9	$1.20	$ 10.80
1968–69	—	—	—
1969–70	—	—	—
1970–71	—	—	—
1971–72	—	—	—
1972–73	22	1.30	28.65
1973–74	57	2.30	131.25
1974–75	109	1.84	200.56
1975–76	142	2.20	312.55
1976–77	314	7.79	2,445.75
1977–78	299	7.05	2,107.95
1978–79	255	7.36	1,876.80
1979–80	189	6.33	1,197.00
1980–81	167	4.95	826.65

consumed small mammals, fruit, birds, and eggs in summer and fall; cotton-tails and corn were the chief foods in winter, mice and insects in spring. *Spilogale* may be locally destructive to poultry, occasionally raids nests, and sometimes catches game birds or songbirds. But the benefits accrued from destruction of injurious insects and small mammals far outweigh any harm done.

Mead (1968) demonstrated that the eastern spotted skunk (*S. putorius*) and the western species (*S. gracilis*) show pronounced differences in their re-productive cycles. In the former, breeding probably occurs in April, and lit-ters are born late in May or in June with an estimated gestation period of 55–65 days; delayed implantation is unknown. The western species breeds in September, but implantation is delayed until April and young are usually born in May after a gestation of 210–230 days. Female western spotted skunks can breed at four or five months of age, whereas nine or ten are re-quired before the eastern species is sexually mature. Litter size in *S. putorius* ranges from three to seven. Newborn are blind, weigh about 9 g (0.3 oz.), and are covered with fine hair that shows the black and white pattern. Their eyes do not open for approximately a month, and they can spray musk at 46 days. They are weaned on about the 54th day. Sexual maturity is attained in both sexes at nine or ten months. Females have eight mammae.

Spilogale is much more alert and active than the striped skunk. It does not hibernate but stays inside the den in a state of slowed physiological activity during most of the winter, relying on fat stored up the preceding fall. On warm winter days, however, it often emerges and wanders about.

Before spraying, the spotted skunk usually performs a warning behavior consisting of a series of "handstands." Following this, the oily musk is accurately emitted in a fine spray for several feet. Spraying is usually done while the animal is on all fours. Although the musk smells of sulfur, the odoriferous agent, civetone, contains none. To most people the smell of a spotted skunk is muskier and more intensively repugnant than the sulfurous normal butyl mercaptan of the striped skunk. It also is longer-lasting. Acidic liquids, such as tomato juice, vinegar, or lemon juice can help neutralize mercaptans by changing them to esters, but this is not possible with civetone, a 17-carbon cyclic ketone.

Self and McKnight (1950) and Ellis (1955) have reported on parasites of the spotted skunk in Oklahoma.

Van Gelder (1959) considered all of the spotted skunks except *S. pygmaea* of southern Mexico to be a single species, *S. putorius*, but most systematists have not followed him, preferring to consider the western spotted skunk a separate species, *S. gracilis*. The subspecies of *S. putorius* in Oklahoma would be *S. p. interrupta* (Hall, 1981).

Mephitis mephitis (Schreber)
Striped Skunk
Viverra mephitis Schreber, 1776 : 444
Mephitis mephitis: Allen *et al.*, 1902 : 115

One of the best known mammals in Oklahoma is the striped skunk, which is first and foremost recognized by its smell. This "essence of skunk" is the

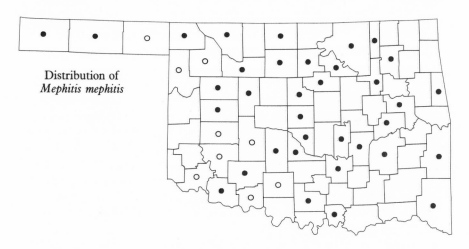

Distribution of
Mephitis mephitis

pungent, sulfurous odor produced by the chemical compound normal butyl mercaptan. Unlike most other mammals, skunks are dark below and light above. A white stripe usually extends from nose to forehead in *Mephitis*. A much broader area of white originates on the crown and runs posteriorly to shoulder level where it splits in two. These stripes usually continue posterolaterally, in some specimens as far as the base of the tail, but the extent of white striping is extremely variable. The blacker the pelt, the higher its value on the fur market (Hall, 1955). Along the tail's undersurface, a narrow band of white progresses rearward, occasionally all the way to the tip. In some specimens it may cover the sides and top of the tail as well; others may have an all-white brush at the tip. The largest of the skunks, *Mephitis* ranges from 2.7 kg to 5.4 kg. (6–12 lbs.) or more, with males usually larger. It is a stout-bodied mammal with moderately short limbs and very dense, long fur. Total lengths of adults vary from just over 500 mm (20 in.) to almost 760 mm (30 in.). Its ambling gait, a sort of "lope," is not unlike that of other members of the family Mustelidae. This species is not likely to be confused with the smaller spotted skunks (genus *Spilogale*), in which the white dorsal stripes are interrupted, or with the rare hog-nosed skunk (*Conepatus mesoleucus*), which is entirely white-backed and inhabits only the Black Mesa region.

Striped skunks are found throughout Oklahoma in all physiognomic regions and seem to prefer habitats ranging from woodland edges and open country to dry upland forests. In western Oklahoma, they show a definite preference for brushy areas and bottomland woods. For refuge, rocky defiles and outcrops often are chosen. Den sites are seldom more than 3 km (2 mi.) from water. Skunks often dig their dens under buildings, use hollow logs, or use burrows dug by other mammals, particularly badgers, armadillos, foxes, and large rodents. Lyle Rexroat, a government pest control agent, reported that, in Kiowa County in 1960 or 1961, he killed about 40 skunks in a prairie dog town with cyanide guns set for coyotes. On a farm near Walters in Cotton County, Pearl Peterson watched an old skunk pull five or six of her kits from a flooded prairie dog hole in the summer of 1966 (Tyler, 1968).

According to Duck and Fletcher (1945), the striped skunk was formerly "The most valuable fur producer in Oklahoma . . . ," and more pelts of this species were taken each year than from any other mammal except the opossum. Between 1938 and 1944, 42 percent of all money paid for furs in the state was for skunk skins, even though they made up only 22 percent of the total number of pelts. The following numbers of striped skunk furs were purchased by Oklahoma fur dealers during the years indicated: 1938–39, 92,948; 1939–40, 95,862; 1940–41, 80,564; 1941–42, 71,443; 1942–43, 54,148; 1943–44, 67,013 (Duck and Fletcher, 1945), and 1951–52, 25,221 (Oklahoma Game and Fish Department, 1952). Price per pelt ranged from $0.63 to $1.89. Table 14 reveals the number of pelts taken and the average price per pelt over the past few years.

Little has actually been recorded about the biology of Oklahoma striped skunks. However, it is probably similar to that of animals occurring in adjacent states, and such information is probably pertinent to Oklahoma skunks. Wade-Smith and Verts (1982) have summarized the biology of this species.

Skunks forage primarily between sundown and dawn, although they are seen occasionally during the day. Because of their long foreclaws, they are excellent diggers. They rely strongly on their keen senses of smell and hearing when searching for food, as their eyesight is poor. Opportunistic feeders, they consume both vegetable and animal matter, the latter consisting principally of insects. In Texas, the percentage of insects in the diet ranged from 96 percent in spring to 52 percent in winter (Davis, 1974). Preference is shown for grubs, ground beetles, grasshoppers, and crickets (Oklahoma Game and Fish Department, 1952). When insects become scarce in winter, skunks depend heavily on small mammals (particularly mice, rats, and cottontails) and on vegetable material (Davis, 1974). Nuts, fruit, berries, eggs, birds, small vertebrates, and carrion are utilized as food. Skunks can inflict considerable damage to poultry and occasionally to game birds and songbirds or their eggs, but on average, their food habits make them much more beneficial than destructive.

Individual skunks—primarily males—are abroad during warm spells all winter (Hamilton, 1937). Males tend to wander farther than females in both spring and fall. Females and young den earlier and remain longer in a state of torpor than do males, which usually den alone. Because females remain in dens throughout the trapping season, they usually survive to breed, thus bolstering local populations. Hall (1955) reported that some dens contain as many as 14 individuals, predominantly females. They emerge in late winter

TABLE 14. Number of striped skunk pelts purchased and
average price paid by Oklahoma fur dealers, 1967–81.
(Oklahoma Dept. Wildl. Conserv.)

Year	No. Pelts Bought	Avg. Price/Pelt	Total
1967–68	82	$0.48	$ 39.36
1968–69	169	0.53	90.25
1969–70	296	0.75	218.90
1970–71	103	0.50	50.80
1971–72	109	0.63	68.67
1972–73	459	0.99	455.90
1973–74	1,547	1.79	2,764.45
1974–75	2,993	2.58	7,369.70
1975–76	2,651	1.32	3,490.06
1976–77	5,466	1.97	10,784.75
1977–78	3,302	1.95	6,438.90
1978–79	4,356	2.19	9,539.64
1979–80	2,710	2.40	6,493.65
1980–81	2,068	1.58	3,267.44

or early spring in a state of emaciation. The number of skunk carcasses along Oklahoma roadsides begins to increase in late February and early March, when males wander widely while seeking females with which to mate. Hall (1955) witnessed males in combat during the last week of February in Kansas. After a gestation period of 63 days, three to seven blind, almost naked kits are born in a nest of dried grass and weed stems (Davis, 1974). Their eyes open between the 17th and 20th days (Hall, 1955). Larger and older females usually produce larger litters (Cahalane, 1961); one litter annually is the rule. The female has 12 mammae and raises the brood; the male lives alone (Hall, 1955). After six or seven weeks, the little skunks are weaned and begin to follow the female, single file. By fall, some of the young are on their own.

If a person moves deliberately and slowly when near a skunk, he is not likely to be sprayed. Skunks have few natural enemies and use their musk defensively. Before they discharge, they usually give several warning behaviors: raising the tail straight up, stamping the front feet, and hissing or growling. Before spraying, the skunk moves so that the anal region points toward its intruder, who by this point should have retreated. The skunk usually will not go through the warning repertoire if the person stands perfectly still or retreats slowly. One who is unfortunate enough to be sprayed can ameliorate the odor with vinegar, tomato juice, or lemon juice, weak acids that change the structure of normal butyl mercaptan from a sulfurous thiol to an ester. Other remedies are gasoline and a fifty-fifty mixture containing oil of bergamot and oil of citronella. For clothing, immersion in ammonia, chloride of lime, dilute sodium hypochlorite, or smoke of burning juniper leaves is effective. Skunk spray is an oily, yellowish secretion from the paired musk glands near the anus and will not cause permanent blindness, as some believe. However, skunks' susceptibility to rabies makes such exposure inadvisable. It is against the law to possess descented skunks because of the inability of current rabies vaccines to protect skunks from getting rabies. In any case, Oklahoma law prohibits the keeping of wild animals in captivity without a license. Because skunks are the principal sylvatic reservoir for rabies in the midcontinental plains, one should avoid handling dead skunks or do so only when wearing gloves and taking extra precautions against coming in contact with their body fluids. Symptoms of active rabies in skunks include aggressive charging, carrying the tail low and trailing when acting aggressively, and apparently having restricted peripheral vision. During aggressive charges, rabid skunks attack only objects that are straight ahead, usually not turning to attack a target that steps aside. But, of course, most skunks are not rabid.

Unless the rigors of starvation are strong enough, carnivores large enough to prey on *Mephitis* seldom do so. One exception is the great horned owl, which takes a considerable toll of skunks.

Available evidence indicates that skunks are major carriers of rabies (Verts, 1967) and leptospirosis (Roth *et al.*, 1963). Other epidemiological diseases, such as distemper and viral infections, sometimes cause massive die-offs, such as the one reported during the spring of 1940 in the Wichita Mountains Wildlife Refuge. It was attributed to a pneumonic epizootic (Halloran and Glass, 1959). Skunks are also especially susceptible to an often fatal filaria worm, great numbers of which sometimes live in skunks' nasal passages and frontal sinuses (Cahalane, 1961). The usual assortment of mammalian ecto- and endoparasites infects them as well. These have been studied in Oklahoma by Self and McKnight (1950). As in any normal animal population, however, diseased skunks constitute only a small percentage of the total.

Two races of the striped skunk occur in Oklahoma and apparently intergrade (Blair, 1939; Hall, 1981). *Mephitis mephitis mesomelas* inhabits eastern sections, and *M. m. varians* is found in the west. Most skunks from central Oklahoma appear to be intergrades.

Conepatus mesoleucus (Lichtenstein)
Hog-nosed Skunk
Mephitis mesoleuca Lichtenstein 1832: pl. 44
[Conepatus] mesoleucus: Merriam, 1902:163

The hog-nosed skunk can easily be distinguished from the other Oklahoma skunks, the common striped skunk (*Mephitis mephitis*) and the much smaller spotted skunks (*Spilogale putorius* and *S. gracilis*). At a distance the entire back and tail appear white, contrasting sharply with the black sides. A few black hairs may be found in the tail, which is shorter than that of *Mephitis* and with much shorter hair. Because of its large front claws and its heavy shoulders, *Conepatus* has earned the epithet "badger skunk" (Cahalane, 1961), while its well-developed, somewhat elongated nosepad, in which the nostrils open downward, accounts for the name "hog-nosed." The nosepad allows it to root about seeking insects, the mainstay of its diet. Females average somewhat smaller than males, and weights of adult *C. m. mearnsi* from Texas range from about 1.1–2.7 kg (2.5–6.0 lbs.) (Davis, 1974). Total body length is usually 560–840 mm (22–33 in.).

In Oklahoma, the hog-nosed skunk is found only rarely in the Black Mesa country at the far western end of the Panhandle. There are only two specimen records for the state—a skull found on the Black Mesa in 1970 and a skin and skull in the U.S. National Museum obtained from Fred Tucker of Kenton, Cimarron County, on 21 December 1927. Glass (1951) reported that another skunk was killed about three miles north of the Black Mesa, probably in the 1940s, by Truman Tucker, and the skin was sent to the state game and fish department, but its whereabouts is now unknown.

The hog-nosed skunk is seldom abundant anywhere in its range. Evidence of its presence is shown by "ploughed" patches of earth where it has rooted, overturning rocks, small logs, and debris in search of food. A favorite root-

Distribution of
Conepatus mesoleucus

ing ground seems to be under piñon pines (*Pinus edulis*). In areas where it is sympatric with *Mephitis*, it seems to make use of similar habitats and, like that species, will occasionally take up residence beneath human dwellings (Cahalane, 1961). Nooks or crannies in rocky places are favored den sites, although the hog-nose may burrow at times. A den will sometimes serve as a nursery (Davis, 1974). To most people, the odor of its musk is indistinguishable from that of *Mephitis*.

Conepatus is primarily insectivorous. In Texas, insects composed about 80 percent of the winter and spring foods and half the diet at other seasons (Davis, 1974). Insects eaten included large beetles and their grubs, grasshoppers, and crickets. Arachnids also were consumed, but in lesser quantities. Some reptiles were eaten throughout the year, but only a few small mammals were taken (during summer and winter). Carrion is also eaten. In summer and fall, vegetation constituted approximately a third of the food, but it was barely represented in winter and spring. Hog-nosed skunks are reported to be fond of ripe prickly pear fruits (Bailey, 1905) as well as various other fruits, berries, and nuts. Poultry may be taken occasionally, and eggs, nestlings, or birds are sometimes consumed.

The species has few enemies. It is mostly nocturnal, although Davis (1974) reported that in central Texas it sometimes forages at midday during winter in a manner similar to that of armadillos. Its pelt is too thin to be of commercial value.

Breeding begins in February in Texas (Davis, 1974), and two or three (rarely four) young are born between late April and early May after a gestation period of some 60 days. By August, most young are weaned and are foraging for themselves. The females have six mammae.

Bailey (1931) reported that *Conepatus* sometimes becomes "moderately fat" in fall, possibly indicating an ability to experience torpor. This probably occurs only during the coldest winter periods.

The type specimen of *Conepatus mesoleucus figginsi*, the race inhabiting Oklahoma, was collected in Furnace Canyon, Baca County, southeastern Colorado, only about eight miles north of the Oklahoma state line (Miller, 1925). This locality is not too far from the northernmost limit of distribution for *Conepatus* in the United States.

Lutra canadensis (Schreber)
River Otter
Mustela lutra Schreber, 1776: pl. 126*b*
Lutra canadensis: Sabine, *in* Franklin 1819–22: 653

The otter is a large, streamlined mustelid with a round tail that is stoutest at the base and tapers evenly to the tip. Webbed toes on very short limbs and a broad, flattened head with small ears are further adaptations for its aquatic life. The dense fur is rich dark brown dorsally, grayish brown below. Males are larger than females and average about 5.4–6.8 kg (12–15 lbs.), although weights up to 10.5 kg (23 lbs.) have been recorded. Length seldom exceeds 1.4 m (4.5 ft.). The only other aquatic mammals that the otter might be con-

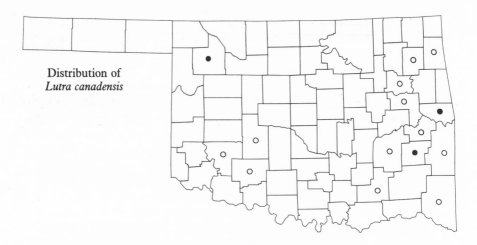

Distribution of
Lutra canadensis

fused with are the mink and muskrat (both much smaller), the beaver (has a broad flat tail), or the nutria (tail is round and scaly).

Otters can catch the swiftest of fish, but crayfish, frogs, and other aquatic animals usually make up most of the diet (Hall, 1955). Birds, mammals, and reptiles are also eaten. Hatcher (1984) reported that the stomachs of two otters taken in Latimer County, Oklahoma, contained predominantly crayfish, three newts (*Notophthalmus viridescens*), a gastropod, and parts of one fish.

After attaining sexual maturity at two years of age, otters mate in March or April and may breed again soon after parturition occurs. Implantation of the blastocyst is delayed for eight months or more, so the total time between fertilization and birth is approximately a year. The two or three blind, toothless young are usually born between late March and May. Their eyes are open by the fifth week of life. The young stay with their mother for about a year, at which time she is preparing to care for a new litter (Davis, 1974).

Dens may be in hollows of trees in or near water, in bank holes, under rocky ledges, in old beaver lodges, or similar situations. Otters do not hibernate. They are active during both daylight hours and dark, but because of their shyness and propensity to wander, they are seldom seen. They can remain submerged while swimming a quarter-mile; however, they are somewhat awkward on land, where the usual gait is a peculiar gallop coupled with a humping of the back (lordosis), which compensates for the shortness of the legs.

Otters usually lead solitary lives, but each will leave his scent at selected locations. Within a family group, their sociability and playfulness are well known. Sensitive and prominent vibrissae and a keen sense of smell probably help offset the otter's less-developed senses of sight and hearing. In some areas, otters are thought to be enemies of muskrats, beaver, and ducks. This may be true in a few places, but is not generally so.

In 1834, August P. Chouteau wrote of shipping more than 19 tons of furs from his trading post near the confluence of the Verdigris, Neosho (Grand), and Arkansas rivers in present-day Muskogee County, northeastern Oklahoma. Sixty-seven of these were otter skins (Foreman, 1926). Captain Randolph B. Marcy, during his exploration of the Red River in 1852, found otters "throughout the valley" (Marcy, 1854). Edwin Palmer, who collected at the Kiowa Agency 17 mi. southeast of Fort Cobb (Caddo County) for the National Museum during the spring of 1867 (Nice, 1931), sent the museum an adult otter skull. Along streams in and near the Wichita Mountains of southwestern Oklahoma, G. W. Conover and an Indian friend named Red Blanket trapped "several otters . . . solely for their hides which were very valuable" in the 1870s (Conover, 1927). James H. Gaut, with the U.S. Biological Survey, visited the Wichitas in 1904 and wrote: "Prof. James Mooney of the Bureau of Ethnology showed me the tanned skin of an otter which had recently been caught in a fish net at Mountain View [Kiowa County]. . . . The former skin has apparently been lost, as there is no record of it in the U.S. National Museum mammal collections" (Halloran and Glass, 1964). Blair (1939) wrote that otters, although rare in 1939, undoubtedly were once common along streams throughout Oklahoma. The only Oklahoma specimen of which he was aware was at the University of Kansas, having been collected in Woodward County, northwestern Oklahoma. At that time, he knew of recent reports from Delaware County (Spavinaw Creek) and Mayes County (Spring Creek), both in the northeastern section of the state. In 1952, the Oklahoma Department of Fish and Game reported that the otter had become "very rare or extirpated . . ." and that the last record of one being trapped was "in 1946 in Sequoyah County" (Oklahoma Fish and Game Department, 1952). This mounted specimen, displayed in the state capitol for many years, is now at the University of Oklahoma.

Since 1971, several otters have been seen or trapped in extreme east central Oklahoma (Bissonette and Maughan, 1978; Hatcher, 1984). Recent water-development projects in the Poteau and Illinois river basins, and the Kerr-McClellan navigation system on the Arkansas River, have created much new habitat that has enabled otters to reoccupy several areas where they had been absent or very rare for decades. In southeastern Oklahoma, five pairs of otters from Louisiana were released into the Wister Wildlife Management Area 21 March 1984, and seven more into McGee Creek Wildlife Management Area on 2 and 5 April 1985, by the Oklahoma Department of Wildlife Conservation (Base, 1986). The races that originally inhabited Oklahoma were *L. c. interior* throughout most of the state and *L. c. texensis* along the southern edge. The Louisiana animals are *L. c. texensis* (Hall, 1981).

Felis concolor Linnaeus
Mountain Lion
Felis concolor Linnaeus, 1771:522

Male cougars are generally much larger than their mates. Young and Gold-man (1946) gave figures for 27 males at least a year old, most from Arizona and Colorado, that averaged 63 kg (140 lbs.); average total length of 31 males was 2.2 m (7 ft. 3 in.). For 19 and 22 females, respectively, the averages were 44 kg (96 lbs.) and 1.9 m (6 ft. 2 in.). The largest of record was taken in Arizona in 1917 and weighed 125 kg (276 lbs.) after the intestines were re-moved; it measured 2.7 m (8 ft. 7 in.) in total length (Young and Goldman, 1946). Individual coloration varies so widely that it is virtually useless in as-signing geographic races. Shades ranging from light brown or gray to rufous or dark tawny have been reported. The tail-tip and backs of the ears are usu-ally black, the venter and rump white. The mountain lion's head appears small for its body size, which is greatest at the hips. The long, rounded tail is more than half the length of the head and body combined.

Deer make up most of the mountain lion's diet. Other prey items include rabbits, porcupines, squirrels, mice and rats, elk, and occasionally domestic stock. Cross (1917) recorded the killing of a pig by a lion near Jefferson in Grant County, Oklahoma, in 1895. Calves, sheep, and goats are also some-times killed by lions, but their favorite domestic animal is the horse, as nu-merous accounts attest.

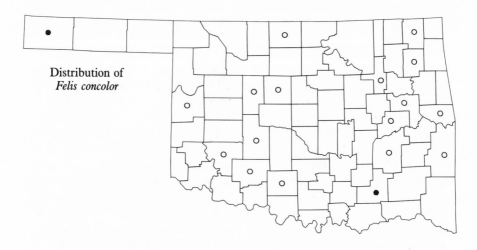

Distribution of
Felis concolor

Mountain lions breed at two to three years of age and pair only during the female's estrus, which is apparently not seasonal (Davis, 1974), although there seems to be a preponderance of spring births. Gestation lasts 87–97 days, and the number of young ranges from two to five, averaging three. At birth, the spotted cubs weigh about 450 g (1 lb.) and have short tails. Their spots disappear with age. They are weaned after two or three months but may remain with their mother for up to two years. Adult females have six functional mammae. They usually mate in alternate years.

The cougar's unmistakable scream has given rise to many folk tales and myths concerning its ferocity and rapacity, but in reality it is a night-wanderer that prefers to avoid man. It roams widely and can travel 40 km (25 mi.) or more in one night. Preferred haunts are the highest, roughest, and most inaccessible regions where deer can be found and man has not intruded. The big cats often wander from one mountain range to another in search of prey, denning beneath rock overhangs or in cliff crevices, thick brush, rock piles, or similar refugia. Pumas are currently classified as "protected predators," and it is illegal to hunt them in Oklahoma. The biology of this species was summarized by Currier (1983).

Historically, the earliest Oklahoma record seems to be "a large panther" mentioned by Lt. J. W. Abert (1845–46) that was flushed by his party in the fall of 1845 from a deep ravine not far from the Canadian River 20 or 30 miles east of "Antelope Buttes" (Antelope Hills), located in northern Roger Mills County. This sighting was probably made a few miles west or southwest of Camargo in present-day Dewey County. In 1851, S. W. Woodhouse (1853), naturalist with the Sitgreaves expedition, reported the sighting of one in Indian Territory near a swamp. On 17 May 1852, Capt. Randolph B. Marcy's expedition killed a lion on one of "the branches of Cache Creek" near its mouth, probably in present-day Cotton County. It measured 2.6 m (8.5 ft.). On 4 July of that same year, another lion was shot as it left a waterhole along Red River in extreme southwestern Oklahoma, more than likely in present-day Harmon or Jackson County (Marcy, 1854). Mead (1899a) described the terrifying scream of two pumas he heard on the Cimarron River in 1868 in what is now Kingfisher County. Conover (1927) recorded the killing of three lions in the mid-1870s in the vicinity of the Wichita Mountains, Comanche County, and that he fired unsuccessfully at a cougar near Marlow, Stephens County. A lion was killed in Grant County in 1895 (Cross, 1917). A skin in the American Museum of Natural History was collected in Indian Territory by J. Q. A. Ward, but neither date nor sex is given. James Gaut (1904) caught one in the Wichitas that sprang his trap and escaped. A veteran forester in the Wichitas, Earl Drummond, reported that the last lion in Comanche County was killed in 1905 and that he last heard one scream in the Wichitas in 1912 (Halloran, 1957). However, long-time caretaker in the Wichitas, Gus McGuire, told Vernon Bailey that the last one killed there was in 1908 (Halloran and Glass, 1959).

Reports of mountain lion sightings persist in Oklahoma. The big cats no doubt wander in occasionally from New Mexico or Arkansas along a major watercourse or through one of the thinly populated regions of the state. However, the distribution of recent sightings or collection of specimens strongly suggests that a few cougars are still native to Oklahoma (Lewis, 1969). Recent records in western Oklahoma include an old skull recovered from a Cimarron County cave in 1938, now in the Oklahoma State University Museum, and the plaster cast of a track taken southeast of Canton Lake, Blaine County, on 13 March 1953 and identified by Bryan Glass as that of a cougar (Merrifield, 1955). On 17 August 1971 one was reported in the Wichitas, and several people watched one near a hayfield about 12 miles west and 2 miles south of Apache, Caddo County, on 7 June 1972 (McClung, 1972). Several reliable lion sightings have been made in the Wichita Mountains Wildlife Refuge very recently (December 1983; August 1984; September 1984), and reports are occasionally received of cougars along the Red River or one of its tributaries in southwestern Oklahoma. An Oklahoma City couple, Brooks and Thula Parkhill, both experienced naturalists, watched an adult at close range for several seconds through binoculars on the morning of 14 May 1978, in Black Mesa State Park in far western Oklahoma (fide, same day, J. D. Tyler; letter to Tyler dated 3 April 1982). A deer hunter killed an adult male lion that weighed 55 kg (121 lbs.) near Reydon, Roger Mills County, on 19 November 1983 (Bean, 1983).

In the eastern part of the state, between 1961 and 1965, twelve issues of the

Daily Oklahoman carried stories of cougar sightings in Craig, Mayes, and Tulsa counties of northeastern Oklahoma (Lewis, 1969). In April 1968, the partially decomposed carcass of a yearling female puma was found at Seven Mile Slough, 10 miles west of Checotah, in McIntosh County. It was estimated to have weighed 68 kg (150 lbs.), and the tail was 711 mm (28 in.) long (Lewis, 1969, 1970). Between Stringtown and Redden in Atoka County, an adult was found dead in late 1975 (Nowack, 1976). Deer, the puma's preferred food, have greatly increased their numbers in the Ozark Mountains and adjacent forests of Arkansas, Missouri, Louisiana, and Oklahoma as man has increasingly vacated the countryside since the end of World War II. Lewis (1969) concluded that a small but viable population of mountain lions had reestablished in this region, hence the recent increase in sightings during the past twenty years. Bissonette and Maughan (1978) cited ten recent records involving a minimum of 14 lions in six southeastern Oklahoma counties. Recent records for Arkansas were summarized by Sealander and Gipson (1973).

In Union County, New Mexico, an adult male weighing 175 pounds was shot by Fred Daniel 36 miles east of Folsom, in the northeast corner of the state, on 20 February 1961 (Golz, 1961). Daniel said that his brother had killed two other lions in the same area since 1961 (*fide* J. D. Tyler). The site of this kill is only 32 miles west of Cimarron County, Oklahoma.

On 12 August 1892, a cub about two or three weeks old was captured near Memphis, Hall County, Texas, in the "Red River Valley" (Prairie Dog Town Fork) and taken to the National Zoo in Washington, where it died in 1900 (Bailey, 1905). A lion alleged to have been killed about 1950 between Hollis, Oklahoma, and Memphis, Texas, may have been the basis of the record shown for Hall County, Texas, on Davis's (1974) map.

Mead (1899*a*) reported that in the 1850s the mountain lion "was occasionally found in central Kansas in its first settlement, was common along the southern line of the state, yet more common in the Indian Territory, now known as Oklahoma. Its habitat was along the timbered streams and the prairies and hills adjacent."

According to the distribution map of Young and Goldman (1946), the subspecies occurring in Oklahoma is *F. concolor stanleyana*. However, they listed no specimens from Oklahoma, and the way that subspecies boundaries on Goldman's map tend to follow the state boundaries separating New Mexico, Colorado, Kansas, Oklahoma, and Texas renders their assignment of subspecies suspect. Probably the specimens from east of the 100th meridian can be logically referred to *F. c. hippolestes* or *stanleyana;* they list three records from just over the line in southwest Kansas, and the recent specimen from northwest New Mexico could just as well belong to any of three subspecies: *stanleyana, hippolestes,* or *azteca.*

Felis rufus Schreber
Bobcat
Felis rufa Schreber, 1777: pl. 109*b*

The bobcat, *Felis rufus*, is larger than a domestic cat, and its very short tail and spotted coat immediately distinguish it from the mountain lion. The varigated color of its upper parts ranges from a grizzled brown to cinnamon to yellowish or gray, and black hairs are almost always mixed in profusion, especially along the spine. The backs of the tufted ears are black and bear a median white spot. The dominant color, however, varies geographically, even seasonally to some extent. The white underparts are usually splotched with black. The tail is only about one-fifth the total length of head and body combined and is 130–155 mm (5– 6 in.) long. There are usually a few black bars atop the tail, but the tip is white. Color is variable but does not conform to geographic differences. Reddish ones have been taken in Cimarron and Washington counties, for example. Likewise, the amount of spotting varies greatly between individuals, again without any relationship to range. Males are larger than females. Total lengths vary from about 650 mm to 900 mm (25–35 in.). Eighteen males, most from Oklahoma, averaged 10.9 kg (24 lbs.) in weight; six comparable females averaged 9 kg (19.8 lbs.), and the overall range was 5.9–15.4 kg (13–34 lbs.) (Young, 1958). The mean weight of 237 bobcats of both sexes from Oklahoma collected between 1979 and 1982 was 7.35 kg (16.2 lbs.) (Rolley, 1983).

The bobcat is found throughout Oklahoma. Bobcats are wily and secretive inhabitants of the rougher broken terrain of western Oklahoma as well as the

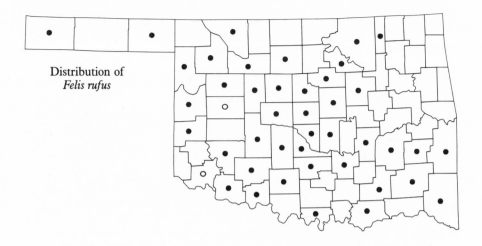

Distribution of
Felis rufus

dense forests, lowlands, and mountains of the east. Although seldom encountered because of their furtive, nocturnal life-style, bobcats are occasionally active during daylight hours. Males have much larger home ranges than females and have ranged 64–77 km (25–30 mi.) in Oklahoma (Gray, in Young, 1958). Rolley (1983) found that the mean home range size of four adult females and seven adult males in southeastern Oklahoma was 14.8 sq. km (5.7 sq. mi.) and 43.2 sq. km (16.6 sq. mi.), respectively. Three home ranges were entirely within forested areas.

Analysis of the stomach contents of 3,538 bobcats from all parts of the United States, but primarily from the west, revealed that rabbits (45 percent of all contents) were the preferred food throughout the year (Sperry, in Young, 1958). Only 57 of these bobcat stomachs were from Oklahoma, but 686 were taken in Texas, 603 in New Mexico, and 13 in Arkansas. Thus, more than one-third of the sample was from the Southwest, and the overall results give a good idea of prey preferred by Oklahoma bobcats. Rodents contributed 46 percent of the total, in the following order: Cricetidae (woodrats, voles, cotton rats, some deer mice, harvest mice, muskrats, and others), 28 percent; Sciuridae (ground and tree squirrels, chipmunks, flying squirrels, prairie dogs, and marmots), 10 percent; Heteromyidae (kangaroo rats and pocket mice), 5 percent; and gophers, porcupines, and other rodents in lesser quantities. Annual averages of other foods were deer (mostly in the form of carrion), 5 percent; livestock (mostly sheep), 2 percent; other mammals (shrews, moles, opossums, raccoons, and skunks), 2 percent; and game birds, non-game birds, poultry, and snakes and lizards (except in winter), 1 percent. Invertebrates, chiefly grasshoppers and beetles, represented only a trace of the total. Rolley's (1983) data on winter food habits are in agreement.

TABLE 15.   Number of bobcat pelts purchased and
average price paid by Oklahoma fur dealers, 1967–81.
(Oklahoma Dept. Wildl. Conserv.)

Year	No. Pelts Bought	Avg. Price/ Pelt	Total
1967–68	7	$ 0.75	$ 5.25
1968–69	27	4.55	122.95
1969–70	50	3.50	174.50
1970–71	45	3.75	169.00
1971–72	49	6.21	304.29
1972–73	199	10.30	2,050.10
1973–74	725	19.90	14,431.10
1974–75	1,458	11.52	16,798.93
1975–76	2,302	37.28	85,822.80
1976–77	3,548	55.49	196,884.50
1977–78	2,244	35.31	79,235.64
1978–79	2,902	83.59	242,578.18
1979–80	2,214	61.61	136,400.35
1980–81	2,782	66.54	185,114.28

Ellis and Schemnitz (1958) found that rabbits (both cottontails and jack rabbits) made up a major part of the contents of 10 stomachs from Cimarron County in far western Oklahoma.

Bobcats are generally solitary. Of 411 Oklahoma specimens examined by Rolley (1983), only 191 (46 percent) were males. Using dental criteria he also calculated the following age structure for 549 animals: 0.5 yrs. (25.7 percent); 1.5 yrs. (31.5 percent); 2.5 yrs. (17.5 percent); 3.5 yrs. (10.4 percent); 4.5 yrs. (6.0 percent); 5.5 yrs. (3.5 percent); ≥ 6.5 yrs. (5.5 percent). Bobcats mate in January or February (usually February in Texas according to Davis, 1974) and are probably promiscuous. In Oklahoma, Rolley (1983) reported that of 220 animals, the pregnancy rate of yearling females was 45.7 percent, significantly lower than that of adults (92.4 percent). After a gestation period of approximately fifty days, two to four young are born in a den that may be under an overhanging rock ledge, in a hollow under a log or root system, in a thicket, or even high in a tree hollow. Mean *in utero* litter size of 154 females from Oklahoma was 2.25 for yearlings and 2.66 for adults (Rolley, 1983). The newborn are blind and covered with spotted fur and weigh only 285–340g (10–12 oz.). In about nine days their eyes open, and they are weaned when about two months of age. Both parents feed the young while the kits are in the den. They remain with their mother until early fall. In Arkansas, males are sexually mature by their second winter, and females when one or two years old (Fritts and Sealander, 1978). Because the hair is brittle, bobcat furs are of little economic value except as trimming for garments. However, demand for "spotted cat furs" by the garment industry in recent years has greatly enhanced the price paid for them by Oklahoma fur dealers (Table 15). Rolley (1985a) reported that Oklahoma populations declined sharply from 1971 to 1981, possibly from trapping pressure. Infrequently and locally, a bobcat sometimes kills small livestock animals, such as sheep or swine, but the total effect of this animal on man's economy is positive, since it devours great numbers of rabbits and rodents potentially damaging to human agricultural interests.

Bobcats have few natural enemies. Occasionally, foxes or great horned owls take the young, and where their ranges overlap, the mountain lion has been known to kill and devour bobcats (Young, 1958). Nunley (1978) found an inverse relationship between the sizes of bobcat and coyote populations in the western United States and attributed direct predation by coyotes to be a major causative factor. Rolley (1985a, 1985b) studied population dynamics and habitat use of Oklahoma bobcats. Parasites of bobcats from Oklahoma and west Texas have been studied by Ellis (1954) and Stone and Pence (1978), respectively. Young (1958) devoted an entire chapter to this interesting aspect of bobcat ecology. Trail and Tumlison (1984) reported on skull anomalies among 285 individuals from Oklahoma.

The western and northwestern form is *Felis rufus baileyi*, the extreme southwestern form is *F. r. texensis*, and the eastern woodland race is *F. r. rufus* (Hall, 1981).

Order Artiodactyla

Deer, Pronghorn, Bison, and Allies

Jack D. Tyler

The artiodactyls are widely distributed throughout much of the world. The mammals in this group are often referred to as ungulates because of the presence of cloven hooves on each foot. In North America, five families occur, three native to Oklahoma: Cervidae (deer, elk), Antilocapridae (pronghorn), and Bovidae (bison).

Cervus elaphus
Wapiti or American Elk
Cervus elaphus Linnaeus 1758:66

Cervus elaphus, the American elk or wapiti, is easily distinguished from the white-tailed deer by its larger size (bulls weighing nearly 272.2 kg or 600 lbs.). Halloran (1968*a*) found that adult male elk butchered at the Wichita Mountains Wildlife Refuge between 1950 and 1965 averaged 255 kg (562 lbs.), two-year-old bulls 213 kg (468 lbs.), and yearlings 161 kg (354 lbs.) The mean weight of adult females was 196 kg (431 lbs.). Compared with herds in other parts of the United States, Oklahoma elk are smaller. This trait might be inherited but may also result from environmental variables such as food, climate, or the lack of calcium in the soils of these granitic mountains.

Elk are generally yellow brown in coloration. The dark brown head and neck (which bears a short mane) contrasts with the dull brownish gray back

351

Distribution of
Cervus elaphus

and sides. The pelage is always darker and redder in summer than in fall and winter, and light and dark colors are usually more intense in bulls. The venter is blackish and the region between the hind legs is white. Wapiti is an Indian name for the elk that means "white deer" and refers to the conspicuous straw- or cream-colored rump. "American elk" derives from the term "elk" used by Europeans for the moose (*Alces alces*).

Males have massive antlers that may attain a length of 1.2 m (4 ft.) or more. Both brow and bez tines develop, and each side of the rack usually bears five or six tines. The entire rack is shed each year between March and May and requires four or five months to grow back fully. Growth ensues immediately after the antlers are dropped.

At birth, male calves have "buttons" which are 2–3 cm (0.78–1.18 in.) long. Yearling bulls develop spikes, but these rarely have brow tines. Young bulls bear proportionately larger racks, but an antler seldom has more than five points. Two-year-olds are often called "raghorns" as a result of their less well developed racks. Females are antlerless.

Formerly, the wapiti enjoyed much wider distribution from southern Canada into California, New Mexico, Arizona, and eastward to northern Georgia. In Oklahoma elk occurred in the western parts of the state at least as far east as the Wichita Mountains, where *C. e. merriami* is known to have lived. Lowery (1974) suggested that the range of *C. e. merriami* might have extended further east because of the specimens which have been recorded in Louisiana. Schwartz and Schwartz (1981) indicated that Wapiti ranged over the entire state of Missouri before the coming of white men. At one time, elk were also quite common in Kansas. During the years from 1859 to 1864, herds of a thousand or more were seen near the village of Lincoln. They remained more or less common in western Kansas until about 1875, but were extirpated prior to 1900 (Hall, 1955; Choate, 1987). Blair (1939) indicated that the herds in western Oklahoma were probably overhunted by settlers, sportsmen, and market hunters. Marcy (1854) noted them in the Wichita Mountains in 1852. Five elk were killed near Mount Sheridan in the Wichitas by General Phillip Sheridan in February of 1869 (Halloran, 1963c). Gaut (1904) reported that an elk was killed on Rainy Mountain in northeast Kiowa County in 1881 and that shed racks were occasionally collected in the same area for a few years thereafter. However, these were the last elk reported in Oklahoma prior to reintroductions in the early 1900s.

A history of the elk herd in the Wichita Mountains was recorded by Halloran (1963c) from whom most of the following comments were taken. A single bull of unknown stock and origin was released into the Wichitas in 1908, a gift from the city of Wichita, Kansas. In 1911, one bull and four cows were brought in from Jackson, Wyoming. These represented the original stock from which the present herd has developed. It is now maintained at about 500 animals. The 1984 count (done by helicopter) tallied 175 bulls, 179 cows, and 100 calves and yearlings (pers. comm., J. Crabtree), but the age ratio and distribution is unknown. The herd is cropped annually by a controlled hunt in early December. Between 1969 and 1972, over 300 elk were removed to eastern Oklahoma in an attempt to reestablish herds there (Stout et al., 1972). They were released into the following wildlife preserves: Cherokee, Cookson, LeFlore, McCurtain, Pushmataha, and Spavinaw. The success has been marginal for these reintroductions because of poaching, wild dogs, and parasitic meningeal worms (Parelaphostrongylus) (Carpenter et al., 1973).

Little is recorded concerning the behavior and ecology of elk in the Wichita refuge. Much of the following was related by Jack Crabtree, refuge biologist. The animals are gregarious except for the mature bulls, which are solitary in spring and summer. No long-term group cohesiveness develops for these elk. Mixed groups of up to 70 or 80 animals may develop during the year, except during the rutting and calving season. These mixed groups consist predominantly of females. Elk usually feed at a slow, walking pace in groups, but they can trot and even gallop. Quite agile, elk have been known to jump fences seven feet high. When startled, a sharp, explosive warning bark is given, and the group may stampede for short distances before stopping to check for danger. If the threat is still evident, the elk often set off single-file at a trot, a pace that can be maintained for hours. Elk can see and hear well, but probably depend on smell to a greater degree to warn them of potential danger.

The breeding season lasts from August to mid-September, ending in November at the latest. After the rack has fully developed, its sensitive velvetlike covering is rubbed off; this usually occurs in October. Then the males begin to "bugle." This flutelike call originates with a low note that explodes upward, rising sharply, then elevates even higher into a shrill, piercing whistle, held a few seconds until it finally trails downward, terminating in three or four coarse "grunts." Its function is probably to establish territories. Rutting season lasts from approximately mid-September through October in the Wichitas. In mid-September mature bulls begin establishing harems that usually average five cows per bull. Younger and less dominant bulls may remain near the harems and attempt to mate. The harem bull expends a considerable amount of time and energy protecting his harem from younger bulls. Frequently, he does not eat during this time and eventually abandons his harem after becoming exhausted. The peak mating period usually extends from September into early October.

Waldrip (1975) studied cow elk habitat in the Wichitas during calving season, and the following remarks are from his work. Cows in spring and summer had a home range that averaged 619 ha (1,548 acres), and they demonstrated no seasonal or yearly habitat shift. All home ranges centered around small mountain complexes. A calf increased the size of its home range with age, and it equaled that of the cow in about two months. Habitat preferred by cows was 25.3 percent closed forest, 65.6 percent intermediate forest interspersed with grasslands, and 9.1 percent open areas. Gestation lasts eight and a half months, and a single calf is born. This usually occurs in May or June, but a few August births have been recorded in the Wichitas. On average, the number of calves per 100 cows was 50 with a survival rate of 94 percent. Incidence of twinning has been as high as 6 percent under extremely favorable range conditions. The pregnancy rate for cows two and one-half years old was about 70 percent, ranging from 30 percent to 100 percent depending on population and environmental conditions. Younger cows had a variable pregnancy rate as high as 40 percent. The female removes herself from the group when the time of parturition nears. Calves are born and hidden in rough terrain, especially boulders and thick woody cover. This probably helps to lower the rate of predation by coyotes and bobcats. The newborn are brownish red with white spots on back and sides; the rump patch is poorly developed. By August, the spots usually disappear. The calf is hidden by the cow for about five weeks and visited by her at least three times per day; at morning, midday, and early evening. Bedding sites are close to boulders and woody cover, areas that are cooler and offer more protection from predators. Even though the calf has a musky smell, the cow locates it by memory and through vocalizations (Waldrip, 1975). The October to December following is the usual period of weaning. White-tailed deer were never observed closer than 45 m (50 yds.) to elk and appeared to avoid feeding with them. Rangers and biologists in the Wichitas reported that elk act with apparent indifference toward the longhorns and bison with which they share the refuge.

The foods of elk in the Wichita Mountains have not been studied but probably consist primarily of grasses, forbs, and shrubs. Common parasites are ticks.

McCullough (1969) has suggested that the red deer of Europe and the wapiti of North America can interbreed in nature. Therefore the two forms are now recognized as a singe species, *C. e. canadensis*. The native subspecies in Oklahoma was *C. elaphus merriami*, but, because of introductions from Wyoming, it is now *C. e. nelsoni*. For perspectives on taxonomy of elk, see Walker (1975), McCullough (1969), and Jones *et al.* (1982).

Odocoileus hemionus (Rafinesque)
Mule Deer
Cervus hemionus Rafinesque, 1817:436
Odocoileus hemionus: Merriam, 1898:100

Mule deer, (*Odocoileus hemionus*), differ from whitetails (*O. virginianus*) in several important respects, notably the way in which the antlers branch dichotomously, the larger ears, and the rounded tail (see whitetail account). The upper pelage is bluish gray in winter (not salt-and-pepper gray, as in the whitetail) and reddish in summer. Ventral areas, as well as a large gular patch, the rump, and tail (except the black tip) are all whitish. A dark patch of coarse hair adorns the forehead, but the muzzle is light in color. The metatarsal gland, 80–130 mm (3–5 in.) long in mule deer, is less than 25 mm (1 in.) in whitetails. Another peculiarity of the mule deer is its high, bound-

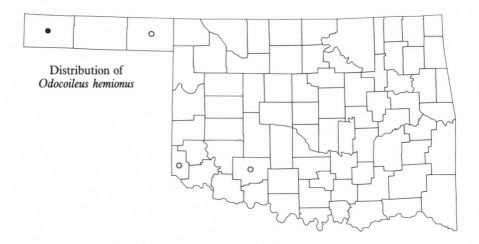

Distribution of
Odocoileus hemionus

ing gait when in full flight. Because size is influenced by many factors, mule deer do not invariably average larger than whitetails.

Mule deer inhabit northwestern Oklahoma and the Panhandle. Infrequent reports indicate that individuals may occasionally wander into southwestern Oklahoma. If so, they would most likely be of the race *O. h. crooki,* which occurs in the contiguous Texas Panhandle (Hall, 1981). Whether or not racial interbreeding occurs is unknown. Clark (1969) reported that mule deer occurred naturally in Oklahoma only in the Mesa de Maya district (Piñon-Juniper Mesas physiognomic region) of northwestern Cimarron County. A transplant of 65 animals by the Oklahoma Department of Wildlife Conservation from Colorado to northwestern Oklahoma in 1965 was unsuccessful (Clark 1967, 1968). Whitetails were released into the Piñon-Juniper Mesas physiognomic region about 1962, and a few could still be seen on the Cimarron River approximately 20 miles to the east in 1969 (Clark and Skryja 1969). However, in 1983, L. E. Dunn (pers. comm., J. D. Tyler) stated that mule deer outnumbered whitetails by more than twenty-five to one along the Cimarron and North Canadian rivers in eastern Beaver County.

Gaut (1904) received reports in the spring of 1904 indicating that the last mule deer seen in the Wichita Mountains was in 1882. This may have been the case, because mule deer historically occurred over the western two-thirds of Kansas, at least in winter (Cockrum 1952). The last mule deer anyone could remember in the vicinity of Mobeetie, Texas, 25 miles west of Beckham County, Oklahoma, was killed in 1896 (Bailey 1905). Bailey (1905), the Texas Game and Fish Department (1945), and Blair (1954) all reported the species from deep canyons near Washburn (Palo Duro Canyon and tributaries) in the south central Texas Panhandle, but, inexplicably, Blair (1939) did not list the mule deer as occurring in Oklahoma.

More open, arid terrain is favored by this species than by its white-tailed cousin. During fall and winter in the Piñon-Juniper Mesas physiognomic region of northwestern Cimarron County, Clark (1968, 1969) found that for retreat and resting cover, mule deer preferred the steep slopes of rocky mesas where grew shrubby one-seeded junipers (*Juniperus monosperma*), hackberries (*Celtis reticulata*), mountain mahogany (*Cercocarpus montanus*), Gambel's oak (*Quercus gambelii*), skunk bush (*Rhus trilobata*), and piñon pines (*Pinus edulis*), subtended with several species of grama grasses (*Bouteloua* spp.) and buffalo grass (*Buchloë dactyloides*). Depending on locality, mule deer may be sedentary (as in Oklahoma), or in mountainous regions they may migrate to low country in winter. Home range size is dependent on food availability and is therefore smallest in summer. Clark (1967) reported that, except for four that died, none of the 65 Colorado deer released in and near Woodward County, northwestern Oklahoma, could be located after five months. He concluded that the species composition and life-form of the vegetation, as well as the topography of the release sites, were ecologically unsuitable to mule deer.

In the Black Mesa region of Oklahoma, Clark (1968) found that, in fall and early winter, mule deer preferred the following foods in approximate order of importance: prickly pear and cholla cacti (*Opuntia* spp.); lamb's quarter (*Chenopodium* sp.); pigweed (*Amaranthus* sp.); various available crops, especially alfalfa (*Medicago sativa*), winter wheat (*Triticum aestivum*), and sorghum (*Sorghum vulgare*); *piñon pine, *mountain mahogany, composites, *one-seeded juniper, toothed euphorbia (*Euphorbia dentata*), beeflower (*Cleome* sp.), *Gambel's oak, *rabbit brush (*Chrysothamnus nauseosus*), *skunk bush, and several grasses and forbs (species marked with an asterisk are well-known foods of mule deer in other states). From studies throughout the West, Rue (1978) compiled a list of seasonal foods eaten by mule deer.

Mule deer are polygamous. Does usually breed at two years of age, bucks at three or four. The height of the rut is normally during November and December but may continue through January. Bucks shed their antlers between mid-January and mid-April, and a new set starts to grow back immediately. Gestation requires approximately 203 days (Asdell 1964). Time of parturition, somewhat dependent on locality, occurs anytime between June and August in Texas (Davis 1974) but usually in May and June over much of the West (Asdell 1964). About 2.7 kg (6 lbs.) is the average weight of a newborn fawn (Davis 1974). Hudson (1959) found an average of 1.66 fawns per doe in Montana. After 60–70 days, the fawns were weaned and began to lose their spots, which were completely gone by September.

The subspecies occurring in Oklahoma is *O. h. hemionus* in the northwest and Panhandle regions and possibly *O. h. crooki* in southwestern Oklahoma (Hall, 1981).

Odocoileus virginianus (Zimmermann)
White-Tailed Deer
Dama virginiana Zimmermann, 1780:24, 129
Odocoileus virginianus: Merriam, 1898:100

The most important big game mammal in Oklahoma is the familiar white-tailed deer, *Odocoileus virginianus*. The mule deer, *O. hemionus*, inhabits primarily the Black Mesa country in the northwestern corner of the Panhandle. A major distinguishing character between the two species is the manner in which the antlers branch: in mule deer, the primary beam, as well as its branches, fork equally and symmetrically, but the tines of a whitetail's rack grow upward from the main lower beam without branching. The enormous ears of a mule deer are also diagnostic, as well as its rounded white tail, tipped with black. The mule deer's tail is surrounded by a large white rump patch and is not held aloft when the animal runs. By contrast, the somewhat flattened tail of *D. virginianus* is longer, dark on top, and usually erect whenever the animal takes flight. Its undersurface and the rump are white, as are the ear linings, insides of the legs, eye rings, bands across the nose, throat patch, and belly. A black spot lies on either side of the chin. Lindzey (1950) discussed pelage color extensively. In general, whitetails have assumed their grayish winter coat by mid-November. This color offers excellent camouflage, and the hair insulates well because it is heavy, dense, and hollow. The

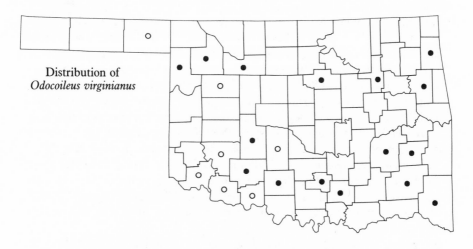

Distribution of
Odocoileus virginianus

molt into the reddish brown summer coat begins in early April and is usually complete by the end of May. By September, the red coat has begun to fade back to gray.

The maximum live weight of an adult buck in Oklahoma is approximately 82 kg (180 lbs.) (Oklahoma Game and Fish Department, 1952), but the average hog-dressed weight (all viscera removed) is 48 kg (106 lbs.), which is equivalent to a live weight of about 60 kg (133 lbs.) (Lindzey, 1950). The average total length, tail length, and shoulder height, respectively, of 73 bucks taken in southeastern Oklahoma were 1,500 mm (59 in.), 250 mm (9.7 in.), and 920 mm (36 in.), and their age classes were 1 1/2 years (40 percent); 2 1/2 years (33 percent); 3 1/2 years (24 percent); 3 1/2 to 5 1/2 years (1.5 percent), and more than 5 1/2 years (1.5 percent) (Lindzey, 1950). Females usually average about 25 percent smaller in all measurements.

Deer frequent edges and clearings in woodlands, where they find the greatest variety of their preferred food plants. Oak-pine forests of the southeast and oaks mixed with hickory and other hardwoods in northeastern Oklahoma provide ideal habitat for feeding and concealment. In much of central Oklahoma, post oak-blackjack forests interspersed with riparian woodlands compose the optimal cover. Timber is essentially restricted to the bottomlands of western Oklahoma, greatly limiting the available deer habitat. Uncontrolled burning and overgrazing by livestock are the primary factors that destroy deer habitat.

The whitetail's choice of diet is largely governed by food availability, and thus varies with locality. Rue (1978) listed seasonally preferred foods, and Atwood (1941) recorded 614 geographically important food species. Acorns are a nutritious staple for deer during fall and winter in Oklahoma and are heavily utilized from late November to mid-March, a time during which competition with cattle is most intense. In southeastern Oklahoma, important fall and winter foods included various parts of several huckleberries (*Vaccinium* spp.), New Jersey tea (*Ceanothus* sp.), dogwoods (*Cornus* spp.), cherry (*Prunus* sp.), greenbriers (*Smilax* spp.), elms (*Ulmus* spp.), oaks (*Quercus* spp.), maples (*Acer* spp.), vibernum (*Vibernum* sp.), and some sedges, grasses, and forbs (Lindzey, 1950). Beginning in June, these additional summer foods were heavily used: grapes (*Vitis* spp.), New Jersey tea, hawthorne (*Crataegus* sp.), dogwood, fringe tree (*Chionanthus* sp.), lespedeza (*Lespedeza* sp.), and beggar's lice (*Desmodium* sp.). Halloran and Glass (1959) reported that greenbrier, elm, grasses, junipers (*Juniperus* spp.), acorns, sumac (*Rhus* spp.), and oak leaves were important foods of deer in the Wichita Mountains Wildlife Refuge. In regions with too many deer, agricultural crops may suffer extensive damage.

The antlers of Oklahoma deer begin regrowing in late April or May after having been shed at some time between December and late March (Oklahoma Department of Wildlife Conservation, 1982). Through the summer they are covered with "velvet," a furlike tissue that supplies them with blood. After full growth is completed in August or September, the bucks start scraping the velvet off on saplings or bushes. This behavior is autoerotic, and the bucks become increasingly aggressive as they assert their dominance. By mid-November, the rut has reached peak intensity, and bucks spend almost all their time and energy in quest of does in heat. Estrus lasts for about 24 hours and occurs at 28-day intervals in females not impregnated during their first heat. Most breeding takes place at night, and each dominant male copulates with several does during the rut. Although female fawns may breed at only six or seven months of age, bucks first breed at about 18 months (Rue, 1978). The gestation period is about 200 days; Armstrong (1950) has described fetal development. Most births in Oklahoma take place in late May or early June, and does bear an average of 1.26 fawns (Lindzey, 1950). First-year does usually bear single fawns, while older does bear two. Triplets are occasionally born, and quintuplets have even been recorded. Females 18 years of age have borne fawns (Rue, 1978). At birth, fawns weigh from 2.3 to 3.7 kg (5–8 lbs.) and are born with their eyes open. Their pelage is a bay or dull red color, dappled with conspicuous white spots. Newborn are usually hidden for 10 to 14 days, with twins being hidden in separate locations. After three or four weeks, the fawns begin to follow their mother and to eat a little solid food. By early fall, they are weaned. Their white spots begin to disappear with the fall molt, but the youngsters remain with their mother until they are sexually mature. A full set of permanent teeth does not develop until they are two years old. Litvaitis and Bartush (1980) studied fawn predation by coyotes in the Wichita Mountains, and additional aspects of fawn biology there were investigated by Bartush and Garner (1979), Bartush and Lewis (1978, 1981), Garner and Morrison (1977, 1980), Garner *et al.* (1976, 1979), Pfister (1984), and Stout (1982).

Home ranges of central Oklahoma deer are about two to six times as large as those in most other parts of the country (Okenfels, 1980), possibly because of the lack of uniformity in food and cover dispersal or to lower quality of available food. In summer, home ranges are smaller and more restricted to riparian forests and wetlands, where the deer seek relief from heat stress and insect pests. Bottomlands also provide the greatest protection from the elements during winter. Lindzey (1950) reported that, in heavily forested southeastern Oklahoma, home ranges averaged about one mile in radius, though some deer undoubtedly ranged farther. Hahn (1945) observed that a radius of one and one-half miles was the maximum home range size for deer in the Edwards Plateau of southwest Texas.

Deer are crepuscular feeders. They normally spend the daytime hours bedded down in thick cover high up on ridges or hillsides, but at night they frequent the low country. Several types of scent glands, vocalizations, and tail movements allow deer to maintain contact (Schwartz and Schwartz, 1981). The flash of the white rump patch and underside of the tail by does is a well-known signal of danger. Deer usually forage head-down, moving into the wind, but nearly always flick their tails just before the head is raised. Several twitches of the tail after danger has passed indicates "all clear." Whitetails may attain speeds up to 56 kph (35 mph) in short spurts and jump obstacles 2.6 m (8.5 ft.) high, and they can swim well. Maximum longevity in the wild is about 12 years, but captives are known to have lived for 19. Does outlive bucks, even without hunting pressures (Rue, 1978).

Parasites and diseases of white-tailed deer have been reported by Whitlock (1939), Van Volkenberg and Nicholson (1943), Anderson (1962), and Rue (1978) and have been summarized by Walker and Becklund (1970). Shaw and Kocan (no date) described 24 parasites from Oklahoma deer, and Kocan *et al.* (1982) and Carpenter *et al.* (1972) also published findings on this subject. Aging techniques were described by Cahalane (1932), Severinghaus (1949), Low and Cowan (1963), Gilbert (1966), and Ranson (1966).

Shortly after Oklahoma Territory was opened to settlement in 1889, market hunting and changes in land use began to reduce the size of the deer population. Only an estimated 500 deer remained in the state in 1917 (Lindzey, 1950). However, the original stock in McCurtain County and in the Wichita Mountains apparently was never extirpated (Lindzey, 1950; Halloran and Glass, 1959). The protection afforded by closed hunting seasons between 1916 and 1933 allowed populations to increase until, by 1940, numbers had reached 5,000–7,000 (Duck and Fletcher, 1945). As a result of annual in-state transplantings begun in 1942 by the Oklahoma Department of Game and Fish, there were approximately 9,500 deer in Oklahoma in 1946 (Oklahoma Game and Fish Department, 1952). Most of these animals were removed from herds in the Wichita Mountains Wildlife Refuge and nearby Fort Sill (Halloran, 1969), although some came from the Lake Murray area in south central Oklahoma and the McAlester Ammunition Depot in Pittsburg County. A 1977 estimate placed the number at 94,000 (Rue, 1978), and one in 1982 at 100,000 (Oklahoma Department of Wildlife Conservation, 1982).

The race that occurs in the eastern part of the state is *O. v. macroura;* that of western Oklahoma is *O. v. texana* (Hall, 1981).

FAMILY ANTILOCAPRIDAE   Pronghorn

Antilocapra americana (Ord)
Pronghorn
Antilope americana Ord, 1815:292
Antilocapra americana: Ord, 1818:149

Because of its superficial resemblance to African antelopes, the pronghorn was believed by many early-day explorers in the American West to be either a true antelope or some type of goat. In fact, its scientific name, *Antilocapra americana*, translates to "American antelope-goat." As this name implies, the species is unique to North America. Some refer to it as the prongbuck, berrendo, or American "antelope," but pronghorn is the preferred name. It is the swiftest of all American mammals, able to run at least 88 km (55 miles) per hour over the spacious shortgrass prairies and sagebrush flats where it lives (Hoover *et al.*, 1959).

Pronghorns are not large ungulates, adult males standing about 865–915 mm (34–36 in.) high at the shoulder, with a total length of about 1,270–1,420 mm (50–56 in.). The tail is 125–180 mm (5–7 in.) long, and the hind

363

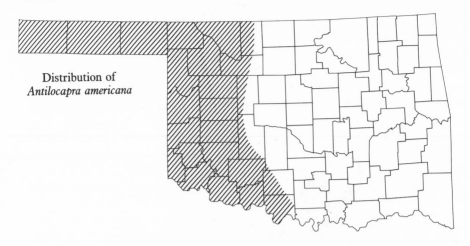

Distribution of
Antilocapra americana

foot measures about 380–430 mm (15–17 in.). Adults seldom weigh much over 46 kg (100 lbs.), and males generally are about 10 percent larger. Weights of both sexes increase with age, and northern animals are bigger overall (Buechner, 1950a; Mitchell, 1971).

The color of a pronghorn's short, coarse pelage is basically light brownish tan, but the chest, belly, sides, and rump (except for the dorsal tail surface) are white. The ventral half of the muzzle, including the cheeks, is also white, as are two broad and distinctive "collars" on the throat and small patches at the bases of the ears. In males, a conspicuous crescent bordering the angle of the jaw and extending upward to eye level, and the dorsal surface of the muzzle, are black. The rump patch, composed of white erectile hairs 10 cm (4 in.) long, is a conspicuous signaling device. The pelage hairs are effective insulation because they are hollow (Hall, 1955).

The pronghorn is the only hollow-horned ruminant that annually sheds its horn sheaths. This occurs soon after the breeding season. In Texas, shedding is from mid-October to early November (Buechner, 1950a); in the Wichita Mountains Wildlife Refuge, it is during November (Halloran and Glass, 1959). Horns, although present in both sexes, are much longer in males (up to 510 mm = 20 in.). "Pronghorn" refers to the diminutive forward-projecting tine about halfway toward the tip; this branching is also unique to horned mammals.

Coronado was probably the first white man to see the pronghorn, and it could have been in present-day Oklahoma because he passed through the northwestern part of the state probably between 1541 and 1542 (Morris *et al.*, 1976). At one time this species probably outnumbered even the great bison herds, and just prior to 1900 a band of pronghorns still roamed near Hobart in Kiowa County (Nelson, 1925). Bailey (1905) reported a small herd still remaining in 1900 about 35 miles northwest of Henrietta in Clay County, northern Texas, approximately 20 miles south of Grandfield in Tillman County, Oklahoma. On the plains around Mobeetie, Texas, 25 miles west of Roger Mills County, Oklahoma, they were "common" in 1901 (Bailey, 1905). In central and western Kansas, Mead (1899b) stated that in 1859 pronghorns were "abundant everywhere in summer, migrating south in winter to the Staked Plains," but Cockrum (1952) reported that numbers in Kansas "fell rapidly after 1890." Sexson and Choate (1981) summarized the history and geography of *Antilocapra* in Kansas. Possibly the earliest documentation of the pronghorn in Oklahoma was on December 8, 1806, near the confluence of the Arkansas River with its Salt Fork, when James B. Wilkinson (Litton, 1957) wrote that "the herds of buffalo, elk, goat [antelope] and deer surpassed credibility." In August, 1820, the S. H. Long Expedition reported "astonishing numbers" along the South Canadian River in western Oklahoma (James, 1823). Marcy (1854) found them "very abundant" along Otter Creek between the North Fork of Red River and the Wichita Mountains during May, 1852. Along the Chisholm Trail near present-day Enid (Garfield County), according to Ben Borroum, "Buffalo, horses, elk, deer, antelope, . . . were all mixed together and it took several hours for them to pass . . . so that we could proceed. . . ." (Drago, 1962). Gaut (1904) indicated that pronghorns were still "numerous" in Old Greer County "as late as 1890," the same year that the last one was seen in Jefferson County (Duck and Fletcher, 1945). They were extirpated from Beaver, Harper, Ellis, and Beckham counties by 1910, but a small band of about 30 animals still survived in Cimarron County to 1945 (Cross, 1917; Duck and Fletcher, 1945). Buechner (1950b) summarized the numerous unsuccessful attempts to reintroduce pronghorns into the Wichita Mountains Wildlife Refuge. Today, pronghorns have made a moderate comeback, and approximately 350–400 animals run free in the Oklahoma Panhandle, primarily in the western two-thirds of Cimarron County (Oklahoma Department of Wildlife Conservation, 1983; *fide* Rod Smith, Western Region Biologist, ODWC, January 15, 1988). The species has been recorded historically in all Oklahoma physiognomic regions except the Cypress-Oak Floodplains, the Oak-Hickory-Pine Ouachita Highlands, and the Oak-Hickory Ozark Plateau.

Pronghorn foods vary widely depending on geographic location, season, availability, competition with livestock (particularly sheep), and moisture content. These ungulates are selective feeders, continually on the move while foraging; thus, overgrazing is unlikely. They relish the buds, flowers, and other succulent parts of food plants. Whenever and wherever available, forbs seem to be preferred (Buechner, 1950a; Hoover et al., 1959; Russell, 1964; Beasom et al., 1981; Sexson et al., 1981). During the colder months, when forbs are unavailable, browse becomes the primary food, especially in more northerly parts of the range (Cole, 1956; Hoover *et al.*, 1959; Dirschl, 1963; Beale and Smith, 1970). Grass is usually of minor importance (but see Schwartz and Nagy, 1976; Skinner, 1922; Hlavachick, 1968). In some regions, cactus (*Opuntia* spp.) contributes significantly to the diet (Russell, 1964; Hlavachick, 1968). Foods have been studied also in several other states conterminous with Oklahoma: western Kansas (Hlavachick, 1968; Sexson *et al.*, 1981), eastern Colorado (Schwartz and Nagy, 1976; Hoover *et al.*, 1959), and eastern New Mexico (Russell, 1964; Beasom *et al.*, 1981).

Two food habits studies have been conducted in Oklahoma, both in the Wichita Mountains Wildlife Refuge. Rouse (1941) reported that of 15 species of plants eaten in winter, resinous skullcap (*Scutellaria resinosa*), stiff-leaved golden aster (*Chrysopsis stenophylla*), narrow-leaved houstonia (*Houstonia angustifolia*), and white heath-aster (*Aster ericoides*) made up the greater part of the diet. Pronghorns also found *Juniperus* highly palatable in the Wichitas during winter, but the abundant grasses there were hardly touched. Of 45 species consumed in late spring and summer (Buechner, 1950*b*), the staples were sensitive brier (*Shrankia uncinata*), stinging nettle (*Tragia ramosa*), and knotweed (*Phyllanthus polygonoides*). Other foods taken in significant quantities included toothed spurge (*Euphorbia dentata*), threecleft greenthread (*Thelesperma trifidum*), and prairie tickseed (*Coreopsis tinctoria*). Grasses constituted only 1 percent of the diet.

Little or no information is available regarding reproduction in Oklahoma; however, it is probably similar to that of surrounding states. In western Texas, Buechner (1950*a*) reported that the rutting season commences as early as the last week of August and may extend into the first week in October. Bucks gather harems that average about seven females. On the Wichita refuge, this takes place in October (Halloran and Glass, 1959). In Colorado, gestation lasts 240–250 days (Tileston, 1962) but is shorter farther south. For instance, Buechner (1950*a*) found that the time of embryonic development encompasses only seven to seven and one-half months (210–225 days) in Trans-Pecos Texas. Time of fawning also varies geographically, being earlier in more southerly parts of the range. In Texas birthing took place between the first part of April and late May in 1947 (Buechner, 1950*a*), and it occurs during May in the Wichita Mountains Wildlife Refuge (Halloran and Glass, 1959), whereas in Colorado parturition peaks the first or second week of June and spans the period between late May and mid-June (Tileston, 1962). Fraternal twins are the rule, but triplets have been recorded, and young does tend to bear single fawns. In Colorado, Tileston (1962) found that the sex ratio among 229 fawns was very near 1:1.

Thirty-one fawns one day old or younger that were weighed by Hoover *et al.* (1959) in eastern Colorado averaged 3 kg (6.75 lbs.), and males were about half a pound heavier than females. Fawn colors are much lighter and more obscure than those of adults and blend extremely well with the surroundings. By two weeks of age the fawns can run well enough to elude predators, and they are independent of their mothers early in the fall (Buechner, 1950a). They are approaching adult size by late fall but do not fully attain it until about two years of age. Both sexes become sexually mature at one year, and does breed regularly at that time; however, they are more successful at breeding after they are two years of age (Tileston, 1962).

The most important predator of the pronghorn is the coyote. This is especially true during severe winters and in major fawning areas. Coyote predation has been documented by Einarsen (1948), Thompson (1949), Udy (1953), Bruns (1969), and others. Only two of 24 pronghorns found dead in the Wichita Mountains Wildlife Refuge showed evidence of coyote predation, and of 100 coyote stomachs collected there, none contained pronghorn remains (Buechner, 1950b). Golden eagles sometimes kill pronghorns, often during winter. Interestingly, they do not always select fawns or disabled animals (see Williams, 1937; Thompson, 1949; Bruns, 1969). Occasional bobcat kills are reported (Einarsen, 1948).

Pronghorns may be infested with a variety of internal helminths, the most important of which seem to be the stomach worm, *Haemonchus contortus*, and the intestinal threadnecked worms, *Nematodirella* spp. and *Trichostrongylus colubriformes* (Lucker and Dikmans, 1945; Bever, 1957; Allen, 1962; Russell, 1964). In the Wichita Mountains Wildlife Refuge, two ticks, *Dermacentor nigrolineatus* (Buechner, 1950b) and *Otobius megnini* (Ellis, 1955), have been reported from pronghorns. Diseases, in particular pinkeye, lumpy jaw (actinomycosis), diarrhea, hemorrhagic septicemia, and pneumonia occasionally affect *Antilocapra;* infrequent unexplained epidemics were reported a century or more ago, when populations were much greater (Van Wormer, 1969).

Methods of aging pronghorns were discussed by Dow (1952), Wright and Dow (1962), and Hoover *et al.* (1959).

Territorial behavior of pronghorns was studied by Bromley (1969) and courtship by Bromley and Kitchen (1974). For a summary of behavior, see Prenzlow (1965), Prenzlow *et al.* (1968), and Kitchen (1974). Literature reviews of *Antilocapra* were prepared by Spillet (1964) and Prenzlow (1965). The biology of this species was summarized by O'Gara (1978).

The race inhabiting Oklahoma is *Antilocapra americana americana* (Miller and Kellogg, 1953).

FAMILY BOVIDAE   Bison and allies

Bison bison (Linnaeus)
Bison
[*Bos*] *bison* Linnaeus, 1758:72
B. [*ison*] *bison* Jordan, 1888:337

The bison is the largest of native North American land mammals. With a conspicuous dorsal hump that slopes gradually to the tail and a shaggy mantle of dark hair over the hump, shoulders, and head, it is unmistakable. The hair is longest on the forehead, beard, breast, and upper forelegs. By contrast, the bison's slimmer midsection and hindquarters appear devoid of hair except for a prominent tuft that tips the short, slender tail. Its glossy black horns are short, curving outward and upward from the head. Pelage color is uniformly blackish brown forward of the shoulders, lighter behind.

In the Wichita Mountains Wildlife Refuge in Comanche County, a herd numbering approximately 625 animals is maintained. Fall (postrut) weights of 55 adult males (five years and older) there averaged 606 kg (1,333 lbs.), and of 79 cows, 391 kg (861 lbs.) (Halloran, 1961). Some weight is lost during the stressful summer rut and spring calving periods, and bison average larger farther north (Park, 1969).

368

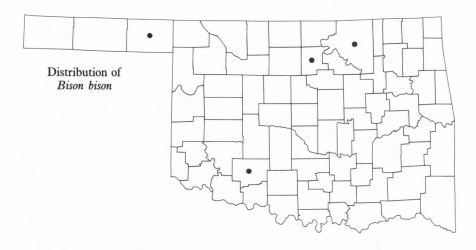

Distribution of
Bison bison

For bison in the Wichita Refuge, Halloran (1961) gave the following average standard measurements of ten adult males: total length, 2,946 mm (116 in.); tail, 394 mm (15.5 in.); hind foot, 605 mm (23.8 in.); ear from notch, 140 mm (5.5 in.); height at shoulder, 1,684 mm (66.3 in.), and for 13 females: 2,637 mm (103.8 in.); 345 mm (13.6 in.); 549 mm (21.6 in.); 132 mm (5.2 in.); and 1,400 mm (55.1 in.).

Most male bison reach sexual maturity at three years, although a few do so at two. Rutting occurs in June and July in the Wichita refuge (Halloran and Glass, 1959). Heifers rarely breed at one year of age, some at two years, but most after they are three. In the Wichita refuge, 6 of 45 heifers (13 percent) bred when two years old, but 24 of 35 (73 percent) mated at three years, and none in their first year. A large percentage of cows three years and older calved every other year (Halloran, 1968b). Cows are polyestrous, so mating may occur several times during the rutting season (Park, 1969). Cows remain in heat for at least two days (Asdell, 1964). Gestation requires about nine months (Brown, 1936), calving usually taking place in late March and early April in the Wichita refuge (Halloran and Glass, 1959), but later farther north. However, it may occur at almost any time of year (Park, 1969). Twins are virtually unknown. Only two instances of twins were recorded among 5,633 births in the Wichita Refuge (Halloran, 1968b). Birth weight is usually between 13 kg and 18 kg (30–40 lbs.) in the Wichitas (*fide* J. A. Howard).

Males slightly but consistently outnumber females at birth (Palmer, 1916; McHugh, 1958; Fuller, 1962); for example, 51 percent of 5,633 calves born on the Wichita refuge were males (Halloran, 1968b). The mother's milk is sparse but very rich, and calves usually suckle for only three or four months (Roe, 1970). The newborn's coat color is bright yellowish red or tawny, and calves are able to run with the herd after only a few days (Garretson, 1938). Young bison usually remain with their mothers until the following spring, or later if she does not conceive that year. The mother and other adults in the herd protect the newborn calves (Garretson, 1938), which are usually weaned in late fall (Davis, 1974). Longevity in the wild state was probably around 25–30 years, but individuals close to 50 years of age are known (Garretson, 1938). There seems to be no completely reliable method of aging bison past 4.5 years (Park, 1969).

In North America bison are generally called "buffalo," but true buffalo of the genus *Bubalus* are confined to Africa and Southeast Asia. It has been estimated that at least 60 million bison roamed the continent prior to 1800 (Seton, 1925–28). This animal was so prevalent during the last century that "buffalo" or "bison" were incorporated into numerous place names. In Oklahoma there is a Buffalo Creek, a Buffalo Springs, and the small town of Bison, all in Garfield County. Another Buffalo Creek in Harper County flows near the town of Buffalo, the county seat. An old stagecoach stopover in Pittsburg County was long known as Buffalo Station.

The first white man to see bison in what is now Oklahoma was probably Coronado, who traveled eastward from New Mexico across the southern Texas Panhandle, then north through northwestern (Beaver County?) Oklahoma between 1540 and 1542 (Seton, 1925–28; Morris *et al.*, 1976). In June 1811, George C. Sibley reported that bison were "plentiful" near what is now Blackwell in Kay County, found 600–800 on the Great Salt Plains (Alfalfa County), and killed 27 from a herd of 30,000 not far to the northwest, at "Rock Saline" on "Buffalo Creek" near the Kansas-Oklahoma border (Sibley, 1812). Not far from the three principal branches of the Kiamichi River (Pushmataha County) in southeastern Oklahoma, Thomas Nuttall recorded that plenty of bison were found for food by his party in May 1819 (Nuttall, 1821).

As the Dragoon expedition of June 1834, commanded by Gen. Henry Leavenworth, marched south and west from Fort Gibson, it first encountered bison near the hamlet of Bromide in Coal or Johnston County (Shirk, 1950). Nathan Boone, son of Daniel Boone, while in north central Oklahoma in 1843, estimated that 100,000 buffalo were being killed annually by white hunters and surmised that they would become rare within a few years (Pelzer, 1917). As the Frémont expedition of 1845 traveled eastward along the South Canadian River in October, the last bison they saw were near Norman in what is now Cleveland County (Mower and Russell, 1972). Captain Randolph B. Marcy in May 1852 observed them along Otter Creek in present-day Tillman or Kiowa County, between the North Fork of Red River and the western reaches of the Wichita Mountains (Marcy, 1854). In 1859, Horace Jones, interpreter at Fort Sill, passed continuous herds of buffalo for over 60 miles

along the 100th meridian, now the western border of the main body of Oklahoma (Hornaday, 1889). In about 1867, George W. Reighard, a hunter from
Dodge City, Kansas, reportedly traveled through a continuous mass of bison
"grazing slowly northward" between Pawnee (probably Pawnee Rock), Kansas, and Fort Supply in the Indian Territory, a distance of 175 miles (Roe,
1970). Colonel John S. Crosby, a member of General Phillip Sheridan's staff
during the Indian campaigns of 1867–68 and 1869 in western Oklahoma,
western Kansas, and the Texas Panhandle, wrote that bison "covered the
whole country in detached herds, numbering from 5,000–20,000, as far as
the eye could see." He further related that one day in 1868, after having
marched from Fort Supply (northwest Woodward County) since daylight,
General Sheridan halted his detachment at 4:00 P.M. on top of the "divide"
between the Cimarron and "Lower Canadian" (probably the North Canadian) rivers (in northern Beaver County?) and asked the 11 members of his
staff to estimate the number of buffalo they had seen that day. Present were
William F. ("Buffalo Bill") Cody and Gen. George A. Custer. The average
estimate: 243,000 (Garretson, 1938). "In 1872, whilst on a scout for about
100 miles south of Fort Dodge to the Indian Territory, we were never out of
sight of buffalo. . . ." (Blackmore, in Dodge, 1877). Dodge City is 55 miles
north of the Oklahoma border. Relying principally on records supplied by
the railroads, Allen (1876) stated that in the immediate vicinity of Fort
Dodge, Kansas, at least 100,000 bison were killed in 1872–73; many of these
were doubtless taken in the Indian Territory. Choate (1987) has chronicled
the extirpation in Kansas. The last buffalo known in Tillman County, southwestern Oklahoma, was killed in 1878, and in Beckham County, in 1885
(Duck and Fletcher, 1945). The final four survivors of the great southern
herd were killed in 1889 in the Texas Panhandle south of the Beaver (North
Canadian) River near Buffalo Springs, a place not far from Cimarron County,
Oklahoma (Garretson, 1938). Park (1969) gave an excellent chronological
recapitulation of the bison's extirpation in North America between 1830
and 1900.

Historically, the bison's most important predators were wolves, which constantly followed the large herds, opportunistically culling the old, the inca-
pacitated, or the very young animals. Even solitary adult bulls were not immune to their attacks. Grizzlies occasionally killed bison. The primary killers
according to Seton (1925–28), however, were the iced-over rivers during the
spring thaw. Thousands of bison drowned each spring, particularly in the
north, when the enormous weight of the crossing herds caused the ice to give
way. Indians with horse and gun took considerable numbers after 1800, as did
bogs, fires, natural precipices, and blizzards (Seton, 1925–28).

Bison are, of course, subject to the same diseases as cattle, but in the wild
seem to have been amazingly free of disease, and no serious epidemics have

been reported in present-day animals (Rorabacher, 1970; Park, 1969). Insect pests include mosquitoes and several species of flies (Park, 1969). Roudabush (1936) could find no fever ticks (*Boophilus annulatus*) on 13 bison at the Wichita refuge in 1935. Stomach worms (*Haemonchus contortus*), a tapeworm (*Moniezia benedini*), and lungworms (*Dictyocaulus viviparous*) are the most important internal parasites (Rorabacher, 1970). Several studies on parasites and diseases of buffalo have been published, for example, Frick (1951), Locker (1953), Choquette *et al.* (1961), Novakowski, *et al.* (1963), and Fuller (1962).

Bison, like cattle, are grazers, but are hardier and less selective of the plants they eat. During winter they simply "muzzle" through the snow to find food. Grass is the chief food on the shortgrass plains (Garretson, 1938; Larson, 1940; Peden, 1976). For example, Peden (1976) reported that bison in northeastern Colorado ate 36 different species of plants, 11 of which contributed significantly to the diet. In terms of both percentage cover and utilization, blue grama (*Bouteloua gracilis*) and buffalo grass (*Buchloë dactyloides*) were the most abundant grasses. However, western wheatgrass (*Agropyron smithii*) appeared to be preferred over either of them. Other species consumed in quantity were red three-awn (*Aristida longiseta*), sedge (*Carex* spp.), scarlet globemallow (*Sphaeralcea coccinea*), sand dropseed (*Sporobolus cryptandrus*), and needle-and-thread (*Stipa comata*). In the Wichita Mountains Wildlife Refuge, the most preferred species were blue grama and sand dropseed, followed by windmill grass (*Chloris verticillata*), *Paspalum* spp., and buffalo grass, but the ubiquitous little bluestem (*Schizachyrium scoparium*) was only sixth in order of preference (Martin *et al.*, 1951). Bison will travel a long way to find water, but can go for long periods without it (Roe, 1970). Feeding chiefly in early morning and late afternoon, bison normally rest and ruminate during mid-day and at night.

Keen of smell but with poor eyesight, bison maintain contact by uttering hoglike grunts. They are ordinarily mild-mannered—even dull—animals, but indicate aggressiveness by a "snort" or a growling, guttural bellow with head up and mouth agape (Park, 1969) and by erecting the tail. Social behavior and herd composition have been studied by Seton (1925–28), Garretson (1938), McHugh (1958), Fuller (1960), Lorr (1974), and others.

The plains bison, *Bison bison bison*, is the only subspecies (Hall, 1981) ever to range into Oklahoma in historic times.

Domesticated and Exotic Species

William Caire

Eight common domesticated species of mammals occur in Oklahoma. These are dogs (*Canis familiaris*), cats (*Felis catus*), horses (*Equus caballus*), donkeys or asses (*Equus asinus*), pigs (*Sus scrofa*), cattle (*Bos taurus*), goats (*Capra hircus*), and sheep (*Ovis aries*).

The dog and cat are primarily kept as pets. However, many are either lost or abandoned, and feral groups may occur. The domestic dog has been known to hybridize with coyotes and in the past with wolves.

Cattle are an important part of Oklahoma's agricultural economy and played a major role in the pioneering of the state. During the late 1800s several cattle trails (the Great Western, the Chisholm, the West Shawnee, the East Shawnee, and the Jones and Plummer trails) crossed Oklahoma. A herd of longhorn cattle is maintained in the Wichita Mountains Wildlife Refuge (Halloran, 1958, 1962, 1965), and they can be found on a number of ranches in Oklahoma. The horse was and still is an important part of the cattle industry in Oklahoma. Today, the horse industry has become a separate entity with a greater emphasis on show horses and racing. No wild horses at present occur in the state, but in the nineteenth century wild mustangs were observed on the prairies by Washington Irving on his tour of the state.

Pigs, goats, and sheep are also important livestock, but to a much lesser extent than cattle and horses. Feral pigs occur in southeastern Oklahoma. Recent reports of feral pigs have come from the Arbuckle Mountains.

In addition to the domesticated species, several exotic species have been brought into the state for various purposes. Numerous exotics exist in zoos and zoological parks for the enjoyment by the public, for educational purposes, and for preservation of threatened forms. Several private ranches and other concerns have a few exotic species (for example, longhorn cattle, Scottish Highland cattle, bighorn sheep, llamas, fallow deer, and axis deer). At

Fort Sill near Lawton there is a small herd of Barbary sheep. Many smaller exotic species of mammals are sold as pets (for example, chinchillas, hamsters, gerbils, European rabbits, European ferrets, kinkajous, coatimundi, and monkeys, to name a few).

Great care should be taken to insure that exotics are not allowed to become established as free-living populations. In most cases when exotics become established, native species are adversely affected.

Species of Unverified Occurrence

William Caire

Because of the close proximity of recorded specimens in adjacent states and the presence of similar habitats in Oklahoma, several additional species of mammals might eventually be found to occur in Oklahoma. These species are the southeastern shrew (*Sorex longirostris*) in Missouri and Arkansas, Botta's pocket gopher (*Thomomys bottae*) in Colorado, and the southern bog lemming (*Synaptomys cooperi*) and the least weasel (*Mustela nivalis*) in Kansas. To date these species have not to our knowledge been collected in Oklahoma, but their possible existence here should not be discounted. A brief account of each follows.

No specimens of the southeastern shrew (*Sorex longirostris*) are known from Oklahoma; however, specimens have been taken in southeastern Missouri (Schwartz and Schwartz, 1981) and northwestern Arkansas (Sealander, 1979) in habitats similar to some in eastern Oklahoma, increasing the chance that this shrew could eventually be found in the state.

The southeastern shrew may be distinguished from the short-tailed shrews (*Blarina carolinensis* and *B. hylophaga*) and the least shrew (*Cryptotis parva*) by a longer tail (usually more than half as long as the body). From the desert shrew (*Notiosorex crawfordi*), it can be separated by its less prominent ears and brownish rather than gray dorsum. *Sorex longirostris* also differs cranially from *Notiosorex* by having five instead of three unicuspid teeth (see key). The third unicuspid of the southeastern shrew is usually smaller than or about equal to the size of the fifth unicuspid. *Cryptotis* has four unicuspids, and the fourth is much smaller, is displaced medially, and is not in view when the skull is examined from the side. *Blarina* has five unicuspids.

The habitat of the southeastern shrew is usually wet environs: stream sides, bogs, marshes, etc. However, specimens have also been taken in upland forest areas.

The subspecies most likely to be found in Oklahoma would be *S. l. longiro-stris* (Hall, 1981).*

Thomomys bottae, Botta's pocket gopher, has been taken within 40 km (25 mi.) of the extreme northwestern edge of Oklahoma near Kim, Colorado (Moulton *et al.*, 1979), and its occurrence in native shortgrass habitats of the piñon-juniper-mesa region of Oklahoma should not be ignored.

To our knowledge, no recent records of the southern bog lemming (*Synaptomys cooperi*) exist from Oklahoma. This small mouse, usually less than 155 mm (6.1 in.) in total length, can be distinguished from other rodents in Oklahoma by its short tail that is rarely longer than the hind foot and by the groove located close to the outside border on each upper incisor. The upper parts are grayish cinnamon brown, and the underparts are plumbeous or cream-colored.

The records of *Synaptomys* closest to Oklahoma are from 22.4 km (14 mi.) southwest of Meade, Meade County, Kansas (Hibbard and Rinker, 1942). The specimens from Kansas were collected from the edge of a marsh or bog area fed by artesian springs. Various grasses, rushes, and sedges composed the dominant vegetation. Prior to the capture of the bog lemmings, over 200 cotton rats (*Sigmodon hispidus*) were removed from the marsh along with several deer mice (*Peromyscus maniculatus*), harvest mice (*Reithrodontomys megalotis*), and shrews (*Cryptotis parva*). Horsetails (*Equisetum* spp.) and a large sedge made up a portion of the lemmings' diet. The horsetail stalks were cut into sections about 5 cm (2 in.) long and stacked into a small pile. Distinctive green fecal droppings frequently were found near or under these piles of vegetation.

Habitat similar to that in Kansas occurs along the Beaver River in northwest Oklahoma, and *Synaptomys* may exist there as isolated remnant populations. Hibbard and Rinker (1942) discuss the destruction of large expanses of suitable bog lemming habitat by the early settlers in southwestern Kansas and northwestern Oklahoma.

Pleistocene fossil records of bog lemmings were collected from the XI Ranch in Beaver County, Oklahoma by Hibbard (1940). He referred this material to *Synaptomys bunkeri*.

The subspecies which might exist in western Oklahoma would be *S. c. paludis* (Hibbard and Rinker, 1942). South central and eastern portions of Kansas harbor a second subspecies, *S. c. gossii*, which may also occur across northern Oklahoma (Hall, 1981).

The least weasel (*Mustela nivalis*) is generally thought of as being a more northern species. It occurs in Canada, the north central United States, and

---

*After completion of this book, Taylor and Wilkinson (1988, Southwestern Nat. 33:248) collected a male southeastern shrew in LeFlore County, Oklahoma.

the Appalachian Mountains. Reports exist from northern Kansas (Choate *et al.*, 1979), and the range of this species is apparently expanding southward (Choate, pers. comm.). Choate (pers. comm.) suggests that it may soon be found to occur between Ponca City and Bartlesville in north central Oklahoma.

Mustela nivalis is a small weasel which is brown above and white below. The tail is uniformly brown. In the winter, Kansas specimens may be mottled white or indistinguishable from summer specimens. It will probably be found most often around watercourses such as lakes, ponds, and streams.*

Several other mammal species might have on occasion occurred in Oklahoma, but valid records and documentation for their presence are lacking.

A record of *Felis pardalis*, the ocelot, exists from 4 km (2 1/2 mi.) northeast of Hedley in the east central Panhandle of Texas (Hall, 1981). This site is approximately 96 km (60 mi.) from the Texas-Oklahoma border. Since the environs in southwestern Oklahoma are similar to those near Hedley, the possibility exists that in the past the ocelot may have also occurred in Oklahoma.

The jaguar, *Felis onca*, might have infrequently wandered into Oklahoma within historic times. Old reports exist from adjacent northeastern New Mexico (Findley *et al.*, 1975) and from central Texas (Hall, 1981).

The javelina, or collared peccary, *Dicotyles tajacu*, formerly was found as far north in Texas as the Red River (Davis, 1974). A record exists from Montague County, Texas, just south of Jefferson County, Oklahoma. Individual or small bands of peccaries may also have occasionally crossed into Oklahoma, but to our knowledge, no record exists for the state.

---

*After completion of this book, Clark and Clark (1988, Prairie Nat. 20:134) collected a female least weasel in Cherokee County, Oklahoma.

Appendix 1
Records of Occurrence

Michael A. Mares

This study was based on the holdings of the following institutions which contained significant collections of Oklahoma mammals. The acronym for each institution precedes the institution name.

ACRONYM	*INSTITUTION*
AMNH	American Museum of Natural History, New York
CAMCO	Biology Department, Cameron University, Lawton, Oklahoma
CSUO	Department of Biology, Central State University, Edmond, Oklahoma
ECENT	Department of Biology, East Central State University, Ada, Oklahoma
FMNH	Field Museum of Natural History, Chicago
FWMSH	Fort Worth Museum of Science and History
KU	Museum of Natural History, University of Kansas, Lawrence
MSU	The Museum, Michigan State University, East Lansing
MVZ	Museum of Vertebrate Zoology, University of California, Berkeley
MWSU	Department of Biology, Midwestern University, Wichita Falls, Texas
NWOSU	Northwestern Oklahoma State University, Alva
OKSU	Museum of Natural and Cultural History, Oklahoma State University, Stillwater
OMNH	Oklahoma Museum of Natural History, University of Oklahoma, Norman
OUBS	University of Oklahoma Biological Station, Madill

TMM   Texas Memorial Museum, University of Texas, Austin
TTU   The Museum, Texas Tech University, Lubbock
UIMNH   Museum of Natural History, University of Illinois, Urbana
UMMZ   Museum of Zoology, University of Michigan, Ann Arbor
USNM   United States National Museum, Washington, D.C.

We examined 19,228 specimens in preparing the distribution maps, species accounts, and identification keys. In this appendix only the specimens actually examined are listed. Literature records of specimens which were not examined are not included. Those literature records and significant sight records (if they contribute substantially to the distribution maps) are represented by an open dot on the maps.

The species are listed alphabetically by scientific name. The specific locality data is arranged alphabetically by county, and within a county the localities are arranged alphabetically from point of reference. In the preparation of this appendix, all obvious errors in spelling and locality data on the specimen tags were corrected. All distances were converted to miles, and fractions of miles were recorded in tenths. The distribution map for each species was prepared from this appendix. A single closed dot within a county indicates that at least one specimen of that species was collected from the county.

Antilocapra americana.—Specimens examined (total 12): Oklahoma Territory, 12 (AMNH).

Antrozous pallidus.—Specimens examined (total 143): CIMARRON COUNTY: Carrizo Creek, 1 (OKSU); Asa Jones barn, Kenton, 5 (OKSU); Regnier Ranch, 2 mi. W, 1 mi. E Kenton, 1 (CSUO); Regnier Ranch, 2 mi. S, 1 mi. E Kenton, 1 (CSUO); north side Black Mesa, 6 mi. N Kenton, 5 (OKSU); Pigeon Cave, 2 mi. E, 0.5 mi. N Kenton, 10 (OKSU); 3 mi. N Kenton, 1 (UMMZ); 5 mi. S Kenton, 1 (ECENT); Pigeon Cave, 28 (OKSU); bat cave, Tesesquite Canyon, 2 (USNM); Tesesquite Bat Cave, 20 (OKSU); Tesesquite Canyon Cave, 1 (OKSU). COMANCHE COUNTY: Cache High School, 8 (OKSU). GREER COUNTY: quarry pond, south side Granite Mt., 3 (OKSU); 1 mi. N Granite, 1 (OKSU). WOODS COUNTY: Merrihew Cave, 4 (OKSU); Merrihew Cave, 1 mi. S Kansas border, 1 (OKSU). WOODWARD COUNTY: Alabaster Caverns, 4 (OKSU), 1 (USNM); Owl Cave, 1 (OMNH); Owl Cave, Alabaster Caverns State Park, 26 (OKSU), 2 (OUBS), 7 (USNM); Woodward County, 9 (OMNH).

Baiomys taylori.—Specimens examined (total 1): COTTON COUNTY: 2 mi. NE Burkburnett, Wichita Co., Texas, 1 (MWSU).

Bassariscus astutus.—Specimens examined (total 18): COMANCHE COUNTY: 2 mi. W, 3 mi. N Porter Hill, 2 (CAMCO). GREER COUNTY:

4 mi. S, 4.5 mi. E Granite, Quartz Mt. State Park, 2 (CAMCO); 5 mi. S, 4 mi. E Granite, 1 (CAMCO). JACKSON COUNTY: 7 mi. E Altus, 1 (CAMCO); 1 mi. E, 4 mi. N Warren, 1 (CAMCO). JEFFERSON COUNTY: 2 mi. S, 1 mi. W Oscar, 1 (OMNH). KIOWA COUNTY: North Fork Red River, W Lone Wolf, 1 (CAMCO); 4 mi. N, 2 mi. W Mountain Park, 1 (CAMCO). MCCLAIN COUNTY: 5 mi. W Norman on SH 9, 1 (OMNH). PONTOTOC COUNTY: T3N, R6E, 2 mi. W Ada, 1 (CAMCO); near Ada, 1 (OKSU); 8.5 mi. W, 1 mi. S Ada, 1 (ECENT); 4 mi. W Roff, 1 (ECENT). TILLMAN COUNTY: 8 mi. E, 2.75 mi. N Manitou, 1 (CAMCO); 4.5 mi. N Tipton, 1 (CAMCO). WOODS COUNTY: Waynoka, 1 (OKSU).

Bison bison.—Specimens examined (total 29): BEAVER COUNTY: Beaver County, 11 (KU). COMANCHE COUNTY: Wichita Mountains, 1 (MSU); Wichita Mountains Wildlife Refuge, 1 (KU), 3 (OKSU), 1 (CSUO). NOBLE COUNTY: 101 Ranch, Bliss, 1 (USNM). OSAGE COUNTY: Fairfax (Arkansas River 10 ft. below water level), 1 (OKSU). COUNTY UNKNOWN: North Fork Beaver River, Neutral Strip, Indian Territory, 1 (AMNH); Indian Territory, 1 (AMNH); Oklahoma, 1 (USNM); Oklahoma Panhandle, Adobe Walls, "between S line of Kansas and N line of Texas" (along Oklahoma Panhandle, caught in 1870s), 6 (MVZ); Teepee Creek, Neutral Strip, Indian Territory, 1 (AMNH).

Blarina carolinensis.—Specimens examined (total 3): MCCURTAIN COUNTY: Flat Swamp, 6 mi. (by road) SE Eagletown, 1 (OKSU); Forked Lake, SE Eagletown, 2 (ECENT).

Blarina hylophaga.—Specimens examined (total 159): ADAIR COUNTY: 2.5 mi. E Stilwell, 2 (UIMNH). ATOKA COUNTY: 20 mi. SW Atoka, 2 (OMNH). BRYAN COUNTY: 4.5 mi. SW Colbert, 1 (OUBS). CARTER COUNTY: T1N, R2W, Sec. 34, SARP Site W5, Wildhorse Creek, 1 mi. E SH 74, 1 (OKSU). CLEVELAND COUNTY: Noble, Oklahoma Territory, 2 (FMNH); campus, University of Oklahoma, Norman, 4 (KU); SE Norman, 2 (KU); southwest edge Norman, 1 (OKSU); 3.2 mi. N Norman, 1 (USNM); 4 mi. S Norman, 1 (OMNH); 5 mi. S Norman, 1 (OMNH); 1 mi. S University of Oklahoma campus, 1 (OMNH). COMANCHE COUNTY: Camp Boulder, Wichita Mountains Wildlife Refuge, 1 (OKSU); Wichita Mountains Wildlife Refuge, 1 (USNM); Quanah Parker Lake, Wichita Mountains Wildlife Refuge, 1 (CAMCO); residential area, Wichita Mountains Wildlife Refuge, 1 (CSUO). CREEK COUNTY: Sapulpa, 3 (KU); 3 mi. S, 1 mi. E jct. Hwy 48 & SH 33, 1 (OKSU). GARVIN COUNTY: T3N, R4W, Sec. 25, SARP Site R5, Rush Creek, 1 (OKSU). JOHNSTON COUNTY: 18 mi. NE Tishomingo, 1 (ECENT). KAY COUNTY: 3 mi. W Indian Hills Lodge, 3 mi. E Arkansas Bridge, Ponca City, 1 (OKSU); 2 mi. S, 6 mi. W Ponca City, 2 (OKSU); north bank

mouth Salt Fork, 1 (OKSU); T26N, R2E, SE 1/4 Sec. 18, 2 (OKSU).
KINGFISHER COUNTY: 12 mi. W Hennessey, 1 (OKSU). KIOWA
COUNTY: 17 mi. SE Ft. Cobb, Kiowa Agency, 1 (USNM). LOGAN
COUNTY: T16N, R4W, Sec. 11, 3 (OMNH). MARSHALL COUNTY:
Shay Crossing of Buncombe Creek, 1 (OUBS). MURRAY COUNTY:
Platt Natl. Park, 5 (KU); Travertine Creek, 1 (OKSU). NOBLE COUNTY:
5 mi. W, 3 mi. N Stillwater, 1 (OKSU); 1 mi. E jct. Hwys 177 & 15 W, 1
(OMNH). OKLAHOMA COUNTY: Edmond, 4 (CSUO); N jct. Dan-
forth & Crowning, Edmond, 1 (CSUO); jct. 10th & Rankin, Edmond, 1
(CSUO); 1600 E. Canary, Edmond, 1 (CSUO). OSAGE COUNTY: Osage
Hills State Park, 1 (OKSU); K. S. Adams Ranch, 12 mi. N, 5 mi. E
Shidler, 1,250 ft., 13 (KU). PAYNE COUNTY: Boomer Lake Dam, 4
(OKSU); Camp Redlands, Lake Carl Blackwell, 1 (OKSU); Lake Carl
Blackwell, 10 (OKSU); northwest end Lake Carl Blackwell, 1 (OKSU);
west side Lake Carl Blackwell, 1 (OKSU); T19N, R1E, SE 1/4 Sec. 18,
Lake Carl Blackwell Area, 1 (OKSU); spillway, near Lake Carl Blackwell,
1 (ECENT); Lakeside Golf Course, 1 (OKSU); Ecology Preserve on SH
51, Oklahoma State University, 1 (OKSU); Insectary Bldg., Dept. of En-
tomology, W Stillwater, 1 (OKSU); riparian area, N Oklahoma State Uni-
versity, Botany & Plant Research Fields, 1 (OKSU); Payne County, 3
(OKSU); Boomer Lake, Stillwater, 3 (OKSU); near Boomer Lake, 1 mi.
N Stillwater, 1 (OKSU); Vets Village, Stillwater, 1 (OKSU); Stillwater, 3
(OKSU); 50 yds. N 619 W. 24th St., Stillwater, 1 (OKSU); 150 yds. S
spillway, Lake Carl Blackwell, Stillwater, 1 (OKSU); 1 mi. N Stillwater, 1
(OKSU); 1 mi. W Stillwater on Hwy 51, 0.25 mi. N, 1 (OKSU); 1.5 mi.
W, 1 mi. N Stillwater, 1 (OKSU); 2 mi. E Stillwater, 1 (OKSU); 2 mi. E
Stillwater, 4 mi. S SH 51, 1 (OKSU); 2 mi. E, 1 mi. S Stillwater, 1
(OKSU); 2 mi. N, 0.5 mi. E Stillwater, 1 (OKSU); 2 mi. S Stillwater,
1 (OKSU); 2 mi. S, 0.5 mi. E Stillwater, 1 (OKSU); 2.5 mi. S Stillwater, 3
(OKSU); 2.5 mi. W Stillwater, 1 (OKSU); 2.5 mi. W Stillwater, W on
Hwy 51, then 0.125 mi. N, 1 (OKSU); 3 mi. N, 0.5 mi. W Stillwater, 1
(OKSU); 3 mi. N, 5 mi. W Stillwater, 1 (OKSU); 3 mi. S Stillwater, 2
(OKSU); 3 mi. W Stillwater, 2 (OKSU); Carberry's Farm, 3 mi. W Still-
water, 1 (OKSU); 4 mi. W, 2 mi. S Stillwater, 2 (OKSU); 4 mi. N, 3 mi. S
Stillwater, 1 (OKSU); 4 mi. W, 3 mi. S Stillwater, 3 (OKSU); Lake Carl
Blackwell, 5 mi. W Stillwater, 1 (OKSU); 6 mi. N, 0.5 mi. E jct. US
Hwy 177 & Lakeview Dr., Stillwater, 1 (OKSU); 6 mi. NE Stillwater, 1
(OKSU); 6 mi. W Stillwater, 1 (OKSU); 7 mi. SE Stillwater, 1 (OKSU); 8
mi. W, 0.75 mi. N Stillwater, 1 (OKSU); 10 mi. W Stillwater, 1 (OKSU); 2
mi. W Yale, 2 (OKSU); T18N, R2E, Sec. 2, 1 (OKSU); 1 mi. N jct. Hwys
51 & 81, 1 (OKSU); 3 mi. N Hwy 51 on Hwy 177, 1 (OKSU); 4.5 mi.
S SH 51 on US Hwy 177, 1 (OKSU). PITTSBURG COUNTY: 9 mi.

SE Eufaula, 1 (OMNH). PONTOTOC COUNTY: 7 mi. NE Ada, 1 (ECENT). POTTAWATOMIE COUNTY: Tecumseh, 2 (KU). ROGERS COUNTY: 7 mi. N Claremore, 1 (OKSU). SEQUOYAH COUNTY: Redland, 2 (USNM). TULSA COUNTY: Mohawk Park, 3 (UMMZ); west side Sequoyah Lake, Tulsa, 1 (OKSU); 7 mi. S, 4 mi. E Tulsa, 1 (OMNH). WASHINGTON COUNTY: Bartlesville, 1 (OKSU).

Canis latrans.—Specimens examined (total 762): ADAIR COUNTY: 4 mi. N US 62 on Tyner Creek, 1 (OKSU). BEAVER COUNTY: 3 mi. E Elmwood, 1 (OKSU); 7 mi. SE Turpin, 1 (OKSU). BECKHAM COUNTY: Gibson Ranch, N Erick, 2 (OKSU); S Sayre, 1 (OKSU). BRYAN COUNTY: 2 mi. N Albany, 3 (OKSU); 1 mi. E, 4 mi. N Bennington, 1 (OKSU); 9 mi. S Bennington, 1 (OKSU); 10 mi. S Bennington, 3 (OKSU); 11 mi. SE Bennington, 4 (OKSU); E Bokchito, 1 (OKSU); 5 mi. S Bokchito, 1 (OKSU); 7 mi. S Bokchito, 1 (OKSU); Bryan County, 2 (OKSU); Caddo, 1 (OKSU); 3 mi. E Caddo, 2 (OKSU); 4 mi. E, 2 mi. N Caddo, 1 (OKSU); 5 mi. E Caddo, 2 (OKSU); 6 mi. E Caddo, 1 (OKSU); 5 mi. W, 1 mi. S Durant, 1 (OKSU). CANADIAN COUNTY: G. Miller Farm, Calumet, 1 (USNM); Neneswander Farm, Calumet, 1 (USNM); Calumet, 8 mi. E at Indian School Rd., 3 (USNM); 1 mi. S Calumet, 1 (OKSU). CHEROKEE COUNTY: Tahlequah, 1 (USNM). CHOCTAW COUNTY: Choctaw County, 1 (OMNH); 3 mi. W Ft. Towson, 2 (OKSU). CIMARRON COUNTY: Boise City, 1 (KU); 6 mi. SW Boise City, 2 (USNM); 8 mi. S Boise City, 1 (OKSU); 8 mi. SW Boise City, 3 (USNM); 10 mi. SW Boise City, 3 (USNM); 12 mi. S Boise City, 1 (OKSU); 14 mi. SW Boise City, 4 (USNM); 15 mi. NW Boise City, 3 (OKSU); 16 mi. N Boise City, 1 (OKSU); 16 mi. W Boise City, 1 (OKSU); 16 mi. W, 3 mi. N Boise City, 1 (OKSU); 17 mi. NW Boise City, 1 (OKSU); 17 mi. W Boise City, 1 (OKSU); 18 mi. SE Boise City, 1 (OKSU); 24 mi. W Boise City, 3 (OKSU); canyon, E North Carrizo Creek, 1 (OKSU); 3 mi. W Felt, 1 (OKSU); 5 mi. NW Felt, 1 (OKSU); 6 mi. NW Felt, 1 (OKSU); 8 mi. NW Felt, 1 (OKSU); 8 mi. W Felt, 1 (OKSU); 10 mi. NW Felt, 1 (OKSU); north side Black Mesa, 5 mi. N Kenton, 1 (OKSU); 1 mi. E Watson Crossing, 1 (OKSU). CLEVELAND COUNTY: Cleveland County, 1 (OMNH); McDaniel Ranch, 1 mi. N, 0.25 mi. E Hollywood, 7 (OMNH); Slatter Ranch, 1 mi. E, 2.5 mi. S Lexington, 2 (OMNH); 7 mi. E Lexington, 1 (OKSU); Logan Ranch, 2 mi. S, 2 mi. E Little Axe, 1 (OMNH); Gill Ranch, 1.75 mi. E McKiddyville, 4 (OMNH); Smith Ranch, 7 mi. E, 1 mi. N McKiddyville, 1 (OMNH); Burkett Ranch, 1 mi. S, 1 mi. E Noble, 2 (OMNH); Followill Ranch, 1 mi. S, 7 mi. E Noble, 3 (OMNH); Goad Ranch, 9 mi. E Noble, 1 (OMNH); McKiddy Ranch, 10 mi. E, 1.5 mi. N Noble, 1 (OMNH); Noble, 5 (USNM); Bruehl Ranch, 4 mi. E Norman, 6 (OMNH); Smith Ranch, 2 mi. S, 1 mi. E Norman, 1

(OMNH); 2 mi. SW Norman, 2 (OUBS); 3 mi. W Norman, 2 (KU); 3 mi. E Norman on Lindsey St., 1 (OMNH); Self Ranch, 6.5 mi. E Norman, 13 (OMNH); 9 mi. E, 5 mi. N Norman, 1 (OMNH); George Ranch, 10 mi. E Norman, 1 (OMNH); McKiddy Ranch, 10 mi. E Norman, 1 (OMNH); 20 mi. E Norman, 1 (OMNH); T8N, R2W, Sec. 16, Norman, 1 (OMNH); Mulden Ranch, 15 mi. E, 3 mi. N Purcell, 7 (OMNH); Skinner Ranch, 9 mi. E, 3 mi. S Purcell, 20 (OMNH); Skinner Ranch, 9 mi. E, 3 mi. S Purcell on Hwy 39, 2 (OMNH); Wheeler Ranch, 13 mi. E, 1 mi. N Purcell, 4 (OMNH); Wheeler Ranch, 13 mi. E, 1 mi. N Purcell on Hwy 39, 1 (OMNH); Vaught Ranch, 3 mi. E, 0.75 mi. S Slaughterville, 3 (OMNH); T10N, R4W, Sec. 3, 1 (OMNH); T8N, R1E, Sec. 7, 1 (OMNH); 1.5 mi. E jct. Hwy 9 & US 77, 1 (OMNH). COMANCHE COUNTY: Chattanooga, 4 (USNM); Comanche County, 1 (OKSU); Ft. Sill, 2 (OMNH); east range, Ft. Sill, 4 (CAMCO); 4 Mile Crossing, 3 mi. N, 2 mi. E Ft. Sill, 1 (CAMCO); 5 mi. N, 3 mi. W Indiahoma, 1 (CAMCO); 7 mi. N, 2 mi. W Indiahoma, 1 (CAMCO); 1 mi. N Lawton on H. E. Bailey Turnpike, 1 (CAMCO); Lake Lawtonka, 1 (CAMCO); Mt. Scott Post Office, 3 (USNM); Deer Creek, Wichita Mountains Wildlife Refuge, 3 (OKSU); Medicine Tank, Wichita Mountains Wildlife Refuge, 1 (OKSU); Wichita Mountains, 6 (USNM); Wichita Mountains Wildlife Refuge, 85 (USNM), 1 (OKSU), 1 (OMNH); Wichita Natl. Forest, 1 (KU). COTTON COUNTY: 1 mi. N, 5.5 mi. W Cookietown, 3 (OKSU); 8 mi. W Cookietown, 4 (OKSU); 3 mi. N, 1 mi. S Randlett, 1 (OKSU); 3 mi. N, 1 mi. W Randlett, 1 (OKSU); 10 mi. S Temple, 9 (OKSU); 10 mi. S, 2 mi. E Temple, 1 (OKSU); 5.5 mi. W Walters, 1 (OKSU). CRAIG COUNTY: 5 mi. S, 0.25 mi. W Big Cabin, 1 (OKSU). CREEK COUNTY: 1 mi. S, 1 mi. W Jennings, 1 (OKSU); Mannford, 1 (USNM). CUSTER COUNTY: 3 mi. W Anthon, 1 (USNM); 4 mi. SW Anthon, 2 (USNM); 7 mi. SW Anthon, 1 (USNM); 9 mi. SW Anthon, 1 (USNM); Butler, 1 (USNM). DELAWARE COUNTY: 4 mi. S Cleora, 1 (OMNH). DEWEY COUNTY: Dewey County, 1 (OKSU); Vici, 1 (OKSU). ELLIS COUNTY: 10 mi. S Arnett, 1 (USNM); Ellis County, 1 (OKSU); Harmon, 2 (OKSU); 15 mi. S Harmon, 1 (OKSU). GARFIELD COUNTY: Drummond, 1 (OKSU); 6 mi. W Enid, 1 (OKSU); 5 mi. E, 1.5 mi. N Goltry, 1 (OKSU). GRADY COUNTY: 4 mi. W Blanchard, 1 (OKSU); 2 mi. E Bradley, 6 (OKSU); Chickasha, 1 (OKSU); Bredwell Ranch, 17 mi. W, 5 mi. S Purcell, 6 (OMNH). HARMON COUNTY: Harmon County, 3 (OKSU); 5 mi. E Hollis, 1 (OKSU); Kromer Ranch, Vinson, 5 (OKSU); Overton Ranch, N Vinson, 1 (OKSU); Vinson, 1 (OKSU). HARPER COUNTY: 7 mi. SW Buffalo, 1 (OKSU); north edge Exp. Range, 1 (OKSU). HUGHES COUNTY: 2 mi. W Atwood, 1 (ECENT); near Holdenville, 4 (OKSU); Hughes County, 5 (OKSU); 1 mi. S, 1.5 mi. W Spaulding, 1 (CAMCO); northwestern part of county, 13 (OKSU). JACKSON COUNTY: 1.5

mi. E Altus, 1 (OKSU). JEFFERSON COUNTY: Jefferson County, 1 (OKSU). JOHNSTON COUNTY: E Connerville, 1 (OKSU); W Connerville, 1 (OKSU); 7 mi. W Mill Creek, 1 (OKSU). KINGFISHER COUNTY: 6 mi. N Goole's Bridge, 1 (OKSU). KIOWA COUNTY: Cooperton, 1 (USNM); 1 mi. N Cooperton, 2 (USNM); 2.75 mi. S, 2.5 mi. E Cooperton, 1 (CAMCO); Kiowa County, 2 (OKSU); 6 mi. N Mountain Park, 2 (CAMCO); 2.5 mi. E Snyder, 1 (CAMCO); 5 mi. E, 2 mi. N Snyder, 1 (CAMCO). LATIMER COUNTY: Brushy Narrows, 1 (OKSU). LEFLORE COUNTY: Cache, 3 (USNM); 6 mi. W, 3 mi. N Spiro, 2 (OKSU). LINCOLN COUNTY: 9 mi. NW Chandler, 1 (OKSU). LOGAN COUNTY: 30 mi. W Stillwater, 1 (OKSU); 12 mi. S jct. SH 51 & I-35, 1 (OKSU). LOVE COUNTY: Love County, 2 (OMNH); 1 mi. N, 2 mi. E, Marietta, 1 (OMNH); 0.25 mi. E Marietta, 1 (OKSU); 2 mi. N, 6 mi. W Marietta, 1 (OKSU); 5.5 mi. N Marietta, 1 (OKSU); 6 mi. N, 1 mi. W Marietta, 1 (OKSU); 6 mi. N, 0.25 mi. E Marietta, 1 (OKSU); 6 mi. W, 4 mi. N Marietta, 1 (OKSU). MAJOR COUNTY: T20N, R11E, SE 1/4, 1 (OKSU). MARSHALL COUNTY: 1 mi. N, 5.5 mi. E Madill, 1 (OMNH); 5 mi. W, 2 mi. S Madill, 2 (OKSU); Lake Texoma, 1 (OKSU). MAYES COUNTY: 3 mi. S, 0.75 mi. E Big Cabin, 1 (OKSU); 4 mi. NE Chouteau, 1 (OKSU). MCCLAIN COUNTY: Hester Ranch, 1 mi. E, 3 mi. N Blanchard, 1 (OMNH); Price Ranch, 4 mi. S Cole, 3 (OMNH); Baxter Ranch, 1 mi. E, 1 mi. N Criner, 2 (OMNH); Hardge Ranch, Criner, 3 (OMNH); Hester Ranch, 1 mi. E, 1 mi. S Dibble, 2 (OMNH); 1 mi. S Dibble, 1 (OKSU); Burkett Ranch, 2 mi. S, 0.5 mi. W Noble, 2 (OMNH); S Purcell, 1 (OKSU); Green Ranch, 1 mi. S, 2 mi. W Purcell, 1 (OMNH); Greene Ranch, 2 mi. W Purcell, 1 (OMNH); 3 mi. N Purcell, 2 (OMNH); 8 mi. W Purcell, 3 (OKSU), 2 (OMNH); 8 mi. S, 2 mi. W Purcell, 1 (OMNH); Oakridge Ranch, 9 mi. W Purcell, 4 (OMNH); Hester Ranch, 12 mi. W Purcell, 4 (OMNH); Hester Ranch, 12 mi. W, 1 mi. S Purcell, 2 (OMNH); Bredwell Ranch, 17 mi. W, 5 mi. S Purcell, 1 (OMNH); Jackson Ranch, 4 mi. S, 4 mi. E Rosedale, 1 (OMNH); Thompson Ranch, 5 mi. E, 4 mi. S Rosedale, 1 (OMNH); 1 mi. W Washington, 3 (OMNH); Mayfield Ranch, 1 mi. S Washington, 1 (OMNH); Sharp Ranch, 3 mi. E Wayne, 2 (OMNH); Wood Ranch, 3 (OKSU); Hester Ranch, 1 mi. W Woody Chapel, 1 (OMNH); Lester Ranch, 1 mi. W Woody Chapel, 2 (OMNH). MCCURTAIN COUNTY: approx. 4 mi. S Broken Bow on Hwy 259, 1 (CSUO); Coffee Ranch, 1 mi. W, 2 mi. S Garvin, 5 (OMNH); Idabel, 1 (OMNH); McCurtain County, 1 (OKSU). MCINTOSH COUNTY: 7 mi. W Eufaula, 1 (OKSU). MURRAY COUNTY: Dougherty, Indian Territory, 2 (FMNH). NOBLE COUNTY: near Sumner, 4 (OKSU). NOWATA COUNTY: 5 mi. E, 1.5 mi. S Nowata, 1 (OKSU). OKLAHOMA COUNTY: Edmond, 1 (OKSU); 5 mi. NE Edmond, 1 (OMNH); 2 mi. E, 1 mi. N Moore, 1 (OMNH); T13N,

R4W, Sec. 10, 1 (OMNH). OKMULGEE COUNTY: Okmulgee County, 2 (ECENT). OSAGE COUNTY: Philips Ranch, 10 mi. SW Bartlesville, 28 (OMNH); 11 mi. SE Fairfax, 1 (USNM); Foraker, 1 (KU); Osage County, 11 (OKSU). PAWNEE COUNTY: 1 mi. N, 2.5 mi. W Hallett, 2 (OKSU); 3 mi. E Hallett, 1 (OKSU); 1 mi. S, 2 mi. W Jennings, 2 (OKSU); 2 mi. E Maramec, 2 (OKSU); 2 mi. E, 1 mi. S Maramec, 2 (OKSU); 2.5 mi. E Maramec, 2 (OKSU); 3 mi. E Maramec, 1 (OKSU); 5 mi. N, 7 mi. W Pawnee, 1 (OKSU); 1 mi. N, 1 mi. W Quay, 2 (OKSU); 2 mi. E, 9.5 mi. N Yale, 1 (OKSU). PAYNE COUNTY: 4 mi. N Cushing, 1 (OKSU); near Glencoe, 2 (OKSU); 2 mi. S, 3 mi. W Glencoe, 1 (OKSU); 4 mi. E, 2 mi. N Glencoe, 1 (OKSU); 4 mi. E, 3 mi. S Glencoe, 2 (OKSU); 4 mi. E, 4 mi. S Glencoe, 6 (OKSU); west end Lake Carl Blackwell, 1 (OKSU); Payne County, 1 (OKSU); 5 mi. W Perkins, 1 (OKSU); 7.5 mi. W Perkins Corner, 1 (OKSU); 11 mi. W, 4 mi. S Perry, 1 (OKSU); near airport, Stillwater, 1 (OKSU); near Stillwater, 1 (OKSU); 1 mi. N Stillwater, 1 (OKSU); 1 mi. W Stillwater, 1 (OKSU); 2 mi. E Stillwater, 1 (OKSU); 3 mi. N Stillwater, 1 (OKSU); 6 mi. N, 2 mi. W Stillwater, 1 (OKSU); near Glencoe, 9 mi. N Stillwater, 1 (OKSU); 9.5 mi. W, 0.75 mi. S. Stillwater, 1 (OKSU); 11 mi. W Stillwater, 1 (OKSU); 15 mi. E Stillwater on Hwy 51, 1 (OKSU); Jardot St., between Grandview & Lakeview St., Stillwater, 2 (OKSU); sheepbarn, near Oklahoma State University, Stillwater, 1 (OKSU); 2 mi. N, 1 mi. E Yost Lake, 3 (OKSU); taken by cyanide gun Fish and Wildlife Service, 1 (OKSU). PITTSBURG COUNTY: 10 mi. S Hartshorne, 1 (OKSU); 8 mi. S McAlester, 1 (OKSU); 10 mi. S McAlester, 1 (OKSU); 11 mi. W, 4 mi. S McAlester, 1 (ECENT); 15 mi. W McAlester, 1 (ECENT); 17 mi. NE McAlester, 1 (OKSU); 0.5 mi. NW U.S. Naval Ammunitions Depot, McAlester, 1 (OKSU); S central U.S. Naval Ammunitions Depot, McAlester, 1 (OKSU); Stuart, 1 (ECENT); 4 mi. E, 1 mi. N Stuart, 1 (ECENT). PONTOTOC COUNTY: E Ada, 1 (OKSU); SW Ada, 1 (OKSU); Pontotoc County, 2 (ECENT). POTTAWATOMIE COUNTY: W Asher, 1 (OKSU); NW McComb, 1 (OKSU); W McComb, 2 (OKSU); 3 mi. E Pink, 1 (OMNH); Skinner Ranch, 9 mi. E, 3 mi. S Purcell, 2 (OMNH); Wheeler Ranch, 13 mi. E, 1 mi. N Purcell, 1 (OMNH). PUSHMATAHA COUNTY: NE Antlers, 1 (OKSU); NW Antlers, 1 (OKSU); S Antlers, 3 (OKSU); SW Antlers, 4 (OKSU); W Antlers, 2 (OKSU); N Finley, 1 (OKSU). ROGER MILLS COUNTY: Taylor Ranch, N Berlin, 8 (OKSU); 1 mi. N Hammon, 12 (OKSU); 5 mi. W Strong City, 4 (OKSU). ROGERS COUNTY: 4 mi. E, 2 mi. S Chelsea, 1 (OKSU); 4 mi. S, 1 mi. E Claremore, 1 (OKSU); 3 mi. N, 1 mi. W Foyil, 1 (OMNH); Rogers County, 3 (UMMZ). TEXAS COUNTY: Texhoma, 1 (OMNH). TILLMAN COUNTY: Frederick, 20 (USNM); 3 mi. N Frederick, 1 (CAMCO); 7 mi. SE Frederick, 1

(CAMCO); NNE corner Frederick Lake, 2 (CAMCO); 4 mi. N, 4 mi. E Grandfield, 2 (OKSU); 4 mi. W, 4.5 mi. S Grandfield, 2 (OKSU); 2.5 mi. N, 5 mi. W Manitou, 1 (OKSU); 3.5 mi. N Manitou, 1 (OKSU); 1 mi. W, 1.75 mi. N Tipton, 1 (CAMCO); 3.5 mi. N, 1 mi. W Tipton, 1 (CAMCO). TULSA COUNTY: Red Fork, 6 (USNM); Tulsa Zoo, 1 (OKSU). WAGONER COUNTY: 2 mi. S Wagoner, 1 (OKSU). WASHITA COUNTY: Elk Creek, 5 mi. W Sentinel, 4 (UIMNH); Washita County, 3 (OKSU); 9 mi. W, 8 mi. S Weatherford, 3 (KU). WOODS COUNTY: 21 mi. NW Alva, 1 (OKSU); 7 mi. NW Freedom, 1 (OKSU). WOODWARD COUNTY: Ft. Supply, 44 (OMNH); 1.6 mi. SE Ft. Supply, Rt. 270, 6 (OMNH); Mutual, 1 (OKSU); Ft. Supply, 3 mi. SE Woodward, 1 (USNM); Woodward County, 3 (KU); NW Sec., 1 (OKSU).

Canis lupus.—Specimens examined (total 13): BEAVER COUNTY: Beaver Creek, Indian Territory, 1 (AMNH). CIMARRON COUNTY: Teepee Creek, Neutral Strip, Indian Territory, 1 (AMNH). COMANCHE COUNTY: Mt. Tarbone, 1 (USNM); Wichita Mountains, 3 (USNM). OTTAWA COUNTY: Afton, 6 (USNM). WOODWARD COUNTY: 7 mi. SW Freedom, 1 (USNM).

Canis rufus.—Specimens examined (total 75): ATOKA COUNTY: near Atoka, 2 (USNM); Redden, 1 (USNM). CHEROKEE COUNTY: 10 mi. S Tahlequah, 1 (USNM). COAL COUNTY: Coalgate, 2 (USNM). COMANCHE COUNTY: Wichita Mts. Wildlife Refuge, 1 (USNM). GARVIN COUNTY: 40 mi. N Ardmore, 1 (USNM). LEFLORE COUNTY: near Big Cedar, 1 (USNM); Gingle Mt., 1 (USNM); Octavia, 1 (USNM); 12 mi. NW Octavia, 1 (USNM); Page, 7 (USNM); near Page, 2 (USNM); Talihina, 1 (USNM); Zafra, 1 (USNM). MCCURTAIN COUNTY: Bethel, 5 (USNM); Broken Bow, 13 (USNM); Broken Bow, 15 mi. N on Cedar Creek, 10 (USNM); Cedar Creek, 2 (USNM); Sherwood, 4 (USNM); Smithville, 12 (USNM). PUSHMATAHA COUNTY: Fewell, 3 (USNM); Nashoba, Garland Creek, 1 (USNM). TILLMAN COUNTY: 20 mi. from Frederick, 1 (USNM). TULSA COUNTY: Red Fork, Indian Territory, 2 (USNM).

Castor canadensis.—Specimens examined (total 48): ALFALFA COUNTY: Aline, 1 (OKSU). BEAVER COUNTY: Beaver, 1 (OKSU). BLAINE COUNTY: Canton, below Canton Reservoir Dam, 1 (OKSU); below dam, Canton Lake, 1 (ECENT); 4 mi. N, 4 mi. W Watonga, 1 (FMNH). CADDO COUNTY: Cobb Creek, 2 mi. S, 1 mi. E Swan Lake Store, 1 (OKSU); Ft. Cobb, 1 (USNM). CANADIAN COUNTY: El Reno, 1 (OKSU); Lake Overholser, 1 (OKSU). CLEVELAND COUNTY: 1 mi. W Noble, 2 (OMNH). COMANCHE COUNTY: East Cache Creek, 2 mi. W Elgin, 1 (CAMCO); Sitting Bear Creek, Ft. Sill, 2 (CAMCO). COTTON COUNTY: N of Main Cache Creek, 1 (OKSU). ELLIS COUNTY: Ellis

County, 1 (OKSU). GRADY COUNTY: 2 mi. S, 2 mi. W Alex, 1 (OMNH). JEFFERSON COUNTY: Beaver Creek, 4 mi. S Waurika, 1 (OKSU). JOHNSTON COUNTY: Nida Pt., Lake Texoma, 1 (OKSU); U.S. Fish Hatchery, Pennington Creek, 1 (OMNH); Rock Creek, 4 mi. W Tishomingo, 1 (OKSU). KIOWA COUNTY: 17 mi. SE Ft. Cobb, 1 (USNM). LEFLORE COUNTY: Poteau, 1 (CSUO). LOGAN COUNTY: 5 mi. N, 3 mi. W Langston, 1 (OKSU). MARSHALL COUNTY: Butcher Pen Creek, Lake Texoma, 1 (OUBS); Mayfield Flats, Lake Texoma, 2 (OUBS); 10 mi. E Madill, 1 (ECENT); 3.5 mi. NE University of Oklahoma Biological Station, 1 (OUBS). MCCLAIN COUNTY: 3 mi. N Purcell, 2 (OMNH). MCINTOSH COUNTY: 10 mi. E, 2 mi. S Hitchita, 1 (ECENT); T11N, R16E, Sec. 3, Hwy I-40, 1 (OMNH). NOBLE COUNTY: 10 mi. NE Perry, 1 (OKSU). OKMULGEE COUNTY: Deep Fork Creek, 1 (ECENT); 5 mi. N Henryetta, 1 (ECENT); Okmulgee, 1 (CSUO). PAYNE COUNTY: arm 4, north side, Lake Carl Blackwell, 1 (OKSU); near Ripley, 1 (CSUO); creek, N of C. E. Donart High School, Stillwater, 1 (OKSU). PONTOTOC COUNTY: 6 mi. SE Ada, 3 (ECENT). POTTAWATOMIE COUNTY: 2 mi. N Harjo, 1 (OMNH). ROGER MILLS COUNTY: Spring Creek Lake Recreation Area, Black Kettle Natl. Grassland, 1 (TTU). STEPHENS COUNTY: Duncan, 1 (CAMCO); 2 mi. E, 2 mi. S Duncan, 1 (CAMCO). TEXAS COUNTY: Texas County, 1 (OKSU).

Cervus elaphus.—Specimens examined (total 9): CHEROKEE COUNTY: Cookson Hills Refuge, 1 (OKSU). COMANCHE COUNTY: Wichita Mountains Wildlife Refuge, 6 (OKSU), 1 (CAMCO); Wichita Mountains, 1 (USNM).

Conepatus mesoleucus.—Specimens examined (total 2): CIMARRON COUNTY: Kenton, 1 (USNM); base southeast end Black Mesa, 2 mi. NE Kenton, 1 (ECENT).

Cryptotis parva.—Specimens examined (total 161): ADAIR COUNTY: Stilwell, Boston Mts., 1 (USNM). BRYAN COUNTY: 5 mi. N Colbert, 2 (TMM). CANADIAN COUNTY: El Reno, 1 (USNM); 5.5 mi. SE Hinton, 1,500 ft., 1 (KU). CHEROKEE COUNTY: Dogwood & Maple, Tahlequah, 2 (OMNH). CHOCTAW COUNTY: 3 mi. E, 1 mi. N Hugo, 1 (OKSU). CLEVELAND COUNTY: Cleveland County, 3 (OMNH); 4 mi. E, 1 mi. S Lexington, 1 (OKSU); Norman, 3 (OMNH); Alameda & 12th St., Norman, 1 (OMNH); 2 mi. SW Norman, 9 (OMNH); 3 mi. S, 7.5 mi. E Norman, 2 (OMNH); 1 mi. S University of Oklahoma campus, 1 (OMNH); Hwy 77, near Purcell, 1 (OMNH); jct. Rock Creek Rd. & South Canadian River, 2 (OKSU); COMANCHE COUNTY: Cache, 1 (CAMCO); Eagle Park, Cache, 1 (CAMCO); 2.5 mi. E Cache, 1 (CAMCO); 3 mi. N Cache, 1 (USNM); Comanche County, 1 (OKSU); Lawton, 5

(CAMCO); Wichita Mountains Wildlife Refuge, 7 (OMNH), 2 (OKSU); Wichita Natl. Forest, 1 (OMNH). CUSTER COUNTY: Thomas, 1 (CAMCO); 3 mi. W, 0.25 mi. N Thomas, 1 (OKSU); Weatherford City Park, 1 (OKSU); 1.25 mi. N, 0.75 mi. W Weatherford, 1 (KU). GARVIN COUNTY: T3N, R3W, Sec. 25, SARP Site R8, Rush Creek, 2.1 mi. E SH 76, 1 (OKSU); T3N, R4W, Sec. 29, SARP Site R5, Rush Creek, 0.5 mi. W SH 76, 1 (OKSU). GRADY COUNTY: 4 mi. W Newcastle, 1 (CSUO). GRANT COUNTY: 1 mi. W, 1 mi. N Hawley, 1 (OMNH). HARPER COUNTY: pasture 26, Southern Great Plains Exp. Range, Ft. Supply, 7 (OKSU). JEFFERSON COUNTY: Rt. 32, near Grady, 1 (OMNH). JOHNSTON COUNTY: 18 mi. NE Tishomingo, 1 (ECENT). KAY COUNTY: 1 mi. S Blackwell, 1 (OKSU); T26N, R2E, SE 1/4 Sec. 18, Ponca City, 2 (OKSU). KINGFISHER COUNTY: Kingfisher, 1 (OMNH); T17N, R5W, Sec. 30, 1 (OMNH). KIOWA COUNTY: 3.5 mi. E Snyder, 1 (CAMCO). LEFLORE COUNTY: 0.5 mi. NW Zoe, 1 (OMNH). LOGAN COUNTY: T16N, R4W, Sec. 11, 2 (OMNH). MAR-SHALL COUNTY: 0.5 mi. E Denison Dam, 1 (OUBS); 0.5 mi. N Willis, 1 (OUBS); 2 mi. N Willis, 1 (OUBS); 4.5 mi. N Willis, 1 (OMNH), 1 (OUBS). MCCURTAIN COUNTY: 14 mi. SE Broken Bow, 1 (OMNH); Forked Lake, SE Eagletown, 2 (ECENT); 2 mi. W Eagletown, 1 (TMM). MUSKOGEE COUNTY: 6 mi. SE Muskogee, 1 (OMNH). NOBLE COUNTY: Lake McMurtry, 5 mi. W, 4 mi. N Stillwater, 1 (OKSU). OKLAHOMA COUNTY: grassland study area, 5 mi. N Vickers, Edmond, 1 (CSUO); 0.65 mi. S Turner Turnpike toll gate on Sooner Rd., 1 (CSUO); T13N, R3W, Sec. 30, 1 (OMNH). OSAGE COUNTY: 5.5 mi. N, 4 mi. E Shidler, 1 (KU). OTTAWA COUNTY: Afton, 1 (OKSU); 2 mi. S, 6 mi. E Afton, 3 (KU). PAYNE COUNTY: Hillcrest Golf Course, 3 (OKSU); Lake Carl Blackwell, 4 (OKSU); south end Lake Carl Blackwell, 1 (OKSU); 5 mi. E Perkins, 1 (OKSU); Lake Sanborn, 2 (OKSU); 0.25 mi. N Sanborn Lake, 2 (OKSU); Stillwater, 4 (OKSU); Boomer Lake, Stillwater, 1 (OKSU); northeast side Boomer Lake, Stillwater, 1 (OKSU); N old golf course, Stillwater, 3 (OKSU); Vet Village, Stillwater, 2 (OKSU); 50 yds. N at 619 W. 24th St., Stillwater, 1 (OKSU); 0.5 mi. N, 0.5 mi. W Stillwater, 1 (OKSU); 1 mi. N Stillwater, 2 (OKSU); 1 mi. N, 1 mi. W Stillwater, 1 (OKSU); 1 mi. N, 2 mi. W Stillwater, 1 (OKSU); 1.5 mi. N Stillwater, 2 (OKSU); 2 mi. S, 0.25 mi. E Stillwater, 1 (OKSU); 2 mi. E, 0.5 mi. S Stillwater, 1 (OKSU); 2 mi. N Stillwater, 2 (OKSU); 2 mi. W Stillwater Airport, 1 (OKSU); 3 mi. N, 0.5 mi. W Stillwater, 1 (OKSU); 3 mi. S Stillwater, 1 (OKSU); 4 mi. W, 3 mi. S Stillwater, 1 (OKSU); 5 mi. NW Stillwater, 2 (OKSU); 5.5 mi. N, 2 mi. E jct. 6th St. & Perkins Rd., Stillwater, 1 (OKSU); 6 mi. N, 4 mi. E Stillwater, 1 (OKSU); 11 mi. W Stillwater, 1 (OKSU). PONTOTOC COUNTY: 3 mi. S, 2 mi.

W Ada, 1 (ECENT); 3 mi. E, 4 mi. N Ada, 1 (ECENT); 7 mi. NE Ada, 3 (ECENT). POTTAWATOMIE COUNTY: 7 mi. SE Tecumseh, 1 (KU). SEMINOLE COUNTY: 1 mi. E, 2 mi. N Maud, 1 (OMNH); Seminole, 1 (OKSU). TULSA COUNTY: Garnett, 5 (UMMZ); Red Fork, Indian Territory, 1 (USNM). WAGONER COUNTY: 4.5 mi. SW Coweta, 600 ft., 1 (OMNH). WOODS COUNTY: 5 mi. S Waynoka, 1,400 ft., 1 (OMNH). WOODWARD COUNTY: above Alabaster Caverns, 1 (OKSU); 3 mi. N Ft. Supply, 1 (USNM); Exp. Station, Woodward, 1 (USNM); 4.5 mi. W Woodward, 1 (USNM).

Cynomys ludovicianus.—Specimens examined (total 187): ALFALFA COUNTY: 5 mi. S Cherokee, 1 (KU); 6 mi. S, 4 mi. E Cherokee, 1 (OMNH); 8 mi. S Cherokee, 1 (OKSU). BEAVER COUNTY: 11 mi. S, 4 mi. W Beaver City, 1 (OKSU); 8 mi. S, 4.5 mi. E Elmwood, 1 (OKSU). BLAINE COUNTY: Hollow Mound Canyon, 12 mi. W Okeene, 1 (OKSU); 1 mi. E Roman Nose State Park, 1 (OKSU); 2 mi. E Roman Nose Park, 2 (OKSU); 5 mi. N Watonga, 1 (OKSU). CANADIAN COUNTY: 3 mi. E, 1 mi. N Piedmont, 1 (CSUO); east edge Yukon, 1 (OKSU). CIMARRON COUNTY: 2 mi. W, 1 mi. S Boise City, 7 (OMNH); 5.1 mi. E, 5.2 mi. S Boise City, 4 (OMNH); 7 mi. N, 2 mi. E Kenton, 1 (OKSU); 8 mi. E Kenton, 4 (OKSU); 1 mi. S, 1 mi. W Wheeless, 1 (OMNH); 1.3 mi. E, 0.5 mi. S Wheeless, 1 (OMNH). CLEVELAND COUNTY: Hospital Farm, N Norman, 1 (OKSU). COMANCHE COUNTY: 3.5 mi. S Cache, 4 (CAMCO); 3 mi. W, 5 mi. S Elgin, 1 (CAMCO); 8 mi. SW Elgin, 2 (CAMCO); 2 mi. S Fletcher, 1 (OKSU); 2 mi. ESE Ft. Sill, 1 (CAMCO); White Wolf Crossing, 4.5 mi. W, 2.25 mi. N Ft. Sill, 7 (CAMCO); Lawton, 1 (OMNH); Cache Rd. at 6th, Lawton, 2 (OKSU); Mt. Scott Post Office, 3 (USNM); Sulphur Flat, Wichita Mountains Wildlife Refuge, 5 (CAMCO); Wichita Mountains Wildlife Refuge, 34 (CAMCO); Wichita Wildlife Refuge, 3 (OMNH). COTTON COUNTY: Chattanooga, 1 (USNM). CUSTER COUNTY: 2 mi. E, 2 mi. N Butler, 1 (CAMCO); 1 mi. N, 0.75 mi. W Thomas, 2 (OKSU); 1 mi. N, 2 mi. W Weatherford, 2 (KU); 15 mi. N Weatherford, 1 (KU). DEWEY COUNTY: 10 mi. NW Canton, 2 (KU); Dewey County, 1 (KU). ELLIS COUNTY: 18 mi. S, 6 mi. E Arnett, 1 (OKSU); 4 mi. NW Ft. Supply on Hwy 180, 1 (OKSU). GARVIN COUNTY: 6 mi. W, 0.75 mi. N Stratford, 1 (ECENT). GRADY COUNTY: 5 mi. E, 2 mi. N Chickasha on Hwy 62, 1 (OKSU). GREER COUNTY: 5 mi. W Granite, 1 (OKSU); Greer County, 7 (OMNH). HARMON COUNTY: 2.5 mi. W, 1 mi. N Hollis, 1 (FWMSH). HARPER COUNTY: T25N, R22W, Sec. 19, 5 mi. N Ft. Supply, 1 (OKSU); Southern Plains Exp. Range, 3 (OKSU); USDA Exp. Range, 1 (OKSU). JACKSON COUNTY: 3.5 mi. E Duke, 6 (CAMCO); 4.5 mi. E Duke, 2 (CAMCO); airplane runway of Republic Gypsum Co., 1

mi. W Duke, 1 (OKSU); 6.2 mi. W Tipton, 4 (ECENT). JEFFERSON
COUNTY: 2.5 mi. S, 1 mi. W Ringling, 2 (OUBS); 3.5 mi. SE Ryan, 3
(OUBS). KAY COUNTY: Ponca Agency, 2 (USNM). KINGFISHER
COUNTY: 5 mi. E Hennessey, 1 (OKSU); 8 mi. E Hennessey, 1 (OKSU).
KIOWA COUNTY: 3 mi. E Snyder, 1 (OUBS); 3 mi. NE Snyder, 2
(OUBS). LOGAN COUNTY: Lovell, 1 (OKSU); 1 mi. N Marshall, 1
(OKSU). MAJOR COUNTY: 4.5 mi. S, 1.5 mi. W Fairview, 1 (OKSU);
3 mi. W Orienta, 2 (OMNH), 4 (USNM); 9 mi. N, 6 mi. E Seiling, 3
(OKSU). MARSHALL COUNTY: 0.75 mi. from University of Oklahoma
Biological Station, 1 (OMNH). MCCLAIN COUNTY: 3 mi. E, 1 mi. S
Blanchard, 1 (CAMCO); Harris Ranch, 2 mi. E, 1 mi. N Lindsay, 1
(OMNH). NOBLE COUNTY: Otoe Indian Reservation, N Morrison, 2
(OKSU). OKLAHOMA COUNTY: Oklahoma City, 3 (USNM). ROGER
MILLS COUNTY: T13N, R25W, W 1/2 NE 1/4 Sec. 3, 1 (OKSU). STE-
PHENS COUNTY: 7 mi. E, 1 mi. S Duncan, 1 (OKSU). TEXAS
COUNTY: 4 mi. N Guymon, 1 (OKSU); 4.5 mi. N, 5.5 mi. W Guymon, 1
(CAMCO); 4.5 mi. W, 3 mi. S Turpin, 1 (KU). WASHITA COUNTY: 0.5
mi. S, 5 mi. E Bessie, 1 (CAMCO). WOODS COUNTY: Alva, 3 (KU);
White Horse Springs, Oklahoma Territory, 6 (FMNH). WOODWARD
COUNTY: USDA Exp. Range, 5 mi. N Ft. Supply, 1 (OKSU); 2 mi. E
Mooreland, 1 (OKSU); 2 mi. N, 1 mi. E Mooreland, 1 (OKSU); 3 mi. E
Mooreland, 1 (OKSU).

Dasypus novemcinctus.—Specimens examined (total 47): BRYAN COUNTY:
10 mi. SE Bennington, 2 (OUBS); Bryan County, 1 (OKSU). CADDO
COUNTY: Red Rock Canyon State Park, 1 (OMNH). CARTER
COUNTY: Lake Murray Park, 1 (OMNH). CLEVELAND COUNTY:
Hollywood, 1 (OMNH); 0.75 mi. E Noble, along South Canadian River
(University of Oklahoma Fisheries Center), 1 (OKSU); 1 mi. E US 77
on Cedar Lane, Norman, 1 (OMNH); Oliver's Woods, 2 mi. S Norman,
1 (OMNH); 4 mi. E Norman, 1 (OMNH); 2 mi. S Slaughterville, 1
(OMNH); 0.25 mi. W Stable, Thunderbird Riding Academy, 1 (OMNH).
COMANCHE COUNTY: 4 mi. N Faxon, 2 (CAMCO); 4 mi. S Sterling, 1
(OKSU); Elm Springs, Wichita Mountains Wildlife Refuge, 1 (USNM);
T2N, R11W, Sec. 26, 1 (OMNH). COTTON COUNTY: Hooper Farm, 1
(OKSU); West Cache Creek, 28 mi. S Lawton, 1 (UIMNH). HASKELL
COUNTY: 6.5 mi. E, 1.5 mi. S Stigler, 1 (OMNH); 2 mi. W Whitefield, 1
(OMNH). JOHNSTON COUNTY: Tishomingo Natl. Wildlife Refuge, 2
mi. S Tishomingo, 1 (OKSU); 3 mi. N Tishomingo, 1 (OKSU); 3 mi. W, 2
mi. N Tishomingo, 1 (OKSU). LEFLORE COUNTY: Kiamichi, S Tali-
hina, 1 (OKSU). LINCOLN COUNTY: Dry Creek, 43 mi. NE Okla-
homa City, 1 (UIMNH). MARSHALL COUNTY: Dark Horse Corner, 1
(OMNH); 1 mi. W University of Oklahoma Biological Station, 1 (OUBS);

5 mi. N Willis, 1 (OMNH). MCCURTAIN COUNTY: 13.5 mi. E, 2.3 mi. N (by road) Broken Bow, 1 (CSUO); 6 mi. W Idabel, 1 (CAMCO). NOBLE COUNTY: 0.75 mi. W Hwy 177 on Orlando Rd., 1 (OKSU); Red Rock, 1 (OKSU). PAYNE COUNTY: Stillwater, 2 (OKSU); 0.1 mi. N Lakeview Dr. on Monroe Ave., Stillwater, 1 (OKSU); 2 mi. W Stillwater, 1 (OKSU); 6 mi. W, 1 mi. N Stillwater, 1 (OKSU). PITTSBURG COUNTY: 12 mi. S McAlester, 1 (ECENT). PONTOTOC COUNTY: 5 mi. NE Ada, 1 (ECENT); 11 mi. S Ada, 1 (ECENT); Lighting Ridge, near Ada, 1 (ECENT); 7 mi. SW Latta, 1 (ECENT); Pontotoc County, 1 (ECENT). POTTAWATOMIE COUNTY: Biology Station #2, 1 (CSUO). PUSHMATAHA COUNTY: T4S, R17E, Sec. 21, 12 mi. E, 2 mi. S Antlers, 1 (OMNH). STEPHENS COUNTY: 1 mi. W Tussey, 1 (OKSU).

Didelphis virginiana.—Specimens examined (total 292): ADAIR COUNTY: 7 mi. W Stilwell, 1 (KU). ALFALFA COUNTY: Great Salt Plains Refuge, 2 (OKSU). BRYAN COUNTY: 0.25 mi. W Colbert, 3 (TMM); Durant, 1 (OUBS). CADDO COUNTY: Ft. Cobb, 2 (USNM). CARTER COUNTY: Ardmore, 1 (OMNH); 4 mi. S, 0.5 mi. E Ardmore, 1 (KU); 1.5 mi. W, 0.75 mi. N Healdton, 1 (ECENT); 7 mi. E Pruitts City, 1 (OKSU). CHEROKEE COUNTY: 3 mi. E Tahlequah, 2 (OKSU). CIMARRON COUNTY: 10 mi. W Felt, 1 (OKSU). CLEVELAND COUNTY: 3 mi. N Lexington, 1 (OMNH); 3 mi. S, 1 mi. E Moore on SH 77, 1 (OKSU); South Canadian River, University of Oklahoma Fisheries Center, 0.75 mi. E Noble, 1 (OKSU); 2 mi. NE Noble, 1 (OMNH); Norman, 7 (OMNH); 1413 Pecan, Norman, 1 (OMNH); 600 E. Lindsey St., Norman, 9 (OMNH); 702 Jenkins, Norman, 1 (OMNH); 0.5 mi. S Norman, 1 (OMNH); Alameda St., 2.5 mi. E Norman, 1 (OMNH); 2.5 mi. NE Norman, 1 (OMNH); 3 mi. E on Hwy 9, Norman, 1 (OMNH); South Canadian River, 3 mi. SE Norman, 2 (KU); 5 mi. E Norman, 2 (OMNH); 9 mi. N Norman, 1 (OMNH); T8N, R2W, Sec. 5, South Base, Norman, 1 (OMNH); Skinner Ranch, 9 mi. E, 3 mi. S Purcell, 1 (OMNH); 2 mi. S Slaughterville, 4 (OMNH); 0.25 mi. S.W. 134th St. on Sunnylane Rd., 1 (OMNH). COMANCHE COUNTY: 1.5 mi. SW Chattanooga, 1 (CAMCO); 4.1 mi. E Elgin, 1 (CAMCO); 3 mi. NW Faxon, 3 (CAMCO); Ft. Sill Game Farm, 1 (USNM); Lawton, 3 (CAMCO); 1 mi. S, 6 mi. E Lawton, 1 (CAMCO); Ft. Sill, 2 mi. W Lawton, 1 (CAMCO); 7.5 mi. W Lawton, 1 (CAMCO); 10.5 mi. S, 2 mi. E Lawton, 1 (CAMCO); Wolf Creek, Lawton, 1 (CAMCO); Medicine Park, 2 (CAMCO); 1.5 mi. N Meers, 1 (OMNH); 5.5 mi. E, 5 mi. N Meers, 1 (CAMCO); Mt. Scott Post Office, 11 (USNM); Wichita Mountains Wildlife Refuge, 6 (USNM); Wichita Natl. Forest, 1 (KU). COTTON COUNTY: Hooper Farm, 1 (OKSU). CRAIG COUNTY: 1 mi. S, 0.75 mi. W Big Cabin, 1 (OKSU). CUSTER COUNTY: 7 mi. W, 4 mi. N Clinton, 1 (OMNH); Weatherford,

1 (KU); 1.25 mi. W Weatherford, 1 (KU). DELAWARE COUNTY: 2 mi. S Colcord, 1 (OKSU); Bill Mitchell Cave, Spavinaw Creek, 4.25 mi. N Colcord, 1 (OMNH); Revine Cave, near Stanburg, 4.25 mi. N Colcord, 500 ft., 1 (OMNH); 10 mi. SE Jay, 1 (OKSU); 3.2 mi. E, 1 mi. N Kansas, 1 (CAMCO). DEWEY COUNTY: 10 mi. NW Canton, 6 (KU); 6 mi. E Seiling, 1 (OKSU). GARFIELD COUNTY: 5.5 mi. W Bison, 1 (OKSU); 3 mi. E Hunter, 1 (OKSU). GARVIN COUNTY: 3 mi. E, 2 mi. S Elmore City, 1 (ECENT). GRADY COUNTY: T3N, R7W, Sec. 11, SARP Site R8, north side Rush Creek, 1 (OKSU). HARPER COUNTY: 3 mi. W May, 1 (OKSU). HASKELL COUNTY: 100 yds. S Stigler, 2 (OMNH). HUGHES COUNTY: 1 mi. N Calvin, 1 (OKSU); 7 mi. N Calvin, 1 (ECENT). JACKSON COUNTY: 0.5 mi. N Blair, 1 (OMNH); 3.25 mi. S Eldorado, 1 (CAMCO); 3 mi. S, 3.5 mi. W Olustee, 1 (CAMCO). JOHNSTON COUNTY: 4 mi. N Mill Creek, 1 mi. E SH 7, 1 (ECENT); 3 mi. E, 8 mi. S Tishomingo, 1 (OUBS). LATIMER COUNTY: Kanniatobbee Creek, 1 (OMNH); Red Oak, 3 (USNM); 10 mi. W, 3 mi. E Talihina, 1 (OKSU). MAJOR COUNTY: 10 mi. W, 6 mi. S Orienta, 1 (OKSU). MARSHALL COUNTY: 1 mi. W Kingston, 1 (OUBS); Marshall County, 1 (OMNH); University of Oklahoma Biological Station, 1 (OMNH); 0.5 mi. W University of Oklahoma Biological Station, 2 (OUBS); 300 yds. SW University of Oklahoma Biological Station, 1 (OUBS); 500 yds. W University of Oklahoma Biological Station, 1 (OUBS); 2 mi. E Willis, 1 (OMNH). MCCLAIN COUNTY: Hester Ranch, 1 mi. W, 1 mi. S Dibble, 1 (OMNH); Johnson Ranch, 2 mi. E Goldsby, 1 (OMNH); South Canadian River, Hwy I-35, SW Norman, 1 (CSUO); Hester Ranch, 12 mi. W, 1 mi. S Purcell, 1 (OMNH); T8N, R4W, NE 1/4 Sec. 11, 1 (OMNH). MCCURTAIN COUNTY: 5 mi. S Broken Bow, 1 (OKSU); 15.5 mi. SE Broken Bow, 1 (OMNH); McCurtain Game Preserve, 1 (ECENT); 2 mi. W Smithville, 1 (OMNH). MCINTOSH COUNTY: 10 mi. E, 1 mi. S Hitchita, 1 (OKSU). MURRAY COUNTY: 5 mi. E Davis, 1 (OKSU); 2 mi. W Sulphur, 1 (ECENT). MUSKOGEE COUNTY: near Ft. Gibson, 1 (OKSU). NOBLE COUNTY: 2 mi. E Billings, 1 (OKSU); 2 mi. S Billings, 2 (OKSU); 5 mi. W Perry, 1 (OKSU); 1 mi. N, 1 mi. E Red Rock, 1 (OKSU); 5 mi. S, 3 mi. E Red Rock, 2 (OKSU). OKFUSKEE COUNTY: Okfuskee County, 1 (OMNH); 2 mi. W Okemah, 1 (OMNH). OKLAHOMA COUNTY: Edmond, 10 (CSUO); Brandywine Apts., Edmond, 1 (CSUO); 6.4 mi. W Edmond, 1 (CSUO); 10 mi. W, 0.5 mi. S Edmond, 1 (CSUO); N Jones, 1 (OKSU); Oklahoma City, 1 (USNM); jct. N.W. 36th & McKinney, Oklahoma City, 1 (OKSU); 4 mi. W jct. Wilshire & Eastern, Oklahoma City, 1 (CSUO); 1505 S.E. 65th, Oklahoma City, 1 (OMNH); Airmens's Diner, Tinker Air Force Base, 1 (CSUO); jct. I-35 & US 60, 1 (OKSU); 13th & Broadway Ext., 1

(CSUO); 5 mi. W Western Ave. on Covell Rd., 1 (CSUO); 1000 blk. E on Westminster Rd., 1 (CSUO). OKMULGEE COUNTY: 3 mi. N Morris, 1 (OKSU); Okmulgee County, 8 (ECENT). OSAGE COUNTY: Phillips Ranch, 10 mi. SW Bartlesville, 1 (OMNH); J. Bower Ranch, 1 mi. E, 1 mi. N Burbank, 1 (OKSU). PAYNE COUNTY: Boomer Lake, 1 (OKSU); 1 mi. N Boomer Lake, 1 (OKSU); 2 mi. N Cushing, 1 (OKSU); 2 mi. NE Glencoe, 1 (OKSU); Hillcrest Golf Course, 1 (OKSU); Lake Blackwell, 1 (OKSU); 5 mi. W Perkins, 1 (OKSU); 3 mi. E, 0.5 mi. N Ripley, 1 (OKSU); Stillwater, 5 (OKSU); College Ave., Stillwater, 1 (OKSU); Lake Carl Blackwell, W Stillwater, 1 (OKSU); N Murry Hall, Oklahoma State University campus, Stillwater, 1 (OKSU); sheepbarn, Oklahoma State University, 1 (OKSU); vacant lot behind 818 N. Lincoln St., Stillwater, 1 (ECENT); W Stillwater, 1 (OKSU); 11th St., Stillwater, 1 (OKSU); 1900 N. Washington St., Stillwater, 1 (OKSU); 400 yds. W Creek Bridge Hwy, Stillwater, 1 (OKSU); 0.25 mi. E Perkins Rd. on Richmond Rd., Stillwater, 1 (OKSU); 0.5 mi. S Stillwater, 1 (OKSU); 1 mi. N Stillwater, 1 (OKSU); 1 mi. NE Stillwater, 1 (OKSU); 1 mi. W Stillwater, 1 (OKSU); 2 mi. S, 2 mi. W jct. 6th & Western Sts., Stillwater, 1 (OKSU); 2 mi. W Stillwater, 3 (OKSU); 3 mi. E Stillwater, 1 (OKSU); 3 mi. N Stillwater, 1 (OKSU); 3 mi. W Stillwater, 1 (OKSU); 5 mi. SW Stillwater, 1 (OKSU); 6.5 mi. N, 2.5 mi. E Stillwater, 1 (OKSU); 7 mi. W Stillwater, 1 (OKSU); 8 mi. W Stillwater, 2 (OKSU), 1 (OMNH); 8 mi. W, 1 mi. N Stillwater, 1 (OKSU); 15 mi. W Stillwater, 1 (OKSU); 15 mi. WSW Stillwater, 2 (OKSU); 0.5 mi. N jct. Hwys 51 & 81, 1 (OKSU); 1 mi. N, 0.25 mi. W jct. Hwys 51 & 51C, 1 (OKSU). PITTSBURG COUNTY: Hartshorne, 11 (USNM); Savanna, 1 (USNM). PONTOTOC COUNTY: 2 mi. E Ada, 4 (ECENT); 3 mi. N Ada, 2 (ECENT); 5 mi. E Ada, 1 (ECENT); 6 mi. SE Ada, 2 (ECENT). POTTAWATOMIE COUNTY: Oklahoma Baptist University, Shawnee, 1 (OKSU); 2 mi. NE Tecumseh, 1 (OKSU); Little River, 7 mi. SE Tecumseh, 1 (KU). PUSHMATAHA COUNTY: 6 mi. S Antlers, 1 (OKSU). ROGERS COUNTY: Catoosa, 1 (UMMZ); T20N, R17E, NW 1/4 Sec. 28, 1 (OKSU). SEMINOLE COUNTY: Konawa, 1 (CAMCO). STEPHENS COUNTY: 0.25 mi. E, 1 mi. S Claud, 1 (OMNH); 4 mi. W, 4.25 mi. N Duncan, 1 (OKSU); Lake Clear Creek, E of Marlow Dr., 1 (CSUO); 11 mi. N, 2 mi. E Ringling, 1 (OKSU). TILLMAN COUNTY: 5 mi. E, 1 mi. N Frederick, 1 (OKSU). TULSA COUNTY: Garnett, 2 (UMMZ); Mohawk Park, 1 (UMMZ); Red Fork, 2 (USNM); Tulsa, 2 (UMMZ); Tulsa County, 1 (OMNH); 2996 E. 56th Pl., Tulsa, 1 (OKSU); 9400 blk. E. 39th Pl., Tulsa, 1 (CSUO); jct. Admiral Pl. & Garnett Rd., Tulsa, 1 (OKSU); jct. 31st St. & S. Boston Ave., Tulsa, 1 (OKSU); 75 yds. N I-44 at E. 31st St., Tulsa, 1 (OKSU). WASHINGTON COUNTY: 4 mi. S Bartlesville on Hwy 75, 5 (OKSU).

WASHITA COUNTY: 3 mi. E, 9 mi. S Weatherford, 1 (KU). WOODS COUNTY: 8 mi. N Alva, 1 (OMNH). WOODWARD COUNTY: Alabaster Caverns, 1 (OKSU); Woodward County, 1 (OMNH).

Dipodomys elator.—Specimens examined (total 2); COMANCHE COUNTY: Chattanooga, 2 (USNM).

Dipodomys ordii.—Specimens examined (total 1,346); ALFALFA COUNTY: Alfalfa County, 1 (OMNH); Great Salt Plains, E Cherokee, 7 (OKSU); 3 mi. E Cherokee, 2 (OMNH); 3 mi. N, 6.5 mi. E Cherokee, 1,170 ft., 1 (OMNH); 3.5 mi. E Cherokee, 9 (OMNH); 4 mi. SE Cherokee, 2 (USNM); 4.5 mi. E Cherokee, 1,170 ft., 4 (OMNH); 5 mi. S Cherokee, 1 (KU); Great Salt Plains Refuge, 5 (OKSU); 8 mi. N Jet, 1,170 ft., 1 (OMNH). BEAVER COUNTY: 1.5 mi. N Beaver, 7 (KU); North Canadian River, 4 mi. S Floris, 6 (KU); 3 mi. NW Slapout, 6 (OMNH); North Canadian River, 7 mi. S Turpin, 4 (KU). BECKHAM COUNTY: 3 mi. W Sayre, 2 (OKSU); 3 mi. W, 1.75 mi. S Sayre, 1 (OKSU); 7 mi. W Sayre, 1 (OKSU). BLAINE COUNTY: 4 mi. N Canton, 1 (OKSU); Canton Lake, 2 (OKSU); 0.25 mi. S Longdale, 0.5 mi. W Canton Lake, 1 (OKSU); Canton Reservoir, 1 (OKSU); between Canton Reservoir & Hwy 58, 1 (OKSU); Canton Shooting Ground, 2 (OKSU); 2 mi. W, 1 mi. N Longdale, 1 (OKSU); 3 mi. W, 1 mi. N Longdale, 1 (OKSU); 2 mi. W Watonga, 1 (OKSU). CADDO COUNTY: Caddo County, 1 (OMNH); 4 mi. W Cogar, 1 (OMNH); Ft. Cobb, 1 (USNM); 5 mi. NE Hinton, 45 (OMNH). CANADIAN COUNTY: T11N, R10W, Sec. 8, Canadian River, 2 (OMNH); 4 mi. W El Reno on US Hwy 66, 6 mi. N, 0.5 mi. W, 1 (OKSU); 6 mi. SE Hinton, 2 (OUBS); north bank South Canadian River, Minco, 1 (USNM); T11N, R9W, Sec. 5, north bank South Canadian River, 4 (OMNH); T12N, R10W, Sec. 17, south bank South Canadian River, 5 (OMNH); 2 mi. S Union City, 1 (OKSU); T11N, R9W, Sec. 5, 10 (OMNH); T12N, R10W, Sec. 17, 10 (OMNH). CIMARRON COUNTY: 3 mi. NE Boise City, 1 (ECENT); 4 mi. N Boise City, 1 (ECENT); 6.7 mi. W, 9.5 mi. S Boise City, 7 (OMNH); 9 mi. W Boise City, 1 (CAMCO); 10.4 mi. W Boise City, 1 (OKSU); 12.5 mi. W Boise City, 3 (OMNH); 13 mi. S Boise City, 5 (ECENT); 14 mi. W Boise City, 7 (OKSU); 15 mi. W Boise City, 2 (OKSU); T4N, R3E, Sec. 12, 15 mi. W Boise City, 1 (OMNH); T4N, R3E, Sec. 12, 15.8 mi. W Boise City, 1 (OMNH); T4N, R3E, Sec. 12, 15.8 mi. W Boise City, 1 (OMNH); 17 mi. W Boise City, 1 (OMNH); 25.4 mi. W Boise City, 1 (OKSU); 0.5 mi. E, 8.3 mi. N Felt, 3 (OMNH); 8 mi. W Griggs, 1 (KU); 9 mi. W Griggs, 2 (KU); Kenton, 1 (OMNH); Kenton, Black Mesa, 2 (CAMCO); 2 mi. E, 6 mi. S Kenton, 13 (CAMCO); 2 mi. S, 6 mi. E Kenton, 4 (CAMCO); 2.5 mi. S Kenton, 3 (CAMCO); 2.5 mi. SE Kenton, 5 (CAMCO); 3.3 mi. S, 1 mi. E Kenton, 1 (OMNH); 2.5 mi. SE Kenton, 4,200 ft., 5 (OMNH); 4 mi. N Kenton, 3

(KU); 4.4 mi. N, 0.4 mi. W Kenton, 1 (OMNH); 3 mi. SE Kenton, 1 (OMNH); 5 mi. N Kenton, 4 (OMNH); 6 mi. N Kenton, 3 (OKSU); 7 mi. SE Kenton, 1 (CAMCO); near Colorado state line, 7 mi. N Kenton, 1 (OKSU); 12 mi. SE Kenton, 1 (CAMCO); Tesesquite Canyon, 1 (OKSU); 3 mi. S Wheeless, 2 (OMNH); T5N, R3E, Sec. 36, 1 (OMNH). CLEVE-LAND COUNTY: R. D. Burns barn, 1 (OMNH); Canadian River, 1 (OMNH); Cleveland County, 1 (OMNH); 1 mi. SW Noble, 1 (UIMNH); 1.3 mi. W Noble, 2 (OMNH), 3 (USNM); Canadian River, S Norman, 1 (OMNH); Norman, 3 (OMNH); near Norman, 2 (OMNH); South Cana-dian River, S Norman, 6 (FWMSH); 0.5 mi. S Norman, 1 (OMNH); 1 mi. E Chickasha Exit, I-35, 950 ft., 1 mi. S Norman, 1 (OMNH); 1 mi. S Nor-man, 3 (OMNH), 1 (OUBS); 1 mi. S, 1 mi. W Norman, 1 (OMNH); 2 mi. S Norman, 1 (OMNH); South Canadian River, 2 mi. S Norman, 2 (OMNH); 2 mi. SW Norman, 3 (OMNH); 2 mi. S, 0.5 mi. E Norman, 1 (USNM); north bank Canadian River, 2.25 mi. S Norman, 1 (USNM); 2.25 mi. S Norman, 6 (OMNH); 2.5 mi. S Norman, 1 (OMNH), 34 (KU); 2.5 mi. SW Norman, 7 (OMNH); South Canadian River, 3 mi. S, 0.5 mi. W Norman, 3 (KU); 3 mi. W, 1.5 mi. S Norman, 2 (TTU); Canadian River, 5 mi. SW Norman, 1 (OMNH); South Canadian River, 5 mi. SW Norman, 1 (OMNH); South Canadian River, 5 mi. W Norman, 2 (OMNH); north bank South Canadian River, 6 mi. W Norman, 1 (OMNH); 1.5 mi. N Purcell, 1 (OMNH); 2.5 mi. S South Canadian River, 4 (USNM); jct. Rock Creek Rd. & South Canadian River, 1 (OKSU); T6N, R1W, Sec. 7, 3 (OMNH); T8N, R3W, Sec. 12, 1 (OMNH); T8N, R2W, NW 1/4 SW 1/4 Sec. 18, 1 (OMNH); T6N, R1W, Sec. 19, 6 (OMNH); T9N, R3W, Sec. 32, 1 (OMNH); T9N, R3W, Sec. 33, 2 (OMNH). COTTON COUNTY: 3 mi. N Burkburnett, 1 (KU); 6 mi. S Randlett, 1 (CAMCO); 5 mi. SE Tay-lor, 900 ft., 1 (OMNH); Red River, 12 mi. S Temple, 1 (TMM). CUSTER COUNTY: 4 mi. E Moorewood, 2 (OKSU); 11 mi. W, 1 mi. N Thomas, 1 (OKSU). DEWEY COUNTY: 3 mi. S Fay, 42 (OMNH); Taloga, 34 (OMNH); 1 mi. N Taloga, 14 (OMNH). ELLIS COUNTY: 8 mi. SE Ar-nett, 3 (USNM); 23 mi. S Arnett, 46 (OMNH); 15 mi. S, 2 mi. E Higgins, Texas, 4 (OKSU); Shattuck, 1 (USNM); 6 mi. NNE Shattuck, 2,335 ft., 2 (OMNH); T18N, R26W, SE 1/4 Sec. 1, 3 (OKSU). GRADY COUNTY: 4 mi. N Minco, 50 (OMNH); T10N, R7W, off Hwy 81 bridge, 4 (OMNH); T10N, R7W, Sec. 3, 2 (OMNH); T10N, R7W, Sec. 10, 5 (OMNH). GRANT COUNTY: 1.5 mi. W, 1.4 mi. N Hawley, 21 (OMNH); 1.7 mi. W, 1.3 mi. N Hawley, 7 (OMNH); 3 mi. NW Pond Creek, 17 (OMNH). GREER COUNTY: abandoned farm, Mangum, 1 (CSUO). HARMON COUNTY: 8 mi. N, 1.5 mi. W Gould, 1 (TTU); 10 mi. S, 1.8 mi. W Gould, 1 (OKSU); Hollis, 1 (FWMSH); 3.5 mi. N Hollis on Hwy 30, 1 (OKSU); 5 mi. N, 1 mi. W Hollis, 1 (FWMSH); 5.25 mi. N, 1 mi. W

Hollis, 2 (FWMSH); 5.5 mi. N, 2 mi. W Hollis, 1 (OKSU); 6 mi. N Hollis, 2 (FWMSH); 6 mi. N, 2 mi. W Hollis, 7 (FWMSH); 6 mi. S, 1.5 mi. W Hollis, 2 (CAMCO); 8 mi. N, 1.5 mi. W Hollis, 2 (FWMSH). 1 (OKSU); 8 mi. N, 1.5 mi. W Kirby's Corner, Hollis, 1 (OKSU); Red River, 8 mi. S Hollis, 3 (FWMSH); 8.5 mi. N Hollis, 3 (FWMSH); 8.5 mi. N, 2 mi. W Hollis, 11 (FWMSH); 8.75 mi. N, 2 mi. W Hollis, 1 (FWMSH); 10 mi. N, 2 mi. W Hollis, 1 (FWMSH); 11 mi. N Hollis, 8 (FWMSH); 13 mi. N Hollis, 8 (FWMSH); 13.5 mi. N Hollis, 1 (OKSU); 13.9 mi. N Hollis, 9 (FWMSH); 17 mi. N, 2.5 mi. W Hollis, 4 (TTU); 19 mi. N, 1.5 mi. E Hollis, 2 (TTU); 6 mi. E, 1 mi. S Vinson, 1,700 ft., 1 (OMNH). HARPER COUNTY: Buffalo Fair Grounds, 1 (UMMZ); 3 mi. S Englewood, Kansas, 2 (MVZ); Great Plains Exp. Range, Ft. Supply, 5 (OKSU); USDA Exp. Station, N Ft. Supply, 4 (OKSU); 1 mi. N Ft. Supply, Southern Plains Exp. Station, 2 (OKSU); 2 mi. W, 2 mi. N Ft. Supply, 1 (OKSU); 3 mi. N Ft. Supply, 2 (OKSU); 3 mi. NNW Ft. Supply, 229 (USNM); 4 mi. N Ft. Supply, 9 (OKSU); USDA SW Great Plains Exp. Range, 4 mi. NW Ft. Supply, 1 (OKSU); T25N, R22W, W 1/2 Sec. 19, 5 mi. N Ft. Supply, 3 (OKSU); 4.5 mi. N Laverne, 1 (UMMZ); Southern Great Plains Exp. Range, 42 (OKSU); USDA Exp. Range, 2 (OKSU). JACKSON COUNTY: 3 mi. S Eldorado, 1 (OKSU); T25N, R23W, SW 1/4 Sec. 6, 4 mi. S Eldorado, 1 (OKSU); 5 mi. SW Eldorado, 1 (UIMNH); 7 mi. W, 1 mi. S Eldorado, 1 (OKSU); Jackson County, 3 (TTU); Red River, 14 mi. S Olustee, 5 (TMM); 8 mi. W Snyder, 2 (OUBS). KINGFISHER COUNTY: 14 mi. W Crescent, 1 (OKSU); 4 mi. W, 1 mi. N Hennessey, 2 (OKSU); 7 mi. SW Hennessey, 1 (OKSU); 14 mi. W Hennessey on Hwy 51, 1 (OKSU); 16 mi. W Hennessey, 2 (OKSU); Kingfisher County, 1 (CSUO); 8 mi. SE Okeene, 1 (OKSU); T16N, R5W, Sec. 11, 3 (CSUO); T17N, R5W, Sec. 30, 5 (OMNH); T17N, R3W, Sec. 32, 1 (OMNH). KIOWA COUNTY: 6.5 mi. W Snyder, 2 (CAMCO); 7.5 mi. S Snyder, 2 (CAMCO). LOGAN COUNTY: T16N, R4W, Sec. 11, 1 (OMNH). MAJOR COUNTY: 2 mi. W Ames, 1 (OKSU), 1 (ECENT); 2.5 mi. S, 1 mi. E Ames, 1 (OKSU); Ewer's Creek, 2 mi. W Bouse Jct., 1 (OKSU); Cleo Springs, 2 (OKSU); 3 mi. S Cleo Springs, 9 (OMNH); 18 mi. W, 3 mi. N Orienta, 1 (OKSU); 5.5 mi. S Waynoka, 3 (OMNH); 5.5 mi. S Waynoka, 1,450 ft., 1 (OMNH); T21N, R11W, SW 1/4 Sec. 4, 1 (OKSU). MCCLAIN COUNTY: 2.7 mi. N Goldsby, 1 (OMNH); 2.7 mi. N, 0.5 mi. W Goldsby, 3 (OMNH); 3 mi. N, 1 mi. E Goldsby, 3 (OMNH); 1 mi. SW Noble, 5 (UIMNH); South Canadian River, 1 mi. SW Noble, 2 (UIMNH); across river from Norman dumps, 1 (OMNH); 1 mi. S Norman, 1 (OMNH); 1 mi. S, 1 mi. W Norman, 1 (OMNH); T8N, R2W, Sec. 10, 1 mi. S, 1 mi. W Norman, 1 (OMNH); 2 mi. S Norman, 1 (OMNH); 2 mi. SW Norman, 1 (OKSU); South Canadian River, N Purcell, 1

(OMNH); South Canadian River, 10.5 mi. N Purcell, 1 (OMNH); east side South Canadian River, 2 (OKSU); south end South Canadian River Bridge, 1 (OKSU); T8N, R2W, Sec. 10, 1 (OMNH); T8N, R2W, Sec. 21, 1 (OMNH); T9N, R3W, Sec. 32, 1 (OMNH). ROGER MILLS COUNTY: Black Kettle Natl. Grasslands, 1 (TTU); 12 mi. NNW Leedey, 1 (OMNH); 2.5 mi. E, 1.5 mi. S Reydon, 12 (CAMCO); Spring Lake Recreation Area, 1 (TTU); T13N, R25W, NW 1/4 Sec. 9, 1 (OKSU). TEXAS COUNTY: Eva, 1 (KU); Beaver River, Guymon, 2 (OKSU); Beaver River, 2 mi. N Guymon, 1 (OKSU); 2.2 mi. W Guymon, 2 (OMNH); 3 mi. N Guymon, 1 (OMNH). 1 (OKSU); 3 mi. NW Guymon, 1 (OKSU); 4.8 mi. N Guymon, 3 (OMNH); 5 mi. N Guymon, 1 (OKSU); 5.5 mi. N Guymon, 2 (OMNH); 5.5 mi. N Guymon, 3,100 ft., 2 (OMNH); 1 mi. W Hooker, 1 (OKSU). TILLMAN COUNTY: 0.5 mi. S, 2.2 mi. E Davidson, 6 (OMNH); 2 mi. S Davidson, 21 (OMNH); 3 mi. S Davidson, 5 (OMNH); 3 mi. E, 1.5 mi. S Davidson, 1 (OKSU); 3 mi. W, 0.5 mi. S Davidson, 1 (OKSU); 3 mi. S, 0.5 mi. E Davidson, 1 (CAMCO); 5.5 mi. S Grandfield, 7 (OMNH); 8 mi. SW Granfield, 1 (OKSU); T5S, R14W, Sec. 7, Red River, 1 (OMNH); 8 mi. S Snyder, 1 (OUBS); 4.5 mi. N, 0.5 mi. W Tipton, 1 (OKSU). WOODS COUNTY: Salt Fork River, 2 mi. N, 3 mi. W Alva, 1 (UIMNH); 6 mi. NW Alva, 1 (OMNH), 8 (OKSU); Salt Fork River, 6 mi. NW Alva, 1 (OKSU); Salt Fork River, 8 mi. S Alva, 1 (UIMNH); 8 mi. NW Alva, 4 (ECENT); 8.5 mi. NW Alva, 1 (OMNH); 10 mi. NW Alva, 1 (ECENT); 11 mi. NW Alva, 2 (ECENT); 13 mi. W, 3 mi. N Alva, 2 (OKSU); 24 mi. NW Alva, 1 (OKSU); 8 mi. N Bouse Jct., 2 (OKSU); 2 mi. E Camp Houston, 1 (OKSU); 2 mi. N, 6 mi. W Cleo Springs, 1 (OKSU); gypsum hills, north bank Cimarron River, 2 mi. W Edith, 1 (USNM); 2 mi. W Edith, 1 (OMNH); 2 mi. SE Freedom, 1 (CAMCO); 5 mi. E Freedom, 2 (OKSU); Waynoka, 59 (OKSU); Waynoka Dunes, 5 (OKSU); 4 mi. S Waynoka Dunes, 1 (OKSU); 0.25 mi. N Cimarron River, S Waynoka, 1 (OKSU); 3 mi. S Waynoka, 19 (OMNH); 3 mi. SW Waynoka, 11 (OMNH); 4 mi. N, 4 mi. W Waynoka, 1 (OKSU); 4.5 mi. W Waynoka, 1 (OKSU); 5 mi. NW Waynoka, 1 (OKSU); 5 mi. S Waynoka, 1,400 ft., 3 (OMNH); 5 mi. S Waynoka, 1,450 ft., 5 (OMNH); Woods County, 1 (OMNH). WOOD-WARD COUNTY: Alabaster Caverns, 1 (OKSU); 2 mi. N, 1 mi. E Alabaster Caverns, 1 (OKSU); Bear Creek, near Selman's Cave, 3 mi. S, 7 mi. W Freedom, 1 (OKSU); 10 mi. SW Freedom, 1 (OKSU); 11 mi. S Freedom, 1 (OKSU); 12 mi. S Freedom, 1 (OKSU); Ft. Supply Dam, 1 (OMNH); 2 mi. E Ft. Supply, 1 (OKSU); Waynoka Sand Dunes, 1 (OMNH); Woodward, 1 (OKSU); Woodward County, 2 (OMNH); 2 mi. NNW Woodward, 1,900 ft., 1 (OMNH); 3.5 mi. WNW Woodward, 1,950 ft., 3 (OMNH); Boiling Springs State Park, 4 mi. N Woodward, 1 (OKSU); 5 mi. S, 2 mi. W Woodward, 17 (OKSU); 11 mi. N Woodward,

1 (OKSU); T23N, R19W, Sec. 29, 1 (OMNH); T24N, R21W, Sec. 25, St. Rd. 34, 1 (OMNH).

Eptesicus fuscus.—Specimens examined (total 179); ADAIR COUNTY: Cave Springs Cave, 5 (OKSU); 3 mi. NNW Chewey, 2 (OMNH); bat cave, 4.5 mi. SSE Kansas, 1 (UIMNH); cave, 5 mi. S Kansas, 2 (OKSU), 1 (TMM). CHEROKEE COUNTY: campus, Northeastern State University, Tahlequah, 2 (CAMCO); Tahlequah, 11 (OMNH). CIMARRON COUNTY: N Carrizo Creek, 1 (OKSU); Carrizo Creek, 6 mi. N Kenton, 1 (OKSU); Dripping Springs, 6 mi. N, 4 mi. E Kenton, 12 (OKSU). DELAWARE COUNTY: 1 mi. W Disney, 2 (OKSU); Stansbury Cave, 1 (OKSU). GARVIN COUNTY: Stratford, 4 (ECENT); Mays Lumber Yard, Stratford, 1 (ECENT). KAY COUNTY: 0.5 mi. E, 0.25 mi. N Pioneer Woman, 1 (OKSU); cave, 0.5 mi. E, 0.25 mi. N Ponca City, 2 (OKSU); limestone caves, 2 mi. E Ponca City, 1 (OKSU). LATIMER COUNTY: campus, Eastern Oklahoma State College, Wilburton, 2 (OKSU); south bank Kanniatobbee Creek, 3.5 mi. N Wilburton, 3 (OMNH). LEFLORE COUNTY: Little River, Honobia, 1 (OKSU); caves, 2.5 mi. E Houston, 1 (OMNH). MAJOR COUNTY: Vickery Cave #2, 1 (OKSU); Vickery Bat Cave, 3 mi. W Bouse Jct., 1 (OKSU); Vickery Cave #1, 3 mi. W, 0.25 mi. S Bouse Jct., 1 (OKSU); Nescatunga Cave, 2.5 mi. W jct. Hwys 281 & 15, 1 (CSUO). MCCURTAIN COUNTY: Beavers Bend State Park, 20 (OKSU); bath house, Beavers Bend State Park, 1 (USNM); Cafe Bldg., Beavers Bend State Park, 1 (OKSU); Beavers Bend State Park, Broken Bow, 2 (OUBS); 2 mi. NE Smithville, 1 (OMNH); 2 mi. W Smithville, 3 (OMNH). OSAGE COUNTY: 2 mi. N Pawhuska, 8 (KU). PAWNEE COUNTY: High School, Cleveland, 7 (OKSU). PUSHMATAHA COUNTY: 7 mi. SE Clayton, 3 (OKSU). TULSA COUNTY: Tulsa, 1 (UMMZ). WASHINGTON COUNTY: 10 mi. SW Bartlesville, 1 (OKSU). WOODS COUNTY: Alva, 1 (CSUO); Alva, Oklahoma Territory, 30 (FMNH); Merrihew Cave, 9 (OKSU); Merrihew Cave, 0.5 mi. S of Kansas Line, 2 (KU); Merrihew Cave, 6 mi. S, 2 mi. W Aetna, Kansas, 3 (KU); Waynoka, 1 (OKSU). WOODWARD COUNTY: Alabaster Caverns State Park, 17 (OKSU); Owl Cave, Alabaster Caverns State Park, 3 (OKSU); Mooreland, 2 (OKSU); 2 mi. E Quinlan, 2 (OKSU).

Erethizon dorsatum.—Specimens examined (total 36); CIMARRON COUNTY: Black Mesa, 1 (OMNH); 4 mi. E Boise City, 1 (OKSU); 10 mi. W Boise City, 1 (OKSU); 12 mi. N, 1 mi. E Boise City, 1 (CAMCO); 13 mi. N Boise City, 1 (ECENT); 15 mi. N Boise City, 1 (ECENT); Felt, 1 (OKSU); 2.5 mi. SE Kenton, 4,200 ft., 1 (OMNH); 4 mi. N Kenton, 1 (OKSU); near Robbers Roost, 6 mi. E Kenton, 1 (OKSU); 4 mi. S Keyes, 1 (KU); T5N, R2E, Sec. 10, 1 (OMNH). COMANCHE COUNTY: 5 mi. S, 4 mi. W Cache, 1 (CAMCO); Geronimo, 1 (CAMCO); 4 mi. N, 3 mi.

W Indiahoma, 1 (CAMCO); Lawton, 2 (CAMCO); 6 mi. S Sterling, 1 (CAMCO); Wichita Mountains Wildlife Refuge, 1 (USNM). CUSTER COUNTY: north end, east side Foss Lake, Washita Natl. Wildlife Refuge, 2 (CAMCO). ELLIS COUNTY: Fargo, 1 (OMNH). GARVIN COUNTY: 3 mi. W Hennepin, 1 (OMNH). GREER COUNTY: approx. 11 mi. W Mangum, 1 (CAMCO). HARMON COUNTY: 8 mi. N, 2 mi. W Hollis, 1 (CAMCO). JACKSON COUNTY: 5 mi. E, 4 mi. S Eldorado, 1 (CAMCO). KIOWA COUNTY: 1.5 mi. S Roosevelt, 1 (CAMCO); Snyder, 1 (CAMCO); 1.5 mi. E Snyder, 1 (CAMCO). LATIMER COUNTY: near Wilburton, 1 (OKSU). MAJOR COUNTY: home of J. D. Gould, 4 mi. E, 1.25 mi. N Chester, 1 (OKSU); Whitlaw Ranch, 10 mi. E Quinlan on Hwy 15, 1 (OMNH). ROGER MILLS COUNTY: 5.2 mi. W Cheyenne, 1 (OKSU); 7 mi. W Cheyenne, 1 (CAMCO); 2 mi. S 4.5 mi. E Reydon, 1 (CAMCO); 4.5 mi. E Reydon, 1 (CAMCO).

Eutamias quadrivittatus.—Specimens examined (total 12); CIMARRON COUNTY: canyon, E of North Carrizo Creek, 1 (OKSU); 0.5 mi. SE Kenton, 1 (OMNH); T4N, R1E, Sec. 5, 3.5 mi. S, 0.5 mi. W Kenton, 1 (OMNH); 2 mi. E, 1 mi. S Kenton, 1 (OMNH); 2 mi. E, 6 mi. S Kenton, 1 (CAMCO); 2.5 mi. E, 3 mi. S Kenton, 1 (CAMCO); 4 mi. SE Kenton, 1 (OMNH); 4.2 mi. S, 0.5 mi. E Kenton, 1 (OMNH); 4.2 mi. S, 0.8 mi. W Kenton, 1 (OMNH); 4.5 mi. SE Kenton, 4,200 ft., 1 (OMNH); rocks above Spring Canyon, Regnier Ranch, 5 mi. S Kenton, 1 (ECENT); 5.5 mi. E, 1.5 mi. S Kenton, 1 (CAMCO).

Felis concolor.—Specimens examined (total 2); ATOKA COUNTY: Hunt Ranch, shore of Lake Eufaula, 4 mi. W, 2.5 mi. N Redden, 1 (OKSU). CIMARRON COUNTY: near Dinosaur Quarry, 8 mi. E Kenton, 1 (OKSU).

Felis rufus.—Specimens examined (total 182); ATOKA COUNTY: 3 mi. N Redden, 3 (USNM); 3 mi. E Wesley, 2 (USNM). BEAVER COUNTY: 6 mi. W Beaver, 1 (OMNH); 4 mi. S, 10 mi. W Gray, 2 (KU). BECKHAM COUNTY: 4 mi. S, 1 mi. E Sayre, 1 (OKSU). BLAINE COUNTY: Canton Lake, 1 (OMNH); 1 mi. S Longdale, 1 (OKSU). BRYAN COUNTY: Mathews Ranch, Armstrong, 1 (OKSU); Davis Ranch, 10 mi. S Bennington, 1 (OKSU). CADDO COUNTY: 3 mi. S Anadarko, 1 (OMNH); near Binger, 3 (OMNH). CANADIAN COUNTY: 5 mi. E, 6 mi. S Geary, 1 (OMNH). CIMARRON COUNTY: Black Mesa, 1 (OMNH); 13 mi. NE Boise City, 1 (OMNH); Squaw Canyon, Brookhart's Sec., 1 (OKSU); Cimarron County, 2 (OMNH); house N of Currumpa Creek, 1 (OKSU); Cienequilla Creek, 4 mi. W Felt, 2 (OKSU); 2.5 mi. SE Kenton, 4,200 ft., 1 (OMNH). CLEVELAND COUNTY: Thunderbird Dam, 10 mi. E Norman, 1 (OMNH); 10 mi. E Norman, 1 (OMNH); Skinner Ranch, 9 mi. E, 3 mi. S Purcell, 1 (OMNH). COMANCHE COUNTY: 5 mi. N, 3.5 mi. W

Chattanooga, 1 (CAMCO); Ft. Sill, 1 (CAMCO); Lawton, 1 (USNM); 2 mi. SSW Medicine Park, 1 (CAMCO); Mt. Scott Post Office, 2 (USNM); summit, Mt. Scott, 1 (USNM); west slope, Mt. Scott, 1 (USNM); Wichita Mountains Wildlife Refuge, 2 (OKSU), 2 (USNM). COTTON COUNTY: 0.5 mi. S Martin Chopple, 1 (OKSU). CREEK COUNTY: near Drumright Creek, 1 (OMNH); 5 mi. SW Drumright, 1 (OKSU); near Slick, 1 (OMNH). DEWEY COUNTY: NW Camargo, 1 (OMNH). ELLIS COUNTY: Ellis County, 1 (OKSU). GARFIELD COUNTY: near Enid, 1 (OKSU). GARVIN COUNTY: near Stratford, 1 (ECENT). GRADY COUNTY: Grady County, 1 (OKSU). HUGHES COUNTY: near Gerty, 1 (ECENT); 4 mi. S Lamar, 1 (OMNH); city lake, Wetumka, 2 (ECENT); R10, Sec. 9, 1.75 mi. N, 0.5 mi. W Wetumka, 1 (OMNH); 3 mi. E Wetumka, 1 (ECENT). KINGFISHER COUNTY: 9 mi. W Crescent, 1 (OKSU). KIOWA COUNTY: 12 mi. N, 5 mi. W Indiahoma, 1 (CAMCO); southwest sector, N Wichita Mountains Wildlife Refuge, 1 (OMNH). LATIMER COUNTY: near Wilburton, 1 (OKSU); 5 mi. N Wilburton, 2 (USNM); 5 mi. SW Wilburton, 1 (USNM). LEFLORE COUNTY: 8 mi. E Big Cedar, 1 (USNM); 16 mi. S Heavener, 4 (USNM); Big Creek, Page, 2 (USNM); 4 mi. NE Page, 1 (USNM); 6 mi. E Page, 1 (USNM); Poteau, 1 (OKSU). LINCOLN COUNTY: 5 mi. NW Chandler, 1 (OKSU); 7 mi. S Cushing, 1 (OKSU); 9 mi. S Cushing, 1 (OKSU); Merrick, 1 (CSUO); SW Wellston, 2 (OKSU). LOGAN COUNTY: 5.5 mi. N, 1.5 mi. E Arcadia, 1 (OMNH); near Cimarron River, S Crescent, 6 (OKSU); N Guthrie, 1 (OKSU); NW Guthrie, 2 (OKSU); 0.5 mi. N Langston University, 1 (OKSU); near Waterloo, 2 (OKSU). LOVE COUNTY: 7 mi. W Thackerville, 1 (OKSU). MAJOR COUNTY: near Fairview, 1 (OKSU); 7 mi. W, 1.5 mi. S Fairview, 2 (OKSU); near Longdale, 1 (OKSU); 12 mi. NE Seiling, 1 (KU). MCCLAIN COUNTY: W Blanchard, 1 (ECENT); Hester Ranch, 1 mi. E, 1 mi. S Dibble, 1 (OMNH). MCCURTAIN COUNTY: Pleasant Hill Area, 8 mi. S Haworth, 1 (OKSU); McCurtain County, 2 (OKSU); Sherwood, 1 (USNM); 5 mi. SE Smithville, 1 (USNM); 30 mi. S Smithville, 1 (USNM). OKLAHOMA COUNTY: S Arcadia, 1 (OKSU); 2.5 mi. E, 0.5 mi. S Edmond, 1 (OMNH); jct. Lake Hawassee Rd. & 10th St., 1 (OKSU); 2 mi. W Luther, 1 (OKSU); Oklahoma City, 1 (OMNH). OSAGE COUNTY: Phillips Ranch, 10 mi. SW Bartlesville, 9 (OMNH); 10 mi. SW Bartlesville, 1 (OMNH); Osage County, 2 (OMNH). PAWNEE COUNTY: Cimarron River, northeast part of county, 1 (OMNH); 12.5 mi. E Glencoe, 1 (OKSU); 1 mi. N, 2.5 mi. W Hallett, 2 (OKSU); Pawnee County, 1 (OKSU); Venuble Sheep Ranch, 5 mi. N, 7 mi. W Pawnee, 1 (OMNH); 8 mi. S Pawnee, 1 (OKSU). PAYNE COUNTY: 2.7 mi. W Hwy 177 on Burris Rd., 1 (OKSU); 1 mi. E SH 108 bridge over Cimarron River, 1 (OKSU); 4 mi. E, 3 mi. N Cushing, 1

(OKSU); 15 mi. N Cushing, 1 (OKSU); Lake Carl Blackwell, 1 (OKSU); Lake Carl Blackwell, 1 mi. NW McMurty Dam, 1 (OKSU); 1.5 mi. S Pierre Beatte Monument, Stillwater, 1 (OKSU); 3 mi. E Stillwater, 1 (OKSU); 9 mi. NE Stillwater, 2 (OKSU); 9 mi. SW Stillwater, 1 (OKSU); Lake Carl Blackwell, 10 mi. W Stillwater, 1 (OKSU); 10 mi. W, 4 mi. S Stillwater, 1 (OKSU); 11 mi. W Stillwater, 2 (OKSU); 12 mi. W Stillwater, 1 (OKSU); 12 mi. E Stillwater, 1 (OKSU); 2.5 mi. S Perkins Rd. on Hwy 51, 1 (OKSU); 8 mi. S, 0.5 mi. E jct. 6th & Western Sts., 1 (OKSU); T20N, R3E, Sec. 21, 1 (OKSU). PITTSBURG COUNTY: 4 mi. N Blocker, 1 (USNM); S U.S. Naval Ammunitions Depot, McAlester, 2 (OKSU); southeast side U.S. Naval Ammunitions Depot, McAlester, 1 (OKSU); U.S. Naval Ammunitions Depot, McAlester, 1 (ECENT); 7.5 mi. SW McAlester, 1 (USNM); 15 mi. E McAlester, 1 (OKSU); Pittsburg County, 4 (OMNH). PONTOTOC COUNTY: 2 mi. SE Ada, 1 (ECENT); 10 mi. W Ada, 1 (ECENT); Pontotoc County, 1 (OMNH). POTTAWATOMIE COUNTY: Smith Ranch, 17 mi. E, 1 mi. N Noble, 2 (OMNH). PUSHMATAHA COUNTY: near Albion, 1 (ECENT); Pushmataha County, 3 (OMNH). ROGER MILLS COUNTY: 7 mi. E, 1 mi. N Cheyenne, 1 (OKSU); Roger Mills County, 1 (OKSU). STEPHENS COUNTY: 4 mi. W, 4 mi. N Duncan, 1 (OKSU); 4 mi. W Marlow, 1 (OKSU); Stephens County, 1 (OKSU). TILLMAN COUNTY: 35 mi. S Indiahoma, 1 (CAMCO); 8.5 mi. E, 0.5 mi. N Manitou, 1 (CAMCO); 1.5 mi. S, 6.25 mi. W Snyder, 1 (CAMCO). WASHINGTON COUNTY: US 75, 1.5 mi. N Ramona, 1 (OKSU). WOODS COUNTY: near Alva, 1 (OKSU). WOODWARD COUNTY: near Woodward, 1 (ECENT).

Geomys bursarius.—Specimens examined (total 1,267); ADAIR COUNTY: 2.5 mi. E Stilwell, 9 (UIMNH). ALFALFA COUNTY: Wheatland Exp. Farm, Cherokee, 8 (OKSU); 2.5 mi. E, 2 mi. S Cherokee, 1 (OMNH); 3 mi. N, 6.5 mi. E Cherokee, 1,170 ft., 3 (OMNH); Great Salt Plains, 1 (OUBS); Great Salt Plains Wildlife Refuge, 9 (OKSU); 2.5 mi. E Vining, 1 (OKSU); Wheatland Exp. Station, 1 (UMMZ). ATOKA COUNTY: 5 mi. E Atoka, 3 (OKSU); Kiedaisch Ranch, 1 mi. S Wardville, 1 (ECENT). BEAVER COUNTY: 2 mi. W Forgan, 5 (OKSU); 3 mi. S, 3 mi. E Slapout, 1 (OKSU). BECKHAM COUNTY: 0.5 mi. S Sayre, 1 (OKSU). BLAINE COUNTY: 0.25 mi. W Canton, 1 (OKSU); 0.5 mi. E Canton, 1 (OMNH); 0.25 mi. W Hwy, Canton Dam, 1 (OKSU); Public Hunting Grounds, Canton Reservoir, 1 (OKSU); Canton Shooting Grounds, 2 (OKSU); between Canton Reservoir & Hwy 58, 1 (OKSU); Canton Reservoir, Fairview Landing, 1 (OKSU); 1 mi. W Longdale, 5 (OKSU); Roman Nose State Park, 6 (OKSU). BRYAN COUNTY: 7 mi. S, 5 mi. W Bennington, 4 (OKSU); Colbert, 3 (TMM); 5 mi. SW Colbert, 12 (TMM); 4 mi. E Durant at old Hwy 70, 8 (OKSU). CADDO COUNTY: Anadarko, 1

(CSUO); 1 mi. N Anadarko, 5 (OKSU); north side Washita River, 1 mi. N Anadarko, 1 (OKSU); Apache, 2 (OKSU); 6 mi. E Binger, 2 (OMNH); Caddo County, 1 (OMNH), 1 (ECENT); Cedar Lake, 100 yds. W west end dam, 50 yds. S, 1 (CSUO); 5 mi. W Cogar, 1 (OMNH), 3 (USNM); 5 mi. N Ft. Cobb, 1 (OKSU); 10 mi. N, 6 mi. W Ft. Cobb, 1 (CAMCO); Hinton, 2 (OKSU); Red Rock Canyon, 1 mi. S Hinton, 6 (OMNH); 1 mi. S Kiwanis, Hinton, 1 (OKSU); 2 mi. N Hinton, 1 (OKSU). CANADIAN COUNTY: Federal Reformatory, El Reno, 1 (OKSU); 0.5 mi. W, 0.5 mi. N El Reno, 2 (OKSU); 6 mi. N, 4 mi. E El Reno, 2 (OKSU); Cottonwood Creek, Piedmont, 1 (CSUO); 4 mi. E, 2 mi. S Union City, 1 (OKSU); 4 mi. E Yukon, 1 (OKSU); T12N, R7W, Sec. 16, 1 (OKSU). CARTER COUNTY: 2 mi. W Ratliff City, 2 (OKSU), 3 (UMMZ); T1N, R2W, Sec. 26, SARP Site W3, south bank Wildhorse Creek, 12 mi. W I-35, 1 (OKSU). CHOCTAW COUNTY: 7 mi. SSE Ft. Towson, 400 ft., 7 (OMNH); 1.5 mi. N Hugo, 2 (KU); 5 mi. N Hugo, 1 (OKSU); opposite Arthur, Texas, near mouth of Boggy River, north side Red River, 4 (USNM); Sawyer, 1 (OKSU); Kiamichi River, Sawyer, 1 (UMMZ). CIMARRON COUNTY: N Boise City, 1 (OKSU); 8 mi. W Boise City, 14 (OKSU). CLEVELAND COUNTY: Cleveland County, 1 (OMNH); 3 mi. N Post Office, Lexington, 2 (OMNH); Moore, 1 (CSUO); Noble, Oklahoma Territory, 2 (FMNH); Norman, 24 (OMNH); Norman environs, 1 (OMNH); Asp & Timberdell, Norman, 20 (OMNH); Duck Pond, Norman, 1 (OMNH); Jenkins & Timberdell, Norman, 2 (OMNH); National Guard Range, Norman, 1 (OMNH); Reeves Park, Norman, 10 (OMNH); Smoking Oak Dr., Norman, 1 (OMNH); Sooner Trailer Park, Norman, 2 (OMNH); South Base, Norman, 2 (OMNH); South Campus, Norman, 9 (OMNH); Southbase Golf Course, Norman, 1 (OMNH); Timberdell & Asp, Norman, 3 (OMNH); University of Oklahoma Golf Course, Norman, 2 (OMNH); 1305 George St., Norman, 1 (OMNH); 2706 Walnut St., Norman, 2 (OMNH); 0.25 blk. W Lindsey & Santa Fe RR, Norman, 2 (OMNH); 0.5 mi. S Norman, west side Jenkins St., 6 (MVZ); E. Robinson, 0.5 mi. E Norman, 1 (OMNH); 0.5 mi. S Norman, 13 (USNM); 0.5 mi. SW Norman, 3 (USNM); 1 mi. N Norman on Hwy 77, 1 (OMNH); 1 mi. S Norman, 2 (OMNH), 1 (USNM), 1 (MVZ); 1.1 mi. E Norman, 1 (OMNH); 1 mi. S, 3 mi. E Norman, 2 (OMNH); 1.4 mi. E Norman, 3 (KU); 1.5 mi. E Norman, 3 (OMNH); 1.5 mi. SW Norman, 6 (USNM); 1.6 mi. E Norman, 1 (OMNH); 1.6 mi. N Norman, 2 (OMNH); 1.7 mi. N Norman, 1 (OMNH), 1 (USNM); 2 mi. S Norman, 1 (OMNH); 2 mi. E Norman, 1 (KU); 2.25 mi. S Norman, 1 (OMNH); 2.3 mi. E Norman, 1 (OMNH); 2.4 mi. E Norman, 1 (OMNH); 2.5 mi. E Norman, 1 (OMNH); 2.5 mi. SW Norman, 3 (OMNH); 2.7 mi. S Norman, 1 (USNM); 2.8 mi. E Norman, 1 (OMNH); 2.8 mi. S Norman, 2 (USNM);

E of city dump, 2.8 mi. S Norman, 1 (MVZ); 2.85 mi. E Norman, 1 (OMNH); 3 mi. E Norman, 4 (OMNH); 3 mi. S Norman, 1 (OMNH); 3 mi. SW Norman, 10 (USNM); 3.5 mi. E Norman, 4 (KU); 4 mi. S Norman, 2 (OMNH); 4 mi. E Norman, 2 (KU); 5 mi. E Norman, 3 (OMNH); 5 mi. E, 1 mi. S Norman, 1 (OMNH); 5 mi. S, 1 mi. W Norman, 2 (OMNH); 5 mi. E, 3 mi. S Norman, 1 (FWMSH); 6.5 mi. SE Norman, 3 (OMNH); 7 mi. S Norman on Hwy 77, 1 (OMNH); 7.2 mi. E Norman, 2 (KU); east bank Little River, 7.2 mi. E Norman, 1 (KU); 12 mi. E, 1 mi. N Norman, 6 (KU); 17.2 mi. E, 1 mi. N Norman, 2 (KU); 2 mi. S Slaughterville, 5 (OMNH). COAL COUNTY: 1 mi. W Coalgate, 3 (OKSU). COMANCHE COUNTY: 0.5 mi. Fletcher, 1 (OKSU); 13 mi. E, 4 mi. N Lawton, 1 (CAMCO). COTTON COUNTY: 3.3 mi. ESE Taylor, 900 ft., 1 (OMNH); 5 mi. SE Taylor, 900 ft., 1 (OMNH); 12 mi. S Temple, 1 (TMM); 8 mi. E Walters, 5 (OKSU). CREEK COUNTY: Cimarron River Bridge, Alton, 1 (OKSU); 7 mi. NE Sapulpa, 1 (OKSU); 15 mi. W Sapulpa, 1 (UIMNH); 2 mi. N Welty, 2 (OKSU). CUSTER COUNTY: Foss Reservoir, Washita Natl. Wildlife Refuge, 1 (OKSU); campus, Southwestern State University, Weatherford, 4 (KU). DELAWARE COUNTY: 3.5 mi. NE Kansas, 2 (UIMNH). DEWEY COUNTY: 5 mi. SW Canton, 1 (KU); 5 mi. W Canton, 4 (KU); Dewey County, 1 (KU); 5 mi. S Vici, 3 (OKSU); 5 mi. SE Vici, 2 (OKSU). ELLIS COUNTY: 2 mi. N Harmon, 2 (FWMSH); Shattuck, 5 (OKSU). GARFIELD COUNTY: Enid, 2 (OKSU); northwest section Enid near Oakwood Rd., 1 (OKSU); University Lake Golf Course, Enid, 1 (FWMSH). GARVIN COUNTY: 3 mi. E Lindsay, 2 (OKSU); northwest corner cemetery, Lindsay, 1 (CSUO); Washita River bottom, Pauls Valley, 1 (UIMNH); Washita River, Pauls Valley, 1 (OKSU); T1S, R1W, Sec. 26, Wildhorse Creek, 1 mi. E SH 74, 1 (OKSU). GRADY COUNTY: 3 mi. W, 0.1 mi. S Blanchard, 1 (OMNH); 1 mi. W Chickasha, 1 (OKSU); 2 mi. E Chickasha, 10 (OKSU); 10 mi. E Chickasha, 1 (OKSU); T3N, R7W, Sec. 11, SARP Site R8, Rush Creek, 10 mi. W SH 29, 1 (OKSU). GRANT COUNTY: 1.4 mi. W, 1 mi. N Hawley, 12 (OMNH); 2 mi. N, 2 mi. W Jefferson, 1 (OMNH). GREER COUNTY: Mangum Cemetery, 1 (OUBS). 3 (UMMZ); 2 mi. S, 0.25 mi. W Mangum, 1 (OKSU); Quartz Mt., 1 (MSU). HARMON COUNTY: Buck Creek, southwest corner state, 1 (TMM); 1.5 mi. N Gould, 1 (TTU); 10.5 mi. S Gould, 1 (OKSU); 1 mi. SW Hollis, 6 (OKSU); 3 mi. W, 7 mi. S Hollis, 1 (OKSU); 8 mi. N Hollis, 1 (TTU); 10 mi. N, 1 mi. W Hollis, 1 (TTU); 13 mi. W Hollis, 1 (CSUO); 13.5 mi. N Hollis, 1 (OKSU); loc. #7, 3 (TTU). HARPER COUNTY: Buffalo Creek & Hwy 64, 2 (UMMZ), 2 (OKSU); Doby Springs, 10 mi. W Buffalo, 4 (OKSU); 3 mi. N Ft. Supply, 7 (USNM); 5 mi. N Ft. Supply, 1 (USNM); Great Salt Plains Refuge, 1 (UMMZ); Southern Plains Exp. Range, 22 (OKSU);

Southern Plains Exp. Station, 7 (UMMZ). HASKELL COUNTY: Keota, 2 (OKSU); 100 yds. S Stigler, 1 (OMNH); 4 mi. NE Stigler on Hwy 2, 2 (OKSU); 5.5 mi. N Stigler, 1 (OKSU); Whitefield, 4 (OKSU). HUGHES COUNTY: 1.5 mi. W, 0.5 mi. S Atwood, 1 (ECENT); north bank South Canadian River, S Holdenville, 4 (OKSU); near Sand Lake, Holdenville Dam, 1 (OKSU); 3 mi. N Wetumka, 1 (ECENT); 3.5 mi. S Wetumka, 1 (ECENT); 6 mi. S, 0.5 mi. W Wetumka, 1 (ECENT). JACKSON COUNTY: 5 mi. SW Eldorado, 2 (UIMNH); 14 mi. S Olustee, 2 (TMM). JEFFERSON COUNTY: 1 mi. E Ringling, 7 (OKSU); 3 mi. S Waurika, 4 (OKSU). JOHNSTON COUNTY: Milburn, 1 (OKSU); 4 mi. N Mill Creek, 1 mi. E SH 7, 1 (ECENT); 1 mi. E, 4 mi. S Tishomingo, 1 (OKSU); 1 mi. E, 5 mi. S Tishomingo, 1 (OKSU); 1 mi. E Tishomingo near Hwy 78, 1 (ECENT); 2 mi. E Tishomingo, 1 (ECENT). KAY COUNTY: 1 mi. E Blackwell, 1 (OKSU); 1 mi. E, 2 mi. N Blackwell, 1 (OKSU); 3 mi. S, 10 mi. W Blackwell, 1 (OKSU); Ponca Agency, 6 (USNM); north edge Ponca City, 1 (OMNH); 2500 W. Central, Ponca City, 1 (OKSU); 2 mi. S, 6 mi. W Ponca City, 1 (OKSU); 3 mi. E Ponca City on Hwy 60, 0.75 mi. on McCord Rd., 1 (OKSU); T26N, R2E, SE 1/4 Sec. 18, Ponca City, 1 (OKSU); T26N, R2E, SE 1/4 Sec. 31, Ponca City, 1 (OKSU); T26N, R3E, SE 1/4 Sec. 31, Ponca City, 1 (OKSU); 1 mi. W, 2.5 mi. S Tonkawa, 1 (OKSU); 10 mi. W, 2.5 mi. S Tonkawa, 1 (OKSU). KINGFISHER COUNTY: 9 mi. W Crescent, 1 (OKSU); 14 mi. W Crescent, 1 (OKSU); Dover, 1 (OKSU); 2 mi. N, 1 mi. W Dover, 1 (OKSU). KIOWA COUNTY: Kiowa Agency, 2 (USNM); 7.5 mi. W, 2.5 mi. S Snyder, 2 (CAMCO); 7.5 mi. W Snyder, 1 (CAMCO). LATIMER COUNTY: 3 mi. W, 1 mi. S Eastern Oklahoma State College campus, 1 (OKSU); 9 mi. W Talihina, 1 (OKSU). LINCOLN COUNTY: Agra, 3 (OKSU); 1.5 mi. N Carney, 1 (OKSU); Chandler, 8 (OKSU); 2.5 mi. W Meeker, 1 (OKSU); 5 mi. W Meeker, 1 (OKSU); Wellston, 7 (OKSU). LOGAN COUNTY: Coyle, 6 (OKSU); 4 mi. NE Coyle on Hwy 33, 2 (OKSU); 2 mi. E Guthrie, 1 (OKSU); Logan County, 1 (CSUO). LOVE COUNTY: 7 mi. S Marietta, 10 (OKSU). MAJOR COUNTY: 2 mi. E, 4 mi. S Ames, 1 (OKSU); 2 mi. W Bouse Jct., 6 (OKSU); 1 mi. S Cleo Springs, 1 (OKSU); 3 mi. S Cleo Springs, 1 (OMNH); 4 mi. SE Cleo Springs, 1 (OKSU); 5.5 mi. S Waynoka, 1 (OMNH). MARSHALL COUNTY: 0.75 mi. field station, 1 (OMNH); Johnson Farm, 1 (OMNH); Marshall County, 15 (OMNH); University of Oklahoma Biology Station, 9 (OMNH), 1 (OKSU); 100 yds. E University of Oklahoma Biological Station, 1 (OMNH); 0.5 mi. W University of Oklahoma Biological Station, 1 (OMNH); 1 mi. E University of Oklahoma Biological Station, 1 (OMNH); 1 mi. W University of Oklahoma Biological Station, 1 (OMNH); 1.5 mi. W University of Oklahoma Biological Station, 1 (OMNH); 2.5 mi. W University of Oklahoma Biological Station, 1 (OUBS); 2 mi. W University of Oklahoma Biological Station, 2 (OUBS); University of Oklahoma Biological Station lawn, 1 (OMNH); Island #2, Lake Texoma, 1 (OMNH); south side Washita River on SH 12, 1 (OKSU), 2 (UMMZ); University of Oklahoma Biological Station, Willis, 2 (OMNH); Willis, 2 (OMNH); 0.25 mi. W Willis, 1 (OUBS); 0.5 mi. W Willis, 2 (OUBS); 0.5 mi. N Willis, 2 (OMNH); 1 mi. E Willis, 670 ft., 1 (OMNH); 1 mi. N Willis, 700 ft., 12 (OMNH); 1 mi. W Willis, 700 ft., 8 (OMNH); 1.5 mi. N Willis, 1 (OUBS); 2 mi. E Willis, 2 (OMNH); 2 mi. E Willis, 0.5 mi. N University of Oklahoma Biological Station, 640 ft., 2 (OMNH); 2 mi. W Willis, 640 ft., 2 (OMNH); 2 mi. W Willis, 690 ft., 1 (OMNH); 2 mi. W Willis, 1 (OUBS); 2.5 mi. NW Willis, 3 (OUBS); 3 mi. W Willis, 1 (OUBS); 3.5 mi. W Willis, 2 (OUBS); 10 mi. N Willis, jct. Hwys 99 & 32, 720 ft., 1 (OMNH). MCCLAIN COUNTY: south side Canadian River, Asher, 2 (UMMZ); 2 mi. W Byars, 3 (UMMZ), 2 (OKSU); 2.7 mi. N, 0.5 mi. W Goldsby, 2 (OMNH); 2.7 mi. N, 5 mi. W Goldsby, 1 (USNM); 3 mi. W Newcastle, 1 (ECENT); 4 mi. W Newcastle, 1 (CSUO); 2 mi. S Noble, 1 (OMNH); T8N, R2W, Sec. 10, 1 mi. S, 1 mi. W Norman, 1 (OMNH); 1 mi. W, 1 mi. S Norman, 1 (OMNH); Rosedale, 1 (OKSU); Wayne, 3 (OKSU); near Wayne, 1 (OKSU); T8N, R2W, Sec. 10, 1 (OMNH). MCCURTAIN COUNTY: 13 mi. SE Broken Bow, 1 (OMNH); 2 mi. SE Idabel, 3 (OKSU). MCINTOSH COUNTY: Eufaula Cemetery, Eufaula, 3 (OKSU), 5 (UMMZ); 11 mi. W Eufaula on Hwy 9, 1 (CSUO); 0.5 mi. S Hitchita, 1 (OKSU). MURRAY COUNTY: 5 mi. W, 2.5 mi. N Sulphur, 1 (ECENT). MUSKOGEE COUNTY: Braggs, 12 (OKSU); Wildlife Conservation Station, Braggs, 1 (UMMZ); 2.25 mi. E Braggs, 1 (UMMZ); 2.5 mi. E Braggs, 1 (UMMZ); Ft. Gibson, 30 (OKSU); 0.5 mi. S Ft. Gibson, 1 (OKSU); 0.5 mi. SE Ft. Gibson, 1 (UIMNH); 1 mi. S Ft. Gibson, 1 (UMMZ); 2 mi. S Ft. Gibson, 1 (OKSU); 3 mi. E Wainwright, 3 (OMNH); 1 mi. E Warner, 5 (OKSU); 2 mi. S Warner, 1 (OMNH). OKFUSKEE COUNTY: 2.5 mi. W Mason, 1 (OKSU); 3 mi. N, 1 mi. E Mason, 1 (OKSU). OKLAHOMA COUNTY: 5 mi. E Central State University, 1 (CSUO); Trosper Park, Del City, 1 (OMNH); Edmond, 4 (CSUO); E Edmond, 1 (OKSU); cemetery, Edmond, 1 (FWMSH); S jct. 2nd & Bryant, Edmond, 1 (CSUO); jct. Blvd. & 9th St., Edmond, 1 (CSUO); 327 E. 10th, Edmond, 3 (CSUO); 5012 N.E. 70th St., Oklahoma City, 1 (CSUO); NW Edmond, sewage plant, Western & Coffee Creek Rd., 1 (CSUO); 2.4 mi. E, 5.8 mi. S Edmond, Witcher, 1 (CSUO); 5 mi. E Edmond, 1 (CSUO), 3 (OKSU); 7 mi. N Edmond, 1 (ECENT); 0.75 mi. W Hiwasee Rd., Jones, 1 (CSUO); 2 blks. E Lake Overholser, 1 (OKSU); 1 mi. N Midwest City, 1 (OKSU); 1.5 mi. E Tinker Field, Midwest City, 1 (OKSU); Dunn's Ranch, Rt. 1, Box 101, Newalla, 1 (OKSU); Oklahoma

City, 9 (CSUO); Oklahoma City Zoo Amphitheatre, 1 (CSUO); N.W. Expressway & N. Portland, Oklahoma City, 1 (CSUO); 3 blks. S 16th & Ann Arbor, 1 (CSUO); 701 N.W. 63rd, Oklahoma City, 1 (CSUO); 2800 S. Eastern, Oklahoma City, 1 (OKSU); 5716 N. Everest St., Oklahoma City, 1 (CSUO); 3 blks. S jct. 16th & Ann Arbor, Oklahoma City, 1 (CSUO); SW corner N. Bryant & N.E. 126th, 1 (CSUO); 0.25 mi. N 234th on May Ave., 1 (CSUO); 0.625 mi. E Spencer, 2 (OKSU); west side Tinker Air Force Base, 1 (OMNH); 2 mi. E Tinker Field, 4 (OKSU); 0.25 mi. S Turner Turnpike toll gate on I-35, 1 (CSUO); 0.65 mi. S Turner Turnpike toll gate on Sooner Rd., 2 (CSUO). OKMULGEE COUNTY: Beggs, 2 mi. N on alt. 75, 2 mi. W, 0.5 mi. N, 1 (OKSU); 4 mi. S, 6 mi. E Nuyaka, 1 (OKSU); Okmulgee County, 1 (ECENT); 3 mi. N Schulter, 1 (ECENT). OSAGE COUNTY: Keystone Reservoir, Osage, 1 (OKSU); T26N, R3E, SE 1/4 Sec. 31, Ponca City, 1 (OKSU); 3.5 mi. E Ponca City on Hwy 60, 0.75 mi. S on Market Rd., 1 (OKSU). PAWNEE COUNTY: 0.5 mi. W Cleveland, 3 (OKSU); 4 mi. N Keystone, 1 (OKSU); G. A. Moore Farm, 2 mi. SW Pawnee, 1 (OKSU). PAYNE COUNTY: Boomer Lake Park, 1 (OKSU); 4 mi. E Coyle on SH 33, 1 (OKSU); Fairlawn Cemetery, 6 (OKSU); 0.25 mi. W SH 177 on Lakeview Rd., 1 (OKSU); campus, Oklahoma State University, 1 (FWMSH); Payne County, 1 (OKSU); Perkins, 2 (CSUO); 1 mi. W Perkins Corner, 9 (OKSU); 3 mi. W, 0.5 mi. S Perkins, 1 (OKSU); 5 mi. E Perkins on SH 33, 1 (OKSU); 0.5 mi. N, 5 mi. E Ripley, 1 (OKSU); 0.25 mi. N Sanborn Lake, 1 (OKSU); Stillwater, 6 (OKSU); Stillwater Cemetery, 2 (OKSU); 120 N. Stallard Dr., Stillwater, 1 (OKSU); Virginia St., Stillwater, 1 (OKSU); Boomer Creek, Stillwater, 1 (OKSU); Boomer Lake Area, Stillwater, 1 (OKSU); Boomer Lake, Stillwater, 4 (OKSU); west Boomer Lake, Stillwater, 1 (OKSU); cemetery, E Stillwater, 3 (OKSU); E edge Stillwater, 1 (OKSU); Golf Course, N Stillwater, 1 (OKSU); Hillcrest Golf Course, Stillwater, 3 (OKSU); just N Western St. & Admiral Ave., Stillwater, 1 (OKSU); 0.25 mi. below Dam, Boomer Lake, Stillwater, 1 (OKSU); 100 yds. W Ag Hall, campus, Oklahoma State University, Stillwater, 1 (OKSU); 0.25 mi. S Stillwater, 1 (OKSU); 0.5 mi. N Stillwater, 2 (OKSU); 0.8 mi. E Stillwater, 1 (OKSU); 1 mi. E Fairlawn Cemetery, Stillwater, 1 (OKSU); 1 mi. N jct. Hwy 51 & Western Ave., 0.125 mi. W, Stillwater, 1 (OKSU); 1 mi. N Stillwater on Boomer Rd., 1 (OKSU); 1 mi. N, 0.5 mi. W Stillwater, 1 (OKSU); 1 mi. S Stillwater, 1 (OKSU); 1 mi. S, 0.75 mi. W Stillwater, 1 (OKSU); 1 mi. SW Stillwater, 5 (OKSU); Izaac Walton League Plot, 1 mi. N Stillwater, 1 (FWMSH); 1 mi. W Stillwater, 1 (OKSU); 1 mi. W, 2 mi. S Stillwater, 1 (OKSU); 1.2 mi. W, 1 mi. N Stillwater, 1 (FWMSH); 1.5 mi. SW Stillwater, 1 (OKSU); 1.5 mi. W, 0.75 mi. S Stillwater, 1 (OKSU); dairy barn, Oklahoma State University, 1.5 mi. W Stillwater, 1 (OKSU); Sanborn,

Izaac Walton Lodge, 1.5 mi. N Stillwater, 2 (FWMSH); 1.75 mi. N, Hwy 40, Stillwater, 2 (OKSU); 2 mi. E, 1.5 mi. N Stillwater, 1 (OKSU); 2 mi. E, 2 mi. S Stillwater, 1 (OKSU); 2 mi. N Stillwater, 4 (OKSU); 2 mi. N, 1 mi. E Stillwater, 1 (OKSU); 2 mi. N, 3 mi. E Stillwater, 1 (OKSU); 2 mi. S Hwy 51 on Western, Stillwater, 1 (OKSU); 2 mi. S Stillwater, 2 (OKSU); 2 mi. S, 0.5 mi. E Stillwater, 2 (OKSU); 2 mi. SE Stillwater, 1 (OKSU); 2 mi. SW Stillwater, 2 (OKSU); 2 mi. W Stillwater, 1 (OKSU); 2 mi. W, 0.4 mi. N Stillwater, 1 (OKSU); 2.5 mi. E, 3 mi. S Stillwater, 1 (OKSU); 3 mi. E, 1.25 mi. N Stillwater, 1 (OKSU); 3 mi. E, 3 mi. S jct. Jardot St. & SH 51, Stillwater, 1 (OKSU); 3 mi. N Stillwater, 2 (OKSU); 3 mi. NW Stillwater, 1 (UMMZ); 3 mi. W Stillwater, 1 (OKSU); 3 mi. W, 0.5 mi. S Stillwater, 1 (UIMNH); 4 mi. E Stillwater, 1 (OKSU); 4 mi. E, 1 mi. S Stillwater, 1 (OKSU); 4 mi. E, 0.5 mi. S Stillwater, 1 (OKSU); 4 mi. N Stillwater, 3 (OKSU); 4 mi. W Stillwater, 3 (OKSU); 4.5 mi. W Stillwater, 1 (OKSU); 5 mi. E, 3 mi. S Stillwater, 1 (OKSU); 5 mi. N Stillwater, 2 (OKSU); 5 mi. W Stillwater, 0.25 mi. N SH 51, 1 (OKSU); 5 mi. W, 0.5 mi. S Stillwater, 2 (OKSU); 5.5 mi. N, 2 mi. E jct. 6th St. & Perkins Rd., Stillwater, 1 (OKSU); 6 mi. E, 1 mi. S, 0.25 mi. E Stillwater, 1 (OKSU); 6 mi. N, 2 mi. E Stillwater, 1 (OKSU); 6 mi. S, 1 mi. E Stillwater, 2 (OKSU); 7 mi. N Stillwater, 1 (OKSU); 7 mi. SE Stillwater, 1 (OKSU); 7.5 mi. SE Stillwater, 1 (OKSU); 8 mi. E, 0.25 mi. S Stillwater, 4 (OKSU); 10 mi. N Stillwater, 1 (OKSU); 25 mi. E, 2.6 mi. S Stillwater, 1 (OKSU); 0.25 mi. W Old Vet Village, 1 (OKSU); S side Cimarron River, 2 mi. SW Yale, 4 (OKSU); 8.5 mi. S jct. SH 51 & I-35, 1 (OKSU); 2.5 mi. S, 0.25 mi. E SH 51 & 177 S, 1 (OKSU); 4 mi. E US Hwy 177 on Mehan Rd., 2.5 mi. S, 1 (OKSU); 7 mi. E, 3 mi. S jct. Hwys 5 & 177, 1 (OKSU); Hwy 40 & Yost Lake Rd., 1 (OKSU); T19N, R1E, SE 1/4 Sec. 18, 1 (OKSU); T18N, R3E, SW 1/4 Sec. 27, 1 (OKSU); T18N, R3E, Sec. 27, 4 mi. E Hwy 177, 2.5 mi. S Mehan Rd., 1 (OKSU). PITTSBURG COUNTY: near Kiowa, 1 (ECENT); McAlester Cemetery, 8 (OKSU); 8 mi. W McAlester, 1 (ECENT). PONTOTOC COUNTY: Ada, 1 (ECENT); Rosedale Cemetery, 3 mi. W Ada, 1 (ECENT); 7 mi. NE Ada, 8 (ECENT); Pontotoc County, 1 (ECENT); Tyrola, 2 (OKSU). POTTAWATOMIE COUNTY: Asher, 7 (OKSU); 2 mi. E Dale, 1 (OMNH); 2.5 mi. E Dale, 1 (OMNH); 0.25 mi. E McLoud, 1 (CSUO); Tecumseh, 4 (KU); 1 mi. W Tecumseh, 1 (OMNH), 2 (KU); 5 mi. W Tecumseh, 4 (KU); 6.5 mi. W Tecumseh, 5 (KU). PUSHMATAHA COUNTY: Antlers, 4 (OKSU); 1 mi. S Finley, 2 (OKSU); T4S, R17E, Sec. 20, 1 (OKSU). ROGER MILLS COUNTY: 1 mi. N Cheyenne, 3 (UMMZ); 1 mi. N Cheyenne on N side Washita River, 1 (OKSU); 1.7 mi. N Cheyenne, 2,000 ft., 3 (OMNH); 2.7 mi. N Cheyenne, 2,000 ft., 1 (OMNH); 2.5 mi. E, 1.5 mi. S Reydon, 1 (CAMCO); Black Kettle Natl. Grasslands, 7.2 mi. W Roll, 1 (TTU).

SEMINOLE COUNTY: 1 mi. S, 2 mi. E, 7.5 mi. N Post Office, Bowlegs, 1 (OMNH); 6.3 mi. N, 2 mi. E Bowlegs, 1 (OMNH); 1 mi. E, 2 mi. N Maud, 1 (OMNH); 1 mi. E, 4 mi. N Maud, 1 (OMNH); 4 mi. W Seminole, 1 (ECENT). SEQUOYAH COUNTY: Redland, 3 (USNM); 1 mi. S Sallisaw, 1 (OKSU); 5.5 mi. W Sallisaw, 1 (ECENT); 2 mi. E Vian, 4 (OKSU). STEPHENS COUNTY: 0.25 mi. E Claud, 6 (OMNH); 0.25 mi. E, 1 mi. S Claud, 1 (OMNH); 0.75 mi. S, 0.25 mi. E Claud, 2 (OMNH); 2 mi. W, 0.5 mi. S Comanche, 1 (OKSU); 4 mi. W, 4.25 mi. N Duncan, 1 (OKSU); 4 mi. S, 6 mi. E Duncan, 1 (CAMCO); 8 mi. W, 0.5 mi. S Duncan, 1 (CAMCO); 1 mi. E Marlow, 4 (OKSU); 2.25 mi. W Marlow, 1 (CAMCO); 9 mi. N, 1 mi. E Ringling, 1 (OKSU); T1N, R6W, Sec. 23, 1 (OMNH). TEXAS COUNTY: Guymon, 3 (OKSU); RR at Hooker, 1 (OKSU). TILLMAN COUNTY: Davidson, 1 (OKSU); Frederick Cemetery, 3 (OKSU); 4 mi. W Frederick, 1 (OKSU); 5.5 mi. S Grandfield, 2 (OMNH); 7 mi. W, 1 mi. S Snyder, 1 (CAMCO); 7.5 mi. W, 2.5 mi. S Snyder, 2 (CAMCO); Tipton Grade School, 1 (OKSU). TULSA COUNTY: Garnett, 4 (UMMZ); Mohawk Park, 16 (OKSU); 8 mi. W Red Fork, 5 (USNM); 5 mi. W Sand Springs Bridge, 5 (OKSU); 2 mi. S Sand Springs, 1 (OKSU); 5 mi. W Sand Springs, 2 (OKSU); 0.25 mi. W jct. Sheridan & 101st, 1 (OKSU); Tulsa, 4 (UMMZ); east bank Arkansas River at 38th St., Tulsa, 1 (OKSU). WAGONER COUNTY: Coweta, 3 (UMMZ); S Arkansas River, Coweta, 5 (OKSU); 2.5 mi. SSW Coweta, 600 ft., 4 (OMNH); 4 mi. N Okay, 1 (OKSU); 4 mi. NW Okay, 2 (UMMZ); 1 mi. S Vann's Lake, 1 (OKSU). WASHINGTON COUNTY: 0.25 mi. E SH 75 on Oglesby Rd., 1 (OKSU). WASHITA COUNTY: 4 mi. E Cordell, 6 (OKSU). WOODS COUNTY: Alva, 8 (FMNH), 2 (OKSU); 4 mi. N Alva, 1 (OKSU); 8 mi. NW Alva, 1 (OMNH), 2 (ECENT); 12 mi. N Alva, 2 (OKSU); 3 mi. E Camp Houston, 2 (OKSU); E side Cimarron River, 6 (UMMZ); E side Cimarron River on Hwy 64, 2 (OKSU); Freedom, 1 (OKSU); Waynoka, 3 (UMMZ); 4.5 mi. W Waynoka, 1 (OKSU); 5 mi. S Waynoka, 1,450 ft., 4 (OMNH). WOODWARD COUNTY: Alabaster Caverns, 2 (OKSU); 1 mi. N, 4 mi. W Mooreland, 1 (OKSU); Southern Great Plains Field Station, 7 (USNM); Woodward, 2 (USNM); 2 mi. NNE Woodward 1,900 ft., 2 (OMNH); 2 mi. NNW Woodward, 1,900 ft., 1 (OMNH); 3.5 mi. WNW Woodward, 1,950 ft., 3 (OMNH); 5 mi. S, 2 mi. W Woodward, 4 (OKSU).

Glaucomys volans.—Specimens examined (total 61); ADAIR COUNTY: Boston Mts., Stilwell, 7 (USNM). CHEROKEE COUNTY: Scraper, 3 (UMMZ). CLEVELAND COUNTY: 1 mi. S Corbett, 1 (OUBS); Hall Park, Norman, 1 (OMNH); 10 mi. E Norman, 2 (OMNH). COAL COUNTY: northwest corner county, 1 (ECENT). COMANCHE COUNTY: 0.5 mi. S Peach Tree Crossing, E Cache Creek, Ft. Sill, 1

(CAMCO). CREEK COUNTY: Sapulpa, 4 (KU). GARVIN COUNTY: 2 mi. S, 1 mi. W Pauls Valley, 1 (ECENT). LATIMER COUNTY: 9 mi. NE Red Oak, 2 (OUBS). MAYES COUNTY: 0.25 mi. S Pryor, 2 (OKSU). MCCURTAIN COUNTY: Beavers Bend State Park, 1 (OUBS). MCIN-TOSH COUNTY: Deep Fork River, Pierce, 1 (FWMSH). OKFUSKEE COUNTY: Okemah, 1 (OKSU). OKLAHOMA COUNTY: Oklahoma City, 1 (USNM). OKMULGEE COUNTY: near Beggs, 1 (OKSU); Ok-mulgee County, 1 (ECENT). PAWNEE COUNTY: 1 mi. E, 1.75 mi. N Pawnee, 1 (KU). PAYNE COUNTY: Payne County, 1 (OKSU); 5 mi. W Perkins, 2 (OKSU); Gallagher Woods, Stillwater, 1 (OKSU); Stillwater Creek, near Stillwater, 1 (OKSU); Stillwater Creek, 0.5 mi. W Stillwater, 2 (OKSU); 2 mi. E, 1 mi. S, Stillwater, 4 (OKSU); 3 mi. S Stillwater, 1 (OKSU); 4 mi. W, 3 mi. S Stillwater, 2 (OKSU); 8 mi. E Stillwater on SH 51, 7 mi. S on SH 108, 1 (OKSU). PITTSBURG COUNTY: near McAlester, 1 (OKSU). PONTOTOC COUNTY: 7 mi. NE Ada, 1 (ECENT); 10 mi. W Ada, 1 (ECENT). TULSA COUNTY: Mohawk Park, 3 (UMMZ); 8 mi. W Red Fork, 4 (USNM); near Tulsa, 1 (OMNH); Tulsa County, 1 (OMNH); 3100 blk. E. 51st St., Tulsa, 1 (CSUO); 4 mi. S Tulsa, 1 (OMNH).

Lasionycteris noctivagans.—Specimens examined (total 4); CLEVELAND COUNTY: 3.5 mi. N Little Axe School, 1 (OMNH). COMANCHE COUNTY: Medicine Bluff, Ft. Sill, 1 (CAMCO). MCCLAIN COUNTY: 2.5 mi. N Newcastle, 1 (ECENT). PAYNE COUNTY: ZTA (sorority) yard, Stillwater, 1 (OKSU).

Lasiurus borealis.—Specimens examined (total 299); ADAIR COUNTY: Cave Springs Cave, 1 (OKSU). ALFALFA COUNTY: 8 mi. N Jet, 1,170 ft., 1 (OMNH). BLAINE COUNTY: Blaine County, 1 (OMNH); 2 mi. W, 0.5 mi. S Longdale, 1 (CAMCO). BRYAN COUNTY: Red River, 3 mi. SE Yuba, 1 (UMMZ). CHOCTAW COUNTY: Ft. Towson, 1 (USNM); 3 mi. N Hugo, 1 (OKSU). CLEVELAND COUNTY: Camp Kickapoo, 2 (OMNH); Cleveland County, 1 (OMNH); Hall Park, Norman, 6 (OMNH); Norman, 26 (OMNH); 1121 Arkansas, Norman, 4 (OMNH); 205 W. Eu-faula, Norman, 1 (OMNH); 815 E. Hughbert St., Norman, 4 (OMNH); campus, University of Oklahoma, Norman, 15 (OMNH), 1 (KU); S Mam-mal Lab, campus, University of Oklahoma, Norman, 2 (OMNH); N Owen Stadium, campus, University of Oklahoma, Norman, 1 (OMNH); Sutton Hall, University of Oklahoma, Norman, 3 (OMNH). COMANCHE COUNTY: Ft. Sill, 1 (CAMCO); Lawton, 3 (CAMCO); 300 N. Ft. Sill Blvd., Lawton, 1 (CAMCO); 1428 Lindy, Lawton, 1 (CAMCO); W Cache Creek at Refuge Boundary, 1 (OKSU); east base Mt. Scott, Wichita Moun-tains, 1 (USNM); Wichita Mountains Wildlife Refuge, 1 (USNM). CUS-TER COUNTY: Weatherford, 4 (KU); 4 mi. NW Weatherford, 1 (OKSU).

DELAWARE COUNTY: Spavinaw Creek, 7.5 mi. SE Jay, 1 (CSUO). DEWEY COUNTY: 10 mi. NW Canton, 3 (KU). GARFIELD COUNTY: 2 mi. E Phillips University, Enid, 1 (KU). GREER COUNTY: quarry pond, south side Granite Mt., 1 (OKSU). HARMON COUNTY: 6.5 mi. SE Vinson, 3 (CAMCO). JOHNSTON COUNTY: Tishomingo Natl. Wildlife Refuge, 640 ft., 1 (USNM). KAY COUNTY: Chilocco Indian School, 1 (OKSU); Kay County, 1 (OKSU); Ponca, 2 (USNM). KIOWA COUNTY: Snyder, 1 (CAMCO). LATIMER COUNTY: Boy Scout Camp, Wilburton, 2 (OMNH); 3.2 mi. N Wilburton, 1 (OMNH). LEFLORE COUNTY: Little River Bridge, Honobia, 1 (OKSU); 10 mi. W Oklahoma Border, Hwy 63, 1 (OUBS); Kiamichi River, S Talihina, 1 (OKSU). LOGAN COUNTY: 4.5 mi. W, 2 mi. W Guthrie, 1 (CSUO). MARSHALL COUNTY: jct. Kingston & Madill Rd., 1 (OUBS); Marshall County, 4 (OMNH); Rainbolt, 1 (OMNH); Dr. Rolland's Farm, 2 (OUBS); University of Oklahoma Biological Station, 2 (OUBS); 0.5 mi. W University of Oklahoma Biological Station, 2 (OMNH); 1.5 mi. W University of Oklahoma Biological Station, 1 (OUBS); 2 mi. W University of Oklahoma Biological Station, 1 (OMNH); Willis, 2 (OMNH); 2.5 mi. W Willis, 1 (KU); 3 mi. N Willis, 1 (OMNH), 1 (OUBS); 3 mi. W Willis, 1 (KU); 4 mi. NNE Willis, 1 (OUBS); 10 mi. N Willis, 1 (OMNH). MAYES COUNTY: 1.9 mi. E Chouteau Creek, Chouteau, 1 (OMNH). MCCUR-TAIN COUNTY: 10 mi. SE Broken Bow, 1 (OMNH); 14 mi. SE Broken Bow, 17 (OMNH), 1 (CAMCO); Little River, 5 mi. SE Eagletown, 1 (OKSU); Glover Creek, 5 (OKSU); 0.25 mi. W Glover, 2 (TMM); Twin Lakes, near Idabel, 1 (OKSU); 6 mi. E, 5 mi. S Idabel, 1 (OKSU); mouth Mt. Fork River, 1 (OKSU); Goff Farm, 2 mi. W Smithville, 1 (OKSU); 2 mi. W Smithville, 14 (OMNH); University of Oklahoma Biological Station, 2 mi. W Smithville, 1 (OMNH); 6 mi. S Tom, 1 (TMM); Glover Creek, 3 mi. E Wright City, 1 (OKSU); 9 mi. N Wright City, 2 (OKSU). MURRAY COUNTY: Platt Natl. Park, 1 (OKSU); Platt Natl. Park (outside), 1 (OMNH). MUSKOGEE COUNTY: Braggs, 1 (OKSU); creek, 4 mi. NE Braggs, 3 (OKSU); Camp Gruber Area, 1 (OKSU); Ft. Gibson, 1 (OKSU); Wallis Farm, 1 mi. S Ft. Gibson, 1 (OKSU), 2 (FWMSH); Muskogee, 1 (OKSU); 1805 Robinson St., Muskogee, 1 (OKSU); Connors College, Warner, 2 (OKSU); Wildlife Conservation Station, 2 (OKSU). OKLAHOMA COUNTY: 2100 N. Redmond, Bethany, 1 (CSUO); Edmond, 5 (CSUO); 105 10th St., Edmond, 1 (CSUO); Midwest City, 1 (CSUO); 715 Procter Pl., Midwest City, 1 (CSUO); Oklahoma City, 1 (CSUO); 10th and Stonewall, Oklahoma City, 1 (CSUO); Skylark, Melrose Ln., 1,150 ft., Oklahoma City, 1 (CSUO); Tinker Field, Oklahoma City, 1 (OMNH); 3029 N. Utah, Oklahoma City, 2 (CSUO); 3714 N.W. 12th, Oklahoma City, 1 (CSUO); 8000 Melrose Ln. Oklahoma City, 3 (CSUO).

OSAGE COUNTY: 2 mi. S Okesa, 1 (UMMZ). OTTAWA COUNTY: Miami, Rt. 1, 1 (CSUO); W Peoria, 1 (OKSU). PAWNEE COUNTY: 1.5 mi. N, 1.4 mi. W Watchorn, 1 (OMNH); 2.6 mi. N, 0.4 mi. E Watchorn, 1 (OMNH). PAYNE COUNTY: W side Murray Hall, Oklahoma State University, 1 (OKSU); County Health Dept., Stillwater, 1 (OKSU); near Stillwater, 5 (OKSU); Stillwater, 27 (OKSU); Stillwater (Oklahoma Rabies Control Center), 4 (CSUO); 2 mi. W Stillwater, 3 (OKSU); 7 mi. S Stillwater, Robert Benton Farm, 1 (OKSU). PITTSBURG COUNTY: Hartshorne, 1 (USNM); south side Hartshorne Lake, 2 (OKSU); Savanna, 1 (USNM). PONTOTOC COUNTY: campus, East Central University, Ada, 2 (ECENT); near Wintersmith Park, Ada, 3 (ECENT); 10 mi. W Ada, 2 (ECENT); 4 mi. S Fitzhugh, 1 (OKSU). PUSHMATAHA COUNTY: Little River, SE Nashoba, 1 (OKSU); Î mi. S Nashoba, 2 (TMM). SEMINOLE COUNTY: 804 McKinley, Seminole, 1 (CSUO). SEQUOYAH COUNTY: Cato Creek Camp Ground, 1 (CSUO); Redland, 2 (USNM). TEXAS COUNTY: Guymon, 1 (CSUO). TULSA COUNTY: Garnett, 1 (UMMZ); 8 mi. W Red Fork, 5 (USNM); Tulsa, 3 (OKSU); 3400 blk. E. 31st, Tulsa, 1 (CSUO). WASHINGTON COUNTY: Bartlesville, 1 (OKSU). WOODS COUNTY: 2 mi. SW Waynoka, 1 (USNM). WOODWARD COUNTY: Alabaster Caverns, 1 (OKSU); 2 mi. E Quinlan, 1 (OKSU).

Lasiurus cinereus.—Specimens examined (total 14); BEAVER COUNTY: 3 mi. S, 2 mi. W Elmwood, 1 (OKSU). BRYAN COUNTY: 10 mi. S, 1 mi. E Boswell, 1 (OMNH). CIMARRON COUNTY: 2.5 mi. SE Kenton, 4,200 ft., 1 (CAMCO); Carrizo Creek, 6 mi. N Kenton, 1 (OKSU). CLEVELAND COUNTY: North Moore Elementary School, Moore, 1 (CSUO); Norman, 1 (OMNH); 4 mi. S Norman, 1 (OMNH). COMANCHE COUNTY: Wichita Mountains Wildlife Refuge, 1 (USNM). MCCURTAIN COUNTY: Glover Creek, 3 mi. E Wright City, 1 (OKSU). OKLAHOMA COUNTY: 300 blk. N.W. 31st, Oklahoma City, 1 (CSUO). PAYNE COUNTY: Stillwater, 2 (OKSU). TEXAS COUNTY: Guymon, 1 (OKSU). TULSA COUNTY: Tulsa, 1 (OKSU).

Lasiurus seminolus.—Specimens examined (total 2); MCCURTAIN COUNTY: Little River, 6 mi. S Eagletown, 1 (OKSU). MURRAY COUNTY: Turner Falls Park, 1 (CSUO).

Lepus californicus.—Specimens examined (total 129); ALFALFA COUNTY: Alfalfa County, 7 (OKSU); Cherokee, 1 (USNM); 3 mi. E, 1.5 mi. N Cherokee, 1,170 ft., 2 (OMNH); 4 mi. E Cherokee, 2 (USNM); 9 mi. E Cherokee, 1 (USNM); 4 mi. SE border Great Salt Plains, 1 (OMNH); 9 mi. E east side Great Salt Plains, 1 (OMNH). BEAVER COUNTY: 5 mi. W, 0.5 mi. S Gray, 2 (KU). BLAINE COUNTY: Canton Reservoir, 1 (OKSU); 0.5 mi. W Canton, 1 (OKSU). CADDO COUNTY: 1 mi. W, 2

mi. S Cyril, 1 (OKSU). CANADIAN COUNTY: Yukon, 1 (KU). CAR-
TER COUNTY: 10 mi. SE Ardmore, 1 (OUBS); 4 mi. N Springer,
1 (USNM). CHEROKEE COUNTY: 4 mi. W, 1 mi. S Tahlequah, 1
(OKSU). CIMARRON COUNTY: 4.6 mi. W Boise City, 1 (OMNH); 6
mi. W Boise City, 2 (OMNH); 17 mi. E, 5 mi. N Boise City, 1 (OMNH);
17 mi. W Boise City, 1 (OMNH); 4.4 mi. N, 1 mi. W Kenton, 1 (OMNH);
1 mi. N, 10 mi. E Wheeless, 1 (OMNH); 1 mi. N. 15 mi. E Wheeless, 1
(OMNH); T4N, R3E, Sec. 36, 1 (OMNH). CLEVELAND COUNTY:
Cleveland County, 1 (OMNH); 1.5 mi. NW Norman, 1 (OMNH); 3 mi. E
Norman, 1 (OMNH); 2 mi. NW Norman, 1 (OMNH); 4 mi. E Norman, 1
(OMNH); 4.5 mi. NE Norman, 1 (USNM); 5 mi. W, 3 mi. N Norman, 1
(OMNH); T9N, R2W, Sec. 19, 1 (OMNH). COMANCHE COUNTY: 3
mi. N Cache, 1 (USNM); 3.5 mi. S Cache, 1 (CAMCO); 1 mi. N, 2 mi. W
Faxon, 1 (CAMCO); 8 mi. SW Lawton, 1 (CAMCO); 2 mi. SSW Medicine
Park, 1 (CAMCO); outside Wichita Natl. Forest, 1 (OMNH); Mt. Scott,
Wichita Mountains, 1 (USNM); Wichita Mountains, 1 (USNM). COT-
TON COUNTY: 15 mi. N Red River, 1 (OKSU); 7 mi. S Temple, 1
(OMNH); 12 mi. W, 3.5 mi. S Walters, 1 (CAMCO). CRAIG COUNTY:
2 mi. N Ketchum, 1 (OKSU). CREEK COUNTY: Sapulpa, 1 (KU).
CUSTER COUNTY: 1 mi. N, 2 mi. W Weatherford, 1 (KU); 1.5 mi. S,
2 mi. W Weatherford, 1 (KU); John Dick Farm, 4 mi. E, 4.25 mi. S
Weatherford, 1 (OKSU). DEWEY COUNTY: 5 mi. SW Canton, 1 (KU);
5 mi. W Canton, 1 (KU); 5.5 mi. SW Canton, 1 (KU). GARFIELD
COUNTY: Enid, 2 (KU); 2 mi. W Enid on Hwy 10, 1 (OKSU). GARVIN
COUNTY: Laytonville, 1 (USNM). GRANT COUNTY: 1.7 mi. W, 1.3
mi. N Hawley, 1 (OMNH). HARMON COUNTY: 8 mi. SW Hollis, 1
(FWMSH); 12.5 mi. N, 3.75 mi. W Hollis, 1 (TTU). HARPER COUNTY:
4.5 mi. N Laverne, 1 (UMMZ). HUGHES COUNTY: 2 mi. E Holden-
ville, 3 (OKSU); 12 mi. S, 1.5 mi. E Holdenville, 1 (ECENT). JACKSON
COUNTY: 6 mi. W, 2.5 mi. N Eldorado, 1 (OKSU); 3 mi. N Headrick, 1
(OMNH). JEFFERSON COUNTY: Starvation Flat, 1 (OKSU). KAY
COUNTY: 3 mi. W Ponca City, 1 (OKSU). MAJOR COUNTY: 5 mi. N,
3 mi. E Cleo Springs, 1 (OKSU). MARSHALL COUNTY: Lake Texoma,
1 (OUBS); University of Oklahoma Biological Station, Lake Texoma, 2
(OMNH); W Madill, 1 (OMNH); on road to Madill from University of
Oklahoma Biological Station, 1 (OMNH); University of Oklahoma Bio-
logical Station, 1 (OMNH); 0.5 mi. W University of Oklahoma Biological
Station, 2 (OUBS); Willis, 1 (OMNH); 0.5 mi. N Willis, 1 (OMNH), 1
(CAMCO). MCCLAIN COUNTY: 10 mi. S Norman, 1 (OMNH). MUS-
KOGEE COUNTY: Braggs, 1 (OKSU); 3 mi. E Wainwright, 1 (OMNH).
NOBLE COUNTY: 0.75 mi. W Hwy 177 on Orlando Rd., 1 (OKSU); 8
mi. N, 2 mi. E Perry, 1 (OKSU). OKLAHOMA COUNTY: jct. Hwy 66

& Council Rd., 1 (CSUO). PAYNE COUNTY: near Stillwater, 1 (OKSU); Stillwater, 3 (OKSU); 2 mi. N Stillwater, 1 (OKSU); 2 mi. N, 1.5 mi. E Stillwater, 1 (OKSU); 3 mi. W, 4 mi. N Stillwater, 1 (OKSU). PITTS-BURG COUNTY: 5 mi. E, 1 mi. S Stuart, 1 (ECENT). POTTAWA-TOMIE COUNTY: Biological Station No. 1, 1 (CSUO); Tecumseh, 2 (KU); 1 mi. W Tecumseh, 2 (OKSU). STEPHENS COUNTY: 4 mi. W, 3.5 mi. N Duncan, 1 (OKSU); 8 mi. W, 2 mi. N Marlow, 1 (CAMCO); 4 mi. E Purnell, 1 (ECENT). TEXAS COUNTY: 6 mi. N, 14 mi. W Guymon, 1 (OMNH). TILLMAN COUNTY: 4 mi. N, 1 mi. W Freder-ick, 1 (CAMCO); 5.5 mi. S Grandfield, 1 (OMNH); 1 mi. W, 2.5 mi. N Tipton, 2 (CAMCO). TULSA COUNTY: Garnett, 4 (UMMZ); 8 mi. W Red Fork, Indian Territory, 4 (USNM). WOODS COUNTY: Alva, 1 (USNM); 12 mi. W, 4 mi. S Alva, Avard, 1 (KU); 2 mi. W, 4 mi. S Dacoma, 1 (OKSU); approx. 12 mi. W Hardtner, 1 (KU); White Horse Springs, Oklahoma Territory, 1 (FMNH). WOODWARD COUNTY: Woodward, 1 (USNM).

Lutra canadensis.—Specimens examined (total 5); LATIMER COUNTY: T5N, R20E, SW 1/4 Sec. 12, in drainage between Fourch Maline River and lake, 2 (OMNH), 1 (OKSU). SEQUOYAH COUNTY: Sequoyah County, 1 (OMNH). WOODWARD COUNTY: mouth of Turkey Creek & Cimarron River, 1 (KU).

Marmota monax.—Specimens examined (total 20); ADAIR COUNTY: 3 mi. NNW Chewey, 1,000 ft., 2 (OMNH). CHEROKEE COUNTY: 0.5 mi. E Peggs, 1 (OUBS). CRAIG COUNTY: 1 mi. S, 6 mi. W Oklahoma-Kansas border on Hwy 2, 1 (OKSU). DELAWARE COUNTY: 4 mi. E, 3 mi. N Jay, 2 (OMNH). LEFLORE COUNTY: Hodgen, 1 (OKSU). MAYES COUNTY: 3.5 mi. N Adair, 1 (OKSU); 1 mi. S Spavinaw, 1 (KU); 1 mi. S Spavinaw Dam, 1 (OKSU). OTTAWA COUNTY: 10 mi. W Mi-ami on Hwy 10, 1 (OMNH); 2 mi. SW Tri-State Monument, 1 (KU). PAYNE COUNTY: Payne County, 1 (OKSU); 1 mi. S Stillwater on 177, 1 (OKSU). SEQUOYAH COUNTY: 11 mi. S Cookson, 1 (CSUO); 0.25 mi. W Strayhorn Landing on SH 100, Lake Tenkiller, 1 (OKSU). WAGONER COUNTY: Snug Harbor, west side Grand River, 1 (OKSU). WASHING-TON COUNTY: near Bar-Dew Lake, 1 (CAMCO); NW Bartlesville, near Bar-Dew, Lake River bottom, 1 (ECENT); 10 mi. NE Bartlesville, 1 (ECENT).

Mephitis mephitis.—Specimens examined (total 127); ADAIR COUNTY: 3 mi. NNW Chewey, 1,000 ft., 2 (OMNH). BLAINE COUNTY: 0.5 mi. W Canton, 1 (OKSU); Hitchcock, 1 (OKSU); near Watonga, 5 mi. W, 3 mi. N Watonga, 1 (MVZ). CARTER COUNTY: 20 mi. W Ardmore, 3 (TTU); Murray State Park, 2 (OUBS). CIMARRON COUNTY: Cold Springs, Garrett Township, 1 (OKSU). CLEVELAND COUNTY: 1 mi. E US 77 on Cedar Lane, 1 (OMNH); campus, University of Oklahoma, Norman, 1 (OMNH); South Canadian River, S Norman, 1 (KU); 1.5 mi. E Norman on Hwy 9, 1 (OMNH); 2 mi. E Norman, 1 (OMNH); 4.5 mi. N Norman, 2 (OMNH); 2 mi. S Slaughterville, 5 (OMNH). COMANCHE COUNTY: Ft. Sill, 1 (CAMCO); 2 mi. N, 1 mi. E Indiahoma, 1 (CAMCO); 3 mi. S, 0.25 mi. E Lawton, 1 (CAMCO); 1.5 mi. N Meers, 1 (OMNH); Mt. Scott, 2 (USNM); Mt. Scott Post Office, 3 (USNM); Wichita Mountains Wildlife Refuge, 7 (USNM); Wichita Natl. Forest, 3 (OMNH), 6 (KU); Wichita Mountains Wildlife Refuge, Cache, 1 (USNM); off Cache Creek, Wichita Natl. Forest, 2 (OMNH); Cow Creek, Wichita Mountains Wildlife Refuge, 1 (USNM); Wichita Mountains Wildlife Refuge, W Graham, 1 (USNM); Greenleaf Cave, Wichita Mountains Wildlife Refuge, 1 (USNM); Mt. Scott, Wichita Mts., 1 (USNM); Panther Creek, Wichita Mountains Wildlife Refuge, 1 (USNM); Post Oak Creek, 1 mi. inside Wichita Natl. Forest, 1 (OMNH); south end Wolf Creek, Wichita Mountains Wildlife Refuge, 1 (USNM). CUSTER COUNTY: T14N, R16E, Sec. 29, 1 (OMNH). DEWEY COUNTY: 5.5 mi. SW Canton, 1 (KU). GARFIELD COUNTY: 5 mi. N, 6 mi. E Enid, 1 (OKSU). GRADY COUNTY: Hwy 277, 1 (OMNH). GRANT COUNTY: 1.5 mi. W, 3 mi. N Hawley, 1 (OMNH). HARPER COUNTY: 2 mi. W May, 1 (OKSU). HUGHES COUNTY: 3 mi. E Wetumka, 1 (ECENT). LEFLORE COUNTY: 6.5 mi. W Heavener, 1 (OMNH). LOGAN COUNTY: 2 mi. N Guthrie on I-35, 1 (OKSU). MAJOR COUNTY: Ewer's Creek, 2 mi. W Bouse Jct., 1 (OKSU). MARSHALL COUNTY: Marshall County, 1 (OUBS); 1 mi. S Powell, 2 (KU); 0.25 mi. N University of Oklahoma Biological Station, 1 (OUBS); 4 mi. W University of Oklahoma Biological Station, 1 (OUBS); Willis, 4 (KU). MCCLAIN COUNTY: 10 mi. W Blanchard on Hwy 62, 1 (OMNH); McClain County, 1 (OKSU); 3 mi. S Norman, 1 (OMNH). MCCURTAIN COUNTY: 14 mi. SE Broken Bow, 2 (OMNH); 15 mi. SE Broken Bow, 1 (OMNH). MCINTOSH COUNTY: 7 mi. E, 3 mi. N Hitchita, 1 (OKSU). MUSKOGEE COUNTY: Wildlife Conservation Station, Braggs, 1 (OKSU). NOBLE COUNTY: 13 mi., 1.5 mi. W Perry, 1 (OKSU). OKLAHOMA COUNTY: Broadway Ext., S Edmond, 1 (CSUO). OSAGE COUNTY: 5 mi. W, 5 mi. S Bartlesville, 1 (OKSU); Philips Ranch, 10 mi. SW Bartlesville, 1 (OMNH). PAWNEE COUNTY: 4 mi. N Bill's Corner, 1 (OKSU); 7.5 mi. N, 2.75 mi. W Pawnee, 1 (KU). PAYNE COUNTY: Elmwood Rd., Stillwater, 1 (OKSU); jct. SH 51 & Western, Stillwater, 1 (OKSU); near Stillwater, 1 (OKSU); Stillwater, 1 (OKSU); Stillwater Airport, 1 (OKSU); Stillwater Creek, W Stillwater, 1 (OKSU); Third & Perkins Rd., Stillwater, 1 (OKSU); 1 blk. E University laundry, Stillwater, 1 (OKSU); 1 mi. E Stallard Dr. on SH 51, Stillwater, 1 (OKSU); 1 mi. N, 1 mi. E Stillwater, 1 (OKSU); 1 mi. W Stillwater,

2 (OKSU); 2 mi. W Stillwater, 1 (OKSU); 3.5 mi. W, 3 mi. N Stillwater, 1 (OKSU); 5 mi. W Stillwater, 0.25 mi. N SH 51, 1 (OKSU); 8 mi. NW Stillwater, 1 (OKSU); 8 mi. S, 3 mi. W Stillwater, 1 (OKSU); 14 mi. N Stillwater, 1 (OKSU); T18N, R2E, Sec. 24, 1 (OKSU). PITTSBURG COUNTY: 2 mi. S Hartshorne, 1 (OKSU); 4 mi. E, 1 mi. S Stuart, 1 (ECENT). PONTOTOC COUNTY: 7 mi. NE Ada, 1 (ECENT); campus, East Central State University, Ada, 1 (ECENT). ROGERS COUNTY: T20N, R15E, E 1/2 E 1/2 SE 1/4 Sec. 26, 4 mi. E Catoosa, 1 (OKSU). SEMINOLE COUNTY: 3 mi. E Seminole on Hwy 7, 906 ft., 1 (CSUO). TEXAS COUNTY: 1 mi. E Guymon, 1 (OMNH). TILLMAN COUNTY: 5.5 mi. S Grandfield, 1 (OMNH). TULSA COUNTY: 8 mi. W Red Fork, 2 (USNM); Tulsa, 1 (UMMZ). WASHINGTON COUNTY: Dewey (via State Health Rabies Control Center), 1 (CSUO). WOODS COUNTY: 6 mi. E Alva, Oklahoma Territory, 2 (FMNH); Cimarron River, Freedom, 1 (OKSU); 3.6 mi. W Waynoka, 1 (OMNH); 3 mi. E Whitehorse, 1 (OKSU).

Microtus ochrogaster.—Specimens examined (total 215); CANADIAN COUNTY: Ft. Reno, 5 (USNM). CHEROKEE COUNTY: Cookson Hills Game Refuge, 1 (OKSU). CLEVELAND COUNTY: 1 mi. S Norman, 2 (OKSU). CRAIG COUNTY: 8 mi. N, 1.5 mi. W Welch, 1 (OMNH). LOGAN COUNTY: Orlando, 1 (USNM). MCINTOSH COUNTY: 5 mi. E, 1 mi. N Checotah, 1 (OMNH). NOBLE COUNTY: 2 mi. S, 0.5 mi. E Red Rock, 1 (OKSU); 1 mi. E jct. Hwys 177 & 15 W, 8 (OMNH); 2.2 mi. N, 1.9 mi. E jct. Hwys 177 & 15 E, 1 (OMNH). NOWATA COUNTY: Paul Buck Ranch, 2 mi. NW Wann, 1 (OKSU). OKLAHOMA COUNTY: Vickers Prairie, west side Bryant, 5 mi. N Edmond, 1 (CSUO); 0.25 mi. N jct. N.W. 234th & N. May, 1 (CSUO). OKMULGEE COUNTY: 3 mi. E, 2 mi. N Okmulgee, 2 (OMNH). OSAGE COUNTY: K.S. Adams Ranch, 12 mi. N, 5 mi. E Shidler, 1,250 ft., 163 (KU). PAWNEE COUNTY: 1.3 mi. N, 1.5 mi. W Watchorn, 1 (OMNH); 1.4 mi. N, 1.9 mi. W Watchorn, 1 (OMNH); 2.3 mi. N, 2.5 mi. E jct. Hwys 177 & 15 E, 1 (OMNH). PAYNE COUNTY: east end Boomer Lake, 1 (OKSU); Payne County, 1 (OKSU); north side Sanborn Lake, 12 (OKSU); Sanborn Lake, 1 (OKSU); 0.25 mi. N Sanborn Lake, 1 (OKSU); SH 51 & Stillwater Creek Bridge, 1 (OKSU); Stillwater, 1 (OKSU); 0.2 mi. W jct. Sangre Rd. & S. 19th St., Stillwater, 1 (OKSU); 3 mi. N, 0.5 mi. W Stillwater, 1 (OKSU); 14 mi. E jct. SH 51 & US Hwy 177, 1 (OKSU). ROGERS COUNTY: 3 mi. N, 1 mi. W Foyil, 1 (OMNH). TULSA COUNTY: Garnett, 1 (TMM).

Microtus pinetorum.—Specimens examined (total 185); ADAIR COUNTY: Boston Mts., Stilwell, 16 (USNM); Stilwell, 7 (UIMNH); 2.5 mi. E Stilwell, 7 (UIMNH). ATOKA COUNTY: 20 mi. SE Atoka, 1 (OMNH). BRYAN COUNTY: 2 mi. W Colbert, 1 (TMM). CADDO COUNTY: T7N, R12W, Sec. 2, SARP Site C4, 1.5 mi. N Washita River on Cobb

Creek, 2 (OKSU). CARTER COUNTY: 3 mi. N Springer, 4 (USNM).
CHEROKEE COUNTY: 3 mi. NW Chewey, 1 (OMNH). CLEVELAND
COUNTY: 2 mi. S, 7 mi. E Noble, 2 (OMNH); Norman, 1 (KU); campus,
University of Oklahoma, Norman, 5 (KU); T8N, R2W, Sec. 10, 6 mi. E,
0.5 mi. N Norman, 1 (OMNH); Oliver's Woods, 1 mi. S Norman, 1
(OMNH); 2 mi. S Norman, 5 (OMNH); 3 mi. E Norman, 2 (OMNH);
3.2 mi. N Norman, 5 (OMNH), 3 (USNM); 3.6 mi. SW Norman, 1
(USNM); 5 mi. S Norman, 1 (OMNH); 10 mi. E Norman, 1 (OMNH);
T6N, R1E, Sec. 31, 1 (OMNH); T8N, R1W, Sec. 21, 1 (OMNH). CO-
MANCHE COUNTY: Elk Mt., 1 (CAMCO); Lake French, Wichita
Mountains Refuge, 4 (USNM); Little Medium Creek, Wichita Mountains
Refuge, 1 (USNM); 2 mi. E Boundary, Wichita Wildlife Fish Hatchery,
1 (OMNH). CREEK COUNTY: Creek County, 1 (KU); Sapulpa, 6
(KU). LATIMER COUNTY: 20 mi. N Wilburton, 1 (OMNH). LOGAN
COUNTY: Logan County, 1 (OMNH). MARSHALL COUNTY: Univer-
sity of Oklahoma Biological Station, Lake Texoma, 1 (OUBS); 0.125 mi.
W University of Oklahoma Biological Station, 1 (OUBS). MCCLAIN
COUNTY: T8N, R4W, 1 (OMNH). MCCURTAIN COUNTY: 5 mi.
S Broken Bow near US Hwy 259, 1 (OKSU); Forked Lake, 5 mi. SW
Eagletown, 1 (ECENT); beneath SH 3 bridge over the Glover River, 1
(OKSU). MUSKOGEE COUNTY: 3 mi. NE Braggs, 2 (OKSU). OKLA-
HOMA COUNTY: E Edmond, 1 (CSUO); Edmond, 1 (CSUO); 3 mi. W
Central State University, Edmond, 1 (CSUO); 4 mi. N, 3 mi. W Oklahoma
City, 1 (OKSU); 8 mi. E Midwest Rd. on N.W. 63rd, Oklahoma City, 1
(CSUO); 1.5 mi. E on N.E. 164th & I-35 N, 0.5 blk. S, 1 (CSUO). OSAGE
COUNTY: Arkansas River, 4 mi. SW Fairfax, 2 (OKSU); 7 mi. N, 5 mi. E
Wynona, 4 (OKSU); 12 mi. NE Wynona, 1 (OKSU). PAWNEE COUNTY:
1.4 mi. N, 1.2 mi. W Watchorn, 1 (OMNH); 1.4 mi. N, 1.4 mi. W Watch-
orn, 1 (OMNH); 2.5 mi. N, 0.5 mi. E Watchorn, 2 (OMNH); Phillips
Camp, N Hwy 15, 1 (OKSU). PAYNE COUNTY: Boomer Lake Dam, 2
(OKSU); spillway, Boomer Lake, 1 (OKSU); 0.5 mi. E Boomer Lake, 4
(OKSU); Cow Creek Reservoir Dam, 1 (OKSU); Camp Redlands, Lake
Carl Blackwell, 1 (OKSU); east bank Lake Carl Blackwell, 1 (OKSU);
Lake Carl Blackwell, 5 (OKSU); spillway, Lake Carl Blackwell, 2 (OKSU);
400 ft. SE Lake Carl Blackwell spillway, 1 (OKSU); near Lake Carl Black-
well, 1 (OKSU); 0.5 mi. N, 0.25 mi. W jct. 51 & 51C near Lake Carl
Blackwell, 1 (OKSU), 1 (ECENT); 1 mi. E Camp Redlands, north end
Lake Carl Blackwell, 1 (OKSU); 4 mi. W Perkins, 1 (OKSU); 1 mi. S, 1
mi. W Progress, 1 (OKSU); Municipal Golf Course, Stillwater, 1 (OKSU);
Vet Village, Stillwater, 1 (OKSU); 1 mi. N, 0.5 mi. E Stillwater, 1 (OKSU);
1 mi. N, 1 mi. W Stillwater, 2 (OKSU); 1 mi. W, 3 mi. S Stillwater, 1
(OKSU); 1.5 mi. N Stillwater, 1 (OKSU); 1.5 mi. W Stillwater on McEl-

roy St., 1 (OKSU); 1 mi. N, 1.6 mi. W Stillwater, 1 (OKSU); 2 mi. N, 1 mi. E Stillwater, 3 (OKSU); 2 mi. W, 4.5 mi. S jct. Hwy 51 & Western St. in Stillwater, 1 (OKSU); 2.25 mi. W, 0.125 mi. N Stillwater on Hwy 51, 1 (OKSU); 3 mi. N, 5 mi. W Stillwater, 1 (OKSU); 3 mi. W Stillwater, 1 (OKSU); 3 mi. W, 2 mi. N Stillwater on SH 51, 1 (OKSU); 4 mi. N, 1 mi. E Stillwater, 1 (OKSU); 4 mi. W, 3 mi. S Stillwater, 1 (OKSU); spillway, Lake Blackwell, 5 mi. W Stillwater, 1 (OKSU); 6 mi. SW Stillwater, 1 (OKSU); 6 mi. W Stillwater, 1 (OKSU); Lowell Farm, 6 mi. E, 2 mi. S Stillwater, 1 (OKSU); 6 mi. W, 3 mi. N Stillwater, 1 (OKSU); 7.4 mi. W Stillwater, 1 (OKSU); 8 mi. E, 0.5 mi. S Stillwater, 1 (OKSU); 9 mi. W, 1 mi. N Stillwater, 1 (OKSU); 1 mi. W Angler's Inn, Hwy 51, 9 mi. W Stillwater, 1 (OKSU); 7 mi. N, 5 mi. E Winona, 1 (UMMZ); 12 mi. NE Winona, 1 (UMMZ); 0.33 mi. SW bridge on SH 51C, 1 (OKSU); 0.125 mi. S, 1 mi. E jct. Hwys 51 & 51C, 1 (OKSU). PONTOTOC COUNTY: 3 mi. W Jessie, 1 (OMNH). POTTAWATOMIE COUNTY: 0.25 mi. E McLoud, 1 (CSUO); Pottawatomie County, 1 (KU). PUSHMATAHA COUNTY: 4 mi. SE Clayton, 1 (OMNH); 1 mi. S Nashoba, 1 (TMM); 15 mi. S Talihina on Little River, 1 (OKSU). TULSA COUNTY: Mohawk Park, 4 (UMMZ); Owasso, 1 (TMM); Tulsa, 1 (OKSU); west side Sequoyah Lake, Tulsa, 2 (OKSU); 13 St. Andrew's Circle between 101st & 111th Sts. on Garnett, Tulsa, 1 (OKSU). WAGONER COUNTY: 4.5 mi. SW Coweta, 600 ft., 1 (OMNH). WASHINGTON COUNTY: 4 mi. S, 0.5 mi. E Limestone Corner, 1 (OMNH); T25N, R2E, Sec. 8, 1 (OMNH).

Mus musculus.—Specimens examined (total 369); ADAIR COUNTY: 1 mi. E Proctor on Hwy 62, 1 (OKSU); 2 mi. S Stilwell, 3 (OKSU). ALFALFA COUNTY: 3 mi. N, 9 mi. E Cherokee, 1,170 ft., 1 (OMNH). BRYAN COUNTY: 5 mi. N Colbert, 1 (TMM); 7 mi. N Durant, 1 (OUBS). CADDO COUNTY: 1.5 mi. S Apache, 1 (CAMCO); 1.5 mi. SE Cyril, 1 (CAMCO); 0.5 mi. S Ft. Cobb, 1 (CAMCO). CANADIAN COUNTY: El Reno, 1 (CSUO); 2 mi. N, 1 mi. W El Reno, 1 (OKSU); 7 mi. W, 1 mi. S El Reno on US Hwy 66, 1 (OKSU); 4 mi. E, 2.25 mi. S Union City, 1 (OKSU). CIMARRON COUNTY: 6 mi. N Kenton, 1 (OKSU); 8 mi. SE Kenton, 1 (CAMCO). CLEVELAND COUNTY: Cleveland County, 3 (OMNH); 1009 S.W. 19th St., Moore, 3 (CSUO); 4 mi. S, 10 mi. E Moore, 1 (OKSU); ATO fraternity house, Norman, 1 (OMNH); city dump, Norman, 3 (OMNH); ΦΓ fraternity house, Norman, 2 (OMNH); Norman, 4 (KU); 421 Foreman, Norman, 1 (OMNH); 603 Rancho Dr., Norman, 1 (OMNH); 1 mi. S, 3 mi. W Norman, 1 (KU); 1.5 mi. S, 1.5 mi. E Norman, 1 (OMNH); 2 mi. E Norman, 1 (OMNH); 2 mi. N, 0.1 mi. W Norman, 1 (OMNH); 3 mi. E Norman, 1 (OMNH); 3 mi. N Norman on SH 77H, 2 (OMNH); 4 mi. SW Norman, 1 (OMNH); 6 mi. E Norman, 3 (OMNH); across street from University of Oklahoma, house east side Jenkins, Norman, 1 (OMNH); Residential Hall, 1 (OMNH); south border, campus, University of Oklahoma, 1 (OMNH); 1.5 mi. W, 1.5 mi. S University of Oklahoma, 2 (OMNH); T9N, R3W, Sec. 31, 1 (OMNH);T6N, R1E, 1 (OMNH); 0.5 mi. E South Canadian River Bridge between I-240 & H. E. Bailey Turnpike, 1 (CSUO). COMANCHE COUNTY: 3.5 mi. S Cache, 1 (CAMCO); 3.5 mi. W Cache on Hwy 62, 1 (OMNH); 5 mi. S, 2 mi. W Cache, 1 (CAMCO); Elgin, 1 (CAMCO); 0.5 mi. E Faxon, 1 (CAMCO); 4 mi. N, 3 mi. E Faxon, 1 (CAMCO); 4 mi. W Fletcher, 1 (CAMCO); Medicine Bluff, White Wolf Crossing, Ft. Sill, 1 (CAMCO); Lake Lawtonka, 1 mi. W Dam, 1 (CAMCO); Lawton, 3 (CAMCO); 3313 Atlanta, Lawton, 1 (CAMCO); 1.5 mi. SE Lawton, 1 (CAMCO); 8 mi. E, 3 mi. N Lawton, 1 (CAMCO); Wichita Mts. Estates, 10 mi. N Lawton, 3 (CAMCO); 5 mi. E Medicine Park, 1 (CAMCO); 0.75 mi. E Mt. Scott, 1 (CAMCO); Wichita Mountains Wildlife Refuge, 2 (USNM); Wichita Wildlife Refuge, 1 (OMNH); T3N, R9W, NW 1/4 Sec. 8, 1 (OMNH). CRAIG COUNTY: 1 mi. S, 0.25 mi. W Big Cabin on Hwy 69, 2 (OKSU); 0.25 mi. E Vinita, 1 (OKSU). CREEK COUNTY: 0.5 mi. E Drumright, 1 (OKSU); Sapulpa, 3 (KU). DELAWARE COUNTY: 2 mi. E Colcord, 1 (OKSU); near Spavinaw Creek, 7.5 mi. SE Jay, 1 (CSUO); 10 mi. SE Jay, 1 (OKSU). DEWEY COUNTY: Dewey County, 1 (KU); 2 mi. E Seiling, 1 (OKSU); 1 mi. N Taloga, 2 (OMNH). GAR-FIELD COUNTY: 19 mi. W, 5 mi. S Enid, 1 (OKSU). GARVIN COUNTY: 1 mi. E, 2.75 mi. S Stratford, 1 (ECENT). GRADY COUNTY: 1 mi. W, 2 mi. S Alex, 1 (OKSU). GRANT COUNTY: 2.3 mi. N, 7.2 mi. W Renfrow, 1 (USNM); 2.3 mi. N, 8 mi. W Renfrow, 4 (USNM). HARMON COUNTY: 6 mi. E, 1 mi. S Vinson, 1,700 ft., 1 (OMNH). HARPER COUNTY: barracks, well 4, Southern Great Plains Exp. Range, Ft. Supply, 1 (OKSU); well 4, Southern Great Plains Exp. Range, Ft. Supply, 2 (OKSU). HASKELL COUNTY: 100 yds. S Stigler, 1 (OMNH). JACK-SON COUNTY: 2 mi. N, 0.5 mi. E Duke, 1 (CAMCO); 1.5 mi. S, 2 mi. E Olustee, 1 (CAMCO); 4 mi. N, 3.5 mi. W Olustee, 1 (CAMCO). JOHN-STON COUNTY: 19 mi. NE Tishomingo, 1 (ECENT). KAY COUNTY: 5 mi. S, 7.5 mi. E Newkirk, 1,100 ft., 5 (OMNH); 5 mi. S, 10.5 mi. E New-kirk, 1,150 ft., 5 (OMNH); 809 Edgewood, Ponca City, 1 (OKSU); T26N, R2E, SE 1/4 Sec. 18, Ponca City, 1 (OKSU). KINGFISHER COUNTY: 2 mi. N, 1 mi. W Dover, 1 (OKSU); T17N, R5W, Sec. 30, 2 (OMNH). KIOWA COUNTY: 1.5 mi. E Snyder, 1 (CAMCO). LATIMER COUNTY: Red Oak, 1 (USNM). LEFLORE COUNTY: Heavener, 1 (OKSU). LIN-COLN COUNTY: 2.5 mi. W Meeker, 1 (OKSU). LOGAN COUNTY: 6 mi. N Edmond, 1 (CSUO); 6 mi. N, 0.75 mi. E Edmond, 1 (CSUO); 0.25 mi. S Guthrie on Pine St., 2 (CSUO); T16N, R4W, Sec. 11, 2 (OMNH). MARSHALL COUNTY: Marshall County, 2 (OUBS); University of Oklahoma Biological Station, 14 (OUBS); 1.3 mi. W University of Oklahoma Biological Station, 1 (OUBS); 0.5 mi. W University of Oklahoma Biological Station, 2 (OUBS); 2 mi. W University of Oklahoma Biological Station, 2 (OUBS); 3.5 mi. W University of Oklahoma Biological Station, 1 (OUBS); 0.5 mi. N Willis, 1 (OUBS); 0.5 mi. SW Willis, 1 (OUBS); 2 mi. W Willis, 1 (OUBS). MAYES COUNTY: Hills Texaco, Hwy 82 & 33, Locust Grove, 1 (OKSU). MCCLAIN COUNTY: McClain County, 1 (OMNH); 1 mi. S, 0.5 mi. W Purcell, 11 (OMNH). MCINTOSH COUNTY: Eufaula, 1 (OKSU); 11 mi. W Eufaula, 2 (CSUO). MURRAY COUNTY: Dougherty, Indian Territory, 2 (FMNH); Travertine Creek, 1 (OKSU); 1 mi. S Wynnewood off US Hwy 77, 1 (OKSU). MUSKOGEE COUNTY: Wildlife Conservation Station, Braggs, 1 (OKSU). NOBLE COUNTY: 2 mi. N, 7.75 mi. E Perry, 3 (OKSU); 3 mi. W Stillwater, 1 (OKSU). NOWATA COUNTY: 2 mi. S South Coffeyville, 1 (OMNH). OKLAHOMA COUNTY: 2 mi. E Central State University, 1.5 mi. N Oakridge Rd., 1 (CSUO); jct. S.E. 15th & Indian Meridian, Choctaw, 1 (CSUO); Edmond, 6 (CSUO); circus grounds, Kelly Ave., N of 2nd St., Edmond, 1 (CSUO); Thatcher Hall, Central State University, Edmond, 1 (CSUO); 0.5 mi. S Edmond, 1 (CSUO); 1.5 mi. N 2nd St. on Kelly Ave., Edmond, 2 (CSUO); 4 mi. N, 5.2 mi. W Edmond, 3 (CSUO); Vickers Prairie, west side Bryant, 5 mi. N Edmond, 1 (CSUO); 6 mi. W Edmond, 3 (CSUO); 6.4 mi. W Edmond, 2 (CSUO); 10 mi. W, 0.5 mi. S Edmond, 4 (CSUO); jct. 10th & Rankin, Edmond, 1 (CSUO); Midwest City, 1 (OKSU); 211 E. Boeing, Midwest City, 1 (OMNH); 2 mi. W Newalla, 1 (CSUO); NE Oklahoma City, 1 (OMNH); Oklahoma City, 4 (OKSU), 1 (CSUO); Southside Sewer Treatment, Oklahoma City, 1 (CSUO); 19th & Meridian, Oklahoma City, 1 (CSUO); 815 N. Hartford, Oklahoma City, 1 (CSUO); S.W. 60th, Oklahoma City, 1 (CSUO); 1 mi. S, 1 mi. W downtown Oklahoma City, 1 (CSUO); S.W. MacArthur Blvd., Oklahoma City, 1 (ECENT); jct. 111th & N. May, Oklahoma City, 2 (CSUO); jct. Penn & Hefner, Oklahoma City, 1 (CSUO); Oklahoma County, 3 (OMNH); 1201 N. Barnes, 1 (CSUO); 2312 S. Broadway, 1 (CSUO); jct. Coltrane & 33rd, 4 (CSUO); jct. East Ave. & N. East, 1 (OMNH); jct. Kelly & N. Britton (103rd St.), 1 (CSUO); 5900 blk. Missouri, 1 (USNM); 0.25 mi. S 4400 blk. N.E. 36th, 1 (CSUO); 0.5 mi. E Sarah Rd. on 122nd St., 5 (CSUO); 0.25 mi. N jct. N.W. 234 & May Ave., 1 (CSUO); 3.1 mi. E on Hwy 66 from I-35, 1 (CSUO); T13N, R3W, Sec. 30, 1 (OMNH); T10N, R3W, Sec. 33, 1 (OMNH). OSAGE COUNTY: 5 mi. S Pawhuska, 1 (OKSU). OTTAWA COUNTY: 5 mi. S Fairland, 1 (OKSU). PAWNEE COUNTY: 7 mi. N, 2.75 mi. W Pawnee, 2 (KU); 1.0 mi. N, 0.5 mi. W Watchorn, 1 (OMNH); 1 mi. E, 3.5 mi. N Yale, 10 (OKSU). PAYNE COUNTY: 0.5 mi. E Boomer Lake, 1 (OKSU); 2.5 mi. SW Cushing, 1 (OKSU); Bennett Dorm, campus, Oklahoma State University, 1 (OKSU); campus, Oklahoma State University, 2 (OKSU);

dairy barn, Oklahoma State University, 3 (OKSU); ABL, Oklahoma State University, Stillwater, 1 (OKSU), 1 (ECENT); Coed Apts, Stillwater, 1 (OKSU); Cordell Hall, Stillwater, 1 (OKSU); field, S jct. 3rd St. & Benjamin, Stillwater, 1 (OKSU); Municipal Airport, Stillwater, 1 (OKSU); Oklahoma State University, Stillwater, 1 (OKSU); Santa Fe RR, NE Stillwater, 1 (OKSU); Vet Village, Stillwater, 1 (OKSU); S jct. 12th St. & Ramsey St., Stillwater, 2 (OKSU); 223 S. Burdick, Stillwater, 1 (OKSU); 706 Connell, Stillwater, 1 (OKSU); 1407 Springfield Dr., Stillwater, 1 (OKSU); 216 N. Stallard Dr., Stillwater, 1 (OKSU); 1625 W. 12th St., Stillwater, 1 (OKSU); Stillwater, 8 (OKSU); 50 yds. SE jct. Jefferson & 11th Sts., Stillwater, 1 (OKSU); Hwy 51, 300 yds. N Stillwater Creek Bridge, W Stillwater, 1 (OKSU); Stillwater Creek, 0.5 mi. W Stillwater, 2 (OKSU); 1 mi. S Stillwater, 2 (OKSU); 1 mi. W, 1 mi. N Stillwater, 1 (OKSU); 1.25 mi. NE Stillwater, 1 (OKSU); 2 mi. S Stillwater, 1 (OKSU); 2 mi. W Stillwater, 1 (OKSU); 3 mi. W Stillwater, 1 (OKSU); 4 mi. W, 2 mi. S Stillwater, 1 (OKSU); 5 mi. W Stillwater, 0.25 mi. N SH 51, 1 (OKSU); Lowell Farm, 6 mi. E, 2 mi. S Stillwater, 1 (OKSU); 300 yds. S swine barns, Stillwater Creek, 1 (OKSU); 0.1 mi. S jct. Hwys 160 & 177, 1 (OKSU); Hwy 177, 3 mi. N Hwy 51, 1 (OKSU). PITTSBURG COUNTY: McAlester, 1 (ECENT); 5 mi. E, 1 mi. S Stuart, 1 (ECENT). PONTO-TOC COUNTY: east side Ada, 1 (ECENT); Ada City Lake, 1 (OKSU); 7 mi. NE Ada, 1 (ECENT). POTTAWATOMIE COUNTY: 3 mi. E Dale, 1 (OMNH); 0.25 mi. E McLoud, 4 (CSUO); 3 mi. NW Shawnee, 1 (OMNH); 4 mi. W, 3 mi. N Shawnee, 4 (OMNH); Tecumseh, 2 (KU); 2 mi. NE Tecumseh, 1 (OKSU); T11N, R5E, NE 1/4, Sec. 1, 1 (CSUO). ROGERS COUNTY: 7.5 mi. W Chelsea, 1 (OKSU). STEPHENS COUNTY: 9 mi. N Ringling, 1 (OKSU). TEXAS COUNTY: 2 mi. E Eva, 3 (KU); Guymon, 1 (OMNH); 2 mi. N Guymon, 3,000 ft., 5 (OMNH); Beaver River, 3.5 mi. SW Optima, 1 (KU). TILLMAN COUNTY: T4S, R14W, Sec. 9, 1 (OMNH); T4S, R15W, Sec. 23, 1 (OMNH); T2S, R14W, Sec. 29, 1 (OMNH). TULSA COUNTY: Garnett, 1 (UMMZ); Red Fork, 1 (USNM); 1.5 mi. N Sperry, 2 (OKSU); 3900 E. 51st, Tulsa, 1 (OKSU); 7 mi. S, 4 mi. E Tulsa, 1 (OMNH); 17 mi. S Tulsa, 2 (OKSU). WAGONER COUNTY: 0.5 mi. S Coweta, 1 (OKSU); 2.5 mi. SSW Coweta, 600 ft., 1 (OMNH); Wagoner, 1 (OKSU). WASHINGTON COUNTY: 3 mi. N Dewey, 2 (OKSU). WOODS COUNTY: Alva, Oklahoma Territory, 13 (FMNH); 6.5 mi. NW Alva, 1 (OMNH); 2 mi. W, 2.5 mi. S Dacoma, 1 (OKSU); 2 mi. W Edith, 1 (OMNH).

Mustela frenata.—Specimens examined (total 5): CLEVELAND COUNTY: Noble, Oklahoma Territory, 1 (FMNH); Norman, 1 (OMNH). PAYNE COUNTY: Stillwater, 1 (OKSU); 8 mi. NW Stillwater, 1 (OKSU). TEXAS COUNTY: near Guymon, 1 (OKSU).

Mustela nigripes.—Specimens examined (total 5): CIMARRON COUNTY:

T3N, R5E, near Boise City, 1 (USNM). CLEVELAND COUNTY: 1 mi.
E Norman, 1 (OMNH). KIOWA COUNTY: Mountain View, 1 (USNM).
TEXAS COUNTY: 8 mi. SE Adams, 1 (OKSU). WOODS COUNTY:
near Hopeton, 1 (NWOSU).

Mustela vison.—Specimens examined (total 70): ATOKA COUNTY: 1 mi.
S, 2 mi. W Atoka, 1 (OMNH). CADDO COUNTY: Ft. Cobb Lake Dam,
1 (CAMCO). CANADIAN COUNTY: southwest shore Lake Overholser,
1 (OMNH); 4 mi. SE Yukon, 2 (OMNH). CLEVELAND COUNTY: 1
mi. W Noble, 1 (CAMCO); 0.5 mi. W I-35 on Robinson St., Norman, 1
(OMNH); 2 mi. S Norman, 1 (OMNH); 2.25 mi. S Norman, 1 (OMNH).
COMANCHE COUNTY: 0.75 mi. W Faxon, 1 (CAMCO). CUSTER
COUNTY: 2 mi. S, 2 mi. W Thomas, 1 (CAMCO). DELAWARE COUNTY:
4.5 mi. above Lake Euche, 1 (CSUO). HUGHES COUNTY: tributary of
Wewoka Creek, 4 mi. W Holdenville, 1 (OMNH). JACKSON COUNTY:
2 mi. E Altus, 1 (CAMCO); 2 mi. N, 1 mi. E Altus, 1 (CAMCO). KING-
FISHER COUNTY: 9 mi. SW Hennessey, 1 (OKSU). LEFLORE
COUNTY: 1.0 mi. SW Summerfield, 1 (OMNH). LINCOLN COUNTY:
20 mi. S Stillwater, 1 (OKSU). MCCURTAIN COUNTY: 5 mi. SE Tom,
1 (ECENT). MUSKOGEE COUNTY: near Taft, 1 (OMNH). NOBLE
COUNTY: 0.75 mi. W Morrison, 1 (OKSU); 1 mi. W Stillwater, 2 (OKSU).
OKLAHOMA COUNTY: 33rd & Broadway, Edmond, 1 (CSUO); Hef-
ner Dam, 1 (CAMCO). OKMULGEE COUNTY: Deep Fork Creek,
13 (ECENT). OTTAWA COUNTY: Ottawa County, 1 (KU). PAYNE
COUNTY: Lake Carl Blackwell, 1 (OKSU); Payne County, 1 (OKSU);
near Stillwater, 8 (OKSU); Stillwater Creek, 3 (OKSU); 2 mi. N Still-
water, 1 (OKSU). PITTSBURG COUNTY: McAlester, 1 (OKSU); Naval
Ammo Depot, 1 (OKSU); 11 (KU). PONTOTOC COUNTY: Pontotoc
County, 1 (ECENT). SEQUOYAH COUNTY: 2 mi. E Sallisaw, 1 (OKSU).
STEPHENS COUNTY: Stephens County, 1 (CAMCO). TILLMAN
COUNTY: 4 mi. E Frederick, 1 (CAMCO). WAGONER COUNTY: 5 mi.
E Broken Arrow, 1 (UMMZ).

Myotis austroriparius.—Specimens examined (total 11): LEFLORE
COUNTY: Little River at Honobia, 1 (OKSU). MCCURTAIN
COUNTY: Mountain Fork River, E Beachtown, 2 (OKSU); Little River,
5 mi. SE Eagletown, 1 (KU), 2 (OKSU); Glover Creek, 1 (OKSU); Little
River, 3 (OKSU); Mountain Fork River, 1 (OKSU).

Myotis grisescens.—Specimens examined (total 222): ADAIR COUNTY:
Adair Bat Cave, 2 (OKSU); Crystal Cave, near Bunch, 1 (OKSU); Cave
Springs Cave, 2 (OKSU); Adair Cave, 3 mi. NNW Chewey, 15 (OMNH);
3.5 mi. NW Chewey, 2 (CAMCO); 2 mi. S Kansas, 4 (UMMZ); Adair
Cave, 5 mi. S Kansas, 1 (OKSU); cave, 5 mi. S Kansas, 30 (OKSU); 5
mi. S Kansas, 4 (FWMSH); cave, 6 mi. S Kansas, 2 (OKSU); Petkoff's

Large Cave, 2 (OKSU); Barren Fork River, 5 mi. S Westville, 1 (OKSU). CHEROKEE COUNTY: Half-moon Cave, 0.5 mi. NW Pigeon, 9 (OKSU); Scraper, 6 (UMMZ). DELAWARE COUNTY: bat cave, 1 (OMNH); Roberts Cave, 6 mi. SSE Cave, 1 (OMNH); 6.5 mi. NW Colcord, 800 ft., 1 (OMNH); Roberts Cave, 6.6 mi. NW Colcord, 800 ft., 29 (OMNH); Stansbury Cave, 6.6 mi. NW Colcord, 1 (OMNH); 1 mi. W Disney, 1 (OKSU); north side Grand Lake Dam, 1 (OKSU); Dunaway Cave, 5 mi. W, 3.5 mi. N Jay, 4 (OKSU); Stansbury Cave, 8 mi. S, 3 mi. E Jay, 5 (OKSU); Spavinaw Creek Cave, 0.20 mi. below Upper Dam, 2 (OKSU); 0.5 mi. NW Upper Spavinaw Lake Dam, 7 (OMNH); 0.5 mi. NW Upper Spavinaw Lake Dam, 800 ft., 13 (OMNH); bat cave, 0.75 mi. NW Upper Spavinaw Dam, 27 (OMNH); near Upper Spavinaw Lake Dam, 800 ft., 1 (OMNH); 0.5 mi. NNW Upper Spavinaw Lake Dam, 800 ft., 1 (OMNH); 0.5 mi. NW Upper Spavinaw Lake Dam, 1 (CAMCO); Spavinaw Creek Cave, 0.75 mi. NW Upper Spavinaw Dam, 8 (OMNH); 0.75 mi. N Upper Spavinaw Lake Dam, 800 ft., 11 (OMNH); cave, 1 mi. N Spavinaw Dam, 1 (OKSU); 1.5 mi. NW Upper Spavinaw Lake Dam, 800 ft., 2 (OMNH); Stansbury Cave, 14 (OMNH). MAYES COUNTY: near Disney, 1 (OKSU); Mayes County, 5 (CSUO); under Pensacola Dam, 2 (OKSU). OTTAWA COUNTY: Washington Hollow Cave, Grand Lake, 2 mi. E, 3 mi. S Fairland, 1 (OKSU).

Myotis keenii.—Specimens examined (total 46): ADAIR COUNTY: Crystal Cave, near Bunch, 11 (OKSU); 4 mi. SW Bunch, 900 ft., 1 (OMNH); Cave Springs Cave, 25 (FWMSH); cave, 5 mi. S Little Kansas, 1 (OKSU). DELAWARE COUNTY: Duncan Cave, near Colcord, 2 (OKSU); 7.5 mi. NE Jay, 950 ft., 1 (OMNH). LEFLORE COUNTY: Kiamichi Mt. Cave, S Muse, 1 (OKSU). MCCURTAIN COUNTY: Beavers Bend State Park, 3 (OUBS). SEQUOYAH COUNTY: 15 mi. N Dwight Mission, 1 (OKSU).

Myotis leibii.—Specimens examined (total 14): CIMARRON COUNTY: North Carrizo Creek, below Black Mesa, 3 (OKSU); mouth North Carrizo Creek, 1 (OKSU). COMANCHE COUNTY: Cache Creek, Wichita Mountains Wildlife Refuge, 1 (OKSU). GREER COUNTY: 1.25 mi. N Granite, 1 (OKSU). KIOWA COUNTY: Windmill Cave, 15 mi. S, 2 mi. W Carnegie, 1 (OKSU); Frisco Mt., 2 (OKSU); Svoboda Cave, 1 mi. W, 1 mi. N Mountain Park, 1 (OKSU); Radziminski Mt. Cave, 2 (OKSU); Svoboda Cave, 1 (OKSU). MCCURTAIN COUNTY: McCurtain Co. Game Preserve, 250 yds. W Mt. Fork River, 1 (OKSU).

Myotis lucifugus.—Specimens examined (total 31): DELAWARE COUNTY: Spavinaw Creek Cave, 7.5 mi. SE Jay, 1 (CSUO). MCCURTAIN COUNTY: Beavers Bend State Park, 24 (OKSU); Youth Camp, Beavers Bend State Park, 6 (OKSU).

Myotis sodalis.—Specimens examined (total 4): ADAIR COUNTY: Adair

Bat Cave, 5 mi. S Kansas, 2 (OKSU). PUSHMATAHA COUNTY: Bowers Trail Cave, 12 mi. S Talihina, 2 (OKSU).

Myotis velifer.—Specimens examined (total 460): BLAINE COUNTY: Blaine County, 2 (OMNH); Salt Creek Canyon, 4 mi. SE Southard, 1 (KU). CANADIAN COUNTY: Ft. Reno, 3 (USNM). CIMARRON COUNTY: Black Mesa State Park, 8 mi. SE Kenton, 1 (CAMCO). CLEVELAND COUNTY: Animal Behavior Lab, University of Oklahoma, Norman, 1 (OMNH). COMANCHE COUNTY: Boulder Canyon, Wichita Wildlife Refuge, 5 (USNM); Cache Creek, Wichita Wildlife Refuge, 12 (USNM). CUSTER COUNTY: Butler, 1 (KU); Weatherford, 1 (OKSU). DEWEY COUNTY: 5 mi. N, 5 mi. W Canton, 1 (KU); 20 mi. N, 2 mi. W Seiling, 1 (OKSU). GARFIELD COUNTY: 1 mi. S, 3.5 mi. W‴Bison, 1 (OKSU); Enid, 2 (KU); main building, Phillips University, Enid, 1 (KU). GREER COUNTY: Bat Cave, 2 (OMNH); Jester Cave, SW Delhi, 2 (OKSU); Jester Cave, 19 (FWMSH); Jester Cave, 3.5 mi. N Jester, 3 (OKSU); 7 mi. S Mangum, 2 (OMNH); Reed Cave, 2 (CSUO); 1 mi. W, 1 mi. S Reed, 3 (OMNH), 5 (USNM); Oklahoma Gypsum Cave, 2 mi. S Reed, 1 (FWMSH); T5N, R24W Sec. 27, 3 mi. SW Reed, 1 (CAMCO); Jester Cave, 12 mi. N Reed, 5 (OKSU); T4N, R24W, Sec.28, 1 (OMNH). HARMON COUNTY: Reed, 2 (CSUO); cave, 3 mi. W, 1.5 mi. S Reed, 8 (OKSU), 11 (KU); 6 mi. SW Reed, 1 (MSU); 1 mi. E, 7 mi. S Vinson, 4 (OKSU); 2 mi. E, 1 mi. S Vinson, 1 (OKSU); 6 mi. E, 1 mi. S Vinson, 2 (OMNH); 6 mi. E, 1 mi. S Vinson, 1,700 ft., 6 (OMNH); 6.5 mi. SE Vinson, 2 (CAMCO); 6.5 mi. ESE Vinson, 1,700 ft., 2 (OMNH). HARPER COUNTY: 2 mi. W May, 2 (OKSU). KINGFISHER COUNTY: 3 mi. W, 3 mi. N Dover, 1 (OKSU). KIOWA COUNTY: Svoboda Cave, 1 mi. N, 1 mi. W Mountain Park, 1 (OKSU); 1 mi. W, 1 mi. N Mountain Park, 1 (OKSU). MAJOR COUNTY: Vickery Cave #2, 3 mi. W Bouse Jct., 1 (FWMSH), 2 (ECENT); Vickery Ranch Cave, 3 mi. W Bouse Jct., 3 (USNM); cave, 3 mi. W Bouse Jct., jct. US Hwys 281 & SH 15, 1 (OKSU); 3 mi. W Bouse Jct., 1 (OKSU); Vickery Cave #2, 7 mi. W Bouse Jct., 1 (OKSU); Cheyenne Valley Cave, 7 (OKSU); Conner's Cave, 6 (OKSU); Corbin Cave, 32 mi. NW Fairview, 1 (KU); 14.7 mi. S, 9.2 mi. W Freedom, 3 (CSUO); Griever Creek, 1 (UMMZ); Griever Creek Cave, 9 (OKSU); Major County, 1 (OKSU), 1 (CSUO); cave, NW Major County, 1 (OKSU); Vickery Cave #2, NW Major County, 2 (FWMSH); Vickery #1, 15 mi. E, 0.25 mi. S Mooreland, 2 (OKSU); Vickery Cave #2, 15 mi. E, 0.25 mi. S Mooreland, 5 (OKSU); 15 mi. E, 0.25 mi. N Mooreland, 4 (OKSU); 15 mi. E, 0.25 mi. S Mooreland, 1 (OKSU); Nescatunga Cave, 3 (CSUO); Corbin Ranch, 4 mi. E Sherman, 55 (KU); Vickery Cave #1, 1 (OKSU); Vickery Cave #2, 9 (OKSU); Vickery Cave #1, Waynoka, 1 (OKSU); Vickery Cave #2, 12 mi. S, 4 mi. W, 0.25 mi. S Waynoka, 1 (OKSU); 12 mi. S Waynoka, 1 (UMMZ);

Whitlaw Terrell Ranch, 2 (OKSU); 26 mi. E Woodward, 1 (OKSU); T22N, R16W, Sec. 15, 2.3 mi. S, 0.4 mi. W jct. Hwys 218 & 15, 1 (OMNH); Vickery Cave #2, 2.5 mi. W jct. 281 & 15, 2 (FWMSH); Nescatunga Cave, 2.5 mi. W jct. Hwys 281 & 15, 17 (CSUO). OKLA-HOMA COUNTY: library, Central State University, Edmond, 1 (CSUO). ROGER MILLS COUNTY: 1.5 mi. S, 2.5 mi. E Reydon, 1 (CAMCO). WASHITA COUNTY: Corn Caves, 5 mi. N, 2 mi. W Corn, 2 (CSUO); T11N, R15W, Sec. 5, 5.5 mi. N, 2 mi. W Corn, 2 (CSUO); Corn Caves, 5 mi. N, 3 mi. W Corn, 4 (CSUO); Corn Cave, 6 mi. N Corn, 1 (CSUO); 5 mi. W, 5 mi. S Weatherford, 5 (KU); Corn Cave, 5 mi. S, 5 mi. W Weatherford, 1 (OKSU). WOODS COUNTY: Merrihew Cave, 2 mi. W, 6 mi. S Aetena (in Barber Co., Kansas), 5 (KU); Anderson Creek Cave, 2 (OKSU); Merrihew Cave, 8 (OKSU); near Waynoka, 4 (KU); 12 mi. S Waynoka, 6 (OKSU); 12 mi. S, 5 mi. W Waynoka, 1 (OKSU). WOOD-WARD COUNTY: Alabaster Cave, 1 (CSUO); Alabaster Cavern, 70 (OKSU), 2 (OMNH), 2 (CSUO); 6 mi. W Alabaster Cavern, 1 (CAMCO); Owl Cave, Alabaster State Park, 1 (OKSU); Anderson Creek Cave, 4 mi. E Camp Huston, 3 (OKSU); Alabaster Cavern, 4 mi. S Freeman, 9 (OKSU); Alabaster Caves, 5 mi. SW Freedom, 4 (OMNH); 5.7 mi. S, 9.2 mi. W Freedom, 26 (CSUO); Alabaster Cavern, 6 mi. S Freedom, 1 (CSUO); Sel-man Cave, 7 mi. SW Freedom, 1 (CSUO); 10 mi. S Freedom, 1 (UMMZ); Icebox Cave, 7 (OKSU); Mooreland, 3 (OKSU); Swigerts cow barn, 0.5 mi. S Mooreland, 3 (OKSU); 16 mi. E, 0.25 mi. S Mooreland, 2 (OKSU); 18 mi. W Mooreland, 1 (OKSU); Owl Cave, 2 (OUBS); 2 mi. E Quinlan, 1 (OKSU); Selmon Cave, 1 (CSUO); 2 mi. W Waynoka, 1 (OKSU); Wood-ward County, 4 (OKSU); 26 mi. E Woodward, 2 (OKSU).

Myotis yumanensis.—Specimens examined (total 83); CIMARRON COUNTY: Carrizo Creek, 1 (OKSU); Cimarron River, 6 (OKSU); Cimarron River, near mouth North Carrizo Creek, 5 (OKSU), 2 (FWMSH); Cimarron River, E mouth North Carrizo Creek, 3 (OKSU); Kenton, 6 (OKSU); Car-rizo Creek, 6 mi. N Kenton, 3 (OKSU); cave, Tesesquite Canyon, 7 mi. SE Kenton, 21 (OKSU); Pigeon Cave, 2 (OKSU); cave, NW Tesesquite Canyon, 13 (OKSU); Tesesquite Canyon Cave, 21 (OKSU).

Nasua nasua.—Specimens examined (total 2); MUSKOGEE COUNTY: T11N, R19E, NW 1/4 Sec. 3, 1 (OMNH). WOODWARD COUNTY: North Canadian River, Woodward, 1 (OKSU).

Neotoma albigula.—Specimens examined (total 74); CIMARRON COUNTY: Black Mesa, 1 (UMMZ); Black Mesa State Park, 3 (UIMNH); Cimarron County, 1 (OMNH); 0.5 mi. E Kenton, 2 (OMNH); T5N, Sec. 24, 1.5 mi. S, 2.75 mi. E Kenton, 1 (OMNH); T5N, R2E, Sec. 34, Black Mesa, 1.5 mi. E, 2.75 mi. S Kenton, 1 (OMNH); 2 mi. N, 1 mi. W Kenton, 4 (OMNH); 2.25 mi. N Kenton, 3 (OMNH); 2.5 mi. SE Kenton, 1 (CAMCO);

2.6 mi. S, 1.5 mi. E Kenton, 1 (OMNH); 3 mi. N Kenton, 1 (OMNH); 3.4 mi. S, 1.2 mi. E Kenton, 2 (OMNH); 3.5 mi. N, 1 mi. E Kenton, 2 (OMNH); 3.6 mi. N, 1.1 mi. W Kenton, 1 (OMNH); 3.6 mi. W, 0.9 mi. E Kenton, 2 (OMNH); 2.5 mi. SE Kenton, 4,200 ft., 3 (OMNH); 4 mi. E Kenton, 1 (OMNH); 4 mi. N Kenton, 11 (KU); 4.2 mi. S Kenton, 4 (OMNH); 4.2 mi. S, 0.5 mi. E Kenton, 4 (OMNH); 4.2 mi. S, 0.8 mi. W Kenton, 4 (OMNH); 4.5 mi. S Kenton, 1 (CAMCO); 5 mi. N Kenton, 4 (OKSU); 5.3 mi. S, 0.5 mi. E Kenton, 2 (OMNH); 6 mi. N Kenton, 8 (OKSU); Black Mesa, Easter Pageant Bluff, 1 (OMNH); Tesesquite Canyon, 5 (OKSU).

Neotoma floridana.—Specimens examined (total 687); ADAIR COUNTY: Adair County, 1 (UMMZ); 2.5 mi. NW Chewey, 800 ft., 1 (OMNH); 2.5 mi. NW Chewey, 900 ft., 2 (OMNH); 3 mi. NNW Chewey, 1,000 ft., 5 (OMNH); 5 mi. SE Flint, 1 (OKSU); 5 mi. S Kansas, 5 (UMMZ); Boston Mts., Stilwell, 8 (USNM); 2.5 mi. E Stilwell, 3 (UIMNH); 7 mi. W Stilwell, 1 (KU). BLAINE COUNTY: between Canton Reservoir & Hwy 58, 1 (OKSU); Canton Lake, 1 (FWMSH); Public Hunting Area, Canton Lake, 4 (USNM); Canton Public Hunting Ground, 2 (OKSU); Canton Reservoir, 1 (OKSU); Fairview Landing, Canton Reservoir, 1 (OKSU); northeast side Canton Reservoir, 1 (OKSU); southeast side Canton Reservoir, 1 (OKSU); Longdale, 1 (USNM); northeast side Canton Reservoir, 0.25 mi. S, 1 mi. W Longdale, 2 (OKSU); 1 mi. W Longdale, 3 (OKSU); 2 mi. W Longdale, 1 (OKSU); Roman Nose State Park, 10 (OKSU); Salt Creek Canyon, 1 (KU); 2 mi. W Watonga, 2 (OKSU). BRYAN COUNTY: 10 mi. SE Bennington, 1 (TMM); 0.5 W Colbert, 3 (TMM); 5 mi. N Colbert, 2 (TMM); 1 mi. N Oberlin, 1 (OUBS). CADDO COUNTY: Caddo County, 1 (OUBS); 4 mi. W Cogar, 5 (OMNH); 5 mi. W Cogar, 3 (OMNH), 2 (USNM); Ft. Cobb, 1 (CAMCO); T9N, R13W, SARP Site C1, above Ft. Cobb Reservoir, 2 (OKSU); 1 mi. S, 0.2 mi. N jct. SH 152 & 146, 1 (OKSU). CANADIAN COUNTY: 6 mi. N, 4 mi. E El Reno, 1 (OKSU); 17 mi. W, 3 mi. S El Reno on US Hwy 66, 1 (OKSU); 5.5 mi. SE Hinton, 1,500 ft., 1 (KU); 8 mi. SE Hinton, 1 (CAMCO); T11N, R10W, Sec. 18, 1 (OMNH). CARTER COUNTY: Arbuckle Mts., 3 mi. N Springer, 3 (MVZ), 3 (USNM). CHEROKEE COUNTY: Cookson Hills Game Refuge, 1 (OKSU); Cookson Hills Wildlife Refuge, approx. 4 mi. N Cookson, 1 (OKSU). CHOCTAW COUNTY: 1.5 mi. N Hugo, 1 (OKSU); 3 mi. E, 1 mi. W Hugo, 1 (OKSU). CLEVELAND COUNTY: Cleveland County, 1 (OMNH); Lake Draper, 1 (CSUO); 4 mi. SE Lexington, 1 (OKSU); 3 mi. E, 1 mi. S Lexington, 1 (OKSU); Noble, Oklahoma Territory, 4 (FMNH); 0.6 mi. W Noble, 1 (USNM); 3 mi. NE Noble, 1 (OMNH); Mathews Farm, Norman, 1 (OMNH); Norman, 1 (OMNH); 3–5 km S Norman, 2 (OMNH); 0.9 mi. N, 2 mi. E Norman on Robinson,

2 (OMNH); 1 mi. S Norman, 1 (OKSU); South Canadian River, 2 mi. S Norman, 11 (KU); 3 mi. E Norman, 1 (OMNH); 3.5 mi. SSE Norman, 1 (USNM); 5 mi. E, 0.5 mi. N Norman, 1 (OMNH), 1 (UIMNH); 5 mi. S Norman, 3 (OMNH); 5 mi. E Norman, 1 (UIMNH); 6 mi. E Norman, 3 (OMNH); 6.2 mi. E Norman, 1,100 ft., 1 (OMNH), 1 (USNM); 6 mi. E, 0.5 mi. N Norman, 1 (OMNH); 6.6 mi. E Norman, 1,100 ft., 1 (OMNH); 8 mi. E Norman, 1 (OMNH); 9 mi. E Norman, 1 (OMNH); 9 mi. E, 1 mi. N Norman, 1 (OMNH); 2 mi. S Slaughterville, 3 (OMNH); jct. Rock Creek Rd. & South Canadian River, 1 (OKSU); Thunderbird Lake, 1 (OMNH). COMANCHE COUNTY: 9 mi. NW Cache, 2 (OMNH); Chattanooga, 1 (USNM); 1 mi. S, 1 mi. E Elgin, 1 (CAMCO); 2 mi. SW Elgin, 1 (CAMCO); 2 mi. SSW Elgin, 2 (CAMCO); 3.75 mi. W, 1.5 mi. S Elgin, 3 (CAMCO); 3 mi. NW Faxon, 1 (CAMCO); 6 mi. E Fletcher, 1 (CAMCO); 2 mi. W Lawton Post Office, 1 (CAMCO); 3 mi. S Lawton, 1 (CAMCO); 10 mi. E, 0.75 mi. N Lawton, 1 (CAMCO); 5 mi. E, 5 mi. N Medicine Park, 1 (CAMCO); Mt. Scott, 1 (OMNH); 0.5 mi. N Mt. Sheridan, 1 (CSUO); Mt. Scott, Wichita Mountains, 7 (USNM); Wichita Mountains, 1 (OMNH); Boulder Camp, Wichita Mountains Wildlife Refuge, 4 (OKSU); Eagle Mt., across from Boulder Camp, Wichita Mountains Wildlife Refuge, 1 (OKSU); Eagle Mt., Wichita Mountains Wildlife Refuge, 1 (OKSU); Hwy 49, east entrance, Wichita Mountains Wildlife Refuge, 1 (OKSU); W Lost Lake, Wichita Mountains Wildlife Refuge, 1 (OKSU); Wichita Mountains Wildlife Refuge, 3 (OKSU); Wichita Natl. Forest, 3 (OMNH); Wichita Wildlife Refuge, 1 (OMNH); 0.25 mi. W Wichita Mountains Wildlife Refuge, 1 (CSUO); 5.4 mi. W east border, Wichita Mountains Wildlife Refuge, 1 (OMNH). COTTON COUNTY: 5 mi. SE Taylor, 900 ft., 3 (OMNH). CREEK COUNTY: Sapulpa, 4 (KU). CUSTER COUNTY: Washita Natl. Wildlife Refuge, W Butler, 1 (OKSU); Foss Reservoir, Washita Natl. Wildlife Refuge, 1 (OKSU). DELAWARE COUNTY: Spavinaw Creek Area, 7.5 mi. SE Jay, 4 (CSUO). DEWEY COUNTY: 5 mi. W Canton, 2 (KU); northeast corner Canton Hunting Area, 1 (OKSU); 1 mi. S, 0.5 mi. E Seiling, 1 (OKSU); 2 mi. S, 2 mi. W Seiling, 1 (KU); 6 mi. S, 2 mi. W Seiling, 2 (KU); 6.5 mi. S, 3 mi. W Seiling, 2 (KU); 7 mi. S, 1.5 mi. W Seiling, 4 (KU); 7 mi. S, 2.5 mi. W Seiling, 3 (KU); 8 mi. S, 5 mi. W Seiling, 2 (KU). GARFIELD COUNTY: 2 mi. E, 1 mi. S Enid, 1 (OKSU). GRADY COUNTY: SARP Site R8, 10 mi. W SH 76, 5.3 mi. N SH 29, 3 (OKSU). GRANT COUNTY: 1 mi. W, 1 mi. N Hawley, 2 (OMNH). HASKELL COUNTY: 6 mi. S Stigler, 1 (OMNH); 6 mi. N, 0.5 mi. E Stigler, 1 (OKSU); 8.5 mi. S Stigler, 1 (OMNH). HUGHES COUNTY: 16 mi. SE Holdenville, 1 (ECENT). JOHNSTON COUNTY: 1 mi. E Tishomingo near Hwy 78, 2 (ECENT). KAY COUNTY: 5 mi. S, 7.5 mi. E Newkirk, 1,100 ft., 1 (OMNH); 5 mi. S, 10.5 mi. E Newkirk, 1,150 ft.,

17 (OMNH); Ponca Agency, 1 (USNM); 7 mi. E, 1 mi. S Ponca City, 1 (OKSU). KINGFISHER COUNTY: 7 mi. W Hennessey, 1 (OKSU). LATIMER COUNTY: south bank Kanniatobbee Creek, 1 (OMNH); Red Oak, 1 (USNM); 10 mi. W, 3 mi. S Talihina, 1 (OKSU); Eastern Oklahoma State College, Wilburton, 1 (OKSU); 0.5 mi. N Eastern Oklahoma State College, Wilburton, 1 (OKSU); Kanniatobbee Creek, 3.5 mi. N Wilburton, 4 (OMNH); south bank Kanniatobbee, 3.5 mi. N Wilburton, 3 (OMNH); northeast bank Kanniatobbee, 3.5 mi. N Wilburton, 1 (OMNH); Robber's Cave State Park, 5 mi. N Wilburton, 1 (KU). LEFLORE COUNTY: 5 mi. S Wister, 1 (OMNH); 0.75 mi. NE Zoe, 5 (OMNH); 1.75 mi. NE Zoe, 1 (OMNH); 2 mi. NE Zoe, 1 (OMNH). LINCOLN COUNTY: Dry Creek, 5 mi. W Stroud, 1 (OKSU). LOGAN COUNTY: Guthrie, 5 (CSUO); 4.5 mi. S, 2 mi. W Guthrie, 2 (CSUO). MAJOR COUNTY: North Canadian River, 3 mi. S Chester, 8 (KU); 3 mi. S, 0.5 mi. E Chester, 4 (KU); 3 mi. S, 1 mi. E Chester, 1 (KU); Vickery Ranch, 1 (OKSU); Nescatunga Cave, 2.5 mi. W jct. Hwys 281 & 15, 1 (CSUO). MARSHALL COUNTY: Marshall County, 1 (OMNH); 0.5 mi. N Paul's Landing, 630 ft., 14 (OMNH); near Buncombe Creek, 0.5 mi. N Shays Crossing, 1 (OUBS); 5 mi. S, 1 mi. W Shay, 1 (OKSU); University of Oklahoma Biological Station, 1 (OUBS), 1 (OKSU); east side Buncombe, across from University of Oklahoma Biological Station, 1 (OUBS); waterfront, 150 yds., University of Oklahoma Biological Station, 1 (OMNH); 0.25 mi. NE University of Oklahoma Biological Station, 1 (OUBS), 1 (OKSU); 0.5 mi. W University of Oklahoma Biological Station, 2 (OUBS); 0.5 mi. E University of Oklahoma Biological Station, 2 (OUBS); 0.5 mi. N University of Oklahoma Biological Station, 2 (OUBS); 0.5 mi. NE University of Oklahoma Biological Station, 2 (OUBS); 1 mi. ENE University of Oklahoma Biological Station, 1 (OMNH); 1 mi. W University of Oklahoma Biological Station, 2 (OUBS); 2 mi. N University of Oklahoma Biological Station, 1 (OMNH); 3 mi. NE University of Oklahoma Biological Station, 1 (OUBS); 3 mi. W University of Oklahoma Biological Station, 1 (OKSU); 0.25 mi. N Willis, 1 (OUBS); 0.5 mi. E Willis, 640 ft., 1 (OMNH); 1 mi. NE Willis, 1 (OUBS); 1 mi. W Willis, 2 (OUBS); 2 mi. W, 1 mi. S Willis, 1 (OMNH), 2 (OUBS); 3 mi. NW Willis, 2 (OUBS); 6 mi. N Bryer Creek, Willis, 1 (OMNH). MAYES COUNTY: 2.5 mi. E Chouteau, 1.0 mi. N Hwy 33, 2 (OMNH); 2.7 mi. E Chouteau, 1.1 mi. N Hwy 33, 1 (OMNH); 2.8 mi. E Chouteau, 1 mi. N Hwy 33, 1 (OMNH); Mayes County, 1 (OMNH); 1 mi. S Spavinaw, 6 (KU). MCCLAIN COUNTY: 5 mi. NW Newcastle, 1 (ECENT); 1.75 mi. N, 3.5 mi. W Newcastle, 1 (ECENT); 1.5 mi. SW Norman, 2 (OMNH); 1 mi. S, 0.5 mi. W Purcell, 1 (OMNH). MCCURTAIN COUNTY: Beavers Bend State Park, 1 (OUBS), 2 (KU); Beavers Bend, 1 (OMNH); Director's Cabin, Beavers Bend State Park, 1 (OMNH); 5 mi. S Broken Bow,

2 (OMNH); 5.7 mi. S Broken Bow, 2 (OMNH); 15 mi. SE Broken Bow, 1 (OMNH); 2 mi. W Smithville, 4 (OMNH); 2.5 mi. W Smithville, 2 (OMNH). MCINTOSH COUNTY: 0.5 mi. W Burney, 1 (OMNH); 11 mi. W Eufaula, 1 (CSUO). MURRAY COUNTY: Dougherty, Indian Territory, 6 (FMNH); 1 mi. SE Sulphur, 1 (UIMNH); Travertine Creek, 2 (OKSU). MUSKOGEE COUNTY: 4 mi. below Ft. Gibson Dam, 1 (OKSU); Arkansas River, 6 mi. SE Ft. Gibson, 1 (OKSU). NOBLE COUNTY: Lake McMurtry, 7 mi. NW Stillwater, 1 (OKSU); 1.4 mi. N, 2.1 mi. W Watchorn, 1 (OMNH); T21N, R2E, NE 1/4 Sec. 3, 1 (OKSU). OKLAHOMA COUNTY: jct. Bryant & Waterloo Rd., 1 (CSUO); on Danforth, 1 (CSUO); Edmond Natural Area, Edmond, 1 (CSUO); N Edmond, 1 (CSUO); jct. N. Boulevard & Danforth, Edmond, 1 (CSUO); jct. Sooner Rd. & Covell Rd., Edmond, 1 (CSUO); 0.3 mi. S Covell on Western, Edmond, 1 (CSUO); 0.75 mi. E Coltrane on Covell, Edmond, 1 (CSUO); 0.8 mi. W Kelly on 15th St., Edmond, 1 (CSUO); 1 mi. NW Edmond, S Danforth, E Golf Course, 1 (CSUO); 1.5 mi. N 2nd St. on Kelly, Edmond, 1 (CSUO); 4 mi. (by road) E Edmond, 2 (CSUO); jct. 2nd & Bryant, 5 mi. E, 1.5 mi. S Edmond, 1 (CSUO); 5 mi. E, 0.75 mi. S, 200 ft. W, Edmond, 1 (CSUO); 6 mi. W Edmond, 2 (CSUO); 7 mi. W, 1 mi. S Edmond, 1 (CSUO); 10 mi. W, 0.5 mi. S Edmond, 5 (CSUO); Sam Gillaspy Farm, 12 mi. E Edmond, 1 (CSUO); 2 mi. SE Jones (by road), 1 (CSUO); 2101 Rolling Hills, 1 (CSUO); 1 mi. W jct. Wilshire & Kelly Rd., N side Oklahoma City, 1 (CSUO); 2 mi. E Choctaw on N.E. 23rd, Oklahoma City, 1 (CSUO); 4 mi. W jct. Eastern & Wilshire, Oklahoma City, 5 (CSUO); 4 mi. E jct. Eastern & Wilshire, Oklahoma City, 1 (CSUO); 0.25 mi. W jct. Western & Danforth, 1 (CSUO); 0.5 mi. N Danforth on May Ave., 3 (CSUO); 0.5 mi. NW jct. 192nd & N. May Ave., 1 (CSUO); 0.5 mi. E on Covell Rd. & Postroad, 1 (CSUO); 0.65 mi. S on Sooner Rd. from Turner Turnpike, 1 (CSUO); 0.75 mi. N jct. I-35 & 66, 150 ft. E, 1 (CSUO); Coffee Creek, 1.5 mi. N Danforth & Coltrane, 2 (CSUO); 3.75 mi. N jct. I-35 & 66, 225 ft. E, 1 (CSUO); 4 mi. N jct. I-35 & 66, 200 ft. E, 1 (CSUO); W Wiley Post Airport, 1 (CSUO). OKMULGEE COUNTY: 1 mi. E Henryetta, 1 (OMNH); 3 mi. S Okmulgee, 1 (OKSU). OSAGE COUNTY: Rock Creek on US 60, W Bartlesville, 4 (OMNH); 10 mi. WSW Fairfax, 1,000 ft., 3 (OMNH); 10 mi. NE Crestwood Country Club on Heartwood Mountain, 1 (OKSU); McClintock Boy Scout Camp, 1 (USNM); Okesa, 9 (UMMZ); Osage Hills State Park, 6 (OKSU); 5 mi. S Pawhuska, 1 (OKSU); 6 mi. N Pawhuska, 9 (OMNH); Sand Creek Falls, 10 mi. NE Pawhuska, 1 (TMM). PAWNEE COUNTY: 7.5 mi. N, 2.75 mi. W Pawnee, 1 (KU); 1.3 mi. N, 1.5 mi. W Watchorn, 2 (OMNH); 1.3 mi. N, 1.6 mi. W Watchorn, 1 (OMNH); 1.5 mi. N, 1.0 mi. W Watchorn, 2 (OMNH). PAYNE COUNTY: northeast shore Boomer Lake, 1 (OKSU); food plot #1, 1 (OKSU); camp area, S Lake Carl Blackwell, 1 (OKSU);

below spillway, Carl Blackwell Lake, 2 (USNM); E Lake Carl Blackwell, 1 (OKSU); east side Lake Carl Blackwell, 3 (OKSU); 0.5 mi. S Hdqtrs. Lake Carl Blackwell, 2 (OKSU); Lake Carl Blackwell, 2 (UIMNH); causeway, Lake Carl Blackwell, 1 (OKSU); 0.125 mi. SE Lake Carl Blackwell, 1 (OKSU); north side arm 4, Lake Carl Blackwell, 1 (OKSU); 1 mi. SSW Lake Carl Blackwell Dam, 1 (OKSU); 1 mi. W Lake Carl Blackwell, 1 (OKSU); northwest part Lake Carl Blackwell, 1 (OKSU); ravine, S Lake Carl Blackwell, 1 (OKSU); spillway, S Lake Carl Blackwell, 1 (OKSU); west arm Lake Carl Blackwell, 1 (OKSU); west end Lake Carl Blackwell, 1 (OKSU); south side Lake Carl Blackwell, 2 (OKSU); 200 yds. E arm 13 Lake Carl Blackwell, 1 (OKSU); 0.25 mi. N arm 13 Lake Blackwell, 2 (ECENT); near Lake McMurtry, 1 (OKSU); Payne County, 1 (OKSU), 1 (ECENT); 3 mi. E, 3.5 mi. S Perkins, 1 (OKSU); 5 mi. W Perkins, 1 (OKSU); Wildlife Research Center & McElroy, Stillwater, 1 (OKSU); Carberry's Farm, Stillwater, 1 (OKSU); jct. Lakeview & Sangre Rd., Stillwater, 1 (OKSU); NW Stillwater, 1 (UMMZ); No. 34 ENW Stillwater, 1 (OKSU); creek, 1900 N. Washington St., Stillwater, 1 (OKSU); spillway, S Boomer Dam, Stillwater, 2 (OKSU); Stillwater, 1 (OKSU); 0.25 mi. W, 2 mi. S Stillwater, 1 (OKSU); 0.05 mi. S SH 51 bridge over Stillwater Creek, 1 (OKSU); 0.5 mi. E Stillwater, 1 (OKSU); 0.5 mi. W dairy barn on Forestry Farm, Stillwater, 1 (OKSU); 1 mi. N Stillwater, 1 (UMMZ); 1 mi. W Stillwater, 2 (OKSU); 1 mi. W, 0.5 mi. S Stillwater, 1 (OKSU); 1.5 mi. N, 2 mi. W Stillwater, 1 (OKSU); 1.5 mi. W Western on Farm Rd., Stillwater, 1 (OKSU); 2 mi. E Stillwater, 1 (OKSU); 2 mi. E, 1.5 mi. S Stillwater, 1 (OKSU); 2 mi. N, 2.5 mi. E Stillwater, 1 (OKSU); 2 mi. N, 4 mi. W Stillwater, 1 (OKSU); 2 mi. S Stillwater, 1 (OKSU); 2 mi. W Stillwater, 2 (OKSU); 2 mi. W, 1 mi. S Stillwater, 1 (OKSU); 2 mi. W, 2 mi. S Stillwater, 1 (OKSU); 2 mi. W, 4 mi. S Stillwater, 1 (OKSU); 2.75 mi. W, 1 mi. S Stillwater, 1 (OKSU); 3 mi. N, 0.5 mi. W Stillwater, 1 (OKSU); 3 mi. N, 0.75 mi. W Stillwater, 1 (OKSU); 3 mi. S Stillwater, 1 (UIMNH); 3 mi. W Stillwater, 4 (OKSU); 3 mi. W, 1 mi. S Stillwater, 1 (OKSU); 4 mi. NE Stillwater, 1 (OKSU); 4 mi. W Stillwater, 1 (OKSU); 4 mi. W Stillwater on Hwy 51, 1 (OKSU); 4 mi. W, 1 mi. S Stillwater, 1 (OKSU); 4 mi. W, 1.5 mi. S Stillwater, 1 (OKSU); 4 mi. W, 2 mi. S Stillwater, 1 (OKSU); 4 mi. W, 5 mi. N Stillwater, 1 (OKSU); 4.5 mi. SW Stillwater, 2 (OKSU), 1 (UMMZ); 4.5 mi. S Oklahoma State University Ecology Preserve, 9 mi. W Stillwater, 1 (OKSU); 5 mi. E Stillwater, 1 (OKSU); 5 mi. E, 0.5 mi. N Stillwater, 1 (OKSU); 5 mi. N Lakeview Dr., 0.5 mi. E US Hwy 177, Stillwater, 2 (OKSU); 5 mi. N Lakeview Rd., 0.1 mi. W Washington St., Stillwater, 1 (OKSU); 5 mi. N Stillwater on Hwy 177, 1 (OKSU); 5 mi. N, 2 mi. E jct. 6th St. & Perkins Rd., Stillwater, 1 (OKSU); 5.5 mi. S, 2 mi. E Stillwater, 1 (OKSU); 5.5 mi. W Stillwater, 1 (OKSU); 6 mi. W Stillwater, 1 (OKSU); 7

mi. W Stillwater, 1 (OKSU); 7.4 mi. W Stillwater, 2 (OKSU); 8 mi. E, 0.25 mi. S Stillwater, 1 (OKSU); 8 mi. N, 1 mi. W Stillwater, 2 (OKSU); 8 mi. S Stillwater, 1 (OKSU); 8 mi. W Stillwater, 1 (OKSU); 9 mi. E, 1 mi. S Stillwater, 1 (OKSU); 9 mi. W Stillwater, 3 (OKSU); 9 mi. W, 1 mi. N Stillwater, 1 (OKSU); Lake Carl Blackwell, 9 mi. W, 2.5 mi. N, Stillwater, 1 (OKSU); 9 mi. W, 2.5 mi. N Stillwater, 1 (OKSU); 10 mi. W Stillwater, 11 (OKSU); 10 mi. W Stillwater, Lake Carl Blackwell, 1 (OKSU); 10 mi. W, 0.5 mi. N Stillwater, 1 (OKSU); Twin Lakes, 10.5 mi. S Stillwater, 2 (OKSU); 11 mi. W Stillwater, 1 (OKSU); 12 mi. W Stillwater, 3 (OKSU); 13.5 mi. E Stillwater, 4 (OKSU); 15 mi. W, 2 mi. N Stillwater, 1 (OKSU); 0.5 mi. E US Hwy 177 on Mehan Rd., 1 (OKSU); 1 mi. S, 3 mi. W Mehan Turn on Hwy 40, 1 (OKSU); 2.5 mi. S, 0.25 mi. E jct. SH 51 & 177 S, 1 (OKSU); 2.7 mi. W Hwy 177 on Burris Rd., 1 (OKSU); 1 mi. N jct. SH 160 & US Hwy 177, 1 (OKSU); 1 mi. N, 0.25 mi. W jct. Hwys 51 & 51C, 1 (OKSU); 0.1 mi. N SH 51, east side Sangre Rd., 1 (OKSU); 3 mi. N SH 51 on Country Club, 1 (OKSU); T19N, R1E, W 1/2 Sec. 17, 1 (OKSU); T19N, R1E, SE 1/4 Sec. 18, 2 (OKSU); T19N, R1E, Sec. 24, 1 (OKSU); T19N, R1E SW 1/4 Sec. 3, 1 (OKSU); T19N, R1W, E 1/2 SE 1/4 Sec. 3, 2 (OKSU). PITTSBURG COUNTY: 2 mi. E McAlester, 1 (OKSU); Lone's Ranch, 4 mi. NW McAlester, 1 (OKSU); Savanna, 1 (USNM). PONTOTOC COUNTY: 4 mi. S Ada, 1 (OKSU); 5 mi. S Ada, 1 (ECENT); 7 mi. NE Ada, 2 (ECENT); 7 mi. SW Ada, 1 (ECENT); 10 mi. W Ada, 1 (ECENT); 10 mi. N Ada, 1 (ECENT); Pontotoc County, 2 (OKSU). POTTAWATOMIE COUNTY: 2 mi. S Earlsboro, 1 (OKSU); 1 mi. W Pink, 3 (OMNH); 3 mi. NW Shawnee, 1 (OMNH); 6 mi. N, 1.5 mi. E Shawnee, 1 (OMNH); 2 mi. E, 0.75 mi. N Tecumseh, 1 (OKSU); Little River, 7 mi. SE Tecumseh, 2 (KU); T11N, R5E, NE 1/4 Sec. 1, 1 (CSUO). PUSHMATAHA COUNTY: 4 mi. SE Clayton, 1 (OMNH); 1 mi. S Nashoba, 4 (TMM); 4.8 mi. S Talihina, 1 (OMNH). ROGERS COUNTY: Bird Creek, 1 (UMMZ); 0.5 mi. E Chelsea City Lake, 1 (OKSU); 5.5 mi. E Claremore, 1 (OMNH); 3 mi. N, 1 mi. W Foyil, 1 (OMNH); U Ranch, 1 (UMMZ). STEPHENS COUNTY: 0.25 mi. E, 1 mi. S Claud, 1 (OMNH); 5 mi. W, 0.5 mi. S Duncan, 1 (CAMCO); T1N, R6W, Sec. 11, 1 (OMNH). TULSA COUNTY: Garnett, 7 (UMMZ); jct. SH 51 & River Rd., 1 (OKSU); Red Fork, Indian Territory, 2 (USNM); 8 mi. W Red Fork, Indian Territory, 2 (USNM); above Arkansas River, 2 mi. W Sand Springs, 1 (OKSU); T19N, R12E, Sec. 11, 1 (OMNH). WAGONER COUNTY: 12 mi. E Wagoner, 1 (OKSU). WASHINGTON COUNTY: SE Hill Crest Presbyterian Church, Bartlesville, 1 (OKSU); 19 mi. W Price Tower, Bartlesville, 1 (ECENT). WOODWARD COUNTY: Woodward County, 4 (OMNH).

Neotoma mexicana.—Specimens examined (total 14); CIMARRON COUNTY:

2.6 mi. S. 1.5 mi. E Kenton, 1 (OMNH); 5 mi. N Kenton. 1 (OKSU); 6 mi. N Kenton. 10 (OKSU); Tesesquite Canyon, 2 (OKSU).

Neotoma micropus.—Specimens examined (total 478); BEAVER COUNTY: 1.5 mi. N Beaver, 2 (KU); 21 mi. S Meade, Kansas, 1 (KU); 3 mi. NW Slapout, 1 (OMNH). BECKHAM COUNTY: south bank North Fork Red River, S Sweetwater, 1 (OKSU). CIMARRON COUNTY: 7.5 mi. S, 10 mi. W Boise City, 3 (KU); 9 mi. W Griggs, 1 (KU); 2 mi. E, 1 mi. S Kenton, 1 (OMNH); 2 mi. E, 0.1 mi. N Kenton, 1 (OMNH); 2 mi. E, 6 mi. S Kenton, 1 (CAMCO); 4 mi. N Kenton, 2 (OKSU); 4.1 mi. S, 0.5 mi. E Kenton, 2 (OMNH); 5 mi. N Kenton, 1 (OKSU); 6 mi. N Kenton, 3 (OKSU); 9 mi. SE Kenton, 7 (CAMCO); 11 mi. SE Kenton, 1 (CAMCO); Lake Etling, Black Mesa State Park, 1 (OMNH); Tesesquite Canyon, 1 (OKSU). GREER COUNTY: north side Granite Mt., 1 (OKSU); 2 mi. N, 5 mi. W Jester, 1 (OKSU); 1 mi. W, 1 mi. S Reed, 2 (OMNH), 2 (USNM); 2.5 mi. SW Reed, 1 (OUBS); 5 mi. NE Reed, 1,700 ft., 1 (OMNH). HARMON COUNTY: jct. Hwy 30 & Elm Fork Red River, 1 (TTU); upper slope Elm Fork River, 1 mi. W jct. Hwy 30 & Elm Fork, 1 (TTU); south bank, 1 mi. W jct. Hwy 30 & Elm Fork Red River, 2 (TTU); 1 mi. W Hwy 30, Elm Fork Red River, 2 (TTU); lower slope, Elm Fork Red River, 2 (TTU); 4.5 mi. N Gould, 1 (TTU); 4.5 mi. N, 0.5 mi. W Gould, 1 (TTU); 10 mi. S Gould, 1 (OKSU); Harmon County, 2 (FWMSH); 2.5 mi. S, 11 mi. E Hollis, 1 (TTU); 4 mi. S Hollis, 1 (FWMSH); 4 mi. S, 1.5 mi. W Hollis, 1 (OKSU); 4.5 mi. S Hollis, 1 (FWMSH); 5 mi. N, 2 mi. W Hollis, 1 (TTU); 5.3 mi. N Hollis, 4 (FWMSH); 5.5 mi. N, 2 mi. W Hollis, 11 (OKSU); 5.5 mi. S Hollis, 54 (FWMSH); 6 mi. N Hollis, 37 (FWMSH); 6 mi. N, 2 mi. W Hollis, 1 (FWMSH), 3 (OKSU); 6.4 mi. S Hollis, 35 (TTU); 7.5 mi. S, 3 mi. E Hollis, 1 (TTU); near Lake Hall, 10 mi. W Hollis, 1 (TTU); 11 mi. N Hollis, 2 (FWMSH); 13 mi. N Hollis, 1 (OKSU), 1 (CSUO); 13.5 mi. N Hollis, 2 (OKSU); 13.5 mi. N Hollis on Hwy 30, 1 (OKSU); 13.9 mi. N Hollis, 1 (FWMSH); 3 mi. E Reed, 6 (OMNH); Spring Lake Recreation Area, 1 (TTU); 6 mi. E, 1 mi. S Vinson, 1,700 ft., 11 (OMNH); 6 mi. S, 1 mi. E Vinson, 1,700 ft., 2 (OMNH); 6.5 mi. SE Vinson, 1 (OMNH); T4N, R26W, NE 1/4 SW 1/4 Sec. 18, 1 (OKSU); T5N, R26W, NE 1/4 SW 1/4 Sec. 32, 1 (TTU). HARPER COUNTY: 3 mi. N Ft. Supply, 50 (USNM); 4.5 mi. N Laverne, 1 (UMMZ); Southern Great Plains Exp. Range, 16 (OKSU); T28N, R20W, Sec. 32, 1 (OMNH). JACKSON COUNTY: 2.5 mi. S, 9.5 mi. E Eldorado, 2 (CAMCO); 3 mi. N, 3.5 mi. E Eldorado, 1 (OKSU); 5 mi. SW Eldorado, 2 (OKSU); 7 mi. E Eldorado, 1 (OKSU); 0.5 mi. N, 1 mi. W Olustee, 1 (CAMCO); 2 mi. W, 3.5 mi. S Olustee, 1 (CAMCO); Red River, 14 mi. S Olustee, 4 (TMM). KIOWA COUNTY: 2 mi. N Cooperton, 1 (CAMCO); 2 mi. S Lugert, 1 (OKSU); Group Camp #2, Quartz Mt. State Park, 1

(OKSU); 8 mi. W Snyder, 1 (CAMCO). MAJOR COUNTY: 6 mi. E Bouse Jct., 1 (OKSU); 3 mi. S Chester, 7 (KU); North Canadian River, 3 mi. S Chester, 23 (KU); 3 mi. S, 0.5 mi. E Chester, 2 (KU); 3 mi. N, 9 mi. W Fairview, 1 (OKSU); Glass Mts., 1 (OKSU); Nescatunga Cave, 2.5 mi. W jct. Hwys 281 & 15, 6 (CSUO); 3 mi. W Orienta, 1 (OKSU); 5 mi. W Orienta, 2 (OMNH); Glass Mts., 5 mi. W Orienta, 2 (USNM); 16 mi. W Orienta, 7 (OKSU); Terril-Whitlaw Ranch, 2 mi. W jct. SH 51 & 281, 1 (OKSU); 5.5 mi. S Waynoka, 1,450 ft., 1 (OMNH); 6 mi. S, 3 mi. E Waynoka, 1 (OKSU); 3 mi. W jct. Hwys 281 & 15, 2 (OKSU). ROGER MILLS COUNTY: 7 mi. N Cheyenne, 2,000 ft., 2 (OMNH); 2.5 mi. E, 1.5 mi. S Reydon, 1 (CAMCO). TEXAS COUNTY: 2 mi. N Guymon, 3,000 ft., 3 (OMNH); 4.5 mi. N Guymon, 3,100 ft., 3 (OMNH); 5.5 mi. N Guymon, 3,100 ft., 1 (OMNH). TILLMAN COUNTY: 2 mi. S Davidson, 1 (OKSU); 5 mi. S Grandfield, 1 (OMNH). WOODS COUNTY: Alva, 7 (USNM); 8 mi. NW Alva, 1 (ECENT); 11 mi. NW Alva, 3 (ECENT); 12 mi. N, 4 mi. S Alva, 3 (KU); cañon, 3 mi. W Alva, Oklahoma Territory, 2 (FMNH); Moccasin Creek, 4 mi. W Camp Houston, 2 (CSUO); north bank Cimarron River, 2 mi. W Edith, 5 (OMNH); 2 mi. W Edith, 1 (USNM); Waynoka, 3 (UMMZ); Waynoka Dunes, 1 (OKSU); 3 mi. S Waynoka, 3 (OMNH); 4 mi. W, 5 mi. N Waynoka, 1 (OKSU); 5 mi. S Waynoka, 1,400 ft., 3 (OMNH); 5 mi. S Waynoka, 1,450 ft., 4 (OMNH); White Horse Springs, 23 (FMNH). WOODWARD COUNTY: Alabaster Caverns, 5 (OMNH); lower camp grounds, Alabaster Caverns State Park, 2 (OKSU); Alabaster Caverns State Park, 1 (OKSU), 1 (OUBS); Boiling Springs State Park, 1,925 ft., 5 (OMNH); Boiling Springs State Park, 4 mi. N Woodward, 1 (OKSU); Hwy 281, northside Cimarron River, 1 (CSUO); Alabaster Caverns State Park, 20 mi. N Mooreland, 1 (OKSU); Woodward, 3 (USNM); Woodward County, 1 (OMNH); 2 mi. NNW Woodward, 1,900 ft., 4 (OMNH); 4 mi. N Woodward, 1 (OKSU); 5 mi. S, 2 mi. W Woodward, 1 (OKSU); T23N, R19W, Sec. 30, 2 (OMNH).

Notiosorex crawfordi.—Specimens examined (total 20); CIMARRON COUNTY: Tesesquite Canyon, 1 (OKSU). COMANCHE COUNTY: 8 mi. N, 2 mi. E Indiahoma, 1 (CAMCO); Wichita Mountains Wildlife Refuge, 1 (OKSU), 1 (USNM). GREER COUNTY: 4.5 mi. W, 1 mi. N Mangum, 1 (CAMCO). HARMON COUNTY: 4 mi. S Hollis, 2 (OKSU); 4 mi. S, 1.5 mi. W Hollis, 1 (OKSU); 5.5 mi. S Hollis, 3 (OKSU). JACKSON COUNTY: 3.5 mi. E Duke, 1 (CAMCO); 3 mi. S, 0.5 mi. W Headrick, 5 (CAMCO). PUSHMATAHA COUNTY: 1 mi. S Nashoba, 1 (TMM). TEXAS COUNTY: 11.5 mi. N, 1 mi. Goodwell, 1 (CAMCO). WOODWARD COUNTY: Trader Creek, Selman, 1 (OKSU).

Nycticeius humeralis.—Specimens examined (total 84); ADAIR COUNTY: Cave Springs Cave, 2 (OKSU); 2 mi. N Lyons, 1 (OKSU); Illinois River, 6 mi. W Watts, 1 (OKSU). BRYAN COUNTY: 10 mi. S, 1 mi. E Boswell, 1 (OMNH). CHEROKEE COUNTY: Barren Fork, Welling, 1 (OKSU). COMANCHE COUNTY: 1 mi. NW Ft. Sill, 1 (CAMCO). JACKSON COUNTY: Altus, 1 (CSUO). LEFLORE COUNTY: Honobia, 1 (OKSU); Little River, Honobia, 8 (OKSU). MARSHALL COUNTY: "Looney Farm," 1 (OMNH); 2 mi. E Willis, University of Oklahoma Biological Station, 650 ft., 1 (OMNH). MAYES COUNTY: 10 mi. E Pryor, 2 (OKSU). MCCURTAIN COUNTY: 14 mi. SE Broken Bow, 12 (OMNH); 15 mi. SE Broken Bow, 1 (OMNH); Forked Lake, S Eagletown, 4 (OKSU); 0.25 mi. W Glover, 2 (TMM); Mountain Fork River at Hochatown Bridge, 1 (OKSU); Goff Farm, 2 mi. W Smithville, 1 (OKSU); 2 mi. W Smithville, 18 (OMNH); 2 mi. NW Smithville, 2 (OKSU); Beech Creek, 6 mi. E, 1.3 mi. S Smithville, 1 (OMNH); University of Oklahoma Biological Station, 1 (OMNH); 9 mi. N Wright City, 1 (OKSU). MURRAY COUNTY: Falls Creek Baptist Assembly, 1 (OKSU); Rock Creek, 1 (OKSU). MUSKOGEE COUNTY: Greenleaf Creek, 1 (OKSU). OKLAHOMA COUNTY: near Skirvin Hotel, 1 (OKSU); Oklahoma City, 1 (CSUO). PAYNE COUNTY: Stillwater, 1 (OKSU). POTTAWATOMIE COUNTY: Oklahoma Baptist University, Shawnee, 1 (OKSU). PUSHMATAHA COUNTY: Pushmataha County, 2 (OMNH). SEQUOYAH COUNTY: Cato Creek Camp Ground, 2 (CSUO); Dwight Mission, 1 (OKSU); Redland, Indian Territory, 4 (USNM). TULSA COUNTY: jct. 4th & Boston, Tulsa, 1 (OKSU); 2300 blk. E. 71st, Tulsa, 1 (CSUO); Tulsa, 1 (CSUO).

Ochrotomys nuttalli.—Specimens examined (total 7); MCCURTAIN COUNTY: 15 mi. SE Broken Bow, 2 (OMNH); 2 mi. S Eagletown, 1 (OKSU); 2.5 mi. W Smithville, 3 (OMNH). PUSHMATAHA COUNTY: 5 mi. E Nashoba, 1 (UMMZ).

Odocoileus hemionus.—Specimens examined (total 6); CIMARRON COUNTY: Cimarron County, 3 (OKSU); 2.5 mi. SE Kenton, 4,200 ft., 1 (OMNH); 7.5 mi. N Kenton, 1 (OKSU); 8 mi. NE Kenton, 1 (OKSU).

Odocoileus virginianus.—Specimens examined (total 54); CADDO COUNTY: 1.5 mi. SW Ft. Cobb. 1 (CAMCO). CHEROKEE COUNTY: Cookson Hills State Game Refuge, 1 (OKSU); 5 mi. W, 4 mi. N Tenkiller Dam, 1 (OKSU). COMANCHE COUNTY: Lawton, 1 (CAMCO); near Lawton, 4 (OKSU); 4 mi. E, 2.5 mi. S Medicine Park, 1 (CAMCO); near Mt. Scott, 4 (USNM); Wichita Game Refuge, 1 (USNM); Quanah Parker Lake, Wichita Mts., 1 (OMNH); Wichita Mountains Wildlife Refuge, 19 (USNM), 2 (OKSU); Wichita Mountains, W Natl. Park, 1 (USNM). DELAWARE COUNTY: 4 mi. S Cleora, 1 (OMNH). ELLIS COUNTY: Ellis County, 1 (OKSU). JOHNSTON COUNTY: 4 mi. W Mill Creek, 1 (OKSU). LATIMER COUNTY: Robber's Cave State Park, 2 (CSUO). MAJOR COUNTY: 18 mi. W, 1.5 mi. S Aline, 1 (OKSU). MCCURTAIN

COUNTY: 2 mi. E, 0.75 mi. S entrance Beavers Bend State Park, 1 (OKSU); Broken Bow deer check stand, 1 (OKSU). MURRAY COUNTY: 10 mi. S, 3 mi. W Davis, 1 (OKSU). PAYNE COUNTY: Stillwater, 1 (OKSU). PITTSBURG COUNTY: U.S. Naval Ammunitions Depot, McAlester, 1 (OKSU). PUSHMATAHA COUNTY: near Mayes, 1 (OKSU); 14 mi. S Talihina, 1 (OKSU). STEPHENS COUNTY: 6.5 mi. W Claud, 1 (OMNH). TULSA COUNTY: 6 mi. W Red Fork, 1 (USNM); died at Tulsa Zoo, 1 (OKSU). WOODWARD COUNTY: Woodward County, 1 (KU).

Ondatra zibethicus.—Specimens examined (total 141); ALFALFA COUNTY: Great Salt Plains Refuge, 1 (OKSU); near mouth Clay Creek, edge Great Salt Plains, 1 (USNM). CADDO COUNTY: Cement, 1 (CAMCO). CLEVELAND COUNTY: Berry Pond, 1 mi. S Moore, 2 (OMNH); City Court House, Norman, 1 (OMNH); corner Robinson & 12th Ave., Norman, 1 (OMNH); Crystal Lake, N Norman, 1 (OMNH); Golf Course Pond, Norman, 1 (OMNH); Norman, 4 (OMNH); Lindsey St. at Duck Pond, Norman, 1 (OMNH); North Campus, Norman, 1 (OMNH); NW side Norman, 1 (OMNH); 1 mi. E Norman, 1 (OMNH); 2 mi. E, 0.5 mi. S Norman, 3 (OMNH); 2 mi. SE Norman, 1 (OMNH); 0.25 mi. SW 134 St. on Sunnylane Rd., 1 (OMNH). CRAIG COUNTY: 1 mi. S Big Cabin turnoff (Will Rogers Turnpike), 1 (OMNH). DELAWARE COUNTY: Flint Creek, 5 mi. SE Colcord, 1 (OKSU); Flint Creek, 1 (OKSU). GARFIELD COUNTY: Enid, 2 (KU). HUGHES COUNTY: Hughes County, 1 (ECENT). JACKSON COUNTY: near Blair, 1 (USNM). KAY COUNTY: Conoco Refinery, Phipp's Traps, 1 (OKSU). KINGFISHER COUNTY: 9 mi. W Crescent, 1 (OKSU); 8 mi. SW Hennessey, 1 (OKSU). KIOWA COUNTY: Snyder, 1 (CAMCO). LEFLORE COUNTY: 7 mi. E, 1 mi. N Keota, 1 (OKSU). MUSKOGEE COUNTY: 5 mi. E, 2 mi. N Muskogee, 1 (OKSU). NOBLE COUNTY: 0.75 mi. W Hwy 177 on Orlando Rd., 1 (OKSU). OKLAHOMA COUNTY: Oklahoma City, 1 (OMNH). OSAGE COUNTY: 1.5 mi. W, 4 mi. N Bartlesville, 2 (OKSU); 1.5 mi. W Shidler, 1 (OKSU). OTTAWA COUNTY: 2.5 mi. NW Cardin, 1 (OKSU). PAYNE COUNTY: fisheries ponds, Lake Carl Blackwell, 1 (OKSU); Lake Carl Blackwell, 17 (OKSU); campus, Oklahoma State University, 2 (OKSU); Payne County, 1 (OKSU); Cimarron River, near Perkins, 1 (OKSU); 0.25 mi. N Swan Rubber Plant, Perkins Rd., 1 (OKSU); pond, near college barns, 2 (OKSU); Sanborn Lake, 3 (OKSU); about 1.5 mi. S Stillwater on US Hwy 177, 1 (OKSU); Boomer Creek, Stillwater, 1 (OKSU); Boomer Lake, Stillwater, 8 (FWMSH); corner Redwood Dr. & Farm Rd., Stillwater, 2 (OKSU); Creech's Pond, Stillwater, 1 (OKSU); Hamm's Lake, 8 mi. W Stillwater, 1 (OKSU); Morningside Park, Stillwater, 1 (OKSU); Stillwater, 3 (OKSU); Stillwater Creek, 1 (OKSU); 0.5

mi. N Stillwater, 3 (OKSU); 0.5 mi. N, 0.5 mi. E Stillwater, 1 (OKSU); 0.5 mi. S dairy barn, 1 (OKSU); 1 mi. E, 4.5 mi. N Stillwater, 1 (OKSU); 1 mi. N Stillwater, 2 (OKSU); 1 mi. N, 0.5 mi. E Stillwater, 1 (OKSU); near pond, N Vet Village, Stillwater, 1 (ECENT); 2 mi. E Stillwater, 1 (OKSU); 2 mi. NE Stillwater, 1 (OKSU); 2 mi. W Stillwater, 1 (OKSU); 2.5 mi. NE Stillwater, 1 (OKSU); 3 mi. N Stillwater, 1 (OKSU); 3 mi. N, 2 mi. E Stillwater, 1 (OKSU); 4 mi. E, 1 mi. N Stillwater, 1 (OKSU); Sanborn Lake, 4 mi. N Stillwater, 3 (OKSU); 4.5 mi. N, 0.5 mi. E Stillwater, 1 (OKSU); 5 mi. NE Stillwater, 6 (OKSU); 6 mi. NE Stillwater on US Hwy 177, 1 (OKSU); 7 mi. E, 1 mi. S Stillwater, 1 (OKSU); Country Club Lake, 8 mi. NE Stillwater, 2 (OKSU); Yost Lake, 8 mi. NE Stillwater, 7 (OKSU). PONTOTOC COUNTY: ʻ6 mi. SE Ada, 3 (ECENT); 5 mi. NE Ada, 1 (ECENT); Wintersmith Park, Ada, 1 (ECENT); 4 mi. N Homer, 1 (ECENT). SEMINOLE COUNTY: 4 mi. S Seminole, 1 (ECENT). TULSA COUNTY: Mohawk Park, 4 (UMMZ); Red Fork, Indian Territory, 1 (USNM). WASHINGTON COUNTY: 3 mi. S Bartlesville, 1 (OKSU). WOODWARD COUNTY: 1 mi. E Supply, 2 (OKSU).

Onychomys leucogaster.—Specimens examined (total 343); ALFALFA COUNTY: Great Salt Plains Refuge, 1 (OKSU); Great Salt Plains, E Cherokee, 1 (OKSU); 3.5 mi. E Cherokee, 2 (OMNH). BEAVER COUNTY: 1.5 mi. N Beaver, 1 (KU); 4 mi. S Floris, 1 (KU); Lake Evans Chambers, 1 (OMNH). BLAINE COUNTY: northeast side Canton Lake, 1 (OKSU); 2 mi. N, 1 mi. W Hydro, 1 (KU); Roman Nose State Park, 1 (OKSU); 2 mi. W Watonga, 2 (OKSU); north bank North Canadian River, 2 mi. W Watonga, 1 (OKSU). CADDO COUNTY: 5 mi. W Cogar, 1 (OMNH). CANADIAN COUNTY: Ft. Reno, 4 (USNM). CIMARRON COUNTY: Black Mesa, 2 (CAMCO); 5.6 mi. N Boise City, 1 (OMNH); 6.7 mi. W, 9.5 mi. S Boise City, 9 (OMNH); 13 mi. S Boise City, 1 (ECENT); 14 mi. W Boise City, 1 (OMNH); T4N, R3E, Sec. 12, 15.8 mi. W Boise City, 1 (OMNH); Cimarron County, 1 (OMNH); 0.5 mi. E, 8.3 mi. N Felt, 2 (OMNH); 9 mi. W Griggs, 1 (KU); 2 mi. E, 6 mi. S Kenton, 1 (CAMCO); 2.5 mi. S Kenton, 1 (CAMCO); 2.5 mi. SE Kenton, 2 (CAMCO); 2.5 mi. SE Kenton, 4,200 ft., 3 (OMNH); 4.1 mi. S, 0.5 mi. E Kenton, 4 (OMNH); 5 mi. N Kenton, 1 (OMNH); 8 mi. SE Kenton, 1 (CAMCO); 9 mi. E, 1 mi. N Kenton, 1 (OMNH); 10 mi. NW Kenton, 1 (CAMCO); 13.5 mi. W Kenton, 2 (OMNH); Lake Etling, 1 (OMNH). CUSTER COUNTY: 4.5 mi. E Moorewood, 3 (OKSU); 0.75 mi. N, 2 mi. E Weatherford, 1 (KU); 7 mi. N, 5 mi. W Weatherford, 2 (KU). DEWEY COUNTY: 5 mi. W Canton, 5 (KU); 5.5 mi. SW Canton, 1 (KU); 1 mi. S, 0.5 mi. E Seiling, 1 (OKSU); 1 mi. N Taloga, 1 (OMNH). ELLIS COUNTY: Davidson Ranch, 8 mi. SE Arnett, 1 (USNM); 15 mi. S, 2 mi. E Higgins,

Texas, 1 (OKSU); 2 mi. N Shattuck, 2,300 ft., 1 (OMNH); 5 mi. NNE Shattuck, 2,335 ft., 5 (OMNH). GRANT COUNTY: 1.5 mi. W, 1.4 mi. N Hawley, 6 (OMNH); 1.7 mi. W, 1.3 mi. N Hawley, 1 (OMNH). GREER COUNTY: T4N, R2W, Sec. 24, 5 mi. SE Mangum, 1 (OMNH). HARMON COUNTY: 4.5 mi. N, 0.5 mi. W Gould, 1 (TTU); 1.5 mi. SW Greer, 1 (OUBS); 2 mi. W, 6 mi. N Hollis, 2 (FWMSH); 2 mi. W, 10 mi. N Hollis, 1 (FWMSH); 2 mi. W, 8.5 mi. N Hollis, 2 (FWMSH); 5 mi. N, 2 mi. W Hollis, 1 (FWMSH); 6 mi. S, 2 mi. W Hollis, 1 (CAMCO); 8.5 mi. N Hollis, 4 (FWMSH); 8.5 mi. N, 2 mi. W Hollis, 1 (OKSU); 11 mi. N Hollis, 3 (FWMSH); 12.5 mi. N, 7.5 mi. E Hollis, 1 (TTU); 13 mi. N Hollis, 3 (FWMSH); 13.5 mi. N Hollis, 2 (OKSU); 13.9 mi. N Hollis, 4 (FWMSH); 17 mi. N, 2.5 mi. W Hollis, 1 (TTU); 1 mi. W Reed, 1 (OMNH); 1 mi. W, 1 mi. S Harmon, Reed County line, Hwy 9, 1 (OMNH); 6 mi. E, 1 mi. S Vinson, 1,700 ft., 2 (OMNH); 6.5 mi. SE Vinson, 2 (OMNH); T4N, R26W, SW 1/4 NW 1/4 Sec. 6, 1 (OKSU). HARPER COUNTY: pasture 25, Southern Great Plains Exp. Range, Ft. Supply, 1 (OKSU); pasture 70, Southern Great Plains Exp. Range, Ft. Supply, 1 (OKSU); Southern Great Plains Exp. Range, Ft. Supply, 31 (OKSU); USDA Exp. Range, 1 (OKSU); USDA Southern Great Plains Exp. Range, 4 mi. NW Ft. Supply, 1 (OKSU); SW 1/4, NW 1/4, Sec. 10-27-24, 3 (UMMZ); T25N, R22W, N 1/2 Sec. 19, 1 (OKSU); T25N, R22W, N 1/2 Sec. 19, USDA Exp. Range, 2 (OKSU). JACKSON COUNTY: 1 mi. W, 5 mi. S Eldorado, 1 (OKSU); 3 mi. S Eldorado, 1 (OKSU); Red River, 14 mi. S Olustee, 1 (TMM). KINGFISHER COUNTY: 14 mi. N Hennessey, 1 (OKSU); T17N, R5W, Sec. 30, 2 (OMNH). MAJOR COUNTY: 2 mi. E, 4 mi. N Cleo Springs, 1 (OKSU); 3 mi. S Cleo Springs, 3 (OMNH), 1 (USNM); 5 mi. SE Cleo Springs, 1 (OKSU). ROGER MILLS COUNTY: Black Kettle Natl. Grassland, Spring Creek Lake Recreation Grounds, 1 (TTU); 1 mi. N Cheyenne, 1 (OKSU); 2.5 mi. E, 1.5 mi. S Reydon, 8 (CAMCO); Spring Lake Recreation Area, 1 (TTU). TEXAS COUNTY: 2 mi. E Eva, 6 (KU); Sand Hills, 4.5 mi. NE Eva, 2 (KU); 4.8 mi. N Guymon, 1 (OMNH); 5.5 mi. N Guymon, 3,100 ft., 1 (OMNH). TILL-MAN COUNTY: 0.5 mi. S, 2.2 mi. E Davidson, 1 (OMNH); 2 mi. S Davidson, 1 (OMNH); 7.5 mi. W, 2.5 mi. S Snyder, 1 (CAMCO). WOODS COUNTY: Alva, Oklahoma Territory, 6 (FMNH); Alva, 2 (USNM); 1.5 mi. N Alva, 1 (OKSU); 6 mi. NW Alva, 1 (OKSU); Salt Fork, 6 mi. NW Alva, 1 (OKSU); 9 mi. NW Alva, 2 (ECENT); 2 mi. E Camp Houston, 1 (OKSU); 2 mi. W Edith, 1 (OMNH); Cimarron River, S Waynoka, 2 (OKSU); Waynoka, 18 (OKSU); Waynoka Dunes, 2 (OKSU); 3 mi. S Waynoka, 2 (OMNH); 3 mi. SW Waynoka, 2 (OMNH), 1 (USNM); 4 mi. S Waynoka, 5 (OKSU); 5 mi. S Waynoka, 1,400 ft., 2 (OMNH). WOOD-WARD COUNTY: above Alabaster Caverns, 1 (OKSU); 8 mi. E Ala-

baster, 1 (CSUO); Bear Creek, Selman Ranch, 1 (OKSU); Camp Supply, 1
(USNM); 5.7 mi. S, 9.2 mi. W Freedom, 2 (CSUO); 3 mi. N Ft. Supply,
78 (USNM); 5 mi. N Ft. Supply, 7 (USNM); Woodward, 1 (USNM); 3
mi. NW Woodward, 2 (OMNH); 5 mi. S, 2 mi. W Woodward, 1 (OKSU);
5 mi. SW Woodward, 3 (USNM); 14 mi. S Woodward on Hwy 183-270, 1
(CSUO).

Oryzomys palustris.—Specimens examined (total 13); BRYAN COUNTY:
5 mi. E Colbert, 3 (OUBS); 5 mi. W Colbert, 1 (TMM). HASKELL
COUNTY: 0.5 mi. W, 0.25 mi. S Garland, 2 (OMNH); 6.5 mi. E, 2 mi. S
Stigler, 1 (OMNH). MARSHALL COUNTY: 3 mi. N Madill, 1 (OMNH);
3.6 mi. N Madill, 2 (OUBS); 4 mi. N Madill, 1 (OUBS). MCCURTAIN
COUNTY: 14 mi. SE Broken Bow, 1 (OMNH); 15 mi. SE Broken Bow, 1
(OMNH).

Pappogeomys castanops.—Specimens examined (total 41); BEAVER COUN-
TY: 4 mi. E Elmwood Post Office, 4 (OKSU); CIMARRON COUNTY:
25 mi. NW Boise City, 2 (OMNH); Pigeon Cave, 2 mi. E, 0.5 mi. N Ken-
ton, 1 (OKSU); T5N, R3E, Sec. 36, 9.25 mi. E, 3.75 mi. S Kenton, 1
(OMNH); 2.5 mi. SE Kenton, 4,200 ft., 11 (OMNH); 2.6 mi. NNE Ken-
ton, 4,200 ft., 1 (OMNH); 4.4 mi. N, 0.4 mi. W Kenton, 1 (OMNH); 5
mi. E, 2 mi. S Kenton, 1 (UIMNH); 5 mi. SE Kenton, 1 (CAMCO); 6 mi.
N Kenton, 4 (OKSU); north side Black Mesa, 6 mi. N Kenton, 1 (OKSU);
Tesesquite Canyon, 7 mi. SE Kenton, 1 (OKSU); 9 mi. SE Kenton, 1
(CAMCO); 10 mi. NW Kenton, 1 (CAMCO); 0.25 mi. S Colorado Line on
North Carrizo Creek, 1 (UIMNH); Tesesquite Canyon, 2 (OKSU); Teses-
quite Canyon, 4 mi. from Hwy 325, 1 (OKSU); T4N, R1E, Sec. 4, 1
(OMNH). TEXAS COUNTY: W Hooker, 5 (OKSU).

Perognathus flavescens.—Specimens examined (total 18); BLAINE COUNTY:
Public Hunting Grounds, Canton, 1 (OKSU). DEWEY COUNTY: Dewey
County, 1 (KU). HARPER COUNTY: 3 mi. N Ft. Supply, 3 (USNM).
ROGER MILLS COUNTY: Spring Lake Recreation Area, 1 (TTU).
WOODS COUNTY: Waynoka, 10 (UMMZ). WOODWARD COUNTY:
1 mi. W, 2 mi. S Woodward, 1 (USNM); 2 mi. S, 4 mi. W Woodward, 1
(USNM).

Perognathus flavus.—Specimens examined (total 166); BEAVER COUNTY:
15 mi. S Beaver, 1 (MVZ); T1N, R21E, Sec. 13, 2 (KU); T1S, R20E,
Sec. 21, 1 (KU); T1S, R21E, Sec. 30, 2 (KU); T1S, R20E, Sec. 33, 1
(KU). CIMARRON COUNTY: Black Mesa, 10 (OMNH), 1 (CAMCO);
Black Mesa State Park, 1 (OKSU); W Boise City, 1 (OMNH); 12 mi. W
Boise City, 1 (OMNH); 12.8 mi. W Boise City, 2 (OMNH); T4N, R3E,
Sec. 12, 14 mi. W Boise City, 1 (OMNH); 14 mi. W Boise City, 4 (OMNH);
Black Mesa, 14 mi. W Boise City, 1 (OMNH); T4N, R3E, Sec. 12, 15.8
mi. W Boise City, 1 (OMNH); 15.8 mi. W Boise City, 2 (OMNH); 17 mi.

W Boise City, 1 (OMNH); 17.6 mi. W Boise City, 1 (OKSU); 18 mi. W Boise City, 1 (OKSU); Cimarron County, 1 (OMNH); 8 mi. W Griggs, 3,900 ft., 1 (KU); Regnier Ranch, 2 mi. S, 1 mi. E Kenton, 3 (CSUO); 2 mi. E, 6 mi. S Kenton, 7 (CAMCO); 3 mi. N Kenton, 5 (UMMZ); 2.5 mi. SE Kenton, 4,200 ft., 1 (OMNH); 3.1 mi. N Kenton, 4,900 ft., 1 (OMNH); 4 mi. N Kenton, 9 (KU); 4 mi. S, 0.5 mi. E Kenton, 1 (OMNH); 2.8 mi. SE Kenton, 4,200 ft., 1 (OMNH); 3.1 mi. N Kenton, 4,950 ft., 4 (OMNH); 5 mi. N Kenton, 1 (OMNH); north side Black Mesa, 6 mi. N Kenton, 2 (OKSU); 6 mi. N Kenton, 1 (OKSU); 8 mi. N Kenton, 2 (OKSU); 8 mi. SE Kenton, 2 (CAMCO); 9 mi. SE Kenton, 1 (CAMCO); 9 mi. N Kenton, 1 (OKSU); T4N, R5E, NW 1/4 Sec. 3, 1 (OMNH); T4N, R3E, Sec. 12, 9 (OMNH). CUSTER COUNTY: 4 mi. W, 4.5 mi. N Weatherford, 1 (OKSU). GREER COUNTY: Reed Cave, 1 (OKSU). HARMON COUNTY: Harmon County, 2 (FWMSH); approx. 2 mi. W, 10 mi. N Hollis, 1 (FWMSH); 5.5 mi. S Hollis, 16 (FWMSH); 6.3 mi. S, 1 mi. E Kirby's Corner, Hollis, 1 (FWMSH); 6 mi. E, 1 mi. S Vinson, 1,700 ft., 18 (OMNH). HARPER COUNTY: Buffalo Fair Grounds, 1 (UMMZ); Southern Great Plains Exp. Range, 2 (OKSU). JACKSON COUNTY: 1 mi. S Olustee, 1 (TMM); Red River, 14 mi. S Olustee, 4 (TMM). MAJOR COUNTY: jct. US Hwy 281 & SH 15, 2 mi. W Bouse Jct., 1 (OKSU); 8 mi. S, 4 mi. E Bouse Jct., 1 (OKSU); Nescatunga Cave, 2.5 mi. W Hwys 281 & 15, 3 (CSUO); 2.5 mi. W jct. Hwys 15 & 281, 3 (CSUO); Vickery Ranch, 2 (OKSU). ROGER MILLS COUNTY: 6 mi. N Cheyenne, 1 (USNM). WOODS COUNTY: 9 mi. NW Alva, 2 (ECENT); Cimarron River on US Hwy 64, 1 (OKSU); 2 mi. W Edith, 1 (USNM); Merrihew Ranch, 1 (OKSU); 1.5 mi. E Tegarden, 1 (OKSU). WOODWARD COUNTY: Alabaster Caverns State Park, 1 (OKSU); 2 mi. N Alabaster Caverns State Park on County Rd., 1 (OKSU); 2.5 mi. N Alabaster Cavern, 1 (OKSU); 2 mi. W Edith, 2 (OMNH); 3 mi. S, 5 mi. W Freedom, 1 (OKSU); 7 mi. W Freedom, 1 (OKSU); 10 mi. S Freedom, 1 (OKSU); 11 mi. S Freedom, 3 (OKSU); 2 mi. E Quinlan, 1 (OKSU); Selman's Ranch, 1 (OKSU).

Perognathus hispidus.—Specimens examined (total 442); BECKHAM COUNTY: 5 mi. NE Elk City, 1 (OMNH); 3 mi. W, 1 mi. S Sayre, 1 (OKSU). BLAINE COUNTY: 1 mi. N Hydro, 3 (KU). BRYAN COUNTY: 2 mi. NW Colbert, 1 (TMM); 5 mi. N Colbert, 1 (TMM); 5 mi. W Colbert, 1 (TMM). CADDO COUNTY: 4 mi. N Hinton, 1 (OKSU). CANADIAN COUNTY: 5 mi. N US Hwy 51, 3 mi. W El Reno, 1 (OKSU). CIMARRON COUNTY: Carrizo Creek on Colorado Line, 1 (OKSU); 2 mi. E, 6 mi. S Kenton, 1 (CAMCO); 2.5 mi. SE Kenton, 1 (CAMCO); 2.5 mi. NNE Kenton, 1 (OMNH); 4 mi. SW Kenton, 1 (CAMCO); 2.5 mi. SE Kenton, 4,200 ft., 1 (OMNH); 4.6 mi. N, 0.2 mi. W Kenton, 2

(OMNH); 3.1 mi. N Kenton, 4,900 ft., 1 (OMNH); 3.1 mi. N Kenton, 4,950 ft., 2 (OMNH); north side Black Mesa, 6 mi. N Kenton, 1 (OKSU); 6 mi. N Kenton, 2 (OKSU); 9 mi. SE Kenton, 1 (CAMCO) CLEVELAND COUNTY: Cleveland County, 3 (OMNH); Noble, 6 (FMNH); 0.5 mi. W Noble, 1 (KU); dump, Norman, 1 (OMNH); 1.5 mi. W Norman, 1 (OMNH); 2 mi. N Norman, 2 (OMNH), 1 (KU); 2.5 mi. NE Norman, 2 (OMNH); 3 mi. E Norman, 9 (OMNH); 3.2 mi. N Norman, 1 (OMNH); 4 mi. S Norman, 1 (OMNH); 5 mi. S Norman, 1 (OMNH); 2 mi. E South Fork Canadian River Bridge & I-35, 1 (CSUO). COMANCHE COUNTY: 1 mi. S Cache, 1 (CAMCO); Chattanooga, 5 (USNM); Comanche County, 1 (OKSU); 3 mi. W, 4 mi. S Elgin, 1 (CAMCO); Ft. Sill, 1 (USNM); 2 mi. W, 7 mi. N Indiahoma, 1 (CSUO); Lake Lawtonka, 1 (CAMCO); Lawton, 2 (USNM); 1 mi. W Cameron University, 3 mi. S Lawton, 1 (CAMCO); Medicine Park, 1 (USNM); near Cache Creek, Mt. Scott, 1 (USNM); SW Mt. Scott, Wichita Wildlife Refuge, 1 (OMNH); Little Medicine Creek, Wichita Mountains Wildlife Refuge, 2 (USNM); 0.5 mi. W Wichita Mountains Wildlife Refuge, 1 (CSUO). COTTON COUNTY: 3 mi. SW Randlett, 1 (MSU); 3.3 mi. ESE Taylor, 900 ft., 2 (OMNH); 5 mi. SE Taylor, 900 ft., 5 (OMNH); Red River, 2 mi. S Temple, 1 (TMM); 12 mi. S Temple, 3 (TMM). CUSTER COUNTY: 2 mi. E Clinton, 1 (OKSU); 4 mi. E Moorewood, 3 (OKSU); 6 mi. W Weatherford, 2 (KU). DEWEY COUNTY: Canton, 1 (KU); 5 mi. W Canton, 11 (KU); 5.5 mi. W Canton, 4 (KU); Dewey County, 3 (KU); 1 mi. S, 0.5 mi. E Seiling, 2 (OKSU); 1 mi. N Taloga, 2 (OMNH). ELLIS COUNTY: 1 mi. W Shattuck, 1 (CSUO); 2 mi. N Shattuck, 2,300 ft., 1 (OMNH); 5 mi. NNE Shattuck, 2,335 ft., 2 (OMNH). GARVIN COUNTY: 5.25 mi. W, 2.25 mi. N Elmore City, 1 (ECENT); T3N, R4W, Sec. 25, SARP Site R5, Rush Creek, 1 (OKSU); T3N, R4W, Sec. 25, SARP Site R9, Rush Creek, 1 (OKSU). GRADY COUNTY: Alex, 1 (OMNH); T3N, R4W, Sec. 29, SARP Site R8, Rush Creek, 0.5 mi. W SH 76, 1 (OKSU); SARP Site R8, 10 mi. W SH 76, 5.3 mi. N SH 29, 1 (OKSU). HARMON COUNTY: 16 mi. S Altus, 1 (FWMSH); 4.5 mi. N Gould, 1 (TTU); 4.5 mi. N, 0.5 mi. W Gould, 1 (TTU); Harmon County, 1 (OUBS); 5.25 mi. S, 2 mi. E Kirby's Corner, Hollis, 1 (OKSU); 5.3 mi. N Hollis, 1 (FWMSH); 5.5 mi. S Hollis, 8 (FWMSH); 13 mi. N Hollis, 1 (FWMSH); 15 mi. N, 1.5 mi. E Hollis, 2 (TTU); 17 mi. N, 2.5 mi. W Hollis, 2 (TTU); 18 mi. N, 9.5 mi. E Hollis, 2 (TTU); 2 mi. E, 3.25 mi. S Kirby's Corner, 5 (OKSU); 2 mi. S, 2 mi. W Reed, 1 (KU); 3 mi. E Reed, 8 (OMNH); Spring Lake Recreation Area, 1 (TTU); 1 mi. S, 6 mi. E Vinson, 3 (OMNH); 6 mi. E, 1 mi. S Vinson, 1,700 ft., 8 (OMNH). HARPER COUNTY: Great Plains Exp. Range, Ft. Supply, 1 (OKSU); 3 mi. N Ft. Supply, 19 (USNM); 3 mi. NNW Ft. Supply, 9 (USNM); T25N, R22W, N 1/2 Sec. 19, 5 mi. N Ft.

Supply, 1 (OKSU); USDA Exp. Range, 5 mi. N Ft. Supply, 1 (OKSU).
HASKELL COUNTY: 1.5 mi. E Porum, 1 (OMNH). JACKSON
COUNTY: 7.5 mi. W, 2.5 mi. N Altus, 1 (CAMCO); 7 mi. E Eldorado, 1
(OKSU); 1.5 mi. S, 2 mi. E Olustee, 1 (CAMCO); 4.5 mi. W, 3 mi. S
Olustee, 1 (CAMCO); 11.5 mi. S, 1.5 mi. W Olustee, 2 (CAMCO); Red
River, 14 mi. S Olustee, 1 (TMM); 11 mi. N US Hwy 62 on SH 34, 1
(OKSU). JEFFERSON COUNTY: 1 mi. E Hastings, 2 (UIMNH). JOHN-
STON COUNTY: 1 mi. W Connerville, 1 (ECENT). KAY COUNTY: 5
mi. S, 7 mi. E Newkirk, 1,100 ft., 2 (OMNH); 5 mi. S, 10.5 mi. E New-
kirk, 1,150 ft., 3 (OMNH); Ponca City, Ponca Agency, 1 (USNM); 4 mi.
W, 5 mi. S Ponca City, 1 (OKSU). KIOWA COUNTY: 6 mi. SE Cooper-
town, 1 (OMNH); 6.5 mi. W Snyder, 1 (CAMCO); 7.5 mi. W Snyder, 2
(CAMCO); 1.8 mi. W Wichita Mt. Refuge, 1.5 mi. S Hwy 49, 1 (CSUO).
LEFLORE COUNTY: 5 mi. N, 2.5 mi. E Bokoshe, 2 (OMNH). LOGAN
COUNTY: 7 mi. N, 2 mi. W Edmond, 1 (CSUO); Logan County, 1
(OMNH); Orlando, 3 (USNM); T16N, R4W, Sec. 2, N bridge on Hwy
74, 1 (OMNH). MAJOR COUNTY: 8 mi. E Alabaster Caverns, 1 (CSUO);
Nescatunga Cave, 2.5 mi. W jct. Hwys 281 & 15, 1 (CSUO); Vickery
Ranch, 3 (OKSU); 5.5 mi. S Waynoka, 1,450 ft., 1 (OMNH). MAR-
SHALL COUNTY: Island No. 1, Lake Texoma, 1 (OUBS); Lake Tex-
oma, 1 (TTU); Marshall County, 1 (OUBS); University of Oklahoma
Biological Station, 2 (OUBS), 1 (OMNH); 0.25 mi. W University of Okla-
homa Biological Station, 1 (OUBS); 1.5 mi. W University of Oklahoma
Biological Station, 1 (OUBS); 2.5 mi. WNW University of Oklahoma Bio-
logical Station, 1 (OUBS); 3.5 mi. NW University of Oklahoma Biological
Station, 2 (OUBS); 0.25 mi. N Willis, 1 (OUBS); 0.5 mi. N, 0.5 mi. W
Willis, 1 (OMNH); 1 mi. W Willis, 670 ft., 1 (OMNH); 1 mi. W Willis,
700 ft., 8 (OMNH); 1 mi. N Willis Post Office, 2 (OUBS); 1 mi. W Willis,
1 (OUBS); 2 mi. E Willis, University of Oklahoma Biological Station, 650
ft., 1 (OMNH); 2 mi. W Willis, 3 (OUBS); 2 mi. W, 1 mi. S Willis, 4
(OKSU); 2.5 mi. NW Willis, 3 (OUBS); 3 mi. E Willis, 1 (OMNH); 3 mi.
W Willis, 1 (OUBS); 3.5 mi. W Willis, 2 (OUBS). MAYES COUNTY: 4
mi. E Pryor, 1 (OKSU). MCCLAIN COUNTY: 4 mi. S, 1.2 mi. W Goldsby, 1 (OMNH); McClain County, 4 (OMNH); T8N, R2W, Sec. 10, 1
(OMNH); T8N, R4W, Sec. 11, 2 (OMNH). MUSKOGEE COUNTY: 3
mi. E Wainwright, 8 (OMNH). NOBLE COUNTY: Arnettville, Okla-
homa Territory, 2 (FMNH); 5 mi. W, 3 mi. N Stillwater, 1 (OKSU). NO-
WATA COUNTY: Paul Buck Ranch, 2 mi. NW Wann, 1 (OKSU).
OKLAHOMA COUNTY: jct. 15th & I-35, Edmond, 1 (CSUO); jct. 122nd
& N. Pennsylvania, Oklahoma City, 1 (CSUO); 0.25 mi. N jct. N.W. 23rd
& N. May, 1 (CSUO). OKMULGEE COUNTY: 3 mi. E, 2 mi. N Ok-
mulgee, 1 (OMNH). OSAGE COUNTY: Osage County, 1 (UMMZ).

PAWNEE COUNTY: Arkansas River, 25 mi. N, 5 mi. E Stillwater, 1 (OKSU); Turkey Island, Arkansas River, 1 (OKSU). PAYNE COUNTY: Boomer Lake, 3 (OKSU); T17N, R1E, Sec. 10, cemetery, 1 (OKSU); Cimarron River floodplain, 1 (OKSU); Cimarron River, 1 (OKSU); Lake Blackwell Dam, 1 (OKSU); Lake Carl Blackwell, 1 (OKSU); Payne County, 1 (OKSU); 1.5 mi. S Progress, 5 (OKSU); 0.25 mi. N Sanborn Lake, 1 (OKSU); Stillwater, 1 (UMMZ); Wildlife Research Center & McElroy St., Stillwater, 1 (OKSU); 0.5 mi. SW jct. Western & Lakeview Sts., Stillwater, 1 (OKSU); 0.5 mi. S Stillwater Creek Bridge on Hwy 51, 1 (OKSU); 1 mi. N Stillwater, 2 (OKSU); 1 mi. S, 1.5 mi. E Stillwater, 1 (OKSU); 1 mi. W Stillwater, 2 (OKSU); 1 mi. W Stillwater on Hwy 51, 0.25 mi. N, 1 (OKSU); 1.5 mi. W Western on Farm Rd., Stillwater, 2 (OKSU); 2 mi. S Stillwater, 1 (OKSU); 3 mi. N, 1 mi. W Stillwater, 1 (OKSU); 3 mi. N, 1.25 mi. E Stillwater, 2 (OKSU); 5 mi. W, 0.5 mi. S Stillwater, 1 (OKSU); 5 mi. W, 2 mi. N Stillwater, 1 (OKSU); 5 mi. W, 0.75 mi. S Stillwater, 1 (OKSU); 5 mi. SE Stillwater, 1 (ECENT); 11 mi. E Stillwater, 1 (OKSU); 13 mi. W, 2.5 mi. N Stillwater, 1 (OKSU); 3 mi. N, 1 mi. W jct. SH 51 & Country Club Rd., 1 (OKSU). PONTOTOC COUNTY: 7 mi. SW Ada, 1 (ECENT). POTTAWATOMIE COUNTY: 0.25 mi. E McLoud, 1 (CSUO). ROGER MILLS COUNTY: 5 mi. N Cheyenne, 2,100 ft., 5 (OMNH); 7 mi. N Cheyenne, 2,000 ft., 3 (OMNH); 2.5 mi. E, 1.5 mi. S Reydon, 3 (CAMCO). ROGERS COUNTY: 0.2 mi. N Oologah Dam Office, Oologah, 1 (OKSU). TEXAS COUNTY: 2 mi. E Eva, 2 (KU). TILLMAN COUNTY: 0.5 mi. W Chattanooga, 1 (OMNH); 3 mi. SE Davidson, 1 (OMNH); 2.8 mi. N Grandfield, 7 (OMNH); 5.5 mi. S Grandfield, 3 (OMNH). TULSA COUNTY: Garnett, 29 (UMMZ); 8 mi. W Red Fork, 3 (USNM); U Ranch, 1 (UMMZ). WAGONER COUNTY: 2.5 mi. SSW Coweta, 600 ft., 2 (OMNH); 4.5 mi. SW Coweta, 600 ft., 1 (OMNH). WOODS COUNTY: Alva, 11 (FMNH), 2 (USNM); 1 mi. E, 3 mi. N Alva, 1 (OKSU); 1.5 mi. N Alva, 1 (OKSU); 5 mi. NW Alva, 1 (KU); 6 mi. NW Alva, 1 (OKSU); 8.5 mi. NW Alva, 1 (OMNH); 2 mi. W Edith, 1 (USNM); 5 mi. S Waynoka, 1,400 ft., 2 (OMNH); 5 mi. S Waynoka, 1,450 ft., 2 (OMNH); White Horse Springs, 2 (FMNH). WOODWARD COUNTY: 8 mi. E Alabaster Caverns, 1 (CSUO); 2 mi. W Edith, 2 (OMNH); 10 mi. S Freedom, 1 (OKSU); Woodward, 1 (USNM).

Peromyscus attwateri.—Specimens examined (total 591); ADAIR COUNTY: 1.5 mi. W Chewey, 1 (OMNH); 3 mi. NNW Chewey, 1,000 ft., 13 (OMNH); 5 mi. S Kansas, 1 (OKSU), 8 (UMMZ); 7 mi. W Stilwell, 1 (KU); 9 mi. S Stilwell, 1 (TMM); Boston Mts., Stilwell, 36 (USNM); T15N, R24E, Sec. 1, 4.5 mi. W Stilwell, 2 (OMNH). BRYAN COUNTY: 9 mi. N, 4 mi. E Bennington, 1 (OMNH). CADDO COUNTY: Hinton, 1 (OMNH). CARTER COUNTY: 3 mi. N Springer, 1 (USNM). CHERO-

KEE COUNTY: 2.5 mi. NW Chewey, 900 ft., 1 (OMNH); Tahlequah, 19 (UMMZ). COMANCHE COUNTY: 9 mi. NW Cache, 1 (OMNH); Elk Mt., Lawton, 2 (CAMCO); Medicine Park, 1 (CAMCO); 3 mi. S Refuge Hdqtrs., 1 (OMNH); 0.25 mi. W Wichita Mountains Wildlife Refuge, 3 (CSUO); 0.5 mi. W Wichita Mountains Wildlife Refuge, 3 (CSUO); 8 mi. W, 3 mi. N Wichita Mountains Wildlife Refuge Visitor Center, 9 (CSUO); Camp Boulder, Wichita Mountains Wildlife Refuge, 3 (OKSU), 1 (OMNH); Eagle Mt., Wichita Mountains Wildlife Refuge, 2 (OKSU); French Lake, Wichita Mountains, 3 (OMNH); Hdqtrs. Area on Cache Creek, Wichita Mountains Refuge, 1 (OKSU); jct. Lost Lake Rd. & Scenic Hwy, 1 (OKSU); Lost Lake Camp Area, 1 (OKSU); 100 yds. W Lost Lake Camp, 2 (OKSU); Lost Lake, Wichita Mountains Wildlife Refuge, 5 (OKSU); Mt. Scott, 7 (OMNH). 24 (USNM); Mt. Scott, Wichita Mountains, 4 (OMNH); Mt. Scott Post Office, 11 (USNM); north side Eagle Mt., Boulder Camp, Wichita Mountains Wildlife Refuge, 1 (OKSU); Pinchot Pasture, W Lake Flats, Wichita Mountains Wildlife Refuge, 1 (OKSU); Wichita Mountains, 3 (OMNH), 123 (USNM); Wichita Mountains Wildlife Refuge, 3 (OMNH), 3 (OKSU). CRAIG COUNTY: 1.75 mi. S, 0.25 mi. W Big Cabin on Hwy 69, 1 (OKSU). CUSTER COUNTY: 6 mi. ENE Clinton, 1 (MSU). DELAWARE COUNTY: Spavinaw Creek, 12 mi. SE Jay, 1 (CSUO); Lake Eucha, 1 (OMNH). JACKSON COUNTY: 11.5 mi. S, 1.5 mi. W Olustee, 2 (CAMCO). JOHNSTON COUNTY: Tishomingo Natl. Wildlife Refuge, 690 ft., 1 (USNM). KIOWA COUNTY: 7 mi. SE Cooperton, 1 (OMNH); Youth Camp #2, Quartz Mt. State Park, 1 (OKSU). LATIMER COUNTY: Red Oak, 9 (USNM); 3 mi. N Wilburton, 1 (OMNH); 3 mi. S Wilburton, 4 (OMNH); 3.5 mi. N Wilburton, 75 (OMNH); 5 mi. N Wilburton, 625 ft., 7 (OMNH); 5.5 mi. N Wilburton, 4 (OMNH). LEFLORE COUNTY: Billy Creek Camp, 7 mi. NW Big Cedar, 2 (OMNH); 2 mi. S Honobia, 3 (OMNH); 1 mi. SW Summerfield, 5 (TMM); 0.75 mi. NE Zoe, 14 (OMNH); 1 mi. NE Zoe, 1 (OMNH); 1 mi. N Zoe, 1 (OMNH); 1.5 mi. N Zoe, 1 (OMNH); 1.5 mi. NW Zoe, 1 (OMNH); 1.75 mi. NE Zoe, 3 (OMNH); 3 mi. NE Zoe, 1 (OMNH). MARSHALL COUNTY: Buncombe Bay, 0.75 mi. N University of Oklahoma Biological Station, 1 (OMNH); N Buncombe, 620 ft., 2 (OMNH); N Paul's Landing, 630 ft., 1 (OMNH); 0.5 mi. N Paul's Landing, 630 ft., 12 (OMNH); 1 mi. ENE University of Oklahoma Biological Station, 7 (OMNH); 3 mi. E Willis, 1 (OMNH); 5 mi. N Willis, 1 (OMNH). MAYES COUNTY: 1.2 mi. N Hwy 33, 3.5 mi. E Chouteau, 3 (OMNH); 3.5 mi. E Chouteau, 1.1 mi. N Hwy 33, 2 (OMNH); Camp Garland, 2 (OKSU); Locust Grove, 4 (UMMZ); 2 mi. S Spavinaw, 4 (OMNH). MC-CURTAIN COUNTY: Beavers Bend State Park, 6 (OMNH); 7 mi. NNE Broken Bow, 4 (OMNH); 2 mi. W Smithville, 12 (OMNH); 2.5 mi. W

Smithville, 4 (OMNH). MCINTOSH COUNTY: 0.5 mi. W Burney, 1 (OMNH). MURRAY COUNTY: Dougherty, Indian Territory, 21 (FMNH); Platt Natl. Park, 2 (OMNH). MUSKOGEE COUNTY: bluff on Grand River, 3 mi. below Ft. Gibson Dam, 1 (OKSU); 4 mi. below Ft. Gibson Dam, 1 (OKSU); east bank Greenleaf Lake, 1 (OKSU); Greenleaf Lake, 1 (OKSU); shore Greenleaf Lake, 1 (OKSU). OSAGE COUNTY: N Cleveland, 3 (OKSU); McClintock Boy Scout Camp, 2 (OKSU); Okesa, 8 (UMMZ); 3 mi. W Okesa, 1 (OMNH); 10 mi. NW Pawhuska, 1 (TMM). PAWNEE COUNTY: 1.3 mi. N, 1.5 mi. W Watchorn, 1 (OMNH). PITTS-BURG COUNTY: 2 mi. S Hartshorne, 1 (OKSU); 3 mi. NE Hart-shorne, 1 (OKSU). PONTOTOC COUNTY: 7 mi. NE Ada, 1 (ECENT); old road near Kerr Lab, 3 (ECENT). PUSHMATAHA COUNTY: 1 mi. S Nashoba, 4 (TMM); Little River, 5 mi. E Nashoba, 1 (OKSU); 5 mi. NW Tuskahoma, 1 (OMNH). ROGERS COUNTY: Catoosa, 12 (UMMZ); U Ranch, 2 (UMMZ). SEQUOYAH COUNTY: Redland, 2 (USNM); 8 mi. N Vian, 3 (OKSU); T13N, R21E, Sec. 3, 1 (OMNH). TULSA COUNTY: 2 mi. W Sand Springs, 1 (OKSU). WASHITA COUNTY: 5 mi. N, 2.4 mi. W Corn, 2 (CSUO).

Peromyscus boylii.—Specimens examined (total 295); CIMARRON COUN-TY: Black Mesa, 1 (OMNH); Black Mesa, 0.25 mi. E Kenton, 1 (OMNH); Cimarron County, 3 (OMNH); 0.25 mi. E Kenton, 1 (OMNH); 0.5 mi. E Kenton, 1 (OMNH); 0.75 mi. E, 0.25 mi. N Kenton, 1 (OMNH); Ken-ton, 6 (OMNH); T5N, R2E, Sec. 34, Black Mesa, 1 mi. E, 2.75 N Ken-ton, 4 (OMNH); 1.25 mi. N Kenton, 4,200 ft., 1 (OMNH); 2 mi. E Kenton, 1 (OMNH); 2 mi. N, 1 mi. W Kenton, 8 (OMNH); 2 mi. E, 6 mi. S Kenton, 1 (CAMCO); 2.5 mi. SE Kenton, 2 (CAMCO); 2.25 mi. N Ken-ton, 14 (OMNH); Regnier Ranch, 2 mi. S, 1 mi. E Kenton, 1 (CSUO); 2.6 mi. S, 1.5 mi. E Kenton, 9 (OMNH); 3 mi. N Kenton, 1 (OMNH), 6 (UMMZ); 3 mi. N, 0.7 mi. W Kenton, 18 (OMNH); 3.4 mi. S, 1.2 mi. E Kenton, 34 (OMNH); 3.5 mi. N, 1 mi. E Kenton, 1 (OMNH); 3.5 mi. N, 1.2 mi. W Kenton, 1 (OMNH); 3.6 mi. S, 0.9 mi. E Kenton, 26 (OMNH); 2.5 mi. SE Kenton, 4,200 ft., 51 (OMNH); 4 mi. S, 0.7 mi. E Kenton, 6 (OMNH); 4 mi. SE Kenton, 8 (OMNH); 4 mi. N Kenton, 6 (KU); 2.6 mi. NNE Kenton, 4,900 ft., 2 (OMNH); 4.2 mi. N, 0.1 mi. W Kenton, 3 (OMNH); 4.2 mi. S Kenton, 3 (OMNH); Regnier's Ranch, 4.2 mi. S Ken-ton, 1 (OMNH); 4.2 mi. S, 0.5 mi. E Kenton, 27 (OMNH); 4.2 mi. S, 0.8 mi. W Kenton, 20 (OMNH); 4.4 mi. N, 0.4 mi. W Kenton, 2 (OMNH); 4.5 mi. SE Kenton, 4,200 ft., 4 (OMNH); 3.1 mi. N Kenton, 4,900 ft., 2 (OMNH); 5.3 mi. S, 0.5 mi. E Kenton, 18 (OMNH).

Peromyscus difficilis.—Specimens examined (total 53); CIMARRON COUN-TY: Black Mesa, 1 (UMMZ); 2.6 mi. S, 1.5 mi. E Kenton, 7 (OMNH); 3 mi. N, 0.7 mi. W Kenton, 5 (OMNH); 3 mi. N Kenton, 1 (UMMZ); 3.5

mi., N, 1 mi. E Kenton, 10 (OMNH); 3.5 mi. N, 1.2 mi. W Kenton, 11 (OMNH); 2.5 mi. SE Kenton, 4,200 ft., 2 (OMNH); 4 mi. N Kenton, 1 (UMMZ); 4.2 mi. N, 0.1 mi. W Kenton, 3 (OMNH); 4.2 mi. S, 0.5 mi. W Kenton, 3 (OMNH); 4.2 mi. S, 0.8 mi. W Kenton, 7 (OMNH); 3.1 mi. N Kenton, 4,950 ft., 2 (OMNH).

Peromyscus gossypinus.—Specimens examined (total 36); BRYAN COUNTY: 7 mi. NE Bokchito, 1 (OMNH); T5S, R13E, Sec. 17, 1 (OMNH). HASKELL COUNTY: 6.5 mi. E, 2 mi. S Stigler, 1 (OMNH). LATIMER COUNTY: Red Oak, Indian Territory, 1 (USNM). LEFLORE COUNTY: 6.5 mi. SW Page, 1 (OMNH); northwest side Rich Mt., 1 (OMNH). MC-CURTAIN COUNTY: 6 mi. N, 2 mi. E Broken Bow, 1 (CAMCO); 14 mi. SE Broken Bow, 3 (OMNH); 15 mi. SE Broken Bow, 11 (OMNH); Mountain Fork River, 2 mi. W Eagletown, 1 (TMM); Glover, 5 (UMMZ); Glover River, 0.25 mi. W Glover, 1 (TMM); 2.5 mi. W Smithville, 5 (OMNH); 3 mi. SSE Tom, 2 (UIMNH). PUSHMATAHA COUNTY: 1 mi. S Nashoba, 1 (TMM).

Peromyscus leucopus.—Specimens examined (total 1,667): ADAIR COUNTY: 1.5 mi. W Chewey, 800 ft., 1 (OMNH); 3 mi. NNW Chewey, 1,000 ft., 4 (OMNH); 5 mi. S Kansas, 5 (UMMZ); Stilwell, 1 (UIMNH); 2.5 mi. E Stilwell, 3 (UIMNH). ALFALFA COUNTY: Alfalfa County, 1 (OKSU); 2 mi. NE Cherokee, 2 (CSUO); 3 mi. N, 6.5 mi. E Cherokee, 1,170 ft., 2 (OMNH); 3 mi. N, 9 mi. E Cherokee, 1,170 ft., 5 (OMNH). ATOKA COUNTY: 6 mi. W, 1 mi. N Atoka, 8 (OMNH). BEAVER COUNTY: Lake Evans Chambers, 6 (OMNH); 3 mi. NW Slapout, 4 (OMNH). BECKHAM COUNTY: 3 mi. W Sayre, 2 (OKSU). BLAINE COUNTY: Blaine County, 5 (OKSU); 1 mi. E Project Office, Canton Lake, 1 (OMNH); 1.5 mi. E Project Office, Canton Lake, 4 (OMNH); 1 mi. W, 0.25 mi. S Project Office, Canton, 1 (OMNH); 1 mi. N, 1 mi. E Project Office, Canton, 1 (OMNH); 1.5 mi. N, 1 mi. E Park Office, Canton, 1 (OMNH); 2 mi. E Project Office, Canton Lake, 3 (OMNH); Fairview Landing, Canton Reservoir, 2 (OKSU); 3 mi. W, 1 mi. N Longdale, 2 (OKSU); Roman Nose State Park, 6 (OKSU); 2 mi. S, 3 mi. W Southard, 3 (OKSU); 2 mi. W Watonga, 2 (OKSU). BRYAN COUNTY: 10 mi. SE Bennington, 5 (TMM); Bryan County, 1 (OKSU); 2 mi. W Colbert, 4 (TMM); 5 mi. N Colbert, 4 (TMM). CADDO COUNTY: 9 mi. E Binger, 7 (OMNH); 4.2 mi. W Cogar, 1 (OMNH); 4.7 mi. W Cogar, 3 (OMNH); Ft. Cobb, 1 (CAMCO); Kiwanis Canyon, 1 mi. S Hinton, 2 (OKSU); 6 mi. E Hinton, 2 (OMNH); Red Rock Canyon, 3 (OMNH); T11N, R11W, Sec. 3, Red Rock Canyon Park, 7 (OMNH); Red Rock Canyon State Park, 2 (OMNH); T11N, R11W, Sec. 3, 2 (OMNH). CANADIAN COUNTY: 3 mi. W El Reno, 1 (OKSU); 11 mi. N El Reno, 1 (OKSU); 17 mi. NW Oklahoma City, 1 (CSUO); T11N, R9W, Sec. 5, north bank South Canadian River, 2 (OMNH); 4 mi. E, 2 mi. S Union City, 2 (OKSU). CARTER COUNTY: Arbuckle Mountains, 3 mi. N Springer, 2 (MVZ); T1S, R3W, Sec. 2, SARP Site W7, Wildhorse Creek, 2 mi. E Hwy 76, 2 (OKSU); 1.4 mi. N Woodford, 975 ft., 3 (OMNH); 2.1 mi. N Woodford, 1,000 ft., 1 (OMNH). CHEROKEE COUNTY: Cookson Hills Game Refuge, 1 (OKSU). CHOCTAW COUNTY: 3 mi. E, 1.5 mi. S Hugo, 2 (OKSU); 3 mi. E, 3 mi. S Hugo, 1 (OKSU); 7 mi. SSE Ft. Towson, 400 ft., 1 (OMNH). CIMARRON COUNTY: Black Mesa State Park, 6 (OMNH); Lake Etling, Black Mesa State Park, 4 (OMNH); Cimarron County, 4 (OMNH); 0.5 mi. E, 8.3 mi. N Felt, 1 (OMNH); 9 mi. E, 1 mi. N Kenton, 1 (OMNH); T5N, R2E, Sec. 34, Black Mesa, 1 mi. E, 2.75 mi. N Kenton, 1 (OMNH); 1.25 mi. N Kenton, 4,200 ft., 8 (OMNH); 2 mi. N, 1 mi. W Kenton, 7 (OMNH); 2 mi. E, 6 mi. S Kenton, 1 (CAMCO); 2.5 mi. SE Kenton, 4 (CAMCO); 2.2 mi. W Kenton, 13 (OMNH); 2.25 mi. N Kenton, 7 (OMNH); 2.6 mi. S, 1.5 mi. E Kenton, 14 (OMNH); 3 mi. N, 0.7 mi. W Kenton, 2 (OMNH); 3 mi. N Kenton, 8 (UMMZ); 3 mi. NE Kenton, 1 (UIMNH); 3.3 mi. S, 1 mi. E Kenton, 15 (OMNH); 3.4 mi. S, 1.2 mi. E Kenton, 1 (OMNH); 3.5 mi. N, 1 mi. E Kenton, 4 (OMNH); 3.6 mi. N, 1.1 mi. W Kenton, 8 (OMNH); 3.7 mi. N, 1.1 mi. W Kenton, 4 (OMNH); 3.9 mi. N, 0.5 mi. W Kenton, 8 (OMNH); 2.5 mi. SE Kenton, 4,200 ft., 34 (OMNH); 4 mi. S, 0.7 mi. E Kenton, 1 (OMNH); 2.6 mi. NNE Kenton, 4,200 ft., 10 (OMNH); 4.1 mi. S, 0.5 mi. E Kenton, 7 (OMNH); 2.6 mi. NE Kenton, 4,200 ft., 3 (OMNH); 4.2 mi. N, 0.1 mi. W Kenton, 1 (OMNH); 4.2 mi. S Kenton, 4 (OMNH); 4.2 mi. S, 0.8 mi. W Kenton, 12 (OMNH); 4.4 mi. N, 0.4 mi. W Kenton, 1 (OMNH); 4.5 mi. SE Kenton, 4,200 ft., 2 (OMNH); 4.6 mi. N, 0.2 mi. W Kenton, 15 (OMNH); 3.1 mi. N Kenton, 4,900 ft., 1 (OMNH); 3.1 mi. N Kenton, 4,950 ft., 7 (OMNH); 5 mi. N, 0.5 mi. W Kenton, 1 (OMNH); 5 mi. N Kenton, 3 (OMNH); 5.3 mi. S, 0.5 mi. E Kenton, 2 (OMNH); 6 mi. N Kenton, 7 (OKSU); T5N, R2E, Sec. 8, 1 (OMNH); T5N, Sec. 11, 1 (OMNH). CLEVELAND COUNTY: Cleveland County, 3 (OMNH); Noble, 20 (FMNH); 0.5 mi. W Noble, 3 (OMNH); 1 mi. SW Noble, 1 (OMNH); 2.5 mi. NE Noble, 1 (OMNH); Norman, 1 (OMNH); 50 yds. S golf course, Norman, 1 (OMNH); 1 mi. S Norman, 1 (OKSU); 2 mi. N Robinson St. on Hwy 77H, Norman, 1 (OMNH); 2.25 mi. S Norman, 4 (OMNH); 3 mi. E Norman, 11 (OMNH); 3 mi. N Norman on SH 77H, 2 (OMNH); 3 mi. S Norman, 2 (OMNH); 3.2 mi. N Norman, 4 (OMNH), 2 (MVZ); 4 mi. S Norman, 1 (OMNH); 4 mi. SE Norman, 1 (OMNH); 5 mi. E Norman, 2 (OMNH); 5 mi. S Norman, 3 (OMNH); 5.6 mi. SE Norman, 1 (OMNH); 6 mi. E Norman, 1 (OMNH); 6 mi. E Norman on Hwy 9, 1 (OMNH); 6.2 mi. E Norman, 1,100 ft., 1 (OMNH); 6.6 mi. E Norman, 1,100 ft., 1 (OMNH); 9 mi. E Norman, 1 (OMNH); city dump, Norman, 1 (OMNH); Oliver's Preserve, 1 mi. S Norman, 1 (OMNH); Oliver's Woods, Norman, 2 (OMNH); South Canadian River, 1 (OMNH); T9N, R3W, 1 (OMNH); T8N, R3W, Sec. 12, 1 (OMNH); T9N, R3W, Sec. 30, 2 (OMNH); T6N, R1E, Sec. 31, 1 (OMNH); T9N, R3W, Sec. 32, 3 (OMNH). COMANCHE COUNTY: 9 mi. W Cache, 1 (OMNH); 12 mi. NW Cache, 1 (CAMCO); Camp Boulder, 2 (OMNH); Comanche County, 1 (OMNH); 8 mi. SW Elgin, 1 (CAMCO); Faxon, 1 (CAMCO); 0.5 mi. S Faxon, 1 (CAMCO); 0.5 mi. E Faxon, 2 (CAMCO); 2.5 mi. NE Faxon, 1 (CAMCO); 2.5 mi. N Faxon, 1 (CAMCO); Ft. Sill, 1 (CAMCO); 1 mi. E Ft. Sill, 1 (CAMCO); Lake Lawtonka, 1 (CAMCO); 0.5 mi. W Lake Lawtonka, 1 (CAMCO); 3 mi. E, 1 mi. N Lawton, 1 (CAMCO); 5.5 mi. N, 1.5 mi. W Lawton, 1 (CAMCO); 5.5 mi. N, 2.5 mi. W Lawton, 1 (CAMCO); 12.5 mi. E, 4 mi. N Lawton, 1 (CAMCO); 20 mi. NW Lawton, 2 (UIMNH); 5 mi. E, 5 mi. N Medicine Park, 1 (CAMCO); 5 mi. N Medicine Park, 1 (CAMCO); 6.5 mi. E, 0.75 mi. N Meers, 1 (CAMCO); creek, near base Mt. Scott, 1 (OMNH); French Lake, Wichita Mountains, 1 (OMNH); Wichita Game Refuge, 1 (OMNH); Wichita Mountains Wildlife Refuge, 3 (OMNH), 2 (OKSU), 2 (UIMNH); Wichita Mountains, 2 (OMNH); 5.7 mi. W east gate Wichita Mountains Wildlife Refuge, 1 (OMNH); 8 mi. W, 3 mi. N Wichita Mountains Wildlife Refuge, 1 (CSUO). COTTON COUNTY: 3 mi. E Randlett, 2 (CAMCO); 3.3 mi. ESE Taylor, 900 ft., 23 (OMNH); 5 mi. SE Taylor, 900 ft., 16 (OMNH); Temple, 7 (UMMZ). CRAIG COUNTY: 2 mi. S Big Cabin on Hwy 69 & 0.125 mi. W, 1 (OKSU); 3.5 mi. E, 0.5 mi. N Centralia, 5 (OMNH); 3.5 mi. W Vinita, 8 (OMNH); 3 mi. E, 2 mi. N Welch, 1 (OKSU); 8 mi. N, 1.5 mi. W Welch, 5 (OMNH). CREEK COUNTY: 5 mi. S Bristow on Hwy 48, 1 (OKSU); corner fence Heyburn Reservoir, 3 (OKSU); 15 mi. W Sapulpa, 2 (UIMNH). CUSTER COUNTY: Washita Natl. Bird Refuge, 1 (OKSU); T15N, R14W, Sec. 7, 2 (OMNH); T15N, R16W, Sec. 16, 1 (OMNH). DELAWARE COUNTY: 7.5 mi. SE Jay, 1 (CSUO); 10 mi. SE Jay, 1 (OKSU); 3 mi. E Ketchum, 1 (OKSU). DEWEY COUNTY: 1 mi. S, 0.5 mi. E Seiling, 1 (OKSU); 1 mi. N Taloga, 3 (OMNH). ELLIS COUNTY: 1 mi. W Shattuck, 1 (CSUO); 2 mi. N Shattuck, 2,300 ft., 17 (OMNH); 5 mi. NNE Shattuck, 2,335 ft., 2 (OMNH). GARFIELD COUNTY: Enid, 1 (OKSU); south boundary, Vance Air Force Base, 2 (OKSU). GARVIN COUNTY: 8 mi. E Pauls Valley on SH 19, 1 (OKSU); T1S, R1W, Sec. 26, SARP Site W4, Wildhorse Creek, 1 mi. E SH 74, 1 (OKSU). GRADY COUNTY: 4 mi. W Newcastle, 1 (CSUO); T3N, R4W, Sec. 29, SARP Site R8, Rush Creek, 0.5 mi. W SH 76, 4 (OKSU); SARP Site R8, 10 mi. W SH 76, 5.3 mi. N SH 29, 1 (OKSU). HARMON COUNTY: Buck Creek, extreme SW corner state, 3 (TMM); 0.5 mi. W Elm Fork Red River on SH 30, 1 (OKSU); Harmon County, 1 (FWMSH); Lake Hall

Area, 10 mi. N, 1 mi. W Hollis, 6 (TTU); 4.5 mi. S, 2 mi. W Hollis, 1
(FWMSH); 5 mi. N Hollis, 1 (FWMSH); 5.5 mi. S Hollis, 6 (FWMSH); 6
mi. N Hollis, 2 (FWMSH); 6 mi. S, 1.5 mi. W Hollis, 1 (CAMCO); 6 mi.
S, 2 mi. W Hollis, 3 (CAMCO); 7.5 mi. S, 3 mi. E Hollis, 1 (TTU); 11 mi.
N Hollis, 5 (FWMSH); 12.5 mi. N, 7.5 mi. E Hollis, 1 (TTU); 13 mi. N
Hollis, 8 (FWMSH); 13.5 mi. N Hollis, 3 (OKSU); 13.5 mi. N Holllis on
SH 30, 2 (OKSU); 13.6 mi. N Hollis, 2 (FWMSH); 13.9 mi. N Hollis, 12
(FWMSH); 13.9 mi. N US 62 in Hollis, 1 (FWMSH); 15 mi. N, 1.5 mi. E
Hollis, 1 (TTU); 6 mi. E, 1 mi. S Vinson, 1,700 ft., 16 (OMNH); gypsum
hills, 13.9 mi. N US 62, 3 (FWMSH). HARPER COUNTY: Doby Springs,
2 (OMNH); pasture 18, Southern Great Plains Exp. Range, Ft. Supply,
1 (OKSU); pasture 28, Southern Great Plains Exp. Range, Ft. Supply, 1
(OKSU); T25N, R22W, N 1/2 Sec. 19, 5 mi. N Ft. Supply, 1 (OKSU);
3 mi. N Ft. Supply, 1 (OKSU); Southern Great Plains Exp. Station, 3
(OKSU); W Scale House, Southern Great Plains Exp. Range, 1 (OKSU);
T27, R24, NE 1/4 Sec. 10, 2 (UMMZ). HASKELL COUNTY: 2.5 mi. E,
1.5 mi. N McCurtain, 2 (OMNH); 6 mi. S Stigler, 1 (OMNH); 8.5 mi. S
Stigler, 3 (OMNH). HUGHES COUNTY: 1 mi. S, 1.5 mi. W Spaulding,
1 (CAMCO). JACKSON COUNTY: Eldorado, 1 (CAMCO); 3.5 mi. S El-
dorado, 1 (CAMCO); 4 mi. SW Eldorado, 1 (OKSU); 3 mi. E, 1.5 mi. N
Friendship, 1 (OKSU); 4.5 mi. S, 4.5 mi. W Olustee, 1 (CAMCO); 14 mi.
S Olustee, 2 (TMM). JEFFERSON COUNTY: Oak Pine, 1 (OKSU);
1 mi. W Terral, 18 (TMM); 5 mi. WSW Waurika, 3 (UIMNH). JOHN-
STON COUNTY: Johnston County, 1 (OMNH). KAY COUNTY: T26N,
R2E, SE 1/4 Sec. 18, 1 (OKSU). KINGFISHER COUNTY: jct. Hwy 51
& Cimarron River, 1 (OKSU); Kingfisher County, 1 (OMNH); T17N,
R5W, Sec. 30, 4 (OMNH); T17N, R6W, Sec. 30, 1 (OMNH). KIOWA
COUNTY: 6 mi. SE Cooperton, 1 (OMNH); 7 mi. SE Cooperton, 5
(OMNH); 1.5 mi. E Snyder, 1 (CAMCO); 7.5 mi. W Snyder, 2 (CAMCO).
LATIMER COUNTY: 3.5 mi. N Wilburton, 3 (OMNH). LEFLORE
COUNTY: 2 mi. S Honobia, 5 (OMNH); 1.5 mi. NE Zoe, 2 (OMNH).
LOGAN COUNTY: jct. Hwy 177 & Cimarron River, 1 (OKSU); 6 mi. N
Edmond, 1 (CSUO); 6 mi. N Edmond, 1.7 mi. E on north side road, 1
(CSUO); below spillway, Liberty Lake, 1 (CSUO); Vickers Study Plot,
jct. Bryant & Waterloo Rd., 1 (CSUO); 0.5 mi. E I-35 on Waterloo Rd.,
1 (CSUO); T16N, R4W, Sec. 2, 2 (OMNH); T16N, R4W, Sec. 11, 4
(OMNH); T19N, R3W, Sec. 20, 1 (OMNH). MAJOR COUNTY: near
Alabaster State Park, 6 (CSUO); canyon, Ewers Creek, 2 mi. W Bouse
Jct., 1 (OKSU); Vickery Ranch, 3 (OKSU); 3 mi. S Waynoka, 3 (OMNH);
5.5 mi. S Waynoka, 1,450 ft., 18 (OMNH). MARSHALL COUNTY:
north end Buncombe, 620 ft., 7 (OMNH); University of Oklahoma Biological Station, 24 (TMM); 1 mi. E Willis, 700 ft., 1 (OMNH); 1 mi. W

Willis, 700 ft., 3 (OMNH); 2 mi. N Willis, 800 ft., 1 (OMNH); 3 mi. E Willis, 630 ft., 1 (OMNH). MAYES COUNTY: 2.5 mi. E Chouteau, 1 mi. N Hwy 33, 2 (OMNH); 3 mi. E Chouteau, 0.75 mi. N Hwy 33, 2 (OMNH); 3.5 mi. E Chouteau on Hwy 33, 2 (OMNH); 2.7 mi. E Chouteau, 0.8 mi. N Hwy 33, 3 (OMNH); 2.7 mi. E Chouteau, 1.2 mi. N Hwy 33, 4 (OMNH); 3.5 mi. E Chouteau, 1.1 mi. N Hwy 33, 7 (OMNH); 2.8 mi. E Chouteau, 0.4 mi. N Hwy, 2 (OMNH); 2.8 mi. E Chouteau, 1.25 mi. N Hwy 33, 1 (OMNH); 2.9 mi. E Couteau, 0.3 mi. N Hwy 33, 1 (OMNH); 3.1 mi. E Chouteau, 1 (OMNH); 3.1 mi. E Chouteau, 0.3 mi. N Hwy 33, 2 (OMNH); 3.1 mi. E Chouteau, 0.75 mi. N Hwy 33, 2 (OMNH); 3.1 mi. E Chouteau, 0.9 mi. N Hwy 33, 7 (OMNH); 3.2 mi. E Chouteau, 1.4 mi. N Hwy 33, 2 (OMNH); 3.25 mi. E Chouteau, 2 (OMNH); 3.4 mi. E Chouteau, 0.4 mi. N Hwy 33, 1 (OMNH); 3.4 mi. E Chouteau, 0.6 mi. N Hwy 33, 1 (OMNH); 3.5 mi. E Chouteau, 1.1 mi. N Hwy 33, 5 (OMNH); 3.6 mi. E Chouteau, 0.6 mi. N Hwy 33, 5 (OMNH); 3.7 mi. E Chouteau, 0.75 mi. N Hwy 33, 1 (OMNH). MCCLAIN COUNTY: 2 mi. W Byars, 3 (OKSU); 3 mi. S Norman, 1 (OMNH); 4 mi. S Norman, 2 (OMNH); 9 mi. W Norman, 5 (OMNH); T8N, R4W, Sec. 11, 5 (OMNH); T8N, R4W, NE 1/4 Sec. 11, 2 (OMNH); T8N, R2W, Sec. 19, 1 (OMNH); T8N, R3N, Sec. 3, 1 (OMNH); T8N, R3W, Sec. 3, 2 (OMNH). MCCURTAIN COUNTY: 2.8 mi. S, 4.5 mi. W Bethel, 4 (OMNH); 5.7 mi. S Broken Bow, 1 (OMNH); 1 mi. W, 1 mi. S Pleasant Hill, 2 (OKSU); 2.5 mi. W Smithville, 4 (OMNH); 3 mi. W Veals Farm, 1 (CSUO); T4, R27, N 1/2 Sec. 33, Veals Farm, 1 (CSUO). MCINTOSH COUNTY: 0.5 mi. W Burney, 4 (OMNH). MURRAY COUNTY: 1.3 mi. S, 2.2 mi. W Davis, 1 (CSUO); Washita River, 10 mi. SE Davis, 1 (OKSU); Murray County, 1 (OMNH); Platt Natl. Park, Sulphur, 1 (OKSU); 12 mi. S Sulphur, 1 (OKSU); Travertine Creek, 1 (OKSU). MUSKOGEE COUNTY: 2.5 mi. NE Camp Gruber, 1 (OKSU); east shore Greenleaf Lake, 1 (OKSU); Greenleaf Lake, 4 (OKSU). NOBLE COUNTY: prairie, near Lake McMurtry, 1 (OKSU); 13 mi. S Ponca City on SH 40, 1 (OKSU); 5 mi. W, 3 mi. N Stillwater, 1 (OKSU); 1.0 mi. E jct. Hwys 177 & 15W, 2 (OMNH); 2.5 mi. N jct. Hwys 177 & 15E, 27 (OMNH). NOWATA COUNTY: 6.5 mi. E, 3 mi. S Nowata, 1 (OMNH); Paul Buck Ranch, 2 mi. NW Wann, 1 (OKSU). OKFUSKEE COUNTY: 2.5 mi. W, 1 mi. N Mason, 1 (OKSU). OKLAHOMA COUNTY: 0.5 mi. E on Covell & Post Rd., Arcadia, 1 (CSUO); Belle Isle Lake, 1 (OKSU); 5 mi. E Central State University, 2 (CSUO); corner of Coltrane & 33rd, Edmond, 1 (CSUO); 0.3 mi. S Covell on Western, Edmond, 1 (CSUO); 0.5 mi. E Post Rd. on Covell, Edmond, 2 (CSUO); 1 mi. S Edmond Rd. on Meridian, 1 (CSUO); 1.5 mi. N of 2nd St. on Kelly Ave., Edmond, 2 (CSUO); 4 mi. N, 5.2 mi. W Edmond, 1 (CSUO); 4.3 mi. E Edmond, 2 (CSUO); 5 mi. E

Edmond, 1 (CSUO); 6.4 mi. W Edmond, 3 (CSUO); 6.5 mi. W Edmond, 1 (CSUO); 10 mi. W, 0.5 mi. S Edmond, 3 (CSUO); jct. 33rd & Broadway, Edmond, 1 (CSUO); jct. 40th & Coachman, Edmond, 2 (CSUO); jct. Sooner Rd. & Covell Rd., Edmond, 3 (CSUO); jct. 15th & I-35, Edmond, 2 (CSUO); pond W Lake Hefner, 1 (CSUO); 4 mi. W jct. Wilshire & Eastern, Oklahoma City, 1 (CSUO); 14 mi. S Oklahoma City, 2 (OMNH); 17 mi. NW Oklahoma City, 1 (CSUO); Oklahoma County, 2 (OKSU); 0.5 mi. E jct. N.E. 164th & I-35, 1 (CSUO); T11N, R4W, Sec. 9, 1 (OMNH); T13N, R4W, NW 1/4 Sec. 27, 1 (CSUO); T13N, R4W, Sec. 27, 2 (OMNH); T13N, R3W, Sec. 30, 1 (OMNH). OKMULGEE COUNTY: 1 mi. E Henryetta, 8 (OMNH); 3 mi. E, 2 mi. N Okmulgee, 1 (OMNH). OSAGE COUNTY: 10 mi. WSW Fairfax, 1,000ft., 13 (OMNH); McClintock Boy Scout Camp, 1 (OKSU); Okesa, 17 (UMMZ); Osage County, 2 (OKSU); Osage Hills State Park, 1 (OKSU); Sand Creek Falls, 10 mi. NE Pawhuska, 2 (TMM); 7 mi. N, 5 mi. E Wynona, 4 (OKSU). OTTAWA COUNTY: Benscoter Farm, 10 mi. SE Quapaw, 1 (OKSU); Lost Creek, near Wyandotte, 1 (OKSU); 3 mi. W Wyandotte, 2 (OMNH); T28N, R23E, SE 1/4 Sec. 23, 1 (FWMSH). PAWNEE COUNTY: Pawnee County, 1 (OMNH); 1 mi. N Ralston, 1 (OKSU); 1.0 mi. N, 0.5 mi. W Watchorn, 6 (OMNH); 1.3 mi. N, 1.5 mi. W Watchorn, 32 (OMNH); 1.3 mi. N, 1.6 mi. W Watchorn, 17 (OMNH); 1.4 mi. N, 1.9 mi. W Watchorn, 4 (OMNH); 1.5 mi. N, 1.0 mi. W Watchorn, 8 (OMNH); 1.5 mi. N, 1.1 mi. W Watchorn, 7 (OMNH); 1.5 mi. N, 1.5 mi. W Watchorn, 37 (OMNH); 2 mi. N, 2 mi. W Watchorn, 5 (OMNH); 2.5 mi. N, 0.5 mi. E Watchorn, 41 (OMNH); 2.5 mi. N, 0.5 mi. W Watchorn, 14 (OMNH); 1 mi. E, 3.5 mi. N Yale, 1 (OKSU). PAYNE COUNTY: 2 mi. N Airport, 1 (OKSU); Boomer Creek, N Boomer Lake, 0.5 mi. E Washington, N of Airport Rd., 1 (OKSU); 1 mi. W Blackwell Club House, 3 (OKSU); 0.5 mi. E Boomer Lake, 1 (OKSU); Boomer Lake Dam, 2 (OKSU); west side Boomer Lake, 1 (FWMSH); sandy wooded floodplain of Cimarron Rd., 1 (OKSU); northwest end Hamm's Lake Area, 1 (OKSU); Cedar Point Campgrounds, west end Lake Carl Blackwell, 1 (OKSU); grasslands, Lake Carl Blackwell, 1 (OKSU); minnow ponds, Lake Carl Blackwell, 1 (OKSU); spillway, S Lake Carl Blackwell, 1 (OKSU); spillway, Lake Carl Blackwell, 4 (OKSU); west end Lake Carl Blackwell, 1 (OKSU); east side Lake Carl Blackwell, 1 (OKSU); south side Lake Carl Blackwell, 1 (FWMSH); Lake Carl Blackwell, 2 (FWMSH); 0.5 mi. N on Hwy 51C toward Lake Carl Blackwell, 0.5 mi. W, 1 (OKSU); 1 mi. E Lake Carl Blackwell, 1 (OKSU); 3 mi. N SH 51, 1 mi. W Lake Carl Blackwell, 1 (OKSU); east bank Lake McMurtry, 1 (OKSU); 0.25 mi. N Lake Sanborn, 2 (OKSU); Oklahoma State University, 1 (OKSU); Aquatic Biology Lab, campus, Oklahoma State University, 1 (OKSU); dump, 0.5 mi. NW

Married Student Housing, Oklahoma State University, 1 (OKSU); Insectary Building, Oklahoma State University, 1 (FWMSH); intramural sports fields, Oklahoma State University, 1 (OKSU); Payne County, 6 (OKSU); 2 mi. S Payne Co. Free Fairgrounds, 1 (OKSU); 1 mi. S, 1 mi. W Progress, 2 (OKSU); 1.5 mi. S Progress, 6 (OKSU); Stillwater, 8 (OKSU); Boomer Lake, Stillwater, 2 (OKSU); north end Boomer Lake, N Stillwater, 1 (FWMSH); college pecan orchard, Stillwater, 3 (OKSU); jct. Lakeview & Sangre Rd., Stillwater, 1 (OKSU); Sanborn Area, Stillwater, 2 (OKSU); NE Stillwater off Western, 1 (OKSU); N Stillwater Creek, 1 (OKSU); Vet Village, Stillwater, 1 (OKSU); Wildlife Research Center on McElroy, Stillwater, 2 (OKSU); 30 yds off rd. at 2300 S. Husband, Stillwater, 1 (KSU); Stillwater Creek on Hwy 51, 50 yds S bridge, 1 (FWMSH); 0.25 mi. S Stillwater Hwy 40, 1 (OKSU); Stillwater Creek, 0.5 mi. S Stillwater, 1 (OKSU); 0.5 mi.. N Stillwater, 1 (OKSU); 0.5 mi. W McElroy & Western, Stillwater, 1 (OKSU); 0.5 mi. W Western on SH 51, Stillwater, 1 (OKSU); 0.5 mi. W, 0.5 mi. S Stillwater, 1 (OKSU); 0.8 mi. E Stillwater, 1 (OKSU); Stillwater Creek, 1 mi. SW Stillwater, 1 (OKSU); 1 mi. N. 0.25 mi. E Stillwater, 1 (OKSU); 1 mi. E Stillwater, 1 (OKSU); 1 mi. N, 1 mi. W Stillwater, 3 (OKSU); 3 mi. NW Stillwater on Valley Acres, 1 (OKSU); Cow Creek, 3.5 mi. NW Stillwater, 1 (OKSU); 4 mi. W, 3 mi. S Stillwater, water, 1 (OKSU); 1 mi. W Stillwater on Hwy 51, 0.25 mi. N, 1 (OKSU); 1 mi. W Stillwater on SH 51, 1 (OKSU); 1 mi. W, 1 mi. N Stillwater, 1 (OKSU); 1 mi. W, 2 mi. N Stillwater, 1 (OKSU); 1.5 mi. W Western St. on Farm Rd. in Stillwater, 2 (OKSU); 1.5 mi. W Stillwater on McElroy Rd., 1 (OKSU); 2 mi. E, 1 mi. S Stillwater, 4 (OKSU); 2 mi. W Stillwater, 1 (OKSU); 2 mi. N Stillwater, 1 (OKSU); 2 mi. N, 6.5 mi. W Stillwater, 6 (OKSU); 2 mi. SW Stillwater, 1 (OKSU); 2 mi. W Stillwater, 0.5 mi. S Hwy 51, 1 (OKSU); 2 mi. W, 1 mi. S Stillwater, 1 (OKSU); 2 mi. W, 2 mi. S Stillwater, 3 (OKSU); 2.5 mi. W Stillwater, 1 (OKSU); 3 mi. W Stillwater, 2 (OKSU); 3 mi. W, 3 mi. N Stillwater, 1 (OKSU); 3 mi. N, 5 mi. W Stillwater, 3 (OKSU); 3 mi. NW Stillwater on Valley Acres, 1 (OKSU); Cow Creek, 3.5 mi. NW Stillwater, 1 (OKSU); 4 mi. W, 3 mi. S Stillwater, 1 (OKSU); 4 mi. W, 16 mi. S Stillwater, 1 (OKSU); 4.5 mi. SW Stillwater, 2 (OKSU); 5 mi. N Lakeview Rd., 0.5 mi. E US Hwy 177, Stillwater, 1 (OKSU); 5 mi. S Stillwater, 1 (OKSU); 5 mi. W, 1 mi. N Stillwater, 1 (OKSU); 5.5 mi. W Stillwater, 3 mi. N SH 51, 1 (OKSU); 6 mi. E Stillwater on Lakeview Dr., 1 (OKSU); 6 mi. W Stillwater, 5 (OKSU); 7 mi. SE Stillwater, 1 (OKSU); 7.5 mi. SE Stillwater, 1 (OKSU); 7.25 mi. SE Stillwater, 1 (OKSU); 8 mi. W, 1 mi. N Stillwater, 4 (OKSU); shore Lake Carl Blackwell, 8.5 mi. W Stillwater, 1 (OKSU); Lake Carl Blackwell, 9 mi. W Stillwater, 4 (FWMSH); 11 mi. W Stillwater, 1 (OKSU); Lake Blackwell, 12 mi. W Stillwater, 1 (OKSU); 13 mi. W, 2 mi. N Stillwater, 3

(OKSU); 15 mi. W, 2 mi. N Stillwater, 1 (OKSU); 0.5 mi. E jct. SH 51 & 51C, 1 (OKSU); 0.3 mi. N jct. Hwys 108 & 51, 1 (OKSU); 1 mi. W, 0.25 mi. S jct. Western & SH 51, 1 (OKSU); 1.4 mi. W jct. McElroy & Orchard Sts., 1 (OKSU); 2 mi. W jct. Hwys 177 & 60, 1 (OKSU); 3 mi. S jct. SH 51 & 51C, 1 (OKSU); T19N, R1E, SW 1/4 Sec. 3, 1 (OKSU); T5E, R19N, Sec. 6, 1 (OKSU). PITTSBURG COUNTY: 2 mi. E McAlester, 1 (OKSU). PONTOTOC COUNTY: 4 mi. S, 1 mi. E Ada, 1 (ECENT); 7 mi. N Ada, 1 (ECENT); 7 mi. NW Ada, 1 (ECENT). POTTAWATO-MIE COUNTY: 0.25 mi. E McLoud, 2 (CSUO); T8N, R4W, Sec. 3, 2 (OMNH). PUSHMATAHA COUNTY: 1 mi. S Nashoba, 2 (TMM); Pushmataha County, 1 (OMNH); T1N, R18E, Sec. 31, 2 (OMNH). ROGER MILLS COUNTY: Spring Creek Lake Recreation Grounds, Black Kettle Natl. Grassland, 7 (TTU); Spring Creek Lake Recreation Area, 2 (TTU). ROGERS COUNTY: Catoosa, 3 (UMMZ); T20N, R15E, NW 1/4 Sec. 26, 4 mi. E Catoosa, 1 (OKSU); 5.5 mi. E Claremore, 1 (OMNH); 7 mi. W, 3 mi. S Claremore, 2 (OMNH); 3 mi, N, 1 mi. W Foyil, 5 (OMNH); 1 mi. N Oologah Dam Office, Oologah, 1 (OKSU); 1 mi. E, 0.5 mi. N south side Oolagah Dam, Oolagah, 1 (OKSU); V Ranch, 3 (UMMZ). SEQUOYAH COUNTY: 4.25 mi. WSW Nicut, 1,000 ft., 1 (OMNH); 8 mi. N Vian, 2 (OKSU). STEPHENS COUNTY: 0.75 mi. E Duncan, 1 (OKSU). TEXAS COUNTY: 2 mi. N Guymon, 3,000 ft., 4 (OMNH); 5.5 mi. N Guymon, 3,100 ft., 1 (OMNH); Texhoma, Beaver River, 1 (OMNH). TILLMAN COUNTY: 3 mi. S, 0.5 mi. E Davidson, 1 (CAMCO); T3S, R14W, Sec. 21, Deep Red Creek, 2 (OMNH); 12.5 mi. S Frederick 41 (TMM); 1.5 mi. E Snyder, 1 (CAMCO); 7.5 mi. W, 0.75 mi. S Snyder, 1 (CAMCO); Tillman County, 1 (OKSU). TULSA COUNTY: Garnett, 12 (UMMZ); Mohawk Park, 9 (UMMZ); N Tulsa, 2 (FWMSH); Tulsa, 5 (UMMZ); 1 mi. N Tulsa, 4 (FWMSH); T19N, R12E, Sec. 11, 1 (OMNH). WAGONER COUNTY: 4.5 mi. SW Coweta, 600 ft., 1 (OMNH). WASHINGTON COUNTY: 3 mi. N Dewey, 1 (OKSU); Washington County, 1 (OMNH). WASHITA COUNTY: 5 mi. N, 2 mi. W Corn, 6 (CSUO); Washita County, 1 (CSUO); 4.5 mi. E, 5 mi. S Weatherford, 1 (OKSU); 5 mi. E, 5 mi. S Weatherford, 1 (OKSU). WOODS COUNTY: Alva, 16 (FMNH); 6 mi. NW Alva, 1 (OMNH), 3 (OKSU); Salt Fork, 6 mi. NW Alva, 1 (OKSU); 8.5 mi. NW Alva, 1 (OMNH); 9 mi. NW Alva, 1 (OKSU); 0.5 mi. S Camp Houston, 1 (CSUO); 2 mi. E Camp Houston, 1 (OKSU); Moccasin Creek, 4 mi. W Camp Houston, 3 (CSUO); 2 mi. W, 2.5 mi. S Dacoma, 1 (OKSU); Waynoka, 1 (UMMZ); Cimarron River, Waynoka, 1 (OKSU); Waynoka Dunes, 3 (OKSU); 5 mi. S Waynoka, 1,400 ft., 4 (OMNH); 5 mi. S Waynoka, 1,450 ft., 25 (OMNH); 5 mi. S Waynoka, 4 (OMNH); White Horse Springs, Oklahoma Territory, 16 (FMNH). WOODWARD COUNTY: Alabaster Caverns, 6 (OMNH);

Boiling Springs State Park, 1 (OMNH); Boiling Springs State Park, 1,925 ft., 13 (OMNH); 1 mi. W Woodward, 1 (OKSU); 3.5 mi. WNW Woodward, 1,950 ft., 1 (OMNH).

Peromyscus maniculatus.—Specimens examined (total 875); ADAIR COUNTY: 3 mi. NNW Chewey, 1,000 ft., 6 (OMNH). ALFALFA COUNTY: 2 mi. NE Cherokee, 2 (CSUO); 3 mi. N, 6.5 mi. E Cherokee, 1,170 ft., 1 (OMNH); 3.5 mi. E Cherokee, 1 (OMNH). ATOKA COUNTY: 6 mi. W Atoka, 1 (OMNH). BEAVER COUNTY: 10.4 mi. E Elmwood, 1 (CAMCO). BECKHAM COUNTY: 3 mi. W, 1 mi. S Sayre, 1 (OKSU). BLAINE COUNTY: 7 mi. W, 2.5 mi. N Canton, 1 (OKSU); northeast side Canton Lake, 2 (OKSU); Canton Public Hunting Area, Longdale, 1 (OKSU); Roman Nose State Park, 3 (OKSU). BRYAN COUNTY: Colbert, 1 (TMM); 0.25 mi. W Colbert, 1 (TMM); 1 mi. W Colbert, 2 (TMM); 5 mi. N Colbert, 2 (TMM); 5 mi. W Colbert, 1 (TMM); 6 mi. NW Colbert, 1 (TMM). CADDO COUNTY: Caddo County, 2 (OMNH); 1.5 mi. E Cyril, 1 (CAMCO); 10 mi. N, 6 mi. W Ft. Cobb, 1 (CAMCO); Hinton, 1 (OMNH); Kiwanis Canyon, 1 mi. S Hinton, 1 (OKSU). CANADIAN COUNTY: 6 mi. E Hinton, 1 (OMNH); T12N, R9W, Sec. 5, north bank South Canadian River, 1 (OMNH); T12N, R10W, Sec. 17, south bank South Canadian River, 1 (OMNH). CARTER COUNTY: T1S, R3W, Sec. 2, SARP Site W7, Wildhorse Creek, 2 mi. E SH 76, 2 (OKSU). CHOCTAW COUNTY: 7 mi. SSE Ft. Towson, 400 ft., 2 (OMNH). CIMARRON COUNTY: Black Mesa, 3 (CAMCO); Black Mesa State Park, 8 (OMNH); Lake Etling, Black Mesa State Park, 2 (OMNH); Boise City, 1 (OKSU); W Boise City, 1 (OMNH); 3 mi. W Boise City, 1 (TTU); Regnier Ranch, 2 mi. S, 1 mi. E Kenton, 1 (CSUO); 2 mi. E, 6 mi. S Kenton, 8 (CAMCO); 2 mi. S, 6 mi. E Kenton, 4 (CAMCO); 2.5 mi. S Kenton, 2 (CAMCO); 2.5 mi. SE Kenton, 3 (CAMCO); 3 mi. N, 0.7 mi. W Kenton, 1 (OMNH); 4 mi. S Kenton, 1 (CAMCO); 4.2 mi. N, 0.1 mi. W Kenton, 1 (OMNH); 6 mi. SE Kenton, 1 (CAMCO); 7 mi. N Kenton, 1 (OKSU); 8 mi. SE Kenton, 2 (CAMCO); 8.5 mi. SE Kenton, 1 (CAMCO); 9 mi. SE Kenton, 3 (CAMCO); Lake Carl Etling, 1 (CAMCO). CLEVELAND COUNTY: Cleveland County, 7 (OMNH); 1 mi. E Noble, 6 (OMNH); 1.6 mi. SW Noble, 3 (OMNH); 2.5 mi. NE Noble, 16 (OMNH); city dump, Norman, 1 (OMNH); south shore from Norman dam, 1 (OMNH); University of Oklahoma, Norman, 1 (OMNH); 0.6 mi. S Norman, 1 (OMNH); 1.5 mi. N Norman, 2 (OMNH); 1.5 mi. S, 1.5 mi. W Norman, 1 (OMNH); 1.7 mi. N Norman, 9 (OMNH); 1.7 mi. S Norman, 1 (OMNH); 2 mi. E Norman, 2 (OMNH); 2 mi. N Norman, 1 (OMNH); 2 mi. S Norman, 3 (OMNH); 2 mi. SW Norman, 8 (OMNH); 2 mi. W, 1 mi. S Norman, 1 (OMNH); 2.25 mi. S Norman, 21 (OMNH); 2.5 mi. S Norman, 1 (OMNH); 3 mi. E Norman, 11 (OMNH); bank Little River, 3 mi. N, 2.5 mi. E Norman, 1 (OMNH); 3 mi. N, 2.5 mi. E Norman, 1 (OMNH); 3 mi. NW Norman, 1 (OMNH); 3 mi. W, 2 mi. S Norman, 1 (OMNH); 3.2 mi. N Norman, 27 (OMNH); 3.4 mi. S, 1.5 mi. E Norman, 8 (OMNH); 3.5 mi. NW Norman, 1 (OMNH); 3.5 mi. SE Norman, 2 (OMNH); 4 mi. S Norman, 6 (OMNH); 4 mi. SE Norman, 2 (OMNH); 5 mi. E Norman, 3 (OMNH); 5 mi. S Norman, 20 (OMNH); South Canadian River, 5 mi. SW Norman, 1 (OMNH); 5.6 mi. S Norman, 10 (OMNH); 6 mi. E, 0.5 mi. N Norman, 1 (OMNH); 6.5 mi. NE Norman, 8 (OMNH); 6.5 mi. SE Norman, 19 (OMNH); 7.4 mi. E Norman, 1 (OMNH); 8 mi. NW Norman, 14 (OMNH); Little River Reservoir, 11.7 mi. E Norman, 6 (OMNH); 11.7 mi. E Norman, 2 (OMNH); 2 mi. N Robinson St., 1 mi. W 77H, 1 (OMNH); island, W Hwy 77H, 1 (OMNH); T9N, R3W, 1 (OMNH); T9N, R3W, Sec. 32, South Canadian River, 2 (OMNH). COAL COUNTY: 1 mi. W, 2 mi. S Coalgate, 2 (OMNH). CO-MANCHE COUNTY: 0.5 mi. N, 2 mi. E Cache, 1 (CAMCO); 2 mi. S, 5 mi. W Cache, 2 (CAMCO); 4 mi. S Cache, 2 (CAMCO); 5 mi. S Cache, 1 (OKSU); 0.25 mi. W Cameron College, 1 (CAMCO); 8 mi. N Chatta-nooga, 1 (OKSU); Faxon, 1 (CAMCO); 3 mi. NW Faxon, 1 (CAMCO); 1 mi. S Ft. Sill, 1 (CAMCO); 1 mi. N Ft. Sill, 1 (CAMCO); 4 mi. W Ft. Sill Post Office, 1 (CAMCO); 4.5 mi. W Ft. Sill Post Office, 2 (CAMCO); NW Lake Lawtonka, Lawton, 1 (CAMCO); southwest shore Lake Lawtonka, 3 (CAMCO); west boundary fence, Lake Lawtonka, 1 (CAMCO); 1 mi. NW dam, Lake Lawtonka, 1 (CAMCO); 1 mi. W dam, Lake Lawtonka, 1 (CAMCO); Wichita Mountains, 10 mi. N, 10 mi. W Lawton, 2 (UIMNH); 12.5 mi. E, 4 mi. N Lawton, 1 (CAMCO); 20 mi. NW Lawton, 1 (UIMNH); Camp Boulder, Wichita Game Preserve, 1 (OMNH); central prairie, Wichita Mountains Wildlife Refuge, 1 (OKSU); Eagle Mt., Wichita Wildlife Refuge, 1 (OMNH); T3N, R14W, NE 1/4 Sec. 30, 1 (OMNH). COTTON COUNTY: 3.3 mi. ESE Taylor, 900 ft., 4 (OMNH); 5 mi. SE Taylor, 900 ft., 5 (OMNH); 5 mi. E, 3 mi. N Temple, 2 (CAMCO). CRAIG COUNTY: 3.5 mi. E, 0.5 mi. N Centralia, 2 (OMNH); 3.5 mi. W Vinita, 3 (OMNH). CUSTER COUNTY: 3 mi. W, 0.25 mi. N Thomas, 1 (OKSU); 3 mi. W, 0.25 mi. S Thomas, 1 (OKSU); 6 mi. W, 2 mi. N Thomas, 2 (OKSU); T15N, R16W, Sec. 16, 1 (OMNH). DELAWARE COUNTY: Spavinaw Creek, 12 mi. SE Jay, 6 (CSUO). ELLIS COUNTY: 13 mi. S, 1 mi. E Higgins, 2 (OKSU); 13.5 mi. S, 1 mi. E Higgins, 1 (OKSU); 1 mi. W Shattuck, 1 (CSUO); 5 mi. NNE Shattuck, 2 (OMNH); 5 mi. NNE Shattuck, 2,335 ft., 2 (OMNH). GARVIN COUNTY: T3N, R4W, Sec. 29, SARP Site R8, Rush Creek, 0.5 mi. W SH 76, 1 (OKSU). GRADY COUNTY: 4 mi. W Newcastle, 1 (CSUO). GREER COUNTY: Quartz Mt. State Park, 4 (OMNH). HARMON COUNTY: Buck Creek, extreme SW Oklahoma, 1 (TMM); 10 mi. S, 0.5 mi. E Gould, 1 (OKSU);

Harmon County, 3 (OMNH); N Hollis, 1 (FWMSH); prairie dog town, 2 mi. W, 1 mi. N Hollis, 1 (FWMSH); 5.5 mi. S Hollis, 9 (FWMSH); 6 mi. S, 1.5 mi. W Hollis, 2 (CAMCO); 8.5 mi. N Hollis, 1 (FWMSH); 11 mi. N Hollis, 1 (FWMSH); 12.5 mi. N, 7.5 mi. E Hollis, 2 (TTU); approx. 13 mi. N Hollis, 1 (FWMSH); 0.5 mi. W Hwy 30 & Elm Fork Red River, 2 (TTU); 8.75 mi. N, 2 mi. W Kirby's Corner, 1 (FWMSH); 6 mi. E, 1 mi. S Vinson, 1,700 ft., 10 (OMNH). HARPER COUNTY: pasture 26, Southern Great Plains Exp. Range, Ft. Supply, 2 (OKSU); pasture 28, Southern Great Plains Exp. Range, Ft. Supply, 1 (OKSU); Southern Great Plains Exp. Range, 2 (OKSU). HASKELL COUNTY: 0.5 mi. E, 4.5 mi. N Garland, 1 (OMNH); 6 mi. S Stigler, 1 (OMNH). HUGHES COUNTY: 1 mi. S, 1.5 mi. W Spaulding, 1 (CAMCO). JACKSON COUNTY: 1 mi. W, 5 mi. S Eldorado, 1 (OKSU); Olustee, 2 (UMMZ); 0.5 mi. N, 1 mi. E Olustee, 1 (CAMCO). JEFFERSON COUNTY: 1 mi. E Hastings, 1 (UIMNH). JOHNSTON COUNTY: 1 mi. E, 3 mi. S, 0.25 mi. E Tishomingo. 2 (OKSU); 2 mi. W Tishomingo, 3 (OKSU). KAY COUNTY: 2 mi. N Nardin, 1 (OKSU); T2S, R2E, Sec. 16, 1 (OKSU); T26N, R2E, SE 1/4 Sec. 18, 3 (OKSU). KINGFISHER COUNTY: T9N, R5W, Sec. 30, 5 (OMNH); T17N, R5W, Sec. 30, 1 (OMNH). KIOWA COUNTY: on banks Elk Creek, Hobart, 1 (OKSU); 6.5 mi. S, 2 mi. E Roosevelt, 1 (OKSU); 4 mi. W, 1.75 mi. N Snyder. 1 (CAMCO). LEFLORE COUNTY: Billy Creek Camp, 7 mi. NW Big Cedar, 1 (OMNH); 1 mi. W Honobia, 2 (OKSU); 2.5 mi. NE Stapp, 1 (OMNH); 2.5 mi. NW Stapp, 4 (OMNH); 1.5 mi. NE Zoe, 1 (OMNH). LOGAN COUNTY: 4.5 mi. S, 2 mi. W Guthrie, 2 (CSUO); Logan County, 1 (OMNH); Vickers Study Plot, jct. Bryant & Waterloo Rd., 2 (CSUO). MAJOR COUNTY: near Alabaster Caverns State Park, 2 (CSUO); 8 mi. E Alabaster Caverns, 1 (CSUO); 2 mi. W Ames, 1 (OKSU); canyon on Ewers Creek, 2 mi. W Bouse Jct., 1 (OKSU); 2 mi. E, 4 mi. N Cleo Springs, 1 (OKSU); 3 mi. S Cleo Springs, 2 (OMNH); 11 mi. SW Cleo Springs, 2 (OMNH); Griever Creek, 1 (UMMZ); 1 mi. E Orienta, 1 (OKSU); Vickery Ranch, 1 (OKSU); 5.5 mi. S Waynoka, 1,450 ft., 4 (OMNH). MAYES COUNTY: 2.25 mi. S Big Cabin, 1 (OKSU); 2.6 mi. E Chouteau, 0.4 mi. N Hwy 33, 1 (OMNH); 2.7 mi. E Chouteau, 0.8 mi. N Hwy 33, 2 (OMNH); 2.8 mi. E Chouteau, 0.4 mi. N Hwy 33, 2 (OMNH); 3.1 mi. E Chouteau, 1 (OMNH); 3.1 mi. E Chouteau, 0.3 mi. N Hwy 33, 22 (OMNH); 3.1 mi. E Chouteau, Hwy 33, 1 (OMNH); 3.2 mi. E Chouteau, 0.5 mi. N Hwy 33, 1 (OMNH); 3.2 mi. E Chouteau, 1.4 mi. N Hwy 33, 1 (OMNH); 3.3 mi. E Chouteau, 0.6 mi. N Hwy 33, 1 (OMNH); 3.6 mi. E Chouteau, Hwy 33, 1 (OMNH); south end low water dam, Grand River, 1 (OKSU). MCCLAIN COUNTY: 4 mi. S, 1.2 mi. W Goldsby, 1 (OMNH); T8N, R4W, Sec. 11, Grass Lake Reservoir Station, 2 (OMNH); Johnson's Pasture, 1 (OMNH); McClain County,

4 (OMNH); 9 mi. W Norman, 2 (OMNH); South Canadian River Bridge, 1 (OKSU); T8N, R4W, NE 1/4 Sec. 11, 1 (OMNH). MCINTOSH COUNTY: 3 mi. NW Faxon, 1 (CAMCO). MURRAY COUNTY: 1.3 mi. S, 2.2 mi. W Davis, 1 (CSUO). MUSKOGEE COUNTY: Wildlife Conservation Station, Braggs, 1 (OKSU); Camp Gruber Area, 1 (OKSU); 2 mi. S Ft. Gibson, 2 (OKSU); 5 mi. SE Muskogee, 1 (OKSU); 6 mi. SE Muskogee, 2 (OMNH); 8 mi. ESE Muskogee, 4 (OMNH); 3 mi. E Wainwright, 22 (OMNH). NOBLE COUNTY: Red Rock Creek, 13 mi. S Ponca City, 2 (OKSU); 5.5 mi. W, 4 mi. N Red Rock, 1 (OKSU); 1.4 mi. N, 2.1 mi. W Watchorn, 4 (OMNH); T22N, R2E, SE 1/4 Sec. 34, 1 (OKSU); 1 mi. E jct. Hwys 177 & 15, 7 (OMNH); 2.5 mi. N jct. Hwys 177 & 15E, 1 (OMNH). NOWATA COUNTY: Paul Buck Ranch, 2 mi. NW Wann, 1 (OKSU). OKLAHOMA COUNTY: E Edmond, 1 (OKSU); 33rd & Broadway, Edmond, 2 (CSUO); Witcher, 1.5 mi. E, 3 mi. S Edmond, 1 (CSUO); jct. 8th & University, Edmond, 1 (CSUO); 0.5 mi. E, 1 mi. N Jones Post Office, 1 (CSUO); Lake Hefner, 2 (OKSU); NE Oklahoma City, 1 (OMNH); Oklahoma City, 2 (OKSU); 0.5 mi. ENE 51st Frontage Rd., Oklahoma City, 1 (OMNH); jct. 122nd & N. Pennsylvania, Oklahoma City, 1 (CSUO); 0.5 mi. N. jct. 150th & N. Rockwell, 5 (CSUO); 0.5 mi. N Memorial on Rockwell, 2 (CSUO); 0.5 mi. E Sarah Rd. on 122nd St., 1 (CSUO); Terra Regal Trailer Park, 1 (CSUO); 4 mi. S of 29th St., 1 (OKSU); T13N, R3W, Sec. 30, 1 (OMNH). OKMULGEE COUNTY: 3 mi. E, 2 mi. N Okmulgee, 2 (OMNH). OSAGE COUNTY: Osage Creek, 8 mi. W Bartlesville, 3 (OKSU); 10 mi. WSW Fairfax, 1,000 ft., 3 (OMNH); 5 mi. S Pawhuska, 1 (OKSU); 1 mi. NW Tulsa, 2 (OKSU). OTTAWA COUNTY: 5 mi. N SH 10 over Spring River, 1 (OKSU); 3 mi. W Wyandotte, 2 (OMNH). PAWNEE COUNTY: 26 mi. N, 4 mi. E Stillwater, 1 (OKSU); 1.0 mi. N, 0.5 mi. W Watchorn, 2 (OMNH); 1.3 mi. N, 1.5 mi. W Watchorn, 3 (OMNH); 1.4 mi. N, 1.9 mi. W Watchorn, 6 (OMNH); 1.5 mi. N, 1.0 mi. W Watchorn, 2 (OMNH); 1.5 mi. N, 1.5 mi. W Watchorn, 2 (OMNH); 2.5 mi. N, 0.5 mi. E Watchorn, 6 (OMNH); 2.6 mi. N, 1.1 mi. W Watchorn, 4 (OMNH); 1 mi. E, 3.5 mi. N Yale, 1 (OKSU). PAYNE COUNTY: Boomer Lake, 4 (OKSU); north side Boomer Lake, 1 (OKSU); northeast side Boomer Lake, 1 (OKSU); 0.5 mi. E Boomer Lake, 1 (OKSU); 1 mi. N Boomer Lake, 1 (OKSU); College Farm, 1 (OKSU); 4 mi. W Cushing, 1 (OKSU); 2 mi. S Ingalls, 1 (OKSU); Lake Carl Blackwell, 14 (OKSU); camp area, S Lake Blackwell, 1 (OKSU); Lake Carl Blackwell Dam, 1 (OKSU); Lake McMurtry, 2 (OKSU); Physical Plant Services dump, N Married Student Housing, Oklahoma State University, 1 (OKSU); 3 mi. E, 3.5 mi. S Perkins, 1 (OKSU); 5.5 mi. N, 2 mi. E jct. 6th St. & Perkins Rd., 2 (OKSU); 6 mi. SE Perkins, 1 (OKSU); 0.25 mi. N Sanborn Lake, 1 (OKSU); 0.1 mi. N SH 51 on Sangre Rd., 1

(OKSU); Sanborn Lake City Park, 0.125 mi. E Stillwater Municipal Airport, 1 (OKSU); Stillwater, 5 (OKSU); near Boomer Lake, Stillwater, 1 (OKSU); Boomer Lake Dam, 3 mi. N Stillwater, 1 (OKSU); by Boomer Lake, N Stillwater, 1 (OKSU); Hillcrest Golf Course, Stillwater, 1 (OKSU); 0.5 mi. E, 4 mi. N Stillwater, 2 (OKSU); 0.5 mi. N Stillwater, 2 (OKSU); 1 mi. E Stillwater, 1 (OKSU); 1 mi. E, 2.5 mi. N Stillwater, 2 (OKSU); 1 mi. N Stillwater, 2 (OKSU); 1 mi. N, 1.5 mi. E Stillwater, 1 (OKSU); 1 mi. N, 2 mi. E Stillwater, 1 (OKSU); 1 mi. W Stillwater, 5 (OKSU); 1 mi. W Stillwater on McElroy St., 2 (OKSU); 1 mi. W Stillwater on SH 51 & 1 mi. S, 1 (OKSU); 1.25 mi. E Boomer Rd. & 32nd St., Stillwater, 1 (OKSU); 1.4 mi. W Orchard & McElroy Sts., Stillwater, 1 (OKSU); 1.5 mi. W Stillwater, 2 (OKSU); 1.5 mi. W, 1 mi. S Stillwater, 1 (OKSU); 2 mi. E Stillwater, 1 (OKSU); 2 mi. E, 1 mi. S Stillwater, 1 (OKSU); 2 mi. N Stillwater, 1 (OKSU); 2 mi. S 19th St. on Sangre Rd., Stillwater, 1 (OKSU); 2 mi. S, 2 mi. W Stillwater, 1 (OKSU); 2 mi. W Stillwater, 3 (OKSU); 3 mi. N, 1 mi. W Stillwater, 1 (OKSU); 3 mi. N, 0.5 mi. W Stillwater, US Hwy 177, 1 (OKSU); 3 mi. S Stillwater, 1 (OKSU); 3 mi. S, 1.5 mi. E Stillwater, 1 (OKSU); 3 mi. W Stillwater, 3 (OKSU); 4 mi. N, 2 mi. W Stillwater, 1 (OKSU); 4 mi. W Stillwater, 1 (OKSU); 5 mi. W Stillwater, 0.25 mi. N SH 51, 1 (OKSU); 8 mi. W, 2 mi. S Stillwater, 1 (OKSU); 9 mi. W Stillwater, 2 (OKSU); 9 mi. W, 1 mi. N Stillwater, 1 (OKSU); Lake Carl Blackwell, 9 mi. W Stillwater, 1 (OKSU); 10 mi. W, 2 mi. N Stillwater, 1 (OKSU); 10 mi. W Stillwater, 1 (OKSU); Twin Lakes, 10.5 mi. S Stillwater, 1 (OKSU); 11 mi. E Stillwater, 1 (OKSU); 12.2 mi. W Stillwater on Hwy 51 & jct. of 51C, 1 (OKSU); 13 mi. W, 2 mi. N Stillwater, 2 (OKSU); 4.5 mi. S on Hwy 177 from Hwy 51, 1 (OKSU); T17N, R1E, Sec. 10, 1 (OKSU). PITTSBURG COUNTY: 12 mi. S Hartshorne, 1 (OKSU). PONTOTOC COUNTY: Pontotoc County, 1 (OKSU). POTTAWATOMIE COUNTY: 1.3 mi. WSW Pink, 3 (OMNH); T11N, R5E, NE 1/4 Sec. 1, 1 (CSUO). ROGER MILLS COUNTY: 5 mi. N Cheyenne, 2,100 ft., 1 (OMNH); 2.5 mi. E, 1.5 mi. S Reydon, 18 (CAMCO). ROGERS COUNTY: 0.5 mi. W Chelsea High School, 1 (OKSU); 8 mi. W, 1.5 mi. S Chelsea, 1 (OKSU); 3 mi. N, 1 mi. W Foyil, 3 (OMNH); 0.5 mi. E Oologah Dam Office, Oologah, 1 (OKSU); 1 mi. N Oologah Dam Office, Oologah, 1 (OKSU). SEMINOLE COUNTY: Seminole, 1 (OKSU). TEXAS COUNTY: 3 mi. NW Guymon, 1 (OKSU); near Palo Duro River, 10 mi. E Hardesty, 1 (TTU). TILLMAN COUNTY: 3 mi. S, 0.5 mi. E Davidson, 1 (CAMCO); T3S, R14W, Sec. 28, 1 (OMNH). TULSA COUNTY: Garnett, 20 (OKSU), 10 (UMMZ); 0.25 mi. E of Memorial Rd. on 46th St. N., Tulsa, 1 (OKSU). WAGONER COUNTY: 2.5 mi. SSW Coweta, 600 ft., 5 (OMNH). WASHINGTON COUNTY: 0.25 mi. S Bartlesville, 2 (OKSU); 11 mi. SW Bartlesville, 1 (OKSU). WASHITA

COUNTY: Clyde Price Farm, 2 mi. W Burns Flat, 1 (TTU); 5 mi. N, 2 mi. W Corn, 3 (CSUO). WOODS COUNTY: 6 mi. NW Alva, 1 (OMNH), 1 (OKSU); 6.5 mi. NW Alva, 2 (OMNH); 8.5 mi. NW Alva, 2 (OMNH); 2 mi. E Camp Houston, 1 (OKSU); 2 mi. W Edith, 7 (OMNH); Waynoka, 1 (UMMZ); 3 mi. SW Waynoka, 4 (OMNH); 5 mi. S Waynoka, 1,400 ft., 2 (OMNH); 5 mi. S Waynoka, 1,450 ft., 7 (OMNH). WOODWARD COUNTY: Selmon Ranch, 8 mi. W Alabaster Caverns, 2 (CSUO); Selman Ranch, 6 mi. SW Freedom, 1 (CSUO); 5.7 mi. S, 9.2 mi. W Freedom, 1 (CSUO); Garrison Property, 9.5 mi. N, 2 mi. E Woodward, 1 (OKSU).

Peromyscus truei.—Specimens examined (total 188); CIMARRON COUN-TY: Cimarron County, 1 (OMNH); Kenton, 1 (OMNH); E Kenton, 1 (OMNH); 0.25 mi. NE Kenton, 1 (OMNH); 0.75 mi. E, 0.25 mi. N Ken-ton, 6 (OMNH); Black Mesa, 0.25 mi. E Kenton, 1 (OMNH); 0.25 mi. E Kenton, 1 (OMNH); 0.5 mi. E Kenton, 1 (OMNH); T4N, R1E, Sec. 5, 4.5 mi. S, 0.5 mi. W Kenton, 1 (OMNH); 1.25 mi. N Kenton, 4,200 ft., 7 (OMNH); 2 mi. E Kenton, 1 (OMNH); Black Mesa, 2 mi. E Kenton, 1 (OMNH); 2 mi. E, 6 mi. S Kenton, 4 (CAMCO); 2.25 mi. N Kenton, 9 (OMNH); 2.5 mi. SE Kenton, 1 (CAMCO); 2.6 mi. S, 1.5 mi. E Kenton, 6 (OMNH); T5N, R2E, Sec. 34, 1 mi. E, 2.75 mi. N Kenton, 1 (OMNH); T5N, R2E, Sec. 18, 1 mi. E, 2.75 mi. N Kenton, Black Mesa, 3 (OMNH); 3 mi. N Kenton, 1 (OMNH); 3 mi. N, 0.7 mi. W Kenton, 3 (OMNH); Black Mesa, 3 mi. NE Kenton, 2 (OMNH); 3 mi. NE Kenton, 1 (UIMNH); 3.4 mi. S, 1.2 mi. E Kenton, 9 (OMNH); 3.5 mi. N, 1 mi. E Kenton, 3 (OMNH); 3.5 mi. N, 1.2 mi. W Kenton, 3 (OMNH); 3.6 mi. N, 1.1 mi. W Kenton, 13 (OMNH); 3.6 mi. S, 0.9 mi. E Kenton, 4 (OMNH); 3.9 mi. N, 0.5 mi. W Kenton, 11 (OMNH); 2.5 mi. S Kenton, 1 (CAMCO); 2.5 mi. SE Kenton, 4,200 ft., 29 (OMNH); 4 mi. S, 0.7 mi. E Kenton, 4 (OMNH); 4 mi. N Kenton, 10 (KU); 2.6 mi. NNE Kenton, 4,200 ft., 1 (OMNH); 4.1 mi. S, 1.9 mi. E Kenton, 6 (OMNH); 4.2 mi. N, 0.1 mi. W Kenton, 1 (OMNH); 4.2 mi. S Kenton, 1 (OMNH); 4.2 mi. S, 0.5 mi. E Kenton, 12 (OMNH); 4.2 mi. S, 0.5 mi. W Kenton, 3 (OMNH); 4.2 mi., S, 0.8 mi. W Kenton, 8 (OMNH); 4.4 mi. N, 0.4 mi. W Kenton, 5 (OMNH); 3.1 mi. N Kenton, 4,200 ft., 1 (OMNH); 3.1 mi. N Kenton, 4,950 ft., 3 (OMNH); Carrizo Creek, 6 mi. N Kenton, 1 (OKSU); 6 mi. N Kenton, 3 (OKSU); 7 mi. N Kenton, 1 (OKSU); Regnier Ranch, 8 mi. S Kenton, 1 (ECENT).

Pipistrellus hesperus.—Specimens examined (total 43): COMANCHE COUNTY: W Cache Creek at Refuge Boundary, 1 (OKSU); Ft. Sill, 1 (CAMCO); Easter Pageant Area, Wichita Mts., 1 (OKSU). GREER COUNTY: Custer Cave, near Granite, 2 (OKSU); north side Granite Mt., 11 (OKSU); quarry pond, south side Granite Mt., 3 (OKSU); Sulphur Springs Pond, north side Granite Mt., 2 (OKSU); 1 mi. N Granite, 3

(OKSU); 1 mi. NE Granite, 2 (OKSU); 1.25 mi. N Granite, 2 (USNM); 1.5 mi. N Granite, 1 (OKSU); southeast corner Quartz Mt. State Park, 1 (OKSU). KIOWA COUNTY: 2 mi. S Lugert, 1 (OKSU); Svoboda Pond, NW Mountain Park, 1 (OKSU); Svoboda Pond, 1 mi. W, 0.5 mi. N Mountain Park, 6 (OKSU); Svoboda Pond, 1 mi. W, 0.5 mi. N Mountain Park, 1 (USNM); north side Radziminski Mt., 4 (OKSU).

Pipistrellus subflavus.—Specimens examined (total 354): ADAIR COUNTY: Adair Cave, 2 (OKSU); Crystal Cave, near Bunch, 21 (OKSU); Spring Cave, 1 mi. N Bunch, 1 (UIMNH); Crystal Cave, 4 mi. SW Bunch, 900 ft., 4 (OMNH); Cave Spring Cave, 3 (UIMNH), 3 (OKSU); 3 mi. NNW Chewey, 1,000 ft., 11 (OMNH); Adair Cave, 3 mi. NNW Chewey, 1,000 ft., 1 (OMNH); 3 mi. NNW Chewey, 1,100 ft., 1 (OMNH); Adair Cave, 3 mi. NW Chewey, 2 (OMNH); Duncan Cave, 3 mi. SSE Colcord, 4 (OKSU); Crystal Cave, 3 (OKSU); Crystal Cave, southwest corner Adair County, 1 (UIMNH); Huggins Ranch, 8 mi. S, 3 mi. E jct. Hwys 59 & 100, 1 (OKSU); cave on Huggins Ranch, 8 mi. S, 5 mi. E jct. Hwys 59 & 100, 1 (OKSU); bat cave, 4.5 mi. SSE Kansas, 16 (UIMNH); bat cave, 5 mi. S Kansas, 10 (OKSU); 2.5 mi. N Lyons, 1 (OKSU); 4 mi. E Oaks, 2 (MSU); Petkoff's Large Cave, 4 (OKSU); Stilwell, 13 (USNM); 7 mi. W Stilwell, Ross Mt. Cave, 4 (KU); 9 mi. S Stilwell, 3 (UMMZ); 25 mi. SW Stilwell, 13 (OKSU); T19N, R24E, Sec. 20, bat cave, 1 (OKSU). CHEROKEE COUNTY: Cherokee County, 3 (OKSU); Cottonwood Cave, 2 (OKSU); 0.5 mi. NW Gideon, 1 (OKSU); Etta Cave, east side Lake Tenkiller, across from Carter's Landing, 1 (CSUO); Muskogee Scout Camp, 1 (OKSU); Scraper, 4 (UMMZ). COMANCHE COUNTY: Penick Tunnel, West Cache Creek, Canton Hunting Area, 1 (OKSU); 5 mi. N, 2 mi. W Meers, 1 (CAMCO); Penick Tunnel, West Cache Creek, Wichita Mountains Wildlife Refuge, 1 (OKSU); Penick Tunnel, Wichita Refuge, 3 (OKSU). CUSTER COUNTY: 5 mi. S, 5 mi. W Weatherford, 2 (KU). DELAWARE COUNTY: 1 mi. E, 3 mi. S Colcord, 1 (OKSU); Duncan Cave, 2.5 mi. SE Colcord, 1,100 ft., 8 (OMNH); Mitchell Farm, Spavinaw Creek, 4.25 mi. N Colcord, 1 (OMNH); Spavinaw Creek, 4.25 mi. N Colcord, 3 (OMNH); Spavinaw Creek, 4.5 mi. N Colcord, 900 ft., 1 (OMNH); 6.6 mi. NW Colcord, 800 ft., 2 (OMNH); Roberts Cave, 6.6 mi. NW Colcord, 800 ft., 6 (OMNH); Stansbury Cave, 6.6 mi. NW Colcord, 10 (OMNH); Twin Caves, 7 mi. SE Disney, Arrowhead Pt., Brand Lake, 1 (ECENT), 1 (FWMSH); Twin Caves, 7 mi. SE Disney, 3 (OKSU); Twin Caves, 8 mi. SE Disney, 1 (OKSU); Twin Caves, 10 mi. SE Disney, 4 (OKSU); Dunaway Cave, 5 mi. W, 3.5 mi. N Jay, 1 (OKSU); Twin Cave, 7 mi. NW Jay, 1,000 ft., 2 (OMNH); 7.5 mi. NE Jay, 950 ft., 1 (OMNH); Spavinaw Creek Cave, 7.5 mi. SE Jay, 3 (CSUO); cave, Spavinaw Creek, 8 mi. SSE Jay, 1 (CSUO); Sutherland Cave, 1 mi. W Maysville, 1 (OKSU);

Cochrans Trout Cave, 3 mi. NW Maysville, 1 (OKSU); 1.5 mi. S, 1 mi. E Spavinaw, 2 (KU); 0.75 mi. W Upper Spavinaw Dam, 13 (KU); cave, 1 mi. N Spavinaw Dam, 2 (OKSU); 0.5 mi. NW Upper Spavinaw Lake Dam, 800 ft., 4 (OMNH); Spavinaw Game Refuge, 1 (CSUO); Black Hollow Cave, south side Spavinaw Lake, 2 (OKSU); Stansbury Cave, 3 (OKSU); Cayton Cave, 6 mi. E Sycamore, 3 (OMNH); Sutherland Cave, 6.5 mi. E Sycamore, 1 (OMNH); Summerfield Creek, 2.5 mi. N Topsy, 1 (OKSU); Wooden Door Cave, 2.5 mi. N Topsy, 1 (OKSU); Wooden Door Cave, 3 mi. N Topsy, 1 (OKSU); Twin Caves, 4 mi. N Trading Post, 2 (ECENT); T22N, R24E, Sec. 32, 2 (OMNH). GREER COUNTY: Jester Cave, 10 mi. S Delhi, 1 (OKSU); Jester Cave, 1 (OKSU); 3.5 mi. N Jester, 2 (OKSU). HARMON COUNTY: 3 mi. W, 1 mi. S Reed, 1 (OKSU); 6.5 mi. SE Vinson, 3 (CAMCO). HUGHES COUNTY: 8.5 mi. SE Wetumka, 1 (OKSU). KAY COUNTY: 0.5 mi. E Main St., Ponca City, 1 (OKSU); 1 mi. E Ponca City, 1 (OKSU). KIOWA COUNTY: Windmill Cave, 15 mi. S, 2 mi. W Carnegie, 1 (OKSU). LATIMER COUNTY: 3.5 mi. N Wilburton, 2 (OMNH). LEFLORE COUNTY: 6.5 mi. W Heavener, 1 (OMNH); Little River Bridge at Honobia, 4 (OKSU); Kiamichi Mt. Cave, 1 (OKSU); Kiamichi Mt. Cave, S Muse, 3 (OKSU); Bear Den Cave, 11 mi. NE Talihina on SH 1, 1 (OKSU); 12 mi. NE Talihina on SH 1, 1 (OKSU); 1.5 mi. NE Zoe, 2 (OMNH). MAJOR COUNTY: 2.5 mi. W Hwy 280, 1 (CSUO); T22N, R16W, Sec. 15, 2.3 mi. S, 0.4 mi. W jct. Hwys 281 & 15, 1 (OMNH); Nescatunga Cave, 2.5 mi. W jct. Hwys 281 & 15, 3 (CSUO); 2.5 mi. W jct. US 281 & Hwy 51, 1 (OKSU); Whitlaw Ranch, 1 (CSUO). MCCURTAIN COUNTY: 14 mi. SE Broken Bow, 13 (OMNH); Forked Lake, S Eagletown, 2 (OKSU); Red River, 1 (OMNH); Rock Creek, 1 (CSUO); 2 mi. W Smithville, 3 (OMNH); 4 mi. E, 3 mi. S Tom, 1 (OKSU); 6 mi. S Tom, 2 (TMM). MURRAY COUNTY: Little Crystal Cave, 2 (OKSU); T15, R15, SE 1/4 Sec. 36, Little Crystal Cave, 1 (OMNH); Mystic Cave, 3 (OKSU); 10 mi. S, 2 mi. E Sulphur, 4 (OMNH); Turner Falls Cave, 2 (OKSU); 0.5 mi. S Turner Falls, 2 (OKSU); 2 mi. S Turner Falls, 1 (OKSU). MUSKOGEE COUNTY: Braggs, 1 (OKSU); Big Greenleaf above Lake, 3 (OKSU); Big Greenleaf Creek, 1 (OKSU). OKLAHOMA COUNTY: Edmond, 1 (CSUO). OTTAWA COUNTY: Boy Scout Cave, 3 (OKSU); 2 mi. S, 2 mi. E Fairland, 1 (OKSU); Ottawa County, 2 (OMNH); W Peoria, 1 (OKSU); 11 mi. S, 2 mi. W Wyandotte, 3 (OKSU). PONTOTOC COUNTY: cave, N Pontotoc, 1 (ECENT). PUSHMATAHA COUNTY: Bower's Trail Cave, 4 (OKSU). SEMINOLE COUNTY: approx. 20 mi. SSE Seminole, 1 (ECENT). SEQUOYAH COUNTY: cave, 5 mi. N Marble City, 1 (OKSU). TULSA COUNTY: Garnett, 4 (UMMZ); 8 mi. W Red Fork, 3 (USNM). WASHITA COUNTY: cave, 0.75 mi. off Hwy, 4 mi. W Cordell on SH 152, 1 (OKSU); Corn

Cave, 3 (CSUO); Water Cave, 5 mi. NE, 2 mi. W Corn, 1 (CSUO); Corn Caves, 5 mi. N, 2 mi. W Corn, 3 (CSUO); T11N, R15W, Sec. 5, 5.5 mi. N, 2 mi. W Corn, 2 (CSUO); Gypsum Caves, 6 mi. W, 4.5 mi. S Weatherford, 2 (OKSU). WOODWARD COUNTY: Alabaster Caverns, 3 (OKSU); Alabaster Caverns, 6 mi. S Freedom, 1 (OKSU).

Plecotus rafinesquii.—Specimens examined (total 5): MCCURTAIN COUNTY: 2.5 mi. W Smithville, 5 (OMNH).

Plecotus townsendii.—Specimens examined (total 222): ADAIR COUNTY: Cave Springs Cave, 3 (OKSU). BLAINE COUNTY: Hitchcock, 1 (OKSU); Salt Creek Canyon, 15 (KU); head Little Branch Salt Creek, 3 mi. SE Southard, 1 (KU). CIMARRON COUNTY: Tesesquite Canyon Cave, 4 (OKSU). COMANCHE COUNTY: 6.5 mi. N, 2 mi. E Indiahoma, 1 (CAMCO); abandoned mine, Wichita Mountains Wildlife Refuge, 1 (OKSU); Cache Creek, Wichita Mountains Wildlife Refuge, 1 (OKSU); Elk Mt., Wichita Mountains Wildlife Refuge, 11 (OMNH); southwest slope Elk Mt., Wichita Mountains Wildlife Refuge, 1 (OMNH); mine shaft, 0.75 mi. below Camp Boulder, Wichita Mountains Wildlife Refuge, 3 (USNM). CUSTER COUNTY: 5 mi. W, 5 mi. S Weatherford, 1 (KU). GREER COUNTY: Jester Cave, 1 (OKSU); 7 mi. S Mangum, 2 (OMNH); 1 mi. S, 2 mi. W Reed, 8 (KU); 3 mi. SW Reed, 1 (CAMCO); 3 mi. W, 1.5 mi. S Reed, 2 (CAMCO), 5 (OKSU); T4N, R24W, Sec. 28, 1 (OMNH). HARMON COUNTY: Reed Tunnel Cave, 4 (OKSU); 1 mi. W, 1 mi. S Reed, 1 (OMNH); T4N, R24W, Sec. 28, 2 mi. W, 1.5 mi. S Reed, 1 (OMNH); 3 mi. SW Reed, 1 (CAMCO); 3 mi. W, 1 mi. S Reed, 1 (OKSU); 3 mi. W, 1.5 mi. S Reed, 1 (CAMCO); 2 mi. E, 1 mi. S Vincent, 1 (OKSU); 7 mi. E, 1 mi. S Vincent, 2 (OKSU), 4 (USNM); 7 mi. E, 1.5 mi. S Vincent, 1 (OKSU); 6 mi. E, 1 mi. S Vinson, 1,700 ft., 5 (OMNH); 6.5 mi. ESE Vinson, 1,700 ft., 6 (OMNH); 6.5 mi. SE Vinson, 2 (OMNH). KIOWA COUNTY: Frisko Mt., 1 (OKSU); 2 mi. S, 1 mi. W Lugert, 3 (KU); Radziminski Mt. Cave, 4 (OKSU); Svoboda Cave, 3 (OKSU). MAJOR COUNTY: Vickery Cave, 3 mi. W Bouse Jct., 1 (OKSU); 3 mi. W, 2 mi. N Bouse Jct., 2 (OKSU); Griever Creek Cave, 1 (OKSU); T22N, R16W, Sec. 15, 2.3 mi. S, 0.4 mi. W jct. Hwys 281 & 15, 1 (OMNH); Nescatunga Cave, 2.5 mi. W jct. Hwys 281 & 15, 13 (CSUO). WASHITA COUNTY: Corn Cave, 5 (OKSU); 4 mi. S, 6 mi. W Weatherford, 2 (OKSU). WOODS COUNTY: 6 mi. S, 2 mi. W Aetna, Kansas, 3 (KU); Anderson Creek Cave, 2 (OKSU); 2 mi. W Edith, 1 (OMNH); cave, 2.5 mi. E Houston, 1 (OMNH); Merrihew Cave, 7 (OKSU); T29, R17W, Sec. 17, Merrihew Cave, 1 (OKSU); Merrihew Cave, 0.5 mi. S Oklahoma-Kansas Line, 43 (KU). WOODWARD COUNTY: Alabaster Caverns, 12 (OKSU); caves, S Freedom, 1 (OKSU); Alabaster Caverns, 4 mi. S Freedom, 5 (OKSU); cave, 6 mi. SW Freedom, 5 (OMNH); 10 mi. S Freedom,

1 (UMMZ); Quinlan Cave, 1 (OKSU); 2 mi. E Quinlan, 2 (OKSU); Ice-box Cave, Selman Ranch, 6 (OKSU); Woodward County, 2 (OUBS).

Procyon lotor.—Specimens examined (total 141): ADAIR COUNTY: 25 mi. SW Stilwell, 4 (OKSU). CADDO COUNTY: Ft. Cobb, 1 (CAMCO). CARTER COUNTY: 9 mi. N, 7 mi. E Ardmore, 1 (KU). CHOCTAW COUNTY: Oil Well Creek, 1 mi. N Ft. Towson, 1 (CSUO). CIMARRON COUNTY: Kenton, 1 (KU); 2.5 mi. SE Kenton, 4,200 ft., 1 (OMNH); 6 mi. N Kenton, 1 (OKSU). CLEVELAND COUNTY: Cleveland County, 2 (OMNH); Noble, 1 (OMNH); 0.25 mi. W jct. Lindsey St. & I-35, Nor-man, 1 (OMNH); 2 mi. S Norman, 1 (OMNH); 5 mi. NW Norman on Hwy 74, 1 (OMNH); 5.5 mi. E Norman, 1 (OMNH); Self Ranch, 6.5 mi. E Norman, 2 (OMNH); Little River, 11 mi. E Norman, 1 (OMNH); Skin-ner Ranch, 9 mi. E, 3 mi. S Purcell on Hwy 39, 2 (OMNH); 2 mi. S Slaughterville, 1 (OMNH); Vaught Ranch, 3 mi. E, 0.75 mi. S Slaugh-terville, 1 (OMNH). COMANCHE COUNTY: 2.5 mi. NW Elgin, 1 (CAMCO); 2.5 mi. N Faxon, 2 (CAMCO); 5 mi. N Faxon, 1 (CAMCO); 2 mi. ENE Ft. Sill, 1 (CAMCO); Lawton, 2 (CAMCO); 1.5 mi. SE Lawton, 1 (CAMCO); 2.5 mi. SE Lawton, 1 (CAMCO); 4 mi. E, 3 mi. S Lawton, 1 (CAMCO); 4.2 mi. E Lawton, 1 (CAMCO); 7 mi. S Lawton. 1 (CAMCO); 2.5 mi. E, 1 mi. N Medicine Park, 1 (CAMCO); 1.5 mi. N Meers, 1 (OMNH); 3 mi. E Meers, 1 (CAMCO); Mt. Scott, 5 (USNM); Cache, Post Oak Camp Ground, Wichita Mountains Wildlife Refuge, 1 (USNM); Wichita Mountains Wildlife Refuge, 4 (USNM), 1 (OMNH); Wichita Natl. Forest, 1 (KU). CUSTER COUNTY: 2.5 mi. SW Thomas, 2 (KU); 1 mi. W, 0.5 mi. S Weatherford, 1 (KU); 8 mi. N, 4 mi. E Weatherford, 1 (KU); T14N, R16E, Sec. 32, 1 (OMNH). DELAWARE COUNTY: 4 mi. SE Colcord, 1 (OKSU). DEWEY COUNTY: 6 mi. E Seiling, 1 (OKSU). GARFIELD COUNTY: 3.1 mi. N Waukomis on US Hwy 81, 1 (OKSU). GARVIN COUNTY: 2 mi. S Antioch, 1 (OMNH). GRADY COUNTY: 5 mi. N, 4 mi. W Chickasha, 1 (OKSU). HARMON COUNTY: 2.5 mi. W, 2 mi. S Reed, 1 (CAMCO). HUGHES COUNTY: Holdenville, 1 (CSUO); Hughes County, 1 (ECENT). JOHNSTON COUNTY: 3 mi. NW Manns-ville, 1 (OKSU). KAY COUNTY: Ponca City, 1 (CSUO). KINGFISHER COUNTY: 14 mi. W Crescent, 1 (OKSU). LATIMER COUNTY: Wil-burton, 1 (OKSU). LINCOLN COUNTY: 3 mi. N, 4 mi. W Meeker, 1 (OKSU). LOGAN COUNTY: T18N, R4W, Sec. 2, 1 (OMNH). MAR-SHALL COUNTY: Willis, 1 (OUBS). MAYES COUNTY: 3 mi. S, 0.5 mi. W Adair, 1 (OKSU). MCCLAIN COUNTY: 10 mi. SW Purcell, 1 (OKSU); 5 mi. E Rosedale, 1 (ECENT). MCCURTAIN COUNTY: 4 mi. S, 4 mi. E Broken Bow, 1 (OKSU); State Game Preserve, 10 mi. N Hochatown, 1 (OMNH). NOBLE COUNTY: S Ponca City, 1 (OKSU); 16 mi. N on Hwy 177, Stillwater, 1 (OKSU). NOWATA COUNTY: 2 mi. S, 2 mi. E Coffeyville, 2 (OKSU). OKFUSKEE COUNTY: 2 mi. E, 5 mi. N Okemah, 2 (OKSU); 10 mi. E Okemah, 1 (OMNH). OKLAHOMA COUNTY: 5 mi. W Edmond, 1 (CSUO); 6 mi. W, 0.75 mi. N Edmond, 1 (CSUO); N Jones, 1 (OKSU); 2 mi. S Canadian River, S Oklahoma City on I-35, 1 (OKSU); 1 mi. W jct. Broadway Ext. & N.W. Hwy, 1 (CSUO); 0.75 mi. W Portland Ave. on N.E. 178th, 1 (CSUO). OSAGE COUNTY: Phillips Ranch, 10 mi. SW Bartlesville, 2 (OMNH); 1 mi. E, 4 mi. N Cleveland, 1 (OKSU); 2 mi. N Pawhuska, 1 (KU). PAWNEE COUNTY: 3 mi. W, 4 mi. S Cleveland, 1 (OKSU). PAYNE COUNTY: Boomer Lake, 1 (OKSU); below Lake Carl Blackwell Dam, 2 (OKSU); Stillwater Creek, near Stillwater, 1 (OKSU); 1625 W. 12th St., Stillwater, 1 (OKSU); Stillwater Creek, 1 mi. W Stillwater, 1 (OKSU); 3 mi. W Stillwater, 1 (OKSU); 3 mi. N, 1 mi. E Stillwater, 1 (OKSU); 5 mi. N Stillwater, 1 (OKSU); 5 mi. W Stillwater, 1 (OKSU); 6 mi. N Stillwater, 1 (OKSU); 6 mi. W Stillwater on Hwy 51, 1 (OKSU); 6.25 mi. E, 1 mi. S Stillwater, 1 (OKSU); 8 mi. W, 0.75 mi. N Stillwater, 1 (OKSU); 9 mi. E Stillwater, 1 (OKSU); 9 mi. W, 3 mi. S Stillwater, Hwys 177 & 51, 1 (OKSU); 10 mi. W Stillwater, 1 (OMNH); near Lake Carl Blackwell, 12 mi. W Stillwater, 1 (OKSU); 5 mi. E Yale on Hwy 51, 1 (OKSU); jct. Airport Rd. & Hwy 177, 1 (OKSU); 4.5 mi. E Mulhall Rd. Exit, I-35, 1 (OKSU); 3 mi. W Hwy 108 on Yost Lake Rd., 1 (OKSU). PITTSBURG COUNTY: S Haywood School, 1 (ECENT); 16 mi. W, 6 mi. S McAlester, 1 (ECENT). PONTOTOC COUNTY: southeast edge Ada, 1 (ECENT); 6 mi. SE Ada, 3 (ECENT); 7 mi. E Ada, 1 (ECENT). POTTAWATOMIE COUNTY: 1 mi. E Maud, 1 (OKSU); 3 mi. E Pink, 1 (OMNH); Shawnee, 1 (CSUO); 2 mi. W, 1 mi. N Shawnee, 1 (OMNH). PUSHMATAHA COUNTY: 1 mi. W, 4 mi. N Antlers, 1 (ECENT); 15 mi. S Talihina, 1 (OKSU). STEPHENS COUNTY: 0.25 mi. E, 0.375 mi. S Claud, 1 (OMNH); 4 mi. W Marlow, 1 (OKSU); 6 mi. E, 3.5 mi. N Marlow, 1 (CAMCO); 12 mi. N Ringling, 1 (OKSU). TEXAS COUNTY: Guymon, 1 (OKSU). TILLMAN COUNTY: 5 mi. E, 2 mi. S Davidson, 1 (CAMCO); 20 mi. from Frederick, 1 (USNM); 4 mi. N, 3 mi. W Tipton, 1 (CAMCO). TULSA COUNTY: 2 mi. S Camelot Inn, 1 (OKSU); Red Fork, Indian Territory, 1 (USNM). WASHINGTON COUNTY: 3 mi. S, 1 mi. W Bartlesville, 1 (OKSU). WOODWARD COUNTY: 3 mi. N Woodward, 1 (OMNH).

Rattus norvegicus.—Specimens examined (total 94): BRYAN COUNTY: Cade, 1 (OKSU). CANADIAN COUNTY: El Reno, 1 (USNM). CLEVELAND COUNTY: Animal Behavior Lab, University of Oklahoma, Norman, 2 (OMNH); city dump, Norman, 1 (OMNH); Insectory, University of Oklahoma, Norman, 1 (OMNH); Residential Hall, Norman, 1 (OMNH); Norman, 7 (KU); 1216 Carter Way, Norman, 1 (OMNH); South Canadian River, 2 mi. S University of Oklahoma, 1 (KU). CO-

MANCHE COUNTY: Lawton, 1 (CAMCO); 1509 A Ave., Lawton, 1 (OKSU); Mt. Scott Post Office, 2 (USNM); T53N, R9W, Sec. 8, Wichita Wildlife Refuge, 1 (OMNH). CUSTER COUNTY: Weatherford, 1 (KU). DELAWARE COUNTY: 10 mi. SE Jay, 1 (OKSU). GARVIN COUNTY: 3 mi. S Stratford, 1 (ECENT). HARPER COUNTY: 3 mi. N Ft. Supply, 1 (USNM); 3 mi. W May, 1 (OKSU). JOHNSTON COUNTY: Tishomingo, 1 (ECENT). MARSHALL COUNTY: Johnson Barn, 1 (OUBS); University of Oklahoma Biological Station, 3 (OUBS). MCCLAIN COUNTY: 0.25 mi. E I-35 southwest corner Purcell, 3 (OKSU). NOBLE COUNTY: 11.5 mi. N Perry, 1 (OKSU); near Red Rock, 2 (OKSU). OKLAHOMA COUNTY: N.E. 10th, 0.5 mi. E Airport, 1 (CSUO); Animal Lab, Central State University, Edmond, 2 (CSUO); Central State University, Edmond, 1 (CSUO); 2 mi. W Jones, 1 (CSUO); downtown Oklahoma City, 1 (OMNH); jct. 19th & Lee St., NE Oklahoma City, 1 (OKSU); 20 mi. E Oklahoma City, 3 (OKSU); 20 mi. E, 0.5 mi. N Oklahoma City, 1 (OKSU); 20 mi. E, 0.5 mi. S Oklahoma City, off Gary Expressway, 1 (OKSU); 0.25 mi. S of 4400 blk. N.E. 36th, 1 (CSUO); jct. 10th & Stonewall, 1 (CSUO). PAWNEE COUNTY: 2 mi. E, 7.5 mi. N Yale, 1 (OKSU). PAYNE COUNTY: Insectary Building, 1 mi. W Oklahoma State University campus, 1 (FWMSH); campus, Oklahoma State University, Stillwater, 1 (OKSU); city dump, W Stillwater, 1 (OKSU); swine barn, Oklahoma State University, Stillwater, 2 (OKSU); Stillwater, 4 (OKSU); 325 W. 3rd St., Stillwater, 1 (OKSU); 100 yds. S Willard Hall, Oklahoma State University, 1 (ECENT); 1 mi. W Stillwater, 2 (OKSU); 1 mi. N, 0.5 mi. W Stillwater, 1 (OKSU); 1 mi. N, 1 mi. W Stillwater, 1 (OKSU); 2 mi. N Stillwater, 1 (OKSU); 3 mi. W Stillwater, 1 (ECENT); 4 mi. W, 2 mi. S Stillwater, 1 (OKSU); 8 mi. W, 1 mi. S Stillwater, 1 (OKSU). PITTSBURG COUNTY: McAlester, 2 (ECENT). PONTOTOC COUNTY: campus, East Central State University, Ada, 8 (ECENT); 1200 N. Broadway, Ada, 1 (ECENT); dump, Ada, 4 (ECENT). ROGERS COUNTY: T20N, R15E, SW 1/4 E 1/2 E 1/2 Sec. 36, 4 mi. E Catoosa, 1 (OKSU). SEMINOLE COUNTY: Seminole, 1 (OKSU). TEXAS COUNTY: 2 mi. E Eva, 2 (KU); S Guymon, 1 (OKSU). TULSA COUNTY: 1.5 mi. N Sperry, 1 (OKSU). WAGONER COUNTY: 4.75 mi. NW Wagoner, 1 (OKSU). WASHINGTON COUNTY: 1 mi. N Dewey on Hwy 75, 1 (OKSU).

Rattus rattus.—Specimens examined (total 39): BRYAN COUNTY: Cade, 1 (OKSU); 1 mi. E Colbert, 1 (OMNH), 1 (KU). CADDO COUNTY: 3 mi. E Randlett, 1 (CAMCO). CARTER COUNTY: NE Ardmore, 1 (FWMSH). CLEVELAND COUNTY: North Base, University of Oklahoma, 1 (OKSU). COMANCHE COUNTY: 3.5 mi. S Cache, 6 (CAMCO); 7 mi. W Elgin, 1 (CAMCO); Lawton, 3 (CAMCO). JACKSON COUNTY:

8 mi. E Eldorado, 3 (CAMCO). MARSHALL COUNTY: north end Buncombe Creek, Lake Texoma, 1 (OMNH); University of Oklahoma Biological Station, 4 (OUBS); 2.5 mi. W University of Oklahoma Biological Station, 5 (OUBS); Willis, 2 (OUBS); 1 mi. W Willis, 1 (OUBS). OKLAHOMA COUNTY: downtown Oklahoma City, 3 (OMNH); 1100 S. Meridian, Oklahoma City, 1 (CSUO); Veazey's Drug, downtown Oklahoma City, 1 (OMNH). PUSHMATAHA COUNTY: 3 mi. NE Antlers, 1 (OKSU). STEPHENS COUNTY: 7.25 mi. W, 4 mi. S Duncan, 1 (OKSU).

Reithrodontomys fulvescens.—Specimens examined (total 190): ADAIR COUNTY: 1.5 mi. W Chewey, 800 ft., 3 (OMNH); Boston Mts., Stilwell, 3 (USNM); Stilwell, 7 (UIMNH); 2 mi. S Stilwell, 3 (OKSU); 2.5 mi. E Stilwell, 16 (UIMNH). CADDO COUNTY: T8N, R12W, Sec. 22, just below Ft. Cobb Reservoir Dam, SARP Site C3, 4 (OKSU). CHOCTAW COUNTY: 7 mi. SSE Ft. Towson, 400 ft., 3 (OMNH); 1.5 mi. N Hugo, 1 (OKSU); 3 mi. E, 1 mi. N Hugo, 1 (OKSU). CLEVELAND COUNTY: Cleveland County, 1 (KU); 2 mi. S, 0.25 mi. W Lexington, 1 (OMNH); Noble, Oklahoma Territory, 1 (FMNH); Norman, 1 (OMNH); city dump, Norman, 2 (OMNH); Thunderbird Lake, Norman, 1 (OMNH); 1.9–3.1 mi. S Norman, 2 (OMNH); 1.5 mi. E Norman, 1 (OMNH); 1.5 mi. S Norman, 1 (OMNH); 1.6 mi. S Lindsey on Jenkins, Norman, 1 (OMNH); 2 mi. S Norman, 1 (OMNH); bank Little River, 3 mi. N, 2.5 mi. E Norman, 1 (OMNH); Little River Reservoir, 11.7 mi. E Norman, 2 (OMNH); T6N, R1E, Sec. 31, 2 (OMNH); T9N, R3W, Sec. 32, 2 (OMNH). COMANCHE COUNTY: 3 mi. E Fletcher, 1 (OKSU); Lake Lawtonka, 1 (CAMCO); Mt. Scott Post Office, near Cache Creek, 4 (USNM); Mt. Scott Post Office, near Medium Creek, 6 (USNM); 0.25 mi. E Mt. Scott, 1 (CAMCO); Pinchot Pasture, Wichita Mountains Wildlife Refuge, 2 (OKSU). CREEK COUNTY: Creek County, 2 (KU); Sapulpa, 5 (KU). DELAWARE COUNTY: 5 mi. SSE Jay, 1 (CSUO). GARVIN COUNTY: T3N, R4W, Sec. 25, SARP Site R5, Rush Creek, 2.1 mi. E SH 74, 2 (OKSU). HASKELL COUNTY: 6 mi. S Stigler, 1 (OMNH). JEFFERSON COUNTY: 5 mi. WSW Waurika, 2 (UIMNH). JOHNSTON COUNTY: Blue River bridge Hwy 7, 1 (OUBS); Tishomingo (N.W. River), 625 ft., 2 (USNM). KAY COUNTY: 7 mi. E, 1 mi. S Ponca City, 2 (OKSU). LATIMER COUNTY: Robber's Cave State Park, 5 mi. N Wilburton, 1 (KU). LEFLORE COUNTY: 1.5 mi. NW Zoe, 4 (OMNH). LOGAN COUNTY: T16N, R4W, Sec. 11, 1 (OMNH). MARSHALL COUNTY: Looney Farm, 1 (OUBS); 0.3 mi. W University of Oklahoma Biological Station, 1 (OUBS); 0.4 mi. W University of Oklahoma Biological Station, 1 (OUBS); 0.5 mi. W University of Oklahoma Biological Station, 1 (OUBS); 3 mi. W Willis, 1 (OUBS); 4 mi. N Willis, 1 (OUBS). MAYES COUNTY: 2.7 mi. E Chouteau, 0.7 mi. N Hwy 33, 2 (OMNH).

MCCLAIN COUNTY: 4 mi. S, 1.2 mi. W Goldsby, 1 (USNM); T8N, R4W, Sec. 11, Grass Lake Reservoir Station, 1 (OMNH). MCCURTAIN COUNTY: Mt. Fork River, 2 mi. W Eagletown, 1 (TMM); 2 mi. W Smithville, 4 (OMNH); 3 mi. SSE Tom, 1 (UIMNH); 5 mi. SE Tom, 1 (UIMNH); T4S, R27E, SW Sec. 33, No. 5, 1 (CSUO). MURRAY COUNTY: 10 mi. SE Davis, 1 (OKSU); Platt Natl. Park, 1 (KU). MUS-KOGEE COUNTY: 3 mi. NE Braggs, 1 (OKSU); 3 mi. E Wainwright, 1 (OMNH). NOBLE COUNTY: Red Fork Creek, 13 mi. S Ponca City, 1 (OKSU). OKLAHOMA COUNTY: Draper Lake, 1 (CSUO); 0.25 mi. N jct. N.W. 234th & N. May, 1 (CSUO); 2 mi. E Central State University, 1.5 mi. N Oakridge Dr., Edmond, 1 (CSUO); 4 mi. E (by road) Edmond, 1 (CSUO); 6.6 mi. W Edmond on Edmond Rd., 1 (CSUO); southeast corner N. Western & 122nd, Oklahoma City, 1 (CSUO). PAYNE COUNTY: Boomer Lake, 2 (OKSU); Lake Carl Blackwell, 3 (OKSU); Lake Carl Blackwell Dam, 2 (OKSU); 0.5 mi. S arm 13 Lake Carl Blackwell, 1 (OKSU); 0.5 mi. SE spillway, Lake Carl Blackwell, 1 (OKSU); east bank Lake McMurtry, 1 (OKSU); near Lake McMurtry, 2 (OKSU); northeast side Boomer Lake, Stillwater, 2 (OKSU); NE Boomer Lake, Stillwater, 1 (OKSU); east side Lake Sanborn, Stillwater, 1 (OKSU); N Stillwater, 1 (OKSU); Stillwater Creek, W Stillwater, 1 (OKSU); 1 mi. W Stillwater, 2 (OKSU); 1 mi. W Stillwater on McElroy St., 2 (OKSU); 1 mi. W, 1 mi. N Stillwater, 3 (OKSU); 1.25 mi. E jct. Boomer Rd. & 32nd St., Still-water, 2 (OKSU); 2 mi. S Stillwater, 1 (OKSU); 2 mi. E, 4 mi. N jct. Main St. & Hwy 51, Stillwater, 2 (OKSU); 2 mi. N, 4 mi. W Stillwater, 2 (OKSU); 3 mi. W, 0.5 mi. S Stillwater, 1 (OKSU); 3 mi. N, 5 mi. W Still-water, 1 (OKSU); 4 mi. S Stillwater, 1 (OKSU); 4 mi. W Western Ave., 2 mi. S Rt. 51, Stillwater, 1 (OKSU); 4 mi. W, 2 mi. S Stillwater, 1 (OKSU); 4 mi. W, 3 mi. S Stillwater, 2 (OKSU); 5.5 mi. N, 2 mi. E jct. 6th St. & Perkins Rd., Stillwater, 1 (OKSU); 6 mi. W Stillwater, 1 (OKSU); 6 mi. W, 2 mi. N Stillwater, 1 (OKSU); 7.4 mi. W Stillwater, 1 (OKSU); Sec. 14 on Lake Carl Blackwell, 8 mi. W Stillwater, 2 (OKSU); 10 mi. W Still-water, 1 (OKSU); 13 mi. W, 1.5 mi. N Stillwater, 1 (FWMSH); 100 yds. N Yost Lake, 1 (OKSU); 1000 yds. N Yost Lake, 1 (OKSU); 1.5 mi. E jct. Hwys 86 & 51, 1 (OKSU); 4.3 mi. N jct. SH 51 & 161, 1 (OKSU). PON-TOTOC COUNTY: Pontotoc County, 2 (OKSU). POTTAWATOMIE COUNTY: 7 mi. SE Tecumseh, 6 (KU). WAGONER COUNTY: 4.5 mi. SW Coweta, 600 ft., 2 (OMNH).

Reithrodontomys humulis.—Specimens examined (total 3): LATIMER COUNTY: Eastern Oklahoma State College Farm, Wilburton, 1 (OKSU); Robber's Cave State Park, 5 mi. N Wilburton, 1 (KU). TULSA COUNTY: Garnett, 1 (UMMZ).

Reithrodontomys megalotis.—Specimens examined (total 22): BEAVER

COUNTY: North Canadian River, 7 mi. S Turpin, 1 (KU). CIMARRON
COUNTY: 3 mi. N Kenton, 1 (OMNH); 3.5 mi. N, 1.2 mi. W Kenton, 1
(OMNH); 4 mi. N Kenton, 1 (UMMZ); 4.1 mi. S, 0.5 mi. E Kenton, 1
(OMNH); 4.6 mi. N, 0.2 mi. W Kenton, 8 (OMNH). ELLIS COUNTY:
2 mi. N Shattuck, 2,300 ft., 1 (OMNH). TEXAS COUNTY: New Beaver
River, 3.5 mi. SW Optima, 8 (KU).

Reithrodontomys montanus.—Specimens examined (total 233): ALFALFA
COUNTY: Great Salt Plains, E Cherokee, 4 (OKSU); 3 mi. N, 6.5 mi. E
Cherokee, 1,170 ft., 3 (OMNH); 3.5 mi. E Cherokee, 1 (OMNH). BEA-
VER COUNTY: 2 mi. W Forgan, 1 (OKSU). BRYAN COUNTY: 5 mi. N
Colbert, 13 (TMM). CANADIAN COUNTY: T11N, R10W, Sec. 18, 1
(OMNH). CHOCTAW COUNTY: 7 mi. SSE Ft. Towson, 400 ft., 1
(OMNH). CIMARRON COUNTY: 13 mi. S Boise City, 1 (ECENT); 13.5
mi. W Boise City, 1 (OMNH); 14 mi. W Boise City, 1 (OMNH); Black
Mesa, 14 mi. W Boise City, 1 (OMNH); 8 mi. W Griggs, 3,900 ft., 7
(KU); 4 mi. N Kenton, 1 (KU); 8 mi. E Keyes, 1 (KU). CLEVELAND
COUNTY: Cleveland County, 6 (OMNH); 2.5 mi. NE Noble, 8 (OMNH);
Norman, 1 (KU); North Campus, University of Oklahoma, Norman, 1
(OUBS); 1.5 mi. N Norman, 1 (USNM), 2 (OMNH); 1.7 mi. N Norman,
5 (OMNH); 2 mi. N Norman, 1 (OMNH); 2 mi. N, 0.1 mi. W Norman, 1
(OMNH); 3 mi. E Norman, 3 (OMNH); 4 mi. S Norman, 1 (OMNH); 10
mi. SW Norman, 1 (OMNH). COMANCHE COUNTY: Comanche
County, 1 (OKSU); Lake Lawtonka, 1 (CAMCO); 20 mi. SW Lawton, 1
(UIMNH); Wichita Mountains Wildlife Refuge, 16 (USNM); top of Elk
Mt., Wichita Mountains Wildlife Refuge, 5 (USNM). COTTON COUN-
TY: 6 mi. W, 4 mi. S Geronimo, 1 (CAMCO); 3.3 mi. ESE Taylor, 900 ft.,
2 (OMNH). CREEK COUNTY: Creek County, 1 (KU); Sapulpa, 1 (KU).
CUSTER COUNTY: 1 mi. N, 2.5 mi. W Weatherford, 1 (KU); 4 mi. N, 2
mi. W Weatherford, 1 (KU). DEWEY COUNTY: 5 mi. W Canton, 2
(KU); 5.5 mi. SW Canton, 1 (KU); 0.5 mi. W Moreland, 1 (OMNH).
ELLIS COUNTY: 2 mi. N Shattuck, 2,300 ft., 2 (OMNH); 5 mi. NNE
Shattuck, 2,335 ft., 2 (OMNH). HARMON COUNTY: 4.5 mi. N Gould,
1 (TTU); 8.5 mi. N, 2 mi. W Hollis, 1 (OKSU); 6 mi. E, 1 mi. S Vinson,
1,700 ft., 1 (OMNH). HARPER COUNTY: near Doby Springs Reservoir,
1 (UMMZ); 3 mi. N Ft. Supply, 10 (USNM); 6 mi. N Ft. Supply, 6
(USNM); Southern Great Plains Exp. Range, 7 (OKSU), 9 (USNM).
JACKSON COUNTY: 1 mi. S Eldorado, 1 (OKSU). JOHNSTON
COUNTY: 2.5 mi. W, 1 mi. N Mannsville, 1 (OUBS). KINGFISHER
COUNTY: Hennessey, 1 (OKSU); T17N, R5W, Sec. 30, 1 (OMNH).
LATIMER COUNTY: Robber's Cave State Park, 1 (ECENT). LIN-
COLN COUNTY: 2 mi. S Carney, 1 (OKSU). MAJOR COUNTY: 5 mi.
S Waynoka, 1,450 ft., 1 (OMNH); 5.5 mi. S Waynoka, 1,450 ft., 1

(OMNH). MARSHALL COUNTY: Engineer Flats, 3 mi. W University of Oklahoma Biological Station, 1 (OUBS). MAYES COUNTY: 2.8 mi. E Chouteau, 0.8 mi. N Hwy 33, 1 (OMNH). MCCLAIN COUNTY: McClain County, 2 (OMNH); 2.5 mi. W, 1.5 mi. N Newcastle, 3 (ECENT); Norman Bridge, 1 (OMNH); 10 mi. SW Norman, 1 (OMNH). MUSKOGEE COUNTY: 3 mi. E Wainwright, 2 (OMNH). NOBLE COUNTY: 1.4 mi. N, 3.1 mi. W Watchorn, 1 (OMNH). NOWATA COUNTY: 6 mi. E South Coffeyville, 700 ft., 1 (OMNH). OKLAHOMA COUNTY: Oklahoma County, 1 (OMNH). OSAGE COUNTY: Adams Ranch, 12 mi. N, 6 mi. E Shidler, 1,250 ft., 6 (KU). PAYNE COUNTY: 0.5 mi. S, 1 mi. W Glencoe, 1 (OKSU); Lake Carl Blackwell, 2 (OKSU); south side Lake Carl Blackwell, 1 (UIMNH); T19N, R1E, Sec. 21, southeast corner Lake Carl Blackwell Area, 1 (OKSU); SE Lake Carl Blackwell Dam, 1 (OKSU); west end Lake Carl Blackwell, 1 (OKSU); sheep barns, Oklahoma State University, 1 (OKSU); 0.1 mi. W Hwy 177 on Sanborn Lodge Area Airport Rd., 1 (OKSU); 1 mi. N Stillwater, 1 (OKSU); 2 mi. N, 2 mi. E Stillwater, 2 (OKSU); 3 mi. W Stillwater, 2 (OKSU); 4 mi. E jct. Lakeview & Perkins Rd., 0.25 mi. N Stillwater, 1 (OKSU); Carberry Ranch, 5 mi. W Stillwater, 1 (OKSU); 7 mi. W on SH 51 & 0.25 mi. S, Stillwater, 1 (OKSU); 16 mi. E Stillwater, 1 (OKSU). PONTOTOC COUNTY: 7 mi. NE Ada, 2 (ECENT); 2 mi. N Roff, 1 (ECENT). ROGER MILLS COUNTY: 2.5 mi. E, 1.5 mi. S Reydon, 7 (CAMCO). ROGERS COUNTY: U Ranch, 1 (UMMZ). SEQUOYAH COUNTY: 4 mi. SW Nicut, 800 ft., 1 (OMNH). TILLMAN COUNTY: 5.5 mi. S Grandfield, 1 (OMNH). TULSA COUNTY: Garnett, 2 (UMMZ). WOODS COUNTY: 1 mi. E, 3 mi. N Alva, 1 (OKSU); 8 mi. NW Alva, 2 (ECENT); 11 mi. NW Alva, 4 (ECENT); Dougherty, Indian Territory, 3 (FMNH); 5 mi. S Waynoka, 1,400 ft., 1 (OMNH); 5 mi. S Waynoka, 1,450 ft., 13 (OMNH); 5 mi. N, 1 mi. W Waynoka, 1 (OKSU). WOODWARD COUNTY: 2 mi. NNW Woodard, 1,900 ft., 1 (OMNH); 5 mi. SW Woodward, 3 (USNM).

Scalopus aquaticus.—Specimens examined (total 264): ADAIR COUNTY: Stilwell, 5 (OKSU); Stilwell Graveyard, 1 (OKSU); 2 mi. W Stilwell, 1 (UMMZ). BECKHAM COUNTY: 2 mi. W Sayre, 1 (OKSU); N Fork Red River, 3 mi. W Sayre, 1 (OKSU); 3 mi. W, 1.5 mi. S Sayre, 1 (OKSU). BLAINE COUNTY: public hunting area, Canton Reservoir, 1 (OKSU); southeast side Canton Lake, 1 (OKSU); 5 mi. E, 5 mi. S Okeene, 1 (OKSU). BRYAN COUNTY: 1 mi. S Blue, 3 (OKSU); Colbert, 3 (TMM); Red River, 3 mi. SE Yuba, 1 (TMM). CADDO COUNTY: 4 mi. W Cogar, 1 (OMNH); 1.5 mi. W Cyril, 1 (OKSU). CANADIAN COUNTY: El Reno, 1 (CSUO); Ft. Reno, 1 (USNM); 5.5 mi. SE Hinton, 1,500 ft., 1 (KU); Methodist Canyon, 1 (ECENT); 3 mi. E Yukon, 1 (OKSU). CARTER COUNTY: Ardmore, 2 (OKSU). CHEROKEE COUNTY: 2 mi. SE

Lowery, 1 (TMM); Scraper, 1 (UMMZ); 8.5 mi. E Tahlequah, 1 (OMNH). CLEVELAND COUNTY: Cleveland County, 1 (OMNH); Moore, 1 (CSUO); Norman, 7 (OMNH); campus, University of Oklahoma, Norman, 2 (OMNH); 811 Timberdell, Norman, 1 (OMNH); 1 mi. E US 77 on Cedar Lane Rd., Norman, 1 (OMNH); 1 mi. N Norman on Hwy 77, 1 (OMNH); 2 mi. S Norman, 1 (OMNH); 2 mi. SW Norman, 1 (OMNH); 2.25 mi. S Norman, 1 (OMNH); 2.8 mi. S Norman, 2 (USNM); 3 mi. E Norman, 2 (OMNH); 3 mi. N Norman, 1 (OKSU); 3.0 mi. S, 7.5 mi. E Norman, 1 (OMNH); University of Oklahoma Golf Course, 1 (OMNH); 0.5 mi. E University of Oklahoma, 1 (OMNH). COMANCHE COUNTY: Cache, 1 (CAMCO); Fletcher, 1 (CAMCO); 6.5 mi. E Ft. Sill, 1 (CAMCO); 8.5 mi. N Indiahoma, 1 (CAMCO); near Cache Creek, Mt. Scott, 2 (USNM); near Medicine Creek, Mt. Scott, 1 (USNM); Mt. Scott, south base Wichita Mountains, 1 (USNM); Mt. Scott, 1 (USNM); Wichita Mountains Wildlife Refuge, 3 (USNM), 1 (OKSU). CRAIG COUNTY: 1 mi. S on Hwy 69, 0.75 mi. W, 1 (OKSU). CREEK COUNTY: 1 mi. E, 0.5 mi. S jct. SH 48 & Hwy 51, 1 (OKSU); 3 mi. E jct. SH 51 & 99, 1 (OKSU). CUSTER COUNTY: Weatherford, 1 (KU). DEWEY COUNTY: 5 mi. W Canton, 1 (KU); 5.5 mi. SW Canton, 1 (KU); Dewey County, 1 (KU). GARFIELD COUNTY: Enid, 1 (KU). GRADY COUNTY: 4 mi. W Newcastle, 1 (CSUO). GRANT COUNTY: 1.4 mi. W, 1 mi. N Hawley, 2 (OMNH). GREER COUNTY: 5 mi. S, 7 mi. W Mangum, 2 (OKSU); 5 mi. NW Willow, 1 (OKSU). HARMON COUNTY: Buck Creek, southwest corner of state, 1 (TMM); 5.5 mi. N, 2 mi. W Hollis, 1 (FWMSH). HARPER COUNTY: 4.5 mi. N Laverne, 2 (UMMZ); pasture 24, Southern Great Plains Exp. Range, Ft. Supply, 1 (OKSU); Southern Great Plains Exp. Range, 1 (OKSU). HUGHES COUNTY: 12 mi. S, 1.5 mi. E Holdenville, 1 (ECENT). JACKSON COUNTY: Red River, 14 mi. S Olustee, 1 (TMM); 3 mi. NE Warren, 1 (OMNH). JOHNSTON COUNTY: 0.5 mi. N Murray State College, Tishomingo, 1 (ECENT). KAY COUNTY: 5 mi. E, 1 mi. S Pioneer Woman Statue, Ponca City, 1 (OKSU); T26N, R2E, W 1/2 NE 1/4 Sec. 19, Ponca City, 1 (OKSU); T26N, R2E, SE 1/4 Sec. 18, 1 (OKSU). LEFLORE COUNTY: 1 mi. SW Summerfield, 1 (TMM). LINCOLN COUNTY: Chandler, 1 (OKSU): 4 mi. N Hwy 62, N Chandler, 1 (OKSU). LOGAN COUNTY: 4 mi. N, 0.5 mi. E Guthrie, 1 (OKSU). LOVE COUNTY: 9 mi. S Ardmore, 1 (OMNH). MAJOR COUNTY: 0.25 mi. N Ames, 1 (OKSU); Griever Creek, 1 (UMMZ). MARSHALL COUNTY: University of Oklahoma Biological Station, 9 (OMNH); 500 yds. NNE University of Oklahoma Biological Station, 2 (OMNH); 0.75 mi. W University of Oklahoma Biological Station, 1 (OUBS); 2 mi. W University of Oklahoma Biological Station, 1 (OUBS); Willis, 1 (UMMZ); 0.5 mi. SW Willis, 1 (OUBS); 0.5 mi. W Willis, 1

(OKSU); 1 mi. W Willis, 1 (UMMZ). MAYES COUNTY: 1.4 mi. E Chouteau, 0.7 mi. N Hwy 33, 1 (OMNH); 4 mi. W, 2.5 mi. N Pryor, 1 (OKSU). MCCLAIN COUNTY: 2.7 mi. N, 0.5 mi. W Goldsby, 4 (OMNH), 4 (USNM); McClain County, 1 (OMNH); 3.5 mi. W, 1 mi. N Newcastle, 1 (ECENT); 5 mi. W Norman, 1 (OMNH); 10 mi. SW Norman, 1 (OMNH). MCCURTAIN COUNTY: 0.25 mi. W Glover, 2 (TMM); T4S, R27E, N 1/2 Sec. 33, Veals Farm, 1 (CSUO). MCINTOSH COUNTY: 11 mi. W Eufaula on Hwy 9, 1 (CSUO); 1 mi. N Hitchita, 1 (OKSU). MUSKOGEE COUNTY: Braggs, 4 (OKSU); Wildlife Conservation Station, Braggs, 1 (OKSU); Ft. Gibson, 1 (OKSU); Muskogee, 1 (OKSU); 3 mi. E Wainwright, 1 (OMNH). NOBLE COUNTY: 7 mi. W, 0.5 mi. S Red Rock, 1 (OKSU). OKFUSKEE COUNTY: 2 mi. W Madison, 1 (OKSU). OKLAHOMA COUNTY: 6713 Gleason Circle, Bethany, 1 (CSUO); 5 mi. E Central State University, 2 (CSUO); Edmond, 3 (CSUO); 1024 N. Kennedy School, Edmond, 1 (CSUO); 1 mi. S Edmond, 1 (OKSU); 3 mi. E Edmond, 1 (CSUO); 5 mi. E Edmond, 1 (CSUO); 10 mi. W, 0.5 mi. S Edmond, 1 (CSUO); T12N, R2E, NE 1/4 Sec. 2, 1 mi. E, 1.25 mi. S Jones, 1 (CSUO); Nicoma Park, 1 (OKSU); Oklahoma City, 3 (CSUO); 1004 N. Council Rd., Oklahoma City, 1 (CSUO); 4000 N.W. 44th, Oklahoma City, 1 (OKSU); 1.5 mi. E Tinker Field, Oklahoma City, 1 (OKSU); 1004 N. Council Rd., 1,250 ft., 1 (CSUO). OKMULGEE COUNTY: 813 S. Alabama St., Okmulgee, 1 (OKSU). OSAGE COUNTY: Osage Indian Territory, 1 (USNM); 6 mi. N Pawhuska, 1 (OMNH); 10 mi. NE Pawhuska, 1 (TMM). OTTAWA COUNTY: 3.9 mi. S (on US 59, 66, 69), 1.5 mi. W Miami, 1 (OKSU). PAWNEE COUNTY: N Morrison, 1 (OKSU); 7.5 mi. N, 2.75 mi. W Pawnee, 1 (KU). PAYNE COUNTY: Boomer Lake, 1 (OKSU); arm 4 Lake Carl Blackwell, 2 (OKSU); 0.125 mi. SE Lake Carl Blackwell, 1 (OKSU); approx. 150 yds. SE jct. McElroy & Perkins, 1 (OKSU); campus, Oklahoma State University, 2 (OKSU); 5 mi. W, 7 mi. S Payne Co.–Creek Co. boundary, 1 (OKSU); 3 mi. S, 3 mi. E Perkins, 1 (OKSU); 0.25 mi. N Sanborn Lake, 1 (OKSU); Boomer Lake Park, Stillwater, 1 (OKSU); Lakeside Golf Course, Stillwater, 1 (OKSU); Sanborn Lake, N Stillwater, 1 (OKSU); Stillwater, 14 (OKSU); 720 Willow Rd., Stillwater, 1 (OKSU); 2006 W. 6th St., Stillwater, 1 (OKSU); 0.25 mi. N Stillwater, 1 (OKSU); 0.5 mi. S Stillwater, 1 (OKSU); 1 mi. E Stillwater, 1 (OKSU); 1 mi. N Stillwater, 1 (OKSU); 2 mi. N, 2 mi. E Stillwater, 1 (OKSU); 2 mi. SE Stillwater, 1 (OKSU); 2 mi. W Stillwater, 4 (OKSU); 2 mi. W, 2 mi. N Stillwater, 1 (OKSU); 3 mi. N, 0.5 mi. W Stillwater on Hwy 177, 1 (OKSU); 3 mi. S Stillwater, 3 (OKSU); 4 mi. E, 1 mi. S Stillwater, 1 (OKSU); 5 mi. W, 0.75 mi. S Stillwater, 1 (OKSU); 8 mi. E Stillwater, 1 (OKSU); 8 mi. E, 0.5 mi. S Stillwater, 1 (OKSU); 8 mi. E, 0.25 mi. S Stillwater, 2 (OKSU); 11 mi. E Stillwater, 1 (OKSU);

T17N, R2E, Sec. 18, 1 (OKSU). PITTSBURG COUNTY: near Kiowa, 1 (ECENT). PONTOTOC COUNTY: Ada, 1 (ECENT). POTTAWATOMIE COUNTY: 2 mi. E Dale, 1 (OMNH); Tecumseh, 2 (KU). PUSHMATAHA COUNTY: 1 mi. S Nashoba, 1 (TMM). ROGERS COUNTY: 5.5 mi. E Claremore, 1 (OMNH). SEMINOLE COUNTY: Seminole, 1 (KU); 4 mi. SE Seminole, 2 (ECENT). SEQUOYAH COUNTY: Dwight Mission, 1 (OKSU). STEPHENS COUNTY: 2 mi. W, 0.5 mi. S Comanche, 1 (OKSU); #54 Camelback, NE Duncan, 1 (CAMCO). TULSA COUNTY: Garnett, 5 (UMMZ); Mohawk Park, 7 (UMMZ); 8 mi. W Red Fork, 3 (USNM). WAGONER COUNTY: SE Broken Arrow, 1 (OKSU). WASHINGTON COUNTY: Dewey, 1 (OKSU). WOODS COUNTY: Alva, 1 (USNM); north bank Salt Fork River, 1.5 mi. N Alva, 1 (OKSU); 2 mi. N Alva, 1 (OKSU). WOODWARD COUNTY: Woodward, 2 (OMNH).

Sciurus carolinensis.—Specimens examined (total 94): ADAIR COUNTY: Stilwell, 2 (USNM); 15 mi. SE Stilwell, 1 (OKSU). ATOKA COUNTY: 9 mi. W Atoka, 1 (KU). CHEROKEE COUNTY: Cherokee County, 1 (OKSU). CHOCTAW COUNTY: T5S, R20E, SE 1/4 Sec. 9, 32 mi. SE Antlers, 1 (CSUO); opposite Arthur, Texas, N of Red River, 4 (USNM); 3.5 mi. E, 1.5 mi. S Hugo, 1 (OKSU). DELAWARE COUNTY: near Jay, 1 (OMNH); 4.5 mi. SE Jay, 900 ft., 1 (OMNH); 10 mi. SE Jay, 2 (OKSU); 2 mi. E, 25 mi. N Ketchum, 1 (OKSU). GARVIN COUNTY: 0.5 mi. S Will Rogers Turnpike at the 92 mi. marker, 1 (OKSU). HUGHES COUNTY: 3 mi. W Calvin, 1 (ECENT); 4 mi. S Gerty, 1 (ECENT); 6 mi. SE Holdenville, 1 (KU). LATIMER COUNTY: Red Oak, 4 (USNM). LINCOLN COUNTY: near Davenport, 1 (OKSU); 5 mi. S, 2 mi. W jct. Hwys 66 & 99, 1 (OKSU). MAYES COUNTY: 0.5 mi. N low water dam on Grand River, 1 (OKSU); 3 mi. S Locust Grove, 1 (OKSU); 3 mi. E Locust Grove, 1 (OKSU); 6 mi. E, 2 mi. N Locust Grove on Hwy 33, 1 (OKSU); 6 mi. W Locust Grove, 3 (CAMCO); 0.25 mi. W Spavinaw Hills Game Refuge, 1 (OKSU). MCCURTAIN COUNTY: 15 mi. SE Broken Bow, 2 (OMNH); bank Red River, 10 mi. S Tom, 1 (OKSU). MURRAY COUNTY: Dougherty, Indian Territory, 1 (FMNH); Dougherty, 3 (USNM). MUSKOGEE COUNTY: 2.25 mi. E Arkansas River on Hwy 10, 300 yds. E Bayou Creek on SH 10, 1 (OKSU); 3 mi. E Arkansas River on Hwy 62, 1 (OKSU); 3 mi. E Wainwright, 1 (OMNH). NOBLE COUNTY: 3 mi. E, 1 mi. N Morrison, 1 (OKSU); jct. #8 Red Rock River near Arkansas River, 1 (OKSU); 0.25 mi. N Red Rock Creek & Arkansas River, 1 (OKSU); 1 mi. E Red Rock Creek & Arkansas River, 1 (OKSU); 8 mi. NE Red Rock River near Arkansas River, 1 (OKSU). NOWATA COUNTY: 5.5 mi. E, 1 mi. S Nowata, 1 (OMNH); 6 mi. E Nowata, 1 (OKSU). OKFUSKEE COUNTY: 9 mi. N, 2 mi. E Paden, 2 (CSUO).

OKMULGEE COUNTY: Okmulgee County, 1 (ECENT). OTTAWA COUNTY: Benscoter Farm, 10 mi. SE Quapaw, 1 (OKSU). PAWNEE COUNTY: 3 mi. E Morrison, 2 (OKSU); 6 mi. NE Morrison, 2 (OKSU); Greasy Creek, 9 mi. E Red Rock, 1 (OKSU); T21N, R7E, S 1/2 Sec. 5, 1 (OKSU). PAYNE COUNTY: 15 mi. E Stillwater, 1 (OKSU). PITTSBURG COUNTY: Hartshorne, 1 (USNM); 2 mi. S Hartshorne, 1 (OKSU); 5 mi. E Stuart, 1 (OUBS). PUSHMATAHA COUNTY: 1 mi. W, 4 mi. N Antlers, 1 (ECENT); Clayton, 1 (OKSU); near Clayton, 1 (OKSU); 1 mi. SE Clayton, 1 (OKSU); 2 mi. W Clayton, 1 (OKSU); 2 mi. NE Cloudy, 1 (OMNH). SEMINOLE COUNTY: 3 mi. S, 6 mi. E Wolf on Hwy 18, 1 (CSUO). SEQUOYAH COUNTY: Redland, 1 (USNM); Tenkiller Dam, 1 (OKSU). TULSA COUNTY: 5.5 mi. N Broken Arrow, 1 (OKSU); Garnett, 6 (OKSU); Zoological Garden Area, Mohawk Park, 4 (USNM); Red Fork, 2 (USNM); Tulsa, 1 (UIMNH). WASHINGTON COUNTY: Bartlesville, 1 (CSUO); Caney River, Bartlesville, 1 (OKSU); 0.5 mi. S Bartlesville, 1 (OKSU); 1 mi. S Caney River, Bartlesville, 2 (OKSU); 4 mi. E Bartlesville, 1 (OMNH).

Sciurus niger.—Specimens examined (total 407): ADAIR COUNTY: 1.5 mi. W Chewey, 800 ft., 2 (OMNH); T5N, R24E, Sec. 1, 4.5 mi. W Stilwell, 1 (OMNH); 1.5 mi. SW jct. US Hwy 59 & SH 100, 1 (OKSU). ATOKA COUNTY: 5 mi. W Wardville, 1 (ECENT). BECKHAM COUNTY: 9 mi. S Elk City, 1 (OKSU); 8 mi. N, 1.25 mi. E Erick, 1 (OKSU); 4 mi. W Sayre, 1 (OKSU). BLAINE COUNTY: Blaine County, 1 (OMNH); Canton Lake, 1 (OMNH); Roman Nose State Park, 3 (OKSU). BRYAN COUNTY: 6 mi. W Colbert, 1 (TMM). CADDO COUNTY: 1.5 mi. N Anadarko, 1 (CAMCO); 4 mi. W Cogar, 1 (OMNH); Ft. Cobb, 1 (USNM); 2 mi. E, 1 mi. S Ft. Cobb, 1 (CAMCO); Red Rock Canyon, Hinton, 2 (OMNH). CARTER COUNTY: 2 mi. N, 2 mi. W Ardmore, 1 (OKSU). CHEROKEE COUNTY: 3 mi. SW Cookson, 2 (OKSU); 6 mi. S Cookson, 1 (OKSU); 5 mi. NW Hulbert, 1 (OKSU); Scraper, 1 (UMMZ); 4 mi. W Tahlequah, 1 (OMNH); 1 mi. N, 4 mi. E Welling, 1 (OKSU); jct. Hwys 100 & 10A, 1 (CSUO). CHOCTAW COUNTY: 3 mi. E, 1.5 mi. S Hugo, 1 (OKSU); Sandy Branch, 2 (OKSU). CLEVELAND COUNTY: Moore, 1 (CSUO); Noble, Oklahoma Territory, 1 (FMNH); 5 mi. E Noble, 6 (OMNH); Brooks & Lahoma St., Norman, 1 (OMNH); Jenkins & Cross Center Dr., Norman, 1 (OMNH); Jenkins & Wilson Center Dr., Norman, 1 (OMNH); Lindsey St., Norman, 2 (OMNH); Oklahoma St., Norman, 1 (OMNH); Norman, 5 (OMNH); 700 Brooks, Norman, 1 (OMNH); 900 blk. Flood, Norman, 1 (OMNH); Elm & Brooks Sts., Norman, 1 (OMNH); 1.5 mi. SW Norman, 1 (OMNH); 2 mi. S Norman, 1 (OMNH); 3 mi. E Norman on Lindsey St., 1 (OMNH); 4 mi. E, 2 mi. N Norman, 2 (OMNH); T8N, R1E, Sec. 35, 1 (OMNH). COAL COUNTY: 0.7 mi.

W, 2 mi. S Coalgate, 1 (OMNH); Lehigh, 1 (OMNH). COMANCHE COUNTY: 9 mi. SW Elgin, 1 (CAMCO); 12 mi. W, 0.5 mi. N Elgin, 1 (CAMCO); 3 mi. NW Faxon, 2 (CAMC0); 3.5 mi. S, 4 mi. E Faxon, 1 (CAMCO); 2 mi. N, 0.25 mi. E Fletcher, 1 (OKSU); 4.5 mi. E, 1 mi. S Fletcher, 1 (CAMCO); Ft. Sill, 2 (CAMCO); east range off SH 277, Ft. Sill, 1 (OKSU); Lawton, 7 (CAMCO); Bell & 12th St., Lawton, 1 (CAMCO); 1703 N. 43rd St., Lawton, 1 (CAMCO); 614 Bell, Lawton, 1 (CAMCO); 1 mi. W Sheridan Rd. on Bishop Rd., S Lawton, 1 (OKSU); 1 mi. S Lawton, 3 mi. S jct. Lee & Sheridan Sts., 1 (CAMCO); 4.25 mi. E, 6 mi. S Lawton, 1 (CAMCO); 6 mi. S Lawton, 1 (OKSU); Wichita Mountains Estates, 10 mi. N Lawton, 1 (CAMCO); West Cache Creek, 12.3 mi. W Lawton, 1 (CAMCO); 5 mi. N, 5 mi. E Medicine Park, 1 (CAMCO); 6.5 mi. E, 0.75 mi. N Meers, 1 (CAMCO); East Cache Creek, Mt. Scott, 1 (USNM); Mt. Scott, near Medicine Creek, Mt. Scott Post Office, 1 (USNM); 4 mi. N Sterling, 2 (OKSU); 4.5 mi. N Sterling, 1 (OKSU); Wichita Mountains Wildlife Refuge, 13 (USNM), 2 (OMNH); 1 mi. N, 0.5 mi. W Wichita Mts. Estates, 1 (CAMCO). COTTON COUNTY: Hooper Farm, 1 (OKSU); 10 mi. N Red River, 1 (OKSU). CRAIG COUNTY: 2 mi. S, 8 mi. W Chelsea, 1 (OMNH); 1 mi. S, 6 mi. W Oklahoma–Kansas Border, N Welch, 1 (OKSU); 8 mi. N, 1.5 mi. W Welch, 1 (OMNH). CREEK COUNTY: 4 mi. N Drumright, 1 (OKSU); Sapulpa, 1 (KU); 7.5 mi. NE Sapulpa, 1 (OKSU). CUSTER COUNTY: 19 mi. W Thomas, 1 (OKSU). DELAWARE COUNTY: 2.5 mi. W Eucha, 1,000 ft., 1 (OMNH); 10 mi. SE Jay, 1 (OKSU). DEWEY COUNTY: 1 mi. W Thomas Gas Plant, 1 (OKSU). GARFIELD COUNTY: 804 E. Elm, Enid, 1 (CSUO). GARVIN COUNTY: 2 mi. W Maysville, 1 (ECENT); 1 mi. N Pauls Valley Airport, 1 (OKSU); 2 mi. S Pauls Valley, 1 (ECENT); 3 mi. NE Stratford, 1 (ECENT). GRADY COUNTY: 109 yds. W Bailey Cemetery, 1 (OMNH); 3 mi. W, 3 mi. N Minco, 1 (OKSU); 8 mi. W, 3 mi. N Minco, 1 (OKSU). GRANT COUNTY: 7 mi. W, 3 mi. N Pond Creek, 1 (CAMCO). HARMON COUNTY: 10 mi. S, 0.5 mi. E Gould, 1 (OKSU); 9 mi. E, 1 mi. S Hollis, 1 (OMNH). HARPER COUNTY: 2 mi. W May, 1 (OKSU); 3 mi. W May, 1 (OKSU). HASKELL COUNTY: 5.5 mi. N, 0.5 mi. W Stigler, 1 (OKSU). HUGHES COUNTY: 4 mi. E Calvin, 1 (ECENT); 1 mi. S, 1.5 mi. W Spaulding, 4 (CAMCO); 3.5 mi. S Wetumka, 1 (ECENT); 7 mi. W Wetumka, 1 (CSUO); 7 mi. SW Wetumka, 1 (ECENT); T7N, R10E, Sec. 29, 1 (OKSU). JACKSON COUNTY: 2.5 mi. SE Duke, 1 (CAMCO); 3.5 mi. S Eldorado, 1 (CAMCO); 3.5 mi. N, 3 mi. E Headrick, 2 (OMNH). JOHNSTON COUNTY: 2.5 mi. NE Mannsville, 1 (OKSU); 2.75 mi. NW Mannsville, 1 (OKSU); 4 mi. N Millcreek, 1 mi. E SH 7, 2 (ECENT); 3 mi. W, 2 mi. N Tishomingo, 1 (OKSU); 4 mi. E Tishomingo, 1 (OKSU). KAY COUNTY: Ponca Agency, 1 (USNM); 9

mi. SW Ponca City, 1 (OKSU); 1 mi. N, 5 mi. E Uncas, 1 (OKSU).
KINGFISHER COUNTY: 14 mi. W Crescent, 1 (OKSU); 2 mi. W Hennessey, 1 (OKSU); 6 mi. SW Hennessey, 1 (OKSU); 10 mi. W Hennessey on SH 51, 1 (OKSU); between Kingfisher & Guthrie, 1 (OKSU). KIOWA COUNTY: 2 mi. E Ft. Cobb, 1 (CAMCO); Kiowa Agency, 17 mi. SE Ft. Cobb, 2 (USNM). LATIMER COUNTY: Red Oak, 6 (USNM); Fourche Maline River, N Wilburton, 1 (OKSU); 2.5 mi. NE Wilburton, 1 (OMNH); 4.5 mi. N Wilburton, 1 (OMNH). LEFLORE COUNTY: 1 mi. W Honobia, 1 (OKSU); 1.5 mi. NE Zoe, 1 (OMNH). LINCOLN COUNTY: 3 mi. N Carney on Hwy 177, 1 (OKSU); 1 mi. S Chandler, 1 (OKSU); 3 mi. N Hwy 62, N Chandler, 1 (OKSU); near Davenport, 1 (OKSU); 1 mi. W Davenport on Rt. 99, 1 (OKSU); 5 mi. N, 6 mi. E Meeker, 1 (OKSU); 3.5 mi. SW Stroud, 1 (OKSU); 1 mi. W Tyron, 1 (OKSU); 5 mi. S, 2 mi. W jct. Hwy 66 & SH 99, 2 (OKSU). LOGAN COUNTY: 3 mi. S, 3 mi. W Marshall, 2 (OKSU); T18N, R4W, Sec. 2, 1 (OMNH). MAJOR COUNTY: Griever Creek, 1 (UMMZ); 1 mi. W, 3.5 mi. S Ringwood, 1 (OKSU). MARSHALL COUNTY: 0.5 mi. N Shay Crossing on Buncombe Creek, 1 (OUBS); University of Oklahoma Biological Station, Lake Texoma, 1 (OMNH); 0.25 mi. N University of Oklahoma Biological Station, 1 (OUBS); 0.5 mi. NE University of Oklahoma Biological Station, 1 (OMNH); 1 mi. W University of Oklahoma Biological Station, 1 (OUBS); 1 mi. E Willis, 1 (OMNH); 5 mi. NE Willis, 1 (OUBS). MAYES COUNTY: 2 mi. S Big Cabin, 1 (OKSU). MCCURTAIN COUNTY: 2 mi. N Broken Bow, 2 (OMNH); 10 mi. SE Broken Bow, 1 (OMNH); 2.5 mi. NE Wilburton, 1 (OMNH). MCINTOSH COUNTY: 1 mi. W, 0.5 mi. N Hitchita, 1 (OKSU); 2 mi. W Warner, 1 (OKSU). MURRAY COUNTY: Dougherty, 2 (USNM); 8 mi. W Mill Creek, 1 (OKSU); 12 mi. S Sulphur, 1 (OKSU); 1 mi. S Wynnewood, 1 (OKSU). MUSKOGEE COUNTY: 3 mi. E Wainwright, 1 (OMNH). NOBLE COUNTY: 1 mi. N, 5 mi. E Morrison, 2 (OKSU); 2 mi. N Morrison, 1 (OKSU); 2 mi. W Morrison, 2 (OKSU); 7 mi. N, 2 mi. E Perry, 1 (OKSU); 5.5 mi. W, 0.5 mi. S Red Rock, 1 (OKSU); 13 mi. N Stillwater, 1 (OKSU). NOWATA COUNTY: 5 mi. E Nowata, 1 (OKSU); 6.5 mi. E, 3 mi. S Nowata, 1 (OMNH). OKFUSKEE COUNTY: 2 mi. W Mason, 1 (OKSU); 2.5 mi. E Mason, 1 (OKSU); 7 mi. E Okemah, 1 (OMNH); 9 mi. N, 2 mi. E Paden, 1 (CSUO). OKLAHOMA COUNTY: Del City Park, 2 (CSUO); Edmond, 3 (CSUO); Fink Park, Edmond, 1 (CSUO); jct. Broadway & N. 2nd St., Edmond, 1 (CSUO); 0.5 mi. E jct. Bryant & 2nd, Edmond, 1 (CSUO); jct. 2nd & Bryant, 5 mi. E, 1.2 mi. S Edmond, 1 (CSUO); 6 mi. W, 4.9 mi. N Edmond, 1 (CSUO); N Jones, 1 (OKSU); 2101 Rolling Hills, Oklahoma City, 2 (CSUO); 5 mi. N, 2 mi. W Oklahoma City, 1 (OKSU); 7 mi. W Oklahoma City, 1 (OKSU); 8000 Melrose

Ln., 1,250 ft., 1 (CSUO); 3500 blk. N.E. 36th, 1 (CSUO). OKMULGEE COUNTY: Okmulgee County, 3 (ECENT); 5 mi. S Okmulgee, 1 (OKSU); 20 mi. SW Okmulgee, 1 (OKSU). OSAGE COUNTY: 5 mi. S Pawhuska, 1 (OKSU); 13 mi. E Pawhuska, 1 (OKSU); 2 mi. S Shidler on Section Rd., 1 (OKSU). OTTAWA COUNTY: 0.25 mi. W Miami on SH 10, 1 (OKSU). PAWNEE COUNTY: Greasy Creek, 9 mi. E Red Rock, 1 (OKSU); T21N, R7E, S 1/2 Sec. 5, 1 (OKSU). PAYNE COUNTY: east side Boomer Lake, 1 (OKSU); below dam, Lake Carl Blackwell, 1 (OKSU); east bank Lake Carl Blackwell, 1 (OKSU); Lake Carl Blackwell, 1 (OKSU); jct. Hwy 177 S & Cimmaron River Bridge, 1 (OKSU); Cleveland, 1 (OMNH); near Forty-north Apartments, 1 (OKSU); 0.5 mi. E Lake McMurtry Dam, 1 (OKSU); campus, Oklahoma State University, 1 (OKSU); dairy farm, Oklahoma State University, 1 (OKSU); 0.5 mi. N Oklahoma State University campus, 1 (OKSU); Payne County, 3 (OKSU); 0.25 mi. E jct. Hwys 33 & 40, near Perkins, 1 (OKSU); 2 mi. E Perkins on Hwy 33, 1 (OKSU); 2.5 mi. W Perkins, 1 (OKSU); 2 mi. S, 3 mi. W Perkins, 1 (OKSU); 3 mi. W, 1 mi. S Perkins Corner, 1 (OKSU); Little Stillwater Creek, 1 (OKSU); Little Stillwater Creek, 1.5 mi. S US 51, 1 (OKSU); Little Stillwater Creek, 1.75 mi. S US 51, 1 (OKSU); agronomy pecan grove, Stillwater, 1 (OKSU); S Stillwater, 1 (OKSU); SE Stillwater, 1 (OKSU); Stillwater, 2 (OKSU); jct. N. Main & Miller St., Stillwater, 1 (OKSU); N. Washington St., Stillwater, 1 (OKSU); 0.25 mi. E Boomer Rd. & 32nd St., Stillwater, 1 (OKSU); 0.25 mi. S Golf Course, Stillwater, 2 (OKSU); 0.25 mi. S Stillwater Sewage Plant, 1 (OKSU); Stillwater Creek, 0.5 mi. W Stillwater, 1 (OKSU); 1 mi. W Stillwater, 1 (OKSU); 1 mi. W, 0.5 mi. S Stillwater, 1 (OKSU); 1 mi. W, 3 mi. S Stillwater, 1 (OKSU); 1 mi. N, 3 mi. W Stillwater, 1 (OKSU); 1.25 mi. N Stillwater, 1 (OKSU); 1.5 mi. W Stillwater, 1 (OKSU); 2 mi. E Stillwater, 1 (OKSU); 2 mi. N, 9 mi. E Stillwater, 1 (OKSU); 2 mi. S Stillwater, 1 (OKSU); 2 mi. S, 0.25 mi. E Stillwater, 1 (OKSU); 2 mi. W Stillwater, 5 (OKSU); 3 mi. E, 1 mi. S Stillwater, 1 (OKSU); 3 mi. E, 2 mi. S Stillwater, 1 (OKSU); 3 mi. E, 3 mi. S Stillwater, 1 (OKSU); 3 mi. E, 4 mi. S Stillwater, 1 (OKSU); 3 mi. N Stillwater, 1 (OKSU); 3 mi. W Stillwater, 2 (OKSU); 3 mi. W, 2 mi. N Stillwater, 1 (OKSU); 4 mi. W Stillwater, 2 (OKSU); 4 mi. S Stillwater on US Hwy 177, 1 (OKSU); 4 mi. W, 0.5 mi. N Stillwater, 1 (OKSU); 4 mi. S, 1 mi. W Stillwater, 1 (OKSU); 4 mi. S, 2 mi. W Stillwater, 1 (OKSU); 4 mi. W, 3 mi. S Stillwater, 3 (OKSU); 5 mi. E Stillwater, 1 (OKSU); 5 mi. E, 3 mi. S jct. SH 177 & 51, 1 (OKSU); 6 mi. W Stillwater, 1 (OKSU); 6 mi. N, 3 mi. W Stillwater, 2 (OKSU); 6 mi. N, 5.5 mi. W Stillwater, 1 (OKSU); 7.5 mi. E, 2 mi. S Stillwater, 1 (OKSU); 8 mi. SE Stillwater, 2 (OKSU); trib. Little Stillwater Creek, 8.5 mi. SE Stillwater, 1 (OKSU); 9 mi. S Stillwater, 1 (OKSU); 10 mi. W, 1 mi. N Stillwater, 2 (OKSU); 13 mi. E, 3 mi.

N Stillwater, 1 (OKSU); 15 mi. E, 20 mi. N Stillwater, 1 (OKSU); 15 mi. W Stillwater on SH 51, 1 (OKSU); W Stillwater on Hwy 33, 1 (OKSU); 1 mi. N Hwy 51 on Hwy 51C, 1 (OKSU); in pecan grove, 1 (OKSU); T19N, R5E, Sec. 6, 1 (OKSU); T19N, R3E, SW 1/4 Sec. 15, 1 (OKSU). PITTS-BURG COUNTY: 4 mi. W Kiowa, 1 (ECENT); 2 mi. E Krebs, 1 (CSUO); Pittsburg County, 1 (OKSU); Savanna, 1 (USNM). PONTOTOC COUNTY: N Ada, 1 (ECENT); 14th St., Ada, 1 (ECENT); 6 mi. N Ada, 1 (ECENT); Pontotoc County, 1 (ECENT). POTTAWATOMIE COUN-TY: 2 mi. S, 1.25 mi. E Pearson, 1 (OKSU); 2 mi. S, 1.25 mi. W Pearson, 1 (OKSU); 9 mi. W Shawnee, 1 (ECENT). PUSHMATAHA COUNTY: 2 mi. W Clayton, 2 (OKSU); 7 mi. NE Clayton, 1 (ECENT); 7 mi. N Clayton, 1 (ECENT). ROGERS COUNTY: T20N, R15E, SW 1/4 Sec. 26, 4 mi. S Catoosa, 1 (OKSU); 10 mi. E Claremore, 1 (OKSU). SEMINOLE COUNTY: Seminole County, 1 (OKSU). SEQUOYAH COUNTY: 2.5 mi. E Akins, 1 (OMNH); 2 mi. S Muldrow, 1 (ECENT). STEPHENS COUNTY: 0.25 mi. E, 0.75 mi. S Claud, 1 (OMNH); 1.25 mi. W, 1.25 mi. S Comanche, 1 (OKSU); 1 mi. W Marlow, 1 (CAMCO); 1 mi. N, 1 mi. E Marlow, 1 (CAMCO); 1 mi. N, 1 mi. W Marlow, 1 (CAMCO); 9 mi. N, 1 mi. E Ringling, 1 (OKSU). TILLMAN COUNTY: 7 mi. W, 6 mi. N Manitou, 2 (CAMCO); 3.25 mi. N, 0.25 mi. E Tipton, 1 (OKSU). TULSA COUNTY: 5 mi. W Bixby, 1 (OKSU); 5.5 mi. N Broken Arrow, 1 (OKSU); 17 mi. N, 7 mi. W Broken Arrow, 1 (OKSU); Garnett, 2 (UMMZ); Mohawk Park, 1 (OKSU); 8 mi. W Red Fork, 11 (USNM); 2 mi. E, 5 mi. N Skiatook, 1 (OKSU); 1.5 mi. N Sperry, 2 (OKSU); Wood-land Animal Hospital, Tulsa, 1 (OKSU); 2 mi. W Tulsa, 1 (OMNH). WASHINGTON COUNTY: 1 mi. S Caney River, Bartlesville, 1 (OKSU); 3 mi. S Bartlesville, 1 (OKSU). WOODS COUNTY: Alva, Oklahoma Ter-ritory, 6 (FMNH); 2 mi. N, 1.5 mi. W Alva, 1 (OKSU); 2 mi. W, 2.5 mi. S Dacoma, 1 (OKSU); 3 mi. SW Waynoka, 1 (USNM), 1 (OMNH). WOOD-WARD COUNTY: Boiling Springs State Park, 1 (OMNH); 0.5 mi. E Mooreland, 1 (OKSU); 3.5 mi. W Mooreland, 1 (OKSU); Woodward, 1 (USNM).

Sigmodon hispidus.—Specimens examined (total 1,622): ADAIR COUNTY: 1.5 mi. W Chewey, 800 ft., 12 (OMNH); 2.5 mi. NW Chewey, 900 ft., 1 (OMNH); 3 mi. NNW Chewey, 1,000 ft., 1 (OMNH); Stilwell, 1 (UIMNH); 2 mi. S Stilwell, 1 (OKSU); 2.5 mi. E Stilwell, 8 (UIMNH); 7 mi. W Stilwell, 2 (KU). ALFALFA COUNTY: 3 mi. E Cherokee, 1 (OMNH); 5.3 mi. S, 8.4 mi. E Driftwood, 2 (KU); Great Salt Plains Wild-life Refuge, 1 (OMNH); 8 mi. N Jet, 1,170 ft., 1 (OMNH); Salt Plains Wildlife Refuge, 1 (OMNH). BEAVER COUNTY: 1.5 mi. N Beaver, 1 (KU); Lake Evans Chambers, 1 (OMNH); 3 mi. NW Slapout, 3 (OMNH). BECKHAM COUNTY: 5 mi. N Texola, 3 (OMNH). BLAINE COUNTY:

3 mi. E Canton on SH 51, 1 (OKSU); 1 mi. E Project Office, Canton Lake, 8 (OMNH); 1 mi. N Canton Lake, 1 (OMNH); Canton Reservoir, 1 (OKSU); 0.5 mi. E Canton Reservoir, 1 (OKSU); 2 mi. N, 1 mi. W Hydro, 1 (KU); 2 mi. W Longdale, 1 (OKSU); Roman Nose State Park, 4 (OKSU); 2 mi. S, 3 mi. W Southland, 1 (OKSU). BRYAN COUNTY: 7 mi. S, 5 mi. W Bennington, 1 (OKSU); 0.25 mi. W Colbert, 6 (TMM); 0.5 mi. W Colbert, 2 (TMM); 5 mi. E Colbert, 1 (OUBS); 5 mi. SW Colbert, 1 (TMM). CADDO COUNTY: Canyon 13, 9 mi. E Binger, 1 (OMNH); 4.2 mi. W Cogar, 1 (OMNH); 5 mi. W Cogar, 4 (OMNH), 1 (USNM); 1.5 mi. SE Cyril, 2 (CAMCO); Washington River, 11 mi. below old Ft. Cobb, 1 (USNM). CANADIAN COUNTY: 3 mi. W El Reno on US Hwy 66, 6 mi. N, 0.5 mi. W, 1 (OKSU); Ft. Reno, 3 (USNM); 17 mi. NW Oklahoma City, 1 (CSUO); 4 mi. E, 2 mi. S Union City, 1 (OKSU). CHEROKEE COUNTY: Cookson Hills Game Refuge, 1 (OKSU); 4 mi. N Cookson Hills Wildlife Refuge, 1 (OKSU); jct. Dogwood & Maple, Tahlequah, 8 (OMNH); 2.25 mi. SE Tahlequah, 2 (OMNH). CHOCTAW COUNTY: 7 mi. SSE Ft. Towson, 400 ft., 10 (OMNH); 1.5 mi. SE Grant, 1 (OKSU); 3 mi. E, 1 mi. N Hugo, 2 (OKSU). CIMARRON COUNTY: 4 mi. N, 4 mi. E Kenton, 1 (OMNH). CLEVELAND COUNTY: bank Canadian River, 1 (OUBS); Cleveland County, 7 (OMNH); NW Cleveland County, 21 (OMNH); 2 mi. S, 0.25 mi. W Lexington, 5 (OMNH); Noble, Oklahoma Territory, 6 (FMNH); 0.25 mi. SE Noble, 1 (OMNH); T8N, R2W, Sec. 27, 0.5 mi. SW Noble, 1 (OMNH); Canadian River Bridge I-35 S, Norman, 2 (OMNH); Hog Creek Arm, Little River Reservoir, Norman, 2 (OMNH); Little River Reservoir, Norman, 2 (OMNH); Little River Reservoir, 7 mi. E Alameda & Classen Hwy 9, Norman, 1 (OMNH); Norman, 6 (OMNH); city dump, Norman, 5 (OMNH); Oliver's Woods, Norman, 3 (OMNH); Police Firing Range, Norman, 1 (OMNH); Bldg. 904, North Campus, University of Oklahoma, Norman, 1 (OMNH); campus, University of Oklahoma, Norman, 2 (KU); S Norman, 1 (OMNH); jct. 12th & Alameda St., Norman, 1 (OMNH); 1.9–3.1 mi. S Norman, 2 (OMNH); Oliver's Woods, 1 mi. S Norman, 2 (OMNH); 0.1 mi. W 77th on Rock Creek Rd., Norman, 2 (OMNH); 1 mi. S Norman, 1,100 ft., 4 (OMNH), 1 (OKSU); 1.5 mi. S Norman, 1 (OUBS); 1.6 mi. S Lindsey on Jenkins, Norman, 1 (OMNH); 1.6 mi. S Norman, 1 (OMNH); 1.7 mi. N Norman, 2 (OMNH), 3 (USNM); Oliver's Woods, 2 mi. S Norman, 2 (OMNH); 2 mi. E Norman, 7 (OMNH); 2 mi. E Porter on Robinson, 0.9 mi. N Norman, 1 (OMNH); 2 mi. N Norman, 2 (OMNH); 2 mi. N Robinson St. on 77th, Norman, 3 (OMNH); 2 mi. NE Norman, 4 (OMNH); 2 mi. S Norman, 4 (OMNH); 2 mi. W, 1 mi. S Norman, 1 (OMNH); 2 mi. S University of Oklahoma campus, Norman, 2 (KU); 2.1 mi. E Norman, 1 (KU); 2.5 mi. S Norman, 1 (KU); 2.7 mi. E Norman, 1 (KU); 3 mi. E Norman,

21 (OMNH); 3 mi. N Norman, 1 (OMNH); 3 mi. N, 2.5 mi. E Norman, 2 (OMNH); 3 mi. N, 10 mi. E Norman, 1 (OMNH); 3 mi. SE Norman, 1 (OMNH); 3 mi. W Norman, 1 (OMNH); 3.5 mi. SE Norman, 1 (OMNH); 4 mi. S Norman, 3 (OMNH); 5 mi. E, 0.5 mi. N Norman, 5 (OMNH); 5 mi. N Norman, 1 (OMNH); 5 mi. S Norman, 7 (OMNH); 6.2 mi. E Norman, 2 (OMNH), 2 (USNM); 6.2 mi. E Norman, 1,100 ft., 2 (OMNH); 6.5 mi. E, 1 mi. N Norman, 1 (OMNH); 6.5 mi. NE Norman, 9 (OMNH); 6.6 mi. E Norman, 1,100 ft., 1 (OMNH); 11.5 mi. E Norman, 3 (OMNH); Little River Reservoir, 11.7 mi. E Norman, 15 (OMNH); T8N, R3W, across river from Norman Dump, 1 (OMNH); Northwest, 13 (OMNH); 2 mi. N Slaughterville, 1 (OMNH); 2 mi. S Slaughterville, 3 (OMNH); 0.5 mi. E South Canadian River Bridge, between I-240 and H. E. Bailey Turnpike, 1 (CSUO); Thunderbird Lake, 3 (OMNH); T8N, R2W, Sec. 16, 1 (OMNH); T9N, R3W, Sec. 30, 31, 32, 1 (OMNH); T9N, R3W, Sec. 33, 1 (OMNH). COAL COUNTY: 1 mi. W, 2 mi. S Coalgate, 1 (OMNH). COMANCHE COUNTY: Cache, 1 (CAMCO); Camp Boulder, 1 (OMNH); Chattanooga, 6 (USNM); Comanche County, 2 (CAMCO); 3.75 mi. W, 1.5 mi. S Elgin, 1 (CAMCO); 8 mi. SW Elgin, 1 (CAMCO); Faxon, 2 (CAMCO); Ft. Sill, 1 (CAMCO); White Wolf Crossing, Ft. Sill, 2 (CAMCO); 1 mi. N Ft. Sill, 1 (CAMCO); Lake Lawtonka, 1 (CAMCO); Medicine Park, Lake Lawtonka, 1 (CAMCO); Lawton, 2 (CAMCO); 2 mi. N, 2 mi. E Lawton, 1 (CAMCO); 3 mi. S Lawton, 1 (CAMCO); 5 mi. E, 2 mi. N Lawton, 1 (CAMCO); 6.5 mi. E, 4 mi. N Lawton, 1 (CAMCO); Wichita Mountains Estates, 10 mi. N Lawton, 1 (CAMCO); 10 mi. E Lawton, 1 (CAMCO); 10 mi. E, 4 mi. N Lawton, 1 (CAMCO); 3 mi. E Meers, 1 (CAMCO); Mt. Scott Post Office, 13 (USNM); Wichita Mountains, 33 (USNM); Lost Lake, Wichita Mountains, 1 (OKSU); Wichita Mountains Wildlife Refuge, 1 (OMNH); Camp Boulder, Wichita Mountains Wildlife Refuge, 2 (OKSU), 1 (OMNH). COTTON COUNTY: 3.3 mi. ESE Taylor, 900 ft., 7 (OMNH); 5 mi. SE Taylor, 900 ft., 10 (OMNH); 5.5 mi. W Walters, 1 (OMNH). CRAIG COUNTY: 1 mi. S, 0.25 mi. W Big Cabin on Hwy 69, 1 (OKSU); 1.75 mi. S, 0.25 mi. W Big Cabin on Hwy 69, 1 (OKSU); 2 mi. S, 0.125 mi. W Big Cabin on Hwy 69, 2 (OKSU); 3.5 mi. E, 0.5 mi. N Centralia, 5 (OMNH). CREEK COUNTY: Sapulpa, 53 (KU). CUSTER COUNTY: 3 mi. W, 0.25 mi. N Thomas, 2 (OKSU); Myrtle Dick Estate, S.E. 155th, 0.25 mi. W Weatherford, 2 (OKSU); 0.5 mi. N, 1 mi. E Weatherford, 1 (KU); 0.75 mi. S Weatherford, 2 (KU); 1 mi. N Weatherford, 1 (KU); 1.5 mi. S, 1 mi. W Weatherford, 1 (KU); T15N, R14W, Sec. 7, 1 (OMNH); T15N, R16W, Sec. 16, 1 (OMNH). DELAWARE COUNTY: 2 mi. E Colcord, 1 (OKSU); 3 mi. E Colcord, 1 (OKSU); 1.5 mi. SE Grant, 1 (OKSU); 4 mi. NW Grove, 2 (KU); 7.5 mi. SE Jay, 1 (CSUO); Lake Eucha, 3 (OMNH). DEWEY COUNTY: 5 mi.

W Canton, 3 (KU); T19N, R13W, Sec. 15, Canton Public Hunting, 1 (ECENT); Dewey County, 7 (KU); 7 mi. W, 2 mi. S Longdale, 1 (OKSU); jct. South Canadian River Bridge & Hwy 183, Taloga, 9 (OMNH); 1 mi. N Taloga, 2 (OMNH). ELLIS COUNTY: 1 mi. W Shattuck, 1 (CSUO). GARFIELD COUNTY: Enid, 2 (OKSU); south fence line, Vance Air Force Base, Enid, 1 (OKSU). GARVIN COUNTY: 8 mi. E Pauls Valley on SH 19, 1 (OKSU). GRADY COUNTY: 3 mi. W, 0.1 mi. S Blanchard, 1 (OMNH); 3 mi. W, 1 mi. S Blanchard, 1 (USNM). GRANT COUNTY: 1 mi. W, 1 mi. N Hawley, 9 (OMNH); 1.4 mi. W, 1 mi. N Hawley, 10 (OMNH); 3 mi. NW Pond Creek, 20 (OMNH); 0.5 mi. N Renfrow, 1 (USNM); 2.3 mi. N, 8 mi. W Renfrow, 6 (USNM). HARMON COUNTY: 5.3 mi. N Hollis, 1 (FWMSH); 5.5 mi. S Hollis, 3 (FWMSH); 6 mi. N Hollis, 4 (FWMSH); Kirby's Corner, 8 mi. N, 1.5 mi. W Hollis, 1 (FWMSH); 9 mi. E, 1 mi. N Hollis, 2 (OMNH); 9 mi. E, 1 mi. S Hollis, 3 (OMNH); 9 mi. S, 1 mi. E Hollis, 3 (OMNH); 10 mi. N. 1 mi. W Hollis, 3 (TTU); 11 mi. N Hollis, 1 (FWMSH); 13.5 mi. N Hollis, 1 (OKSU); 6 mi. E, 1 mi. S Vinson, 1 (OMNH); 6 mi. E, 1 mi. S Vinson, 1,700 ft., 3 (OMNH). HARPER COUNTY: pasture 19, Southern Great Plains Exp. Range, Ft. Supply, 1 (OKSU); pasture 20, Southern Great Plains Exp. Range, Ft. Supply, 1 (OKSU); pasture 26, Southern Great Plains Exp. Range, Ft. Supply, 1 (OKSU); Southern Great Plains Exp. Range, 3 mi. NW Ft. Supply, 11 (USNM); 3 mi. N Ft. Supply, 4 (USNM). HASKELL COUNTY: 0.5 mi. W, 0.25 mi. S Garland, 1 (OMNH); 8 mi. SE Stigler, 2 (OKSU); 8.5 mi. S Stigler, 1 (OMNH). HUGHES COUNTY: 9 mi. E, 1 mi. N Holdenville, 4 (OMNH); 3.5 mi. S Wetumka, 2 (ECENT). JACKSON COUNTY: 5 mi. W Altus, 1 (OKSU); 3.5 mi. E Duke, 1 (CAMCO); 3.5 mi. S Eldorado, 1 (CAMCO); 1.5 mi. S, 1.5 mi. E Olustee, 2 (CAMCO); 4.5 mi. S, 4.5 mi. W Olustee, 1 (CAMCO). JOHNSTON COUNTY: 2 mi. W Tishomingo, 3 (OKSU); Blue River, 9 mi. E Tishomingo, 3 (OMNH). KAY COUNTY: 5 mi. S, 7.5 mi. E Newkirk, 1,100 ft., 4 (OMNH); 5 mi. S, 10.5 mi. E Newkirk, 1,150 ft., 29 (OMNH); 11.5 mi. SE Newkirk, 1 (OMNH); 1 mi. E Ponca City, 1 (OKSU); T25N, R2E, Sec. 8, Ponca City, 3 (OKSU). KINGFISHER COUNTY: Hwy 51 & Cimarron River, 2 (OKSU); Kingfisher County, 1 (OMNH); T16N, R4W, Sec. 11, 1 (OMNH); T9N, R7W, Sec. 13, 1 (OMNH); T17N, R5W, Sec. 30, 1 (OMNH). KIOWA COUNTY: 1.5 mi. E Snyder, 1 (CAMCO). LATIMER COUNTY: first ridge N, Eastern Oklahoma State College, 2 (OKSU); Robber's Cave State Park, 1 (CSUO); 9 mi. W Talihina, 1 (OKSU); 10 mi. W Talihina, 2 (OKSU); campus, Eastern Oklahoma State College, Wilburton, 1 (OKSU); hill behind boy's dorm, Wilburton, 1 (OKSU); pasture, S campus, Wilburton, 1 (OKSU); Robber's Cave State Park, 5 mi. N Wilburton, 4 (KU). LEFLORE COUNTY: 5 mi. N, 2.5 mi. E Bokoshe, 2

(OMNH); 2.5 mi. NW Stapp, 4 (OMNH); 5 mi. S Wister, 8 (OMNH); 0.5 mi. NW Zoe, 2 (OMNH); 1.5 mi. NE Zoe, 1 (OMNH); 1.5 mi. NW Zoe, 4 (OMNH). LOGAN COUNTY: Baggerly Woods, 0.25 mi. N Waterloo Rd. on Bryant, 3 (CSUO); 0.25 mi. N jct. Waterloo Rd. & Bryant, 1 (CSUO); 5 mi. N Edmond on Bryant, 0.4 mi. N Waterloo Rd., 1 (CSUO); field NW jct. Waterloo & Bryant Rd., 1 (CSUO); Hwy 74 & Cimarron River, 1 (CSUO); Cimarron River, S Crescent, 1 (CSUO); T16N, R4W, NE 1/4 Sec. 11, 4 mi. S Crescent, 1 (OKSU); near Guthrie, 1 (OKSU); Logan County, 6 (OMNH); Orlando, 2 (USNM); T16N, R4W, Sec. 2, 1 (OMNH); T16N, R4W, Sec. 10, 1 (OMNH); T16N, R4W, Sec. 11, 3 (OMNH). MAJOR COUNTY: near Alabaster Caverns State Park, 1 (CSUO); northeast bank Cimarron River, Cleo Springs, 1 (USNM); 3 mi. S Cleo Springs, 1 (OMNH). MARSHALL COUNTY: north end Buncombe, 620 ft., 1 (OMNH); 3.6 mi. SE Kingston, 2 (OMNH); 1 mi. W Madill, 1 (OKSU); Marshall County, 1 (OUBS); 0.5 mi. N Paul's Landing, 630 ft., 1 (OMNH); University of Oklahoma Biological Station, 11 (OUBS), 2 (OMNH); 100 yds. N University of Oklahoma Biological Station, 1 (OUBS); 0.25 W University of Oklahoma Biological Station, 1 (OMNH), 3 (OUBS); 0.25 mi. N University of Oklahoma Biological Station, 1 (OUBS); 0.25 mi. NW University of Oklahoma Biological Station, 1 (OUBS); 0.3 mi. W University of Oklahoma Biological Station, 1 (OUBS); 0.5 mi. W University of Oklahoma Biological Station, 5 (OUBS); 0.5 mi W University of Oklahoma Biological Station, 640 ft., 1 (OMNH); 0.5 mi. N University of Oklahoma Biological Station, 700 ft., 1 (OMNH); 0.8 mi. W University of Oklahoma Biological Station, 3 (OUBS); 1 mi. N University of Oklahoma Biological Station, 1 (OMNH); 1 mi. E University of Oklahoma Biological Station, 2 (OUBS); 1 mi. W University of Oklahoma Biological Station, 8 (OUBS); 1.25 mi. W University of Oklahoma Biological Station, 1 (OUBS); 1.5 mi. W University of Oklahoma Biological Station, 2 (OUBS); 1.7 mi. W University of Oklahoma Biological Station, 200 yds. S Willis Rd., 1 (OUBS); 2 mi. NW University of Oklahoma Biological Station, 1 (OUBS); 2 mi. W University of Oklahoma Biological Station, 7 (OUBS); 3 mi. W University of Oklahoma Biological Station, 3 (OUBS); Engineers Flats, 4 mi. W University of Oklahoma Biological Station, 1 (OUBS); Willis, 1 (OUBS); W Willis, 700 ft., 2 (OMNH); N Willis, 800 ft., 1 (OMNH); 0.5 mi. N Willis, 1 (OUBS); 0.5 mi. W Willis, 1 (OUBS); 0.5 mi. E Willis, 690 ft., 4 (OMNH); 0.5 mi. N, 0.5 mi. W Willis, 2 (OMNH); 0.5 mi. S, 0.5 mi. E Willis, 2 (OUBS); 1 mi. W Willis, 2 (OUBS); 1 mi. E Willis, 630 ft., 21 (OMNH); 1 mi. W Willis, 700 ft., 1 (OMNH); 1.5 mi. N Willis, 1 (OUBS); 2 mi. E Willis, 630 ft., 16 (OMNH); 2 mi. N Willis, 800 ft., 2 (OMNH); 3 mi. NW Willis, 1 (OUBS); 3 mi. W Willis, 1 (OUBS); 3.5 mi. N Willis, 1 (OMNH); 4.5 mi.

N Willis, 1 (OUBS); 5 mi. N Willis, 1 (OUBS); 5.5 mi. N Willis, 1 (OUBS); jct. Hwys 99 & 32, 10 mi. N Willis, 720 ft., 1 (OMNH). MAYES COUNTY: 2.5 mi. E Chouteau, 1.0 mi. N Hwy 33, 2 (OMNH); 3.2 mi. E Chouteau, 0.5 mi. N Hwy 33, 1 (OMNH). MCCLAIN COUNTY: 2 mi. W Byars, 3 (OKSU); 2.7 mi. N, 0.5 mi. W Goldsby, 2 (OMNH), 1 (USNM); 4 mi. S, 1.2 mi. W Goldsby, 2 (OMNH), 2 (USNM); Johnson's pasture, 1 (OMNH); McClain County, 9 (OMNH); 1 mi. S Norman, 9 (OMNH); 9 mi. W Norman, 1 (OMNH); 1 mi. S, 0.5 mi. W Purcell, 4 (OMNH); T8N, R4W, NE 1/4 Sec. 11, 3 (OMNH); T8N, R4W, Sec. 11, 2 (OMNH). MCCURTAIN COUNTY: 5.7 mi. S Broken Bow, 10 (OMNH); 15 mi. SE Broken Bow, 2 (OMNH); Mt. Fork River, 2 mi. W Eagletown, 1 (TMM); 3 mi. W Eagletown, 1 (TMM); 3 mi. SSE Tom, 4 (UIMNH); 4.5 mi. SE Tom, 3 (UIMNH); 5 mi. SE Tom, 2 (UIMNH); T4, R27, Sec. 35, Veals Farm, 1 (CSUO). MCINTOSH COUNTY: 5 mi. E, 1 mi. N Checotah, 5 (OMNH). MURRAY COUNTY: Dougherty, Indian Territory, 7 (FMNH); Rock Creek Camp Ground, Platt Natl. Park, 5 (KU). MUSKOGEE COUNTY: Wildlife Conservation Station, Braggs, 3 (OKSU); 2.5 mi. NE Wildlife Conservation Station, Braggs, 2 (OKSU); Camp Gruber, 3 mi. NE Braggs, 1 (OKSU); Huggins Farm, 0.5 mi. S Ft. Gibson, 9 (FWMSH); Greenleaf Lake, 1 (OKSU); Greenleaf Lake Lodge, 1 (OKSU); Muskogee, 1 (CSUO); 1 mi. S Muskogee, 1 (OMNH); 5 mi. SE Muskogee, 1 (OKSU); 3 mi. E Wainwright, 6 (OMNH). NOBLE COUNTY: Red Rock Creek, 13 mi. S Ponca City, 2 (OKSU); 5 mi. W Red Rock, 1 (OKSU); 5 mi. W, 3 mi. N Stillwater, 1 (OKSU); 5 mi. N, 6 mi. W Stillwater, 1 (OKSU); 1 mi. E jct. Hwys 177 & 15 W, 2 (OMNH); T23N, R2E, SW 1/4 Sec. 26, 1 (OKSU). NOWATA COUNTY: 2 mi. S South Coffeyville, 3 (OMNH); Paul Buck Ranch, 2 mi. NW Wann, 1 (OKSU). OKFUSKEE COUNTY: 2 mi. W, 0.25 mi. S Mason, 1 (OKSU). OKLAHOMA COUNTY: jct. Bryant & Waterloo, 3 (CSUO); 0.5 mi. N Central State University on Chartrand & Crown, 3 (CSUO); 5 mi. E Central State University, 5 (CSUO); Hwy 74 & Cimarron River, 1 (CSUO); Del City Park, 2 (CSUO); Edmond, 2 (CSUO); E Edmond, 1 (OKSU); 327 E. 10th Street, Edmond, 1 (CSUO); jct. N. Boulevard & Danforth, Edmond, 1 (CSUO); jct. Bryant & Danforth, Edmond, 1 (CSUO); jct. Coltrane & 33rd, Edmond, 3 (CSUO); jct. 33rd & Blvd., Edmond, 1 (CSUO); jct. 33rd & Broadway, Edmond, 5 (CSUO); jct. Waterloo & Bryant, Edmond, 2 (CSUO); Vickers Study Plot, Edmond, 13 (CSUO); 0.1 mi. S Edmond, 2 (CSUO); E Eastern Ave., 0.1 mi. S Edmond, 1 (CSUO); 0.2 mi. W Boulevard on Sorghum Mill Rd., Edmond, 2 (CSUO); 0.5 mi. N Danforth on May Ave., Edmond, 4 (CSUO); 0.5 mi. S S. 15th & 0.5 mi. W Bryant, Edmond, 2 (CSUO); 0.5 mi. W Bryant, 0.5 mi. S S. 15th, Edmond, 2 (CSUO); 0.8 mi. W of Kelly St. on 15th, Edmond, 1 (CSUO); 1 mi. N Edmond, 1 (CSUO); 1 mi. N 2nd St. on Kelly Ave., Edmond, 1 (CSUO); 1.5 mi. N 2nd St. on Kelly Ave., Edmond, 1 (CSUO); 3 mi. N, 4 mi. E Edmond, 1 (OKSU); 4 mi. E Edmond, 3 (CSUO); 5 mi. E Edmond, 2 (CSUO); 5 mi. N Edmond on Bryant (Vickers Prairie), 2 (CSUO); west side Bryant Rd., 5 mi. N Edmond (Vickers Prairie), 2 (CSUO); 6 mi. W Edmond, 2 (CSUO); 6.8 mi. W Edmond, 1 (CSUO); 8 mi. W, 4.8 mi. N Edmond, 1 (CSUO); 1 mi. S Edmond Rd. on Meridian, 6 (CSUO); Lake Hefner Area, 1 (CSUO); N Lake Hefner, 100 yds. W Portland Ave., 1 (CSUO); N.E. 10th, 0.2 mi. E of Sooner Rd., 3 (CSUO); 0.65 mi. S Turner Turnpike on Sooner Rd., 1 (CSUO); Oklahoma City, 3 (CSUO); Lake Hefner Area, Oklahoma City, 4 (CSUO); Oklahoma City Zoo, 1 (OKSU); Oklahoma County, 1 (OMNH); 4 mi. W jct. Eastern & Wilshire, 1 (CSUO); 10320 N. Kelly, Oklahoma City, 1 (CSUO); 5900 blk. S. Missouri, Oklahoma City, 1 (OMNH), 1 (USNM); 3401 S.W. 29th, 1 (CSUO); jct. 122nd St. & Penn, Oklahoma City, 8 (CSUO); 14 mi. S Oklahoma City, 1 (OMNH); southeast corner N. Western & 122nd St., 1 (CSUO); 0.25 mi. N N. 234th & May, 1 (CSUO); 0.5 mi. W Bryant on 15th St., 1 (CSUO); 0.5 mi. N N.W. 192nd on May Ave., 2 (CSUO); 0.5 mi. N 1923 N. May Ave., 1 (CSUO); 0.5 mi. NW 10th & Council Rd., 1 (CSUO); 1 mi. W Council Rd. & N.W. 10th, 1 (CSUO); 3.1 mi. E jct. Hwy 66 & I-35 N, 2 (CSUO); Terra Regal Trailer Court, 1 (CSUO); across Hwy from Tinker Field, 2 (OKSU); 1 mi. E Will Rogers Airport, 1 (OMNH); T13N, R4W, Sec. 27, 1 (OMNH); T13N, R3W, Sec. 30, 1 (OMNH). OKMULGEE COUNTY: 1 mi. E Henryetta, 1 (OMNH); 3 mi. E, 2 mi. N Okmulgee, 5 (OMNH). OSAGE COUNTY: Arkansas River, 4 mi. SW Fairfax, 1 (OKSU); Osage Hills State Park, 3 (OKSU); 5 mi. S Pawhuska, 1 (OKSU); 7 mi. NE Pawhuska on US 60, 2 (OMNH). OTTAWA COUNTY: 2 mi. S, 6 mi. E Afton, 1 (KU); 5 mi. S Fairland, 2 (OKSU). PAWNEE COUNTY: 7 mi. N, 2.75 mi. W Pawnee, 3 (KU); 7.5 mi. N, 2.75 mi. W Pawnee, 1 (KU); Arkansas River, 2 mi. S, 5 mi. E Stillwater, 1 (OKSU); 28 mi. N, 2 mi. E Stillwater, 1 (OKSU); 2.5 mi. N, 0.5 mi. E Watchorn, 6 (OMNH). PAYNE COUNTY: S Boomer Dam, 1 (OKSU); 0.5 mi. E Boomer Lake Dam, 1 (OKSU); W Boomer Lake, 6 (OKSU); west side Boomer Lake, 1 (OKSU); southwest slope Boomer Lake, 3 (OKSU); Boomer Lake, 5 (OKSU); southeast slope Boomer Lake, 2 (OKSU); northeast shore Boomer Lake, 1 (OKSU); 0.5 mi. E Boomer Lake, 1 (OKSU); 4 mi. W Cushing, 1 (OKSU); 2 mi. NE Glencoe, 1 (OKSU); Cedar Pt., Lake Carl Blackwell, 1 (OKSU); Lake Carl Blackwell, 12 (OKSU); SW Lake Blackwell, 1 (OKSU); west end Lake Blackwell, 1 (OKSU); 0.5 mi. SE spillway, Lake Carl Blackwell, 1 (OKSU); 2 mi. N Lake Carl Blackwell Hdqtrs., 1 (OKSU); Lake McMurtry, 1 (OKSU); dairy barn, Oklahoma State University, 1 (OKSU); intramural field, Oklahoma State University, 1 (OKSU); 1 mi. N Life Science Building, Oklahoma State University, 1 (FWMSH); old golf course, N Married Students Housing, campus, Oklahoma State University, 1 (OKSU); Physical Plant Services Dump, N Married Students Housing, Oklahoma State University, 1 (OKSU); Payne County, 2 (OKSU); just NE jct. 6th & Perkins, 3 (OKSU); 1.5 mi. S Progress, 3 (OKSU); Sanborn Lake, 3 (OKSU); 0.25 mi. N Sanborn Lake, 3 (FWMSH); Stillwater Airport, 1 (OKSU); back of Stillwater Airport, 6 (FWMSH); Berry Park, Stillwater, 1 (OKSU); Boomer Lake Dam, Stillwater, 1 (OKSU); Boomer Lake, N Stillwater, 2 (FWMSH); N Boomer Lake, Stillwater, 1 (OKSU); northeast side Boomer Lake, Stillwater, 2 (ECENT); east side Boomer Lake, Stillwater, 1 (ECENT); below dam, Boomer Lake, Stillwater, 1 (OKSU); campus, Oklahoma State University, Stillwater, 1 (OKSU); College Golf Course, Stillwater, 2 (OKSU); Golf Course, Stillwater, 2 (OKSU); east edge Stillwater, 2 (OKSU); field N Virginia St., 2 blks. E Stallard Dr., Stillwater, 1 (OKSU); Hillcrest Golf Course, Stillwater, 5 (OKSU); Isaac Walton League, Stillwater, 3 (OKSU); Isaac Walton Lodge, 3 mi. N Stillwater, 1 (OKSU); Lovell Farm, 6 mi. E, 2 mi. S Stillwater, 1 (OKSU); Sec. 24, east side, Lake Carl Blackwell, 7.5 mi. W, 0.5 mi. N Stillwater, 1 (OKSU); near McElroy & Western, Stillwater, 1 (OKSU); Municipal Golf Course, Stillwater, 2 (OKSU); N Stillwater, 1 (OKSU); NW section Stillwater, 1 (OKSU); swine barn, Oklahoma State University, Stillwater, 1 (OKSU); Stillwater, 10 (OKSU); area bounded by Perkins Rd., 6th St., 3rd St., Dryden St. & Benj St., Stillwater, 3 (OKSU); E 500 blk. Perkins Rd., Stillwater, 1 (OKSU); southwest corner jct. SH 51 & Jardot St., Stillwater, 1 (OKSU); water plant, Stillwater, 1 (OKSU); west edge Stillwater, 1 (OKSU); 50 yds. N of 619 W. 24th St., Stillwater, 1 (OKSU); 100 yds. NE jct. Tyler St. & N. Main, Stillwater, 1 (OKSU); 300 yds. N Creek Ridge on Hwy 51, Stillwater, 1 (OKSU); 0.5 mi. E Stillwater, 2 (OKSU); 0.5 mi. N Stillwater, 1 (OKSU); 0.5 mi. W, 0.25 mi. N Stillwater, 2 (OKSU); 0.5 mi. N, 0.5 mi. E Stillwater, 1 (OKSU); 0.5 mi. N jct. Lakeview & Sangre Rd., Stillwater, 2 (OKSU); 0.8 mi. E Stillwater, 1 (OKSU); 0.8 mi. W Stillwater, 1 (OKSU); 1 mi. E, 0.5 mi. N Stillwater, 1 (OKSU); 1 mi. E, 2 mi. N Stillwater, 1 (OKSU); 1 mi. E, 6 mi. N Stillwater, 3 (OKSU); 1 mi. N Stillwater, 3 (OKSU); Boomer Lake, 1 mi. N Stillwater, 1 (OKSU); 1 mi. N, 1 mi. E Stillwater, 1 (OKSU); 1 mi. N, 1 mi. W Stillwater, 3 (OKSU); 1 mi. S SH 51 on Stillwater Creek, 1 (OKSU); 1 mi. S, 1 mi. W Stillwater, 2 (OKSU); 1 mi. W Stillwater, 13 (OKSU); 1 mi. W, 0.25 mi. N Stillwater on Hwy 51, 1 (OKSU); 1.25 mi. E jct. Boomer Rd. & 32nd St., Stillwater, 1 (OKSU); 1.25 mi. E Stillwater, 1 (OKSU); 1.25 mi. W Stillwater, 1 (OKSU); 1.3 mi. W, 15 mi. N Stillwater, 1 (OKSU); 1.5 mi. E Stillwater, 1 (OKSU); 1.5

mi. W Western on Farm Rd., Stillwater, 2 (OKSU); 2 mi. E Stillwater, 1 (OKSU); 2 mi. E, 2 mi. N Stillwater, 3 (OKSU); 2 mi. N Stillwater, 9 (OKSU); 2 mi. N, 1 mi. W Stillwater, 1 (OKSU); 2 mi. N, 1.5 mi. E Stillwater, 1 (OKSU); 2 mi. S Stillwater, 9 (OKSU); 2 mi. S, 0.5 mi. E Stillwater, 5 (OKSU); 2 mi. SE Stillwater, 1 (UIMNH); 2 mi. W Airport, Stillwater, 4 (OKSU); 2 mi. W Stillwater, 5 (OKSU); 2 mi. W, 1 mi. S Stillwater, 1 (OKSU); 2 mi. W, 2 mi. N Stillwater, 1 (OKSU); 2.5 mi. W Stillwater, 2 (OKSU); 2.5 mi. W, 1 mi. S Stillwater, 1 (OKSU); 3 mi. E Stillwater, 1 (OKSU); 3 mi. N Stillwater, 1 (OKSU); 3 mi. N, 1 mi. W Stillwater, 1 (OKSU); 3 mi. NE Stillwater, 1 (OKSU); 3 mi. S, 1 mi. E Stillwater, 1 (OKSU); 3 mi. W Stillwater, 2 (OKSU); 3 mi. W, 0.5 mi. S Stillwater, 1 (FWMSH); 3.5 mi. W Stillwater, 4 (OKSU); 4 mi. E, 0.5 mi. S Stillwater, 1 (OKSU); 4 mi. N Stillwater, 1 (OKSU); 4 mi. N, 2.5 mi. E Stillwater, 2 (OKSU); 4 mi. N, 3 mi. W Stillwater, 1 (OKSU); 4 mi. NW Stillwater, 1 (OKSU); 4 mi. W Stillwater, 6 (OKSU); 4 mi. W Stillwater, 0.5 mi. S Hwy 51, 1 (OKSU); 4 mi. W, 1 mi. S Stillwater, 1 (OKSU); 4 mi. W, 2 mi. S Stillwater, 7 (OKSU); Lake Carl Blackwell, 5 mi. NW Stillwater, 1 (OKSU); Lake Carl Blackwell spillway, 5 mi. W Stillwater, 1 (OKSU); 5 mi. W Stillwater, 0.25 mi. N SH 51, 2 (OKSU); 5 mi. W, 2 mi. N Stillwater, 1 (OKSU); 6 mi. N Stillwater, 1 (OKSU); 6 mi. N, 2 mi. E Stillwater, 1 (OKSU); 6 mi. N, 2.5 mi. E Stillwater, 1 (OKSU); 7 mi. SE Stillwater, 1 (OKSU); 7 mi. W Stillwater, 1 (OKSU); 7.5 mi. SE Stillwater, 1 (OKSU); 7.4 mi. W Stillwater, 7 (OKSU); Lake Carl Blackwell, 7.4 mi. W Stillwater, 1 (OKSU); 8 mi. NW Stillwater, 1 (OKSU); near Lake Carl Blackwell, 8 mi. W Stillwater, 1 (OKSU); near Oklahoma State University Ecology Preserve, 8 mi. W Stillwater, 1 (OKSU); 8.25 mi. W Stillwater, 1 (OKSU); 10 mi. W Stillwater, 2 (OKSU); 12 mi. W Stillwater, 1 (OKSU); 13 mi. W, 1.5 mi. N Stillwater, 6 (FWMSH); 13.5 mi. E Stillwater, 2 (OKSU); college pecan orchard, 2 (OKSU); Vet's Village Pond, 1 (OKSU); east side Vet's Village Pond, 2 (OKSU); north side Vet's Village Pond, 3 (OKSU); 0.5 mi. N northwest corner Vet's Village, 1 (OKSU); 1 mi. E Hwy 18, 1 mi. N Hwy 51, 1 (ECENT); 2 mi. N jct. SH 51 & 51C, 1 (OKSU); 3 mi. W Hwy 177, 0.25 mi. SH 51, 1 (UIMNH); 3 mi. N, 1 mi. W jct. Hwys 51 & 51C, 1 (OKSU); 3 mi. S jct. SH 51 & 51C, 1 (OKSU); 6.3 mi. W, 0.5 mi. N jct. Western & 6th St., 1 (OKSU); 0.5 mi. E Western on S. 19th St., 1 (OKSU); 3.25 mi. W SH 108, 1 mi. N of 108 Salvage Yd., 1 (OKSU); T19N, R2E, SW 1/4, 1 (OKSU); T19N, R3E, SW 1/4 Sec. 30, 2 (OKSU). PITTSBURG COUNTY: 3 mi. NE Hartshorne. 1 (OKSU); 4 mi. NW McAlester, 3 (OKSU). PONTOTOC COUNTY: Ada, 1 (ECENT); 2 mi. S Ada, 1 (ECENT); 3 mi. SW Ada, 3 (ECENT); 7 mi. NE Ada, 1 (ECENT); 200 yds. from lake on road near Kerr Research Lab, 1 (ECENT); 0.5 mi. N Kerr Research Lab, 1

(ECENT). POTTAWATOMIE COUNTY: T11N, R5E, NE 1/4 Sec. 1, near SE of Indian Meridian, 1 (CSUO); 4 mi. W, 3 mi. N Shawnee, 1 (OMNH); Tecumseh, 4 (KU); 6 mi. W Tecumseh, 1 (KU); 6.5 mi. W Tecumseh, 2 (KU); Little River, 7 mi. SE Tecumseh, 3 (KU); T11N, R5E, NE 1/4 Sec. 1, 1 (CSUO). ROGER MILLS COUNTY: Spring Creek Lake Recreation Grounds, Black Kettle Natl. Grassland, 1 (TTU); 5 mi. N Cheyenne, 2,100 ft., 1 (OMNH); 6 mi. N Cheyenne, 1 (USNM); 7 mi. N Cheyenne, 2,000 ft., 12 (OMNH); 2.5 mi. E, 1.5 mi. S Reydon, 2 (CAMCO); Spring Lake Recreation Area, 3 (TTU). ROGERS COUNTY: 4 mi. W Catoosa, 7 (TMM); 0.5 mi. N Oologah, 1 (OKSU). SEMINOLE COUNTY: 6 mi. SE Konowa, 1 (ECENT); New Lima, 1 (ECENT). SE-QUOYAH COUNTY: 4 mi. SW Nicut, 800 ft., 1 (OMNH); 5.5 mi. W Sallisaw, 1 (ECENT). STEPHENS COUNTY: 0.15 mi. E Claud, 1 (OMNH); 0.25 mi. E, 1 mi. S Claud, 1 (OMNH); 0.25 mi. E, 1.25 mi. S Claud, 3 (OMNH); 0.5 mi. E, 1.25 mi. S Claud, 2 (OMNH); 9 mi. N, 1 mi. W Ringling, 1 (OKSU). TEXAS COUNTY: Beaver River, N Guymon, 1 (OKSU); 2 mi. N Guymon, 3,000 ft., 8 (OMNH); 4.25 mi. N Guymon, 3,100 ft., 1 (OMNH); 5.5 mi. N Guymon, 3,100 ft., 2 (OMNH). TILLMAN COUNTY: 0.5 mi. W Chattanooga, 6 (OMNH); 3 mi. SE Davidson, 3 (OMNH); 5.5 mi. S Grandfield, 1 (OMNH). TULSA COUNTY: Garnett, 20 (UMMZ); Mohawk Park, 1 (UMMZ); 6 mi. E of Hwy 169, N on 76th St. 0.125 mi. S, Owasso, 1 (OKSU); Red Fork, 5 (USNM); near Airport, Tulsa, 1 (OKSU); east bank Arkansas River at 31st St., Tulsa, 1 (OKSU); east bank Arkansas River at 38th St., Tulsa, 1 (OKSU); east bank Arkansas River at Lawton Ave., Tulsa, 1 (OKSU); 3900 blk. on 51st St., Tulsa, 2 (OKSU); 7 mi. S, 4 mi. E Tulsa, 3 (OMNH); 6 mi. N, 1 mi. W jct. I-244 & Cincinnati St., 2 (OKSU); T19N, R12E, Sec. 11, 1 (OMNH). WAGONER COUNTY: 5 mi. E Wagoner, 2 (OKSU). WASHINGTON COUNTY: Bartlesville, 1 (USNM); Copan, 1 (CSUO); 2 mi. N Dewey, 1 (OMNH). WOODS COUNTY: Alva, 1 (USNM); 11 mi. NW Alva, 1 (ECENT); 12 mi. N Alva, 1 (OKSU); Moccasin Creek, 4 mi. W Camp Houston, 6 (CSUO); 2 mi. W, 2.5 mi. S Dacoma, 1 (OKSU). WOODWARD COUNTY: Alabaster Caverns, 3 (OKSU); Boiling Springs State Park, 1,925 ft., 4 (OMNH); Ft. Supply, 5 (USNM); Boiling Springs, 2 mi. S Woodward, 2 (USNM); 5 mi. S, 2 mi. W Woodward, 1 (OKSU); 14 mi. S Woodward on Hwy 183-270, 1 (CSUO).

Spermophilus spilosoma.—Specimens examined (total 79): BEAVER COUN-TY: 10 mi. N, 12 mi. E Beaver, 1 (KU). CADDO COUNTY: T9N, R12W, Sec. 2, 2.5 mi. S, 3 mi. E jct. Hwys 58 & 152, 3 (OKSU). CIMAR-RON COUNTY: 13 mi. S Boise City, 1 (ECENT); 14 mi. W Boise City, 2 (OKSU); 15 mi. W Boise City, 1 (OKSU). COMANCHE COUNTY:

Wichita Mountains Wildlife Refuge, 3 (USNM). DEWEY COUNTY: 5.5 mi. SW Canton, 1 (KU). HARMON COUNTY: 3.5 mi. S, 1 mi. W Hollis, 1 (FWMSH); 4.5 m. S Hollis, 2 (FWMSH); 5.5 mi. S Hollis, 1 (FWMSH); 8 mi. N, 1.5 mi. W Hollis, 1 (TTU). HARPER COUNTY: Fort Supply, 39 (USNM); T25N, R22W, N 1/2 Sec. 19, 5 mi. N Ft. Supply, 2 (OKSU); Southern Plains Exp. Range, 5 (OKSU); 14 mi. N, 1 mi. E Woodward, 1 (OKSU). JACKSON COUNTY: 2 mi. E, 0.5 mi. S Elmer, 1 (CAMCO). MAJOR COUNTY: 3 mi. S Waynoka, 1 (OMNH). TEXAS COUNTY: 4.5 mi. N Guymon, 3,100 ft., 2 (OMNH); 5.5 mi. N Guymon, 3,100 ft., 1 (OMNH); 6 mi. E, 1 mi. S Hardesty, 1 (CAMCO); 7 mi. E, 1 mi. S Hardesty, 1 (CAMCO). TILLMAN COUNTY: 3 mi. N, 5 mi. W Davidson, 1 (OKSU). WOODWARD COUNTY: Woodward, 7 (USNM).

Spermophilus tridecemlineatus.—Specimens examined (total 258): ALFALFA COUNTY: 3.5 mi. E Cherokee, 2 (OMNH); 6 mi. S, 4 mi. E Cherokee, 1 (USNM). BEAVER COUNTY: Lake Evans Chambers, 1 (OMNH). BECKHAM COUNTY: 5 mi. NE Elk City, 1 (OMNH). BLAINE COUNTY: Canton Lake, 1 (OMNH). BRYAN COUNTY: 5 mi. SW Colbert, 1 (TMM). CADDO COUNTY: Apache, 1 (USNM). CANADIAN COUNTY: 2 mi. NW El Reno, 1 (OMNH); Fort Reno, 3 (USNM). CIMARRON COUNTY: Black Mesa, 1 (OMNH); 3 mi. E, 1 mi. S Boise City, 1 (CAMCO); 4 mi. E, 2.5 mi. S Boise City, 2 (CAMCO); 14 mi. E Boise City, 1 (OMNH). CLEVELAND COUNTY: Noble, 14 (FMNH); Kraettli Apts., University of Oklahoma, Norman, 1 (OMNH); Kraettli Apts., Norman, 1 (OMNH); Norman, 4 (OMNH); Reaves Park, Norman, 6 (OMNH), 1 (USNM); North Base, University of Oklahoma, Norman, 1 (OMNH); University of Oklahoma Golf Course, Norman, 2 (OMNH); Norman, 1,100 ft., 1 (OMNH); 0.5 mi. S Norman, 1 (USNM); 2 mi. N Norman, 1 (OMNH); 3 mi. E Norman, 4 (OMNH); 3.1 mi. N Norman, 1 (USNM); 8 mi. S Norman, 1 (OMNH); 10 mi. S Norman, 2 (OMNH); North Base, University of Oklahoma, 2 (OKSU); T10N, R4W, Sec. 11, 1 (OMNH). COMANCHE COUNTY: 8 mi. SW Elgin, 1 (CAMCO); Ft. Sill, 3 (CAMCO); Lawton, 1 (USNM); airport, Lawton, 1 (CAMCO); Cameron University, Lawton, 1 (CAMCO); 2 mi. E, 1 mi. N Lawton, 1 (CAMCO); 5 mi. S Lawton on Hwy 281, 1 (CAMCO); 9 mi. E Lawton, 1 (CAMCO); Mt. Scott Post Office, 14 (USNM); Wichita Mountains Refuge, 3 (USNM); T4N, R10E, NE 1/4 Sec. 31, 1 (OMNH). COTTON COUNTY: 13 mi. N Red River, 1 (OKSU). CUSTER COUNTY: Thomas Cemetery, 4 (OKSU); campus, Southwestern State University, Weatherford, 1 (KU). DEWEY COUNTY: 5 mi. W Canton, 2 (KU); 5.5 mi. SW Canton, 3 (KU); 5.5 mi. W Canton, 1 (KU); Dewey County, 1 (KU). ELLIS COUNTY: 4 mi. NW Ft. Supply on Hwy 180, 1 (OKSU). GARFIELD COUNTY: Golf Course, SE Enid, 1 (OKSU); 7 mi. N, 1 mi. E Garber, 1 (OKSU). GARVIN COUNTY: north end Wacker Park, Pauls

Valley, 2 (OKSU); 0.5 mi. S Wynnewood on US 77, 1 (OKSU). GREER COUNTY: 5 mi. W Granite, 1 (OKSU); 5 mi. E, 2 mi. S Mangum, 1 (OKSU). HARMON COUNTY: 1 mi. W, 1 mi. S Reed, 1 (OMNH). HARPER COUNTY: 3 mi. N Ft. Supply, 3 (USNM); T25N, R22W, N 1/2 Sec. 19, 5 mi. N Ft. Supply, 2 (OKSU). JACKSON COUNTY: 7 mi. W, 2.5 mi. N Altus, 1 (CAMCO); 3.5 mi. E Duke, 1 (CAMCO); 3.5 mi. S, 4 mi. W Olustee, 1 (CAMCO). JEFFERSON COUNTY: Waurika Cemetery, 1 (OKSU). KAY COUNTY: Ponca City Country Club, 1 (OKSU). KINGFISHER COUNTY: 1 mi. W Hennessey, 1 (OKSU). KIOWA COUNTY: Hobart Cemetery, 5 (OKSU); Snyder Graveyard, 2 (OUBS); 1.5 mi. E Snyder, 4 (OUBS). LOGAN COUNTY: 8 mi. E Guthrie, 1 (USNM); Orlando, 4 (USNM). MAJOR COUNTY: 5 mi. N, 10 mi. W Fairview, 1 (OKSU); 3 mi. W Orienta, 1 (OMNH). MARSHALL COUNTY: Engineers Flats, 4 mi. W University of Oklahoma Biological Station, 1 (OUBS); University of Oklahoma Biological Station, 1 (OUBS); 1 mi. W University of Oklahoma Biological Station, 2 (OUBS); 2 mi. W University of Oklahoma Biological Station, 1 (OKSU); 0.25 mi. W Willis, 1 (OUBS); 1 mi. N Willis, 1 (OUBS). MUSKOGEE COUNTY: 3 mi. E Wainwright, 2 (OMNH). NOBLE COUNTY: Arnettville, Oklahoma Territory, 1 (FMNH); Billings, 1 (UMMZ). OKLAHOMA COUNTY: Lake Hefner Golf Course, 1 (CSUO); 2 mi. N Kickingbird Golf Course, 1 (CSUO); E Oklahoma City, 1 (OKSU); Lincoln Park Zoo, Oklahoma City, 1 (OKSU); north end Hefner Golf Course, Oklahoma City, 2 (OKSU); Oklahoma City Zoo, 1 (OKSU). OKMULGEE COUNTY: 1 mi. E Schulter, 2 (ECENT). OSAGE COUNTY: 5 mi. N Sand Springs, 1 (UMMZ); 12 mi. N, 5 mi. E Shidler, 1,250 ft., 1 (KU). PAYNE COUNTY: Boomer Lake, 1 (OKSU); park, W side Boomer Lake, 1 (OKSU); blk. W Vet's Village on Midi, 1 (OKSU); Married Student Housing, campus, Oklahoma State University, 1 (OKSU); 0.25 mi. N Oklahoma State University campus, 1 (OKSU); dump area near Poultry Research Area, Oklahoma State University, 1 (OKSU); campus, Oklahoma State University, Stillwater, 1 (OKSU); cemetery, E Stillwater, 2 (OKSU); Fairlane Cemetery, Stillwater, 3 (OKSU); intramural field, N Married Student Housing, Stillwater, 1 (OKSU); northwest end Boomer Lake, Stillwater, 1 (OKSU); poultry farm, Stillwater, 1 (OKSU); south side Stillwater, 1 (OKSU); S cemetery, Stillwater, 1 (ECENT); Stillwater, 6 (OKSU); 0.25 mi. E Stillwater, 1 (OKSU); 0.8 mi. E Stillwater, 1 (OKSU); 1 mi. E Stillwater on Hwy 51, 1 (OKSU); Sanborn Lake, 1 mi. N Stillwater, 1 (OKSU); 1 mi. N, 0.66 mi. W Stillwater, 1 (OKSU); 2 mi. W Stillwater, 1 (OKSU); Fairlawn Cemetery, 2 mi. E Stillwater, 1 (ECENT); Stillwater Country Club Golf Course, 3.5 mi. SW Stillwater, 1 (OKSU); Stillwater Cemetery, Stillwater, 5 (OKSU), 2 (ECENT); Stillwater Local Cemetery, 2 (OKSU); Vet. Medicine Driveway, 1 (OKSU); 1 blk. W Vet Village, 1

(OKSU); west end Boomer Lake, Stillwater, 1 (OKSU). POTTAWA-
TOMIE COUNTY: Tecumseh Cemetery, 1 (OKSU). TEXAS COUNTY:
2 mi. E Eva, 4 (KU); Coldwater Creek, S Guymon, 2 (OMNH); NE
Guyman, 1 (OMNH). TILLMAN COUNTY: Frederick Cemetery, 7
(OKSU). TULSA COUNTY: Garnett, 1 (UMMZ); Mohawk Park, Tulsa,
1 (OKSU), 6 (KU), 15 (UMMZ). WOODS COUNTY: Alva, 8 (FMNH),
2 (USNM); White Horse Springs, 1 (FMNH). WOODWARD COUNTY:
3 mi. SW Freedom, 1 (OKSU); Woodward, 3 (USNM).

Spermophilus variegatus.—Specimens examined (total 12): CIMARRON
COUNTY: Black Mesa, 1 (OMNH); Clark Ranch, 15 mi. N, 6 mi. W
Boise City, 1 (ECENT); 1.7 mi. E Kenton, 2 (OMNH); 3 mi. SE Kenton,
1 (OMNH); 2.5 mi. SE Kenton, 4,200 ft., 1 (OMNH); 4 mi. N Kenton, 2
(KU); 4.2 mi. S Kenton, 2 (OMNH); 4.2 mi. S, 0.5 mi. E Kenton, 1
(OMNH); canyon, east side North Carrizo Creek., 6 mi. N Kenton, 1
(OKSU).

Spilogale gracilis.—Specimens examined (total 1): CIMARRON COUNTY:
3.5 mi. N, 1.2 mi. W Kenton, 1 (OMNH).

Spilogale putorius.—Specimens examined (total 71): ALFALFA COUNTY:
east side Salt Fork Arkansas River, 9.5 mi. E Cherokee, 1 (USNM); 3 mi.
E Jet, 1 (OKSU). ATOKA COUNTY: 5 mi. E Atoka, 1 (CAMCO).
BLAINE COUNTY: 1.5 mi. W Longdale, 1 (OKSU); 2 mi. W Longdale,
1 (OKSU); 6 mi. N, 5 mi. W Watonga, 1 (MVZ). CADDO COUNTY:
near Anadarko, 1 (CSUO). CHOCTAW COUNTY: near Hugo, 1 (OKSU).
CLEVELAND COUNTY: 1 mi. N Moore, 1 (OMNH); 20 yds. E Chautau-
qua on Timberdell Rd., Norman, 1 (OMNH). COMANCHE COUNTY:
Ft. Sill, 1 (CAMCO), 1 (USNM); S Arbuckle Range, Ft. Sill, 1 (CAMCO);
0.5 mi. SE Ft. Sill Depot, 1 (USNM); Lawton, 2 (CAMCO); Mt. Scott, 4
(USNM); Wichita Mountains Wildlife Refuge, 1 (OKSU). CUSTER
COUNTY: Custer, 1 (CAMCO). GARFIELD COUNTY: 4 mi. W, 3 mi.
N Hunter, 1 (OKSU). GRADY COUNTY: 3 mi. W Chickasha, 1
(OMNH). HASKELL COUNTY: 15 mi. W, 2 mi. N Stigler, 1 (CSUO).
JACKSON COUNTY: 7 mi. W Altus, 1 (CAMCO); 1 mi. S Blaine, 1
(OKSU); 3.5 mi. N Olustee, 1 (CAMCO). KIOWA COUNTY: 0.75 mi. S
Hobart, 1 (KU). LEFLORE COUNTY: 6 mi. SE Wister, 1 (KU). LIN-
COLN COUNTY: 7 mi. E Chandler, 1 (OMNH); 10 mi. E Stroud, 1
(OMNH). MARSHALL COUNTY: 1.5 mi. W University of Oklahoma
Biological Station, 1 (OUBS); 2 mi. W University of Oklahoma Biological
Station, 1 (OUBS). MUSKOGEE COUNTY: Muskogee, 1 (OKSU).
NOBLE COUNTY: 7 mi. E Perry, 1 (OKSU). OKFUSKEE COUNTY: 5
mi. N Henryetta, 1 (ECENT). OKLAHOMA COUNTY: between 4th
and 5th on Rankin, Edmond, 1 (CSUO); Oklahoma City, 1 (CSUO); jct.
S.E. 25th & I-35, Oklahoma City, 1 (CSUO). OKMULGEE COUNTY:

Schulter, 1 (ECENT). PAYNE COUNTY: Boomer Lake, 1 (OKSU); College Apiary, Stillwater, 2 (OKSU); 1 mi. N Stillwater, 1 (OKSU); 1.5 mi. E Stillwater, 1 (OKSU); 2 mi. N, 1 mi. W Stillwater, 1 (OKSU); 2 mi. E, 3 mi. S Stillwater, 1 (OKSU); 5 mi. E Stillwater, 1 (OKSU); near Yost Lake, 1 (OKSU). PITTSBURG COUNTY: Kiowa, 1 (ECENT); Kiowa Agency, 1 (USNM). POTTAWATOMIE COUNTY: 10.2 mi. E Shawnee on I-40, 1 (OMNH); Sante Fe Cut, NW Tecumseh, 1 (KU); Little River, 7 mi. SE Tecumseh, 1 (KU). TILLMAN COUNTY: 1 mi. S Manitou, 1 (CAMCO); 1.25 mi. W, 3 mi. N Tipton, 1 (CAMCO). TULSA COUNTY: Mohawk Park, 1 (UMMZ); Tulsa, 2 (UMMZ). WASHITA COUNTY: 3 mi. E, 0.75 mi. N Lake Valley, 1 (KU). WOODS COUNTY: Alva, Oklahoma Territory, 5 (FMNH); Alva, 1 (USNM), 3 (MCZ). INDIAN TERRITORY: Marsh Valley, Oklahoma, 1 (USNM).

Sylvilagus aquaticus.—Specimens examined (total 33): BRYAN COUNTY: 1 mi. S Blue, 1 (OKSU). CHEROKEE COUNTY: Illinois River near Sparrowhawk Camp, 3 mi. E Tahlequah, 1 (OKSU). CHOCTAW COUNTY: 32 mi. SE Antlers, 0.25 mi. NW Sobol Cemetery, 1 (CSUO). CLEVELAND COUNTY: Canadian River, S Norman, 1 (OMNH); Hwy 35, Norman, 1 (OMNH); 3 mi. E Norman, 1 (OMNH); near city dump, 3 mi. S Norman, 2 (USNM); Capshaw marsh, 9 mi. E Norman, 1 (OMNH). COMANCHE COUNTY: Ft. Sill, East Cache Cr., 1 (CAMCO); 1 mi. ENE Ft. Sill, 1 (CAMCO). LATIMER COUNTY: Red Oak, 3 (USNM). LEFLORE COUNTY: 6.5 mi. W Heavener, 1 (OMNH). LINCOLN COUNTY: NE Chandler, 1 (OKSU); 3 mi. W, 1 mi. S Carney, 1 (OKSU). LOVE COUNTY: 5 mi. S, 5 mi. E Marietta, 1 (OKSU); T56S, R3E, SE 1/4 SW 1/4 Sec. 31, 1 (OKSU). MCCURTAIN COUNTY: 5.5 mi. N Broken Bow, 1 (OKSU); 10 mi. E Broken Bow, 1 (OKSU); 6.5 mi. W Heavner, 1 (OMNH); 2 mi. W Smithville, 1 (OMNH). PAYNE COUNTY: 7 mi. NW Stillwater, 1 (OKSU). PITTSBURG COUNTY: Hartshorne, 1 (USNM). POTTAWATOMIE COUNTY: Little Rock, 7 mi. SE Tecumseh, 1 (KU). ROGERS COUNTY: Catoosa, 4 (UMMZ). SEMINOLE COUNTY: 5 mi. NW Sasakwa, 1 (CAMCO). TULSA COUNTY: Mohawk Park, 1 (UMMZ). WASHINGTON COUNTY: 8 mi. N Collinsville, 1 (OKSU).

Sylvilagus audubonii.—Specimens examined (total 55): BEAVER COUNTY: 10.4 mi. E Elmwood, 1 (CAMCO). CIMARRON COUNTY: Boise City, 1 (OMNH); N Canadian River, S Boise City, 1 (OMNH); 3 mi. W Boise City, 1 (CAMCO); 4 mi. N Boise City, 1 (UIMNH); 4.5 mi. E, 0.5 mi. S Boise City, 1 (CAMCO); 17 mi. W Boise City, 1 (OMNH); Cimarron County, 1 (OMNH); 3 mi. WSW Felt, 1 (UIMNH); Kenton, 1 (OMNH); 0.5 mi. SE Kenton, 1 (OMNH); 2 mi. S, 4 mi. E Kenton, 1 (OMNH); 2 mi. S, 5 mi. E Kenton, 2 (OMNH); 2.1 mi. E, 0.8 mi. S Kenton, 1

(OMNH); 2.5 mi. S Kenton, 1 (CAMCO); 2.5 mi. S, 4 mi. E Kenton, 1 (OMNH); 3 mi. N Kenton, 2 (UMMZ); 3 mi. NE Kenton, 2 (UIMNH); 3 mi. S Kenton, 1 (ECENT); 2.5 mi. S Kenton, 4,200 ft., 3 (OMNH); 2.5 mi. SE Kenton, 4,200 ft., 3 (OMNH); 4 mi. NE Kenton, 1 (UIMNH); 5 mi. N Kenton, 2 (OKSU); 6 mi. N Kenton, 3 (OKSU); 6 mi. S, 2 mi. E Kenton, 1 (CAMCO); 8 mi. S Kenton, 1 (ECENT); Tesesquite Canyon, 2 (OKSU); Tesesquite Canyon, 4.4 mi. from hwy, 2 (OKSU). COMANCHE COUNTY: Chattanooga, 1 (USNM); Wichita Mountains, 1 (USNM); Wichita Mountains Refuge, 2 (USNM); Wichita Natl. Forest, 1 (OMNH). GRANT COUNTY: 2.3 mi. N, 8 mi. W Renfrow, 1 (USNM). HARMON COUNTY: 2.25 mi. W, 0.75 mi. N Hollis, 2 (TTU). HARPER COUNTY: 3 mi. N Ft. Supply, 2 (USNM). JACKSON COUNTY: 2 mi. SSE Duke, 1 (CAMCO). TEXAS COUNTY: 2 mi. E Eva, 2 (KU). WOODS COUNTY: 4 mi. S Waynoka, 1 (CSUO). WOODWARD COUNTY: 3 mi. N Supply, 1 (USNM).

Sylvilagus floridanus.—Specimens examined (total 402): ADAIR COUNTY: 3 mi. NNW Chewey, 1,000 ft., 2 (OMNH); Stilwell, 14 (USNM); 2 mi. from Stilwell, 1 (OKSU); 7 mi. W Stilwell, 1 (KU). ALFALFA COUN-TY: 7 mi. W, 3 mi. S Jet, 1 (OKSU). BEAVER COUNTY: 5 mi. E, 3 mi. N Elmwood, 1 (OKSU); N Canadian River, 4 mi. S Floris, 1 (KU). BLAINE COUNTY: 1 mi. W Longdale, 2 (OKSU); Roman Nose State Park, 1 (OKSU); Salt Creek Canyon, 2 (KU). BRYAN COUNTY: 6 mi. N Bennington, 1 (TMM); 7 mi. S, 5 mi. W Bennington, 1 (OKSU); Red River, 3 mi. S Yuba, 1 (TMM). CADDO COUNTY: Caddo County, 1 (OMNH); 9 mi. NW Cyril, 1 (OKSU); Ft. Cobb, 1 (USNM); 12 mi. E Hinton, 9 mi. N Hwy 152, 1 (CSUO); 1 mi. S, 0.2 mi. W jct. SH 152 & 146, 1 (OKSU). CANADIAN COUNTY: El Reno Federal Reformatory, 1 (CSUO); 3 mi. E, 1 mi. S Union City, 1 (OKSU). CHOCTAW COUNTY: 4 mi. SSW Ft. Towson, 400 ft., 1 (OMNH); 6 mi. NE Hugo, 1 (USNM). CIMARRON COUNTY: 6.6 mi. W Boise City, 1 (OKSU); 8 mi. E Felt, 1 (UIMNH). CLEVELAND COUNTY: Little River Reservoir, 1 (OMNH); 1009 S.W. 19th St., Moore, 1 (CSUO); airport pond, N Norman, 1 (OMNH); Norman, 10 (KU); campus, University of Oklahoma, Norman, 2 (KU); 817 W. Timberdell Rd., Norman, 1 (OMNH); 2 mi. N Norman, 1 (OMNH); 2.25 mi. SW Norman, 1 (OMNH); 2.25 mi. S Norman, 2 (OMNH); 2.5 mi. S Norman, 2 (OMNH); 3 mi. E Norman, 3 (OMNH), 1 (CAMCO); 6 mi. E Norman, 1 (OMNH). COAL COUNTY: 0.7 mi. W, 2 mi. S Coalgate, 1 (OMNH). COMANCHE COUNTY: 4.5 mi. SE Cache, 1 (USNM); 4.5 mi. S, 1 mi. W Cache, 1 (CAMCO); 6.5 mi. S, 1 mi. W Cache, 1 (CAMCO); 8 mi. SW Elgin, 1 (CAMCO); Lawton, 1 (CAMCO); 1.5 mi. SE Lawton, 1 (CAMCO); 4 mi. W Lawton, 1 (USNM); 5 mi. E, 2 mi. N Lawton, 1 (CAMCO); 8 mi. E, 6 mi. N Lawton, 1 (CAMCO); 9 mi.

E, 6 mi. N Lawton, 2 (CAMCO); 5.5 mi. E, 0.5 mi. N Meers, 1 (CAMCO); Mt. Scott, Wichita Mountains, 8 (USNM); Wichita Mountains, 6 (USNM); Wichita Mountains Wildlife Refuge, 1 (OKSU); Wichita Natl. Forest, 1 (OMNH); 1 mi. E Wichita Mountains Wildlife Refuge, 1 (CSUO). COTTON COUNTY: Hooper Farm, 3 (OKSU); 6.3 mi. N Red River on US Hwy 281, 1 (TMM); 5 mi. SE Taylor, 900 ft., 1 (OMNH). CRAIG COUNTY: 1 mi. S, 0.25 mi. W Big Cabin, 1 (OKSU); 1 mi. S, 6 mi. N Oklahoma-Kansas Border at Hwy 2, N Welch, 1 (OKSU). CREEK COUNTY: 2 mi. E, 0.25 mi. N Drumright, 1 (OKSU); Sapulpa, 4 (KU); 6.5 mi. NE Sapulpa, 1 (OKSU). CUSTER COUNTY: 5 mi. NE Stafford, 2(OMNH); 15 mi. N Weatherford, 1 (KU). DEWEY COUNTY: 5.5 mi. SW Canton, 3 (KU); 7 mi. W Canton, 1 (KU); 10 mi. NW Canton, 1 (KU); Dewey County, 1 (KU); 1 mi. S, 1 mi. W Seiling, 1 (OKSU). ELLIS COUNTY: 7 mi. SE Arnett, 1 (USNM); 8 mi. SE Arnett, 2 (USNM); 18 mi. S, 6 mi. E Arnett, 1 (OKSU); 15 mi. S, 2 mi. E Higgins, Texas, 1 (OKSU). GARFIELD COUNTY: Enid, 1 (KU); 3 mi. S Garber, 1 (OKSU). GARVIN COUNTY: 2 mi. S Pauls Valley, 1 (ECENT); 1 mi. S Stratford, 1 (ECENT); 1 mi. E, 1 mi. N Stratford, 2 (ECENT); Wynnewood, 3 (ECENT). GRADY COUNTY: 1 mi. N, 3 mi. W Chickasha, 2 (OKSU). GRANT COUNTY: 3 mi. S Medford, 2 (OKSU); 3 mi. NW Pond Creek, 1 (OMNH). HARMON COUNTY: 8 mi. N, 1.5 mi. W Hollis, 1 (TTU); 8 mi. SW Hollis, 2 (FWMSH); 9 mi. E, 1 mi. S Hollis, 3 (OMNH); T4N, R26W, NE 1/4 Sec. 6, 1 (OKSU). HARPER COUNTY: 3 mi. N Ft. Supply, 21 (USNM); 4.5 mi. N Laverne, 3 (UMMZ); Southern Plains Exp. Range, 4 (OKSU); pasture 26, Southern Plains Exp. Range, 2 (OKSU); pasture 39, Southern Plains Exp. Range, 3 (OKSU); Supply, 1 (USNM). HASKELL COUNTY: 2.5 mi. E, 2 mi. N McCurtain, 2 (OMNH); 6 mi. N, 1 mi. W Stigler, 1 (OKSU); 8 mi. E, 2 mi. N Stigler, 1 (OMNH). HUGHES COUNTY: 9 mi. E, 1 mi. N Holdenville, 1 (OMNH); 1 mi. S, 1.5 mi. W Spaulding, 1 (CAMCO). JACKSON COUNTY: 1 mi. S, 2 mi. E Altus, 1 (OKSU); 2 mi. N, 3 mi. W jct. Maine & Broadway Sts., Altus, 1 (OKSU); 5 mi. S Altus, 1 (OMNH); 4 mi. W, 0.5 mi. S Eldorado, 1 (OKSU); Red River, 14 mi. S Olustee, 2 (TMM). JEFFERSON COUNTY: 2 mi. NE Hastings, 1 (UIMNH); Starvation, 1 (OKSU); 5 mi. W Waurika, 1 (UIMNH). JOHNSTON COUNTY: 1 mi. S Milburn near Hwy 78, 2 (ECENT). KAY COUNTY: 3.5 mi. E, 4 mi. N Blackwell, 1 (OKSU). KINGFISHER COUNTY: 14 mi. W Crescent, 1 (OKSU); Goole's Bridge, 2 (OKSU); 4 mi. SW Hennessey, 1 (OKSU); 7 mi. E Hennessey on Hwy 51, 1 (OKSU). KIOWA COUNTY: 1.5 mi. N Cooperton, 1 (CAMCO); 4.5 mi. W, 1 mi. S Lone Wolf, 1 (OMNH); 3 mi. E, 1 mi. S Snyder, 2 (OMNH). LATIMER COUNTY: 11 mi. W, 3 mi. S Talihina, 1 (OKSU); W Wilburton, 1 (OKSU); 3 mi. N Wilburton, 1

(OMNH); 7 mi. NE Wilburton, 3 (CSUO). LEFLORE COUNTY: 3 mi. W Hodgens, 1 (OKSU). LINCOLN COUNTY: 4 mi. S Carney, 1 (OKSU). LOGAN COUNTY: Logan County, 1 (OMNH); 19 mi. W, 2 mi. S Stillwater, 1 (OKSU). LOVE COUNTY: 3 mi. E Marietta, 1 (OMNH). MAJOR COUNTY: 1 mi. N, 3 mi. E Fairview, 1 (OKSU); Glass Mt., 5 mi. W Orienta, 2 (USNM); 1 mi. W, 3.5 mi. S Ringwood, 1 (OKSU). MARSHALL COUNTY: 1 mi. S, 1 mi. W Fobb, 1 (OUBS); Lake Texoma, 1 (OUBS); Marshall County, 3 (OUBS); University of Oklahoma Biological Station, 2 (OMNH), 1 (UMMZ); 0.5 mi. W University of Oklahoma Biological Station, 1 (OUBS); 1 mi. W University of Oklahoma Biological Station, 1 (OMNH), 1 (OUBS); 2 mi. W University of Oklahoma Biological Station, 2 (OMNH); 1 mi. S, 2 mi. W Willis, 1 (OUBS); 3 mi. W Willis, 1 (OUBS); 6 mi. N Willis, 1 (OMNH). MAYES COUNTY: 3.25 mi. S Big Cabin, 1 (OKSU); 3 mi. E Locust, 2 (OKSU); 3 mi. E Locust Grove, 1 (OKSU); 9 mi. N Pryor, 1.5 mi. W Hwy 69, 1 (OKSU). MCCLAIN COUNTY: 8 mi. S, 1 mi. W Blanchard, 1 (OMNH); 10 mi. SW Norman, 1 (OMNH). MCCURTAIN COUNTY: 14 mi. SE Broken Bow, 2 (OMNH); McCurtain County, 1 (OMNH); 2 mi. W Smithville, 1 (OMNH); 2.5 mi. W Smithville, 3 (OMNH); 3 mi. E Wainwright, 1 (OMNH). MCINTOSH COUNTY: 5 mi. E Checotah, 1 (OMNH); 4 mi. S Hanna School, 2 (ECENT). MUSKOGEE COUNTY: Wildlife Conservation Station, Braggs, 1 (OKSU); Camp Gruber, 1 (OKSU); Ft. Gibson, 1 (USNM); 8 mi. E Muskogee, 1 (OKSU); 3 mi. E Wainwright, 1 (OMNH); 4 mi. E, 5 mi. S Warner, 1 (OMNH). NOBLE COUNTY: 10 mi. S Billings, 2 (OKSU); 10 mi. W Billings, 1 (OKSU); Otoe Indian Reservation, N Morrison, 1 (OKSU); 5.5 mi. W Red Rock, 1 (OKSU); 0.75 mi. W Hwy 177 on Orlando Rd., 1 (OKSU); T21N, R2E, NE 1/4 Sec. 3, 1 (OKSU). OKLAHOMA COUNTY: 19.4 mi. N Bethany on Rockwell, 1 (CSUO); 4.6 mi. W Edmond, 1 (CSUO); jct. 2nd & Oakridge, 1 (CSUO); 23 Oakwood Dr., 1 (CSUO); Midwest City, 1 (OKSU); northeast corner S.E. 29th & Eastern, Oklahoma City, 1 (OKSU); 5 mi. N, 2 mi. W Oklahoma City, 2 (OKSU); 4 mi. N, 3 mi. W Oklahoma City, 1 (ECENT); Wedgewood Amusement Park, 1 (OKSU); 4 mi. N Nicoma Park on Westminster, 1 (OKSU). OKMULGEE COUNTY: 4 mi. E Council Hill, 1 (OKSU). OSAGE COUNTY: 8 mi. W Bartlesville, 1 (OKSU); 3 mi. S, 6 mi. E Shidler, 2 (KU); 10 mi. N, 5 mi. E Shidler, 1 (KU); Adam's Ranch, 12 mi. N, 5 mi. E Shidler, 1,250 ft., 1 (KU). PAYNE COUNTY: 0.5 mi. S Cushing, 1 (ECENT); 2 mi. S, 1.5 mi. E Cushing, 1 (OKSU); 0.5 mi. S, 1 mi. W Glencoe, 1 (OKSU); east side Lake Carl Blackwell, 1 (OKSU); 0.5 mi. W Lake Carl Blackwell Station, 1 (OKSU); 1 mi. W Oklahoma State University, 1 (OKSU); 1 mi. W Oklahoma State University dairy barn, 1

(OKSU); 1.8 mi. S, 3.8 mi. E Drummond Hall, Oklahoma State University campus, 1 (OKSU); College Farm, Perkins, 6 (OKSU); 4 mi. E Perkins, 1 (OKSU); east side Boomer Lake, Stillwater, 3 (OKSU); Sanborn Lake Area, N Stillwater, 1 (OKSU); Stillwater, 3 (OKSU); E Stillwater, 1 (OKSU); 2 mi. W Stillwater Airport, 1 (OKSU); 100 yds. N Water Plant, Stillwater, 1 (OKSU); 1 mi. N Stillwater, 2 (OKSU); 1 mi. W Stillwater, 1 (OKSU); 1 mi. N, 1.5 mi. E Stillwater, 1 (OKSU); 1.5 mi. W Boomer Station, 0.5 mi. S Stillwater, 1 (OKSU); 2 mi. S Stillwater, 1 (OKSU); 2 mi. W Stillwater, 2 (OKSU); 2 mi. S, 0.5 mi. E Stillwater, 1 (OKSU); 2 mi. N, 1 mi. E Stillwater, 1 (OKSU); 2 mi. W, 1.5 mi. S Stillwater, 1 (OKSU); 2 mi. N, 3 mi. W Stillwater, 1 (OKSU); 3 mi. NW Stillwater, 1 (OKSU); 3 mi. S Stillwater, 2 (OKSU); 3 mi. W Vet's Village, Stillwater, 1 (OKSU); 4 mi. N Stillwater, 1 (OKSU); 4 mi. W, 0.5 mi. N Stillwater, 2 (OKSU); Animal Husbandry Farm, Oklahoma State University, 4 mi. N, 15 mi. W Stillwater, 1 (OKSU); 5 mi. W Stillwater, 1 (OKSU); 6 mi. W, 1 mi. N Stillwater, 1 (OKSU); 6.5 mi. E Stillwater on Hwy 51, 1 (OKSU); 8 mi. E, 0.25 mi. S Stillwater, 1 (OKSU); 9 mi. S Stillwater, 1 (OKSU); 9 mi. S Stillwater on Hwy 177, 1 (OKSU); 12 mi. E Stillwater on SH 51, 1 (OKSU); 4.5 mi. E, 0.5 mi. S jct. US Hwy 177 & SH 33, 1 (OKSU); 4.5 mi. S SH 51 on US Hwy 177, 1 (OKSU); 7 mi. E, 3 mi. S jct. SH 51 & SH 177, 1 (OKSU). PITTSBURG COUNTY: 6 mi. N McAlester, 1 (ECENT); 8 mi. W McAlester, 1 (ECENT); Savanna, 1 (USNM). PONTOTOC COUNTY: Wintersmith Park, Ada, 1 (ECENT); 10 mi. W Ada, 1 (ECENT); 3.25 mi. S Pearson, 1 (OKSU). POTTAWATOMIE COUNTY: Tecumseh, 6 (KU); 1 mi. W Tecumseh, 1 (UMMZ); 3 mi. SE Tecumseh, 1 (KU). PUSHMATAHA COUNTY: 6 mi. S Antlers, 1 (OKSU); Clayton, 1 (OMNH); Pushmataha County, 1 (OMNH); T2N, R19E, Sec. 20, 1 (OMNH). ROGERS COUNTY: Bird Creek, 2 mi. W Catoosa, 1 (UMMZ); 9 mi. W Chelsea, 1 (OKSU); Garnett Prairie, 1 (UMMZ); 3 mi. NE Garnett, 1 (UMMZ). STEPHENS COUNTY: 0.125 mi. E, 0.375 mi. S Claud, 1 (OMNH); 4 mi. SSE Corum, 1 (UIMNH); 5 mi. E, 4 mi. S Duncan, 1 (CAMCO); 5 mi. S, 8 mi. W Duncan, 1 (OKSU); 6 mi. NW Marlow, 1 (USNM); 9 mi. N, 1 mi. W Ringling, 1 (OKSU). TILLMAN COUNTY: 4 mi. NW Grandfield, 1 (OKSU); 5.5 mi. S Grandfield, 2 (OMNH); 3 mi. E, 8 mi. N Tipton, 1 (CAMCO); 5 mi. W, 2 mi. S Tipton, 1 (OKSU); T4S, R14W, Sec. 9, 1 (OMNH). TULSA COUNTY: Garnett, 11 (UMMZ); 3 mi. N Liberty School, 1 (OKSU); 8 mi. W Red Fork, 1 (USNM); 1.5 mi. N Sperry, 3 (OKSU). WAGONER COUNTY: 5 mi. N Wagoner, 1 (OKSU); 8 mi. W Wagoner, 1 (OKSU). WOODS COUNTY: Alva, Oklahoma Territory, 1 (FMNH); 12 mi. W, 4 mi. S Alva, 1 (KU); 19 mi. NW Alva, 1 (OKSU); Waynoka, 1 (UMMZ); 3 mi. S Waynoka, 1

(OMNH); 5 mi. S Waynoka, 1,400 ft., 1 (OMNH). WOODWARD
COUNTY: Woodward County, 2 (OMNH); T25N, R18W, SW corner
Sec. 18, 1 (OMNH); T24N, R14W, Secs. 23– 24, 1 (OMNH).

Tadarida brasiliensis.—Specimens examined (total 754): BEAVER
COUNTY: T4S, R13E, Sec. 7, 1 (OKSU). CIMARRON COUNTY:
Pigeon Cave, 5 (OKSU); Tesesquite Canyon Cave, 3 (OKSU). CLEVE-
LAND COUNTY: Law Bldg., University of Oklahoma campus, Norman,
1 (OMNH); Norman, 1 (OMNH); Zoology Bldg., University of Okla-
homa, Norman, 2 (OMNH). COMANCHE COUNTY: Cameron Univer-
sity, Lawton, 1 (CAMCO); Lawton, 4 (CAMCO); 3 mi. W Lawton, 1
(CAMCO). CUSTER COUNTY: Weatherford, 2 (KU). GARFIELD
COUNTY: Enid, 1 (OKSU). GREER COUNTY: Bat Cave 13, 15
(OMNH); north side Granite Mt., 1 (OKSU); south side Granite Mt., 1
(OKSU); 1 mi. N Granite, 1 (OKSU); Greer County, 9 (OMNH); Lincoln
Bat Cave, 44 (FWMSH); 7 mi. S Mangum, 10 (OMNH); Reed Cave, 12
(CSUO); 1 mi. S Reed, 1 (USNM); 1 mi. W, 1 mi. S Reed, 4 (OMNH); 1.5
mi. S, 2.25 mi. W Reed, 20 (KU); 1.5 mi. SW Reed, 1,700 ft., 27
(OMNH); 1.5 mi. SW Reed, 2,100 ft., 1 (OMNH); 1.5 mi. W, 1.5 mi. S
Reed, 2 (OMNH); 2 mi. S Reed, 1 (OMNH); 2 mi. W Reed, 1 (USNM);
T5N, R24W, Sec. 27, 3 mi. SW Reed, 7 (CAMCO); 3 mi. W, 1.5 mi. S
Reed, 7 (CAMCO); 3 mi. W, 0.5 mi. S Reed, 1 (CAMCO); T4N, R23W,
Sec. 27, 3 (OMNH). HARMON COUNTY: north bank North Fork Red
River, 0.5 mi. N, 1 mi. W Reed, 5 (CSUO); 6 mi. E, 1 mi. S Vinson, 1,700
ft., 1 (OMNH). JACKSON COUNTY: 1 mi. S, 8.5 mi. E Eldorado, 1
(CAMCO). LEFLORE COUNTY: 7 mi. E, 1 mi. N Keota, 1 (OKSU).
MAJOR COUNTY: cavern, Vickery Ranch, 2 mi. W Bouse Jct., 9
(OKSU); cavern, Vickery Ranch, 3 mi. W Bouse Jct., 7 (OKSU); Vickery
Ranch Cave, 3 mi. W Bouse Jct., 3 (USNM); Conners Cave, 18 (OKSU);
Corbin Ranch, 32 mi. NW Fairview, 3 (MVZ); Corbin Cave, Corbin
Ranch, 32 mi. NW Fairview, 86 (KU); Griever Creek, 11 (UMMZ); Major
County, 2 (MSU); Vickery Cave, 15 mi. E Mooreland, 2 (OKSU); 15 mi.
E, 0.25 mi. N Mooreland, 1 (OKSU); Nescatunga Cave, 6 (CSUO); Vick-
ery Cave, 21 (OKSU); Vickery Cave #1, 7 (OKSU), 1 (ECENT); Vickery
Cave, 4 mi. W jct. Hwys 281 & 15, 1 (OKSU); Vickery Cave System, 8
(CSUO); Vickery Ranch, 1 (OKSU); Vickery Ranch Cave #1, 1 (USNM);
12.5 mi. S, 4 mi. W Waynoka, 1 (OKSU); Vickery Cave, 2.5 mi. W jct. US
281 & Hwy 15, 8 (CAMCO); 2 mi. W jct. Hwys 15 & 281, 2 (CSUO);
Nescatunga Cave, 2.5 mi. W jct. Hwys 281 & 15, 86 (CSUO); cave, Terrill-
Whitlaw Ranch, 3 mi. W jct. Hwys 281 & 15, 62 (OKSU); Conners Cave,
5 mi. S, 2 mi. E jct. US Hwy 281 & SH 15, 1 (TTU); T22N, R16W, Sec.
5, 4 (OMNH). MARSHALL COUNTY: Willis, 1 (OMNH). MCCLAIN

COUNTY: Alex High School, Blanchard, 1 (CSUO). MCCURTAIN COUNTY: Beavers Bend State Park, 1 (OKSU). MURRAY COUNTY: Dougherty, Indian Territory, 2 (FMNH); T15, R1E, SE 1/4 Sec. 36, Little Crystal Cave, 1 (OMNH). PAYNE COUNTY: Stillwater, 3 (OKSU). PITTSBURG COUNTY: McAlester, 1 (CSUO). WOODS COUNTY: 2 mi. W Edith, 4 (OMNH); Merrihew Cave, 6 mi. S, 2 mi. W Aetna, Kansas, 4 (KU); Merrihew Cave, 0.5 mi. S Oklahoma-Kansas line, 2 (MVZ), 50 (KU); Merrihew Cave, 54 (KU); Woods County, 2 (MSU). WOODWARD COUNTY: Alabaster Caverns, 2 (FWMSH); Alabaster Caverns State Park, 22 (OKSU); Owl Cave, Alabaster Caverns State Park, 1 (OKSU); Selman Ranch, 6 mi. W Alabaster Caverns State Park, 3 (OKSU); 3 mi. W Bouse Jct., 1 (OKSU); Selman's Cave, 3 mi. S Freedom, 2 (OKSU); 3 mi. S, 7 mi. W Freedom, 38 (OKSU); cave on Bear Creek, 3 mi. S, 7 mi. W Freedom, 2 (OKSU); Selman's Cave, 4 mi. S, 6 mi. W Freedom, 1 (OKSU); T26N, R19W, Sec. 22, 5.3 mi. S, 7 mi. W Freedom, 3 (OMNH); Selman's Cave, 6 mi. SW Freedom, 1 (OKSU); 6 mi. S, 6 mi. W Freedom, 1 (OKSU); Owl Cave, 1 (OMNH); Selman Cave, 3 (OMNH); Selman's Cave, 9 (OKSU); Woodward County, 5 (OKSU).

Tadarida macrotis.—Specimens examined (total 3): OKLAHOMA COUNTY: 900 blk. NE 13th, 1 (CSUO). TEXAS COUNTY: 4 mi. S Elkhart, Kansas, 1 (KU); Guymon, 1 (OKSU).

Tamias striatus.—Specimens examined (total 59): ADAIR COUNTY: 5 mi. S Kansas, 3 (UMMZ); Stilwell, 2 (USNM). CHEROKEE COUNTY: Scraper, 7 (UMMZ); 2 mi. S Scraper, 1 (OMNH). DELAWARE COUNTY: Jay, 1 (CSUO); 4 mi. S Jay, 1 (UIMNH); 8 mi. W Jay, 1 (UIMNH); 10 mi. SE Jay, 2 (OKSU); 10 mi. SW Jay, 1 (OKSU); 12 mi. SE Jay, 1 (CSUO); Lake Eucha, 1 (OMNH); 2 mi. W New Eucha, 1 (OKSU); 7 mi. E Rose on SH 33, 1 (OKSU). LATIMER COUNTY: 1 mi. N Red Oak, 1 (OUBS); 9 mi. NE Red Oak, 1 (OUBS); 3 mi. N Wilburton, 1 (OMNH); near Degnan School, 3 mi. N Wilburton, 1 (OKSU); 4 mi. NE Wilburton, 1 (OMNH). LEFLORE COUNTY: Kiamichi Creek, 2 (OMNH); 1 mi. NE Zoe, 2 (OMNH); 1.5 mi. NE Zoe, 1 (OMNH); 3 mi. NE Zoe, 2 (OMNH); 5.2 mi. W Stapp—Zoe, School House, 1 (OMNH). MAYES COUNTY: 5 mi. S Locust Grove, 1 (OKSU); 7 mi. W Locust Grove, 2 (OKSU). MCCURTAIN COUNTY: 6.5 mi. N Broken Bow, 1 (OKSU); 2 mi. W Smithville, 1 (OMNH). MUSKOGEE COUNTY: 4 mi. S Greenleaf Lake on SH 10, 1 (OKSU). OTTAWA COUNTY: 2 mi. N Peoria, 1 (OKSU); Benscoter Farm, 10 mi. SE Quapaw, 1 (OKSU). PITTSBURG COUNTY: 6 mi. E, 1 mi. S Kiowa, 2 (ECENT). PUSHMATAHA COUNTY: 1 mi. W, 4 mi. N Antlers, 1 (ECENT); 1 mi. S Nashoba, 1 (TMM). SEQUOYAH COUNTY: 3 mi. E Bunch, 2 (OKSU); 2.5 mi. NW

Marble City, 2 (OKSU). TULSA COUNTY: Grove, 1 (CSUO); Red Fork, 2 (USNM). WAGONER COUNTY: Ft. Gibson Public Hunting Area, 1 (CSUO); 14 Mile Creek, 3 mi. E Ft. Gibson Reservoir, 1 (CSUO); 8 mi. W Wagoner, 2 (OKSU).

Taxidea taxus.—Specimens examined (total 66): ALFALFA COUNTY: Hwy 11, Great Salt Plains National Wildlife Refuge, 1 (CAMCO). BLAINE COUNTY: 2.5 mi. N Canton, 1 (CAMCO); 4 mi. S Hitchcock, 1 (OKSU); 5 mi. N Okeene, 1 (OKSU). CADDO COUNTY: 8.5 mi. W Binger, 1 (OMNH); 2 mi. SE Carnegie, 1 (CAMCO); 2 mi. S, 0.5 mi. W Ft. Cobb, 1 (CAMCO). CIMARRON COUNTY: 14 mi. W Boise City, 1 (OKSU); 3 mi. E Kenton, 1 (OKSU). CLEVELAND COUNTY: 6 mi. NW Norman, 1 (OMNH). COMANCHE COUNTY: Chattanooga, 1 (USNM); Bentley Ranch, 3 mi. W Lawton, 1 (OKSU). CUSTER COUNTY: 5 mi. SW Anthon, 1 (USNM); 6 mi. SW Anthon, 1 (USNM); 5 mi. E Butler, 1 (OMNH). DEWEY COUNTY: Camargo, 1 (OKSU). ELLIS COUNTY: Ellis County, 1 (OKSU); 10 mi. SE Higgins, Texas, 1 (MVZ); 4 mi. N Peek, 1 (USNM). GARFIELD COUNTY: Kremlin, 1 (OKSU). GARVIN COUNTY: Hwy I-35 between Wayne & Pauls Valley, 1 (OMNH). GRADY COUNTY: 2 mi. W Tabler, 1 (OMNH). GRANT COUNTY: 6 mi. N, 3.5 mi. E Wakita, 2 (OKSU). HARPER COUNTY: 3 mi. E May, 2 (OKSU). HUGHES COUNTY: 2 mi. W Calvin, 1 (ECENT). JACKSON COUNTY: 5 mi. E Altus, 1 (OKSU); 9 mi. S, 13 mi. E Altus, 1 (ECENT); 7 mi. W, 1 mi. S Eldorado, 1 (OKSU); 2.6 mi. E Headrick, 1 (OMNH); 2 mi. S, 2.25 mi. W Olustee, 1 (CAMCO). JOHNSTON COUNTY: Earl Gray Ranch, 4 mi. NE Mill Creek, 1 (OMNH). KINGFISHER COUNTY: N Cimarron River, 1 (MSU). KIOWA COUNTY: 3.5 mi. W Snyder, 1 (OUBS). LOGAN COUNTY: W Stillwater, 1 (OKSU). MCCLAIN COUNTY: Sonner Fish Farm, 3 mi. E, 1 mi. S Goldsby, 2 (OMNH); 3 mi. W Newcastle, 1 (ECENT). NOBLE COUNTY: T22N, R1E, Sec. 13, 1 (OKSU). OKLAHOMA COUNTY: 5 mi. W Edmond, 1 (CSUO); 5.5 W Edmond on 2nd, 1 (CSUO); northwest part county, 1 (CSUO); jct. 74th & Anderson Rd., Oklahoma City, 1 (CSUO); Rt. 35, 119th St. S, 1 (OKSU). OSAGE COUNTY: 10 mi. SE Fairfax, 1 (USNM). PAWNEE COUNTY: 3.5 mi. N Morrison, 1 (OKSU). PAYNE COUNTY: 2 mi. E Glencoe, 1 (OKSU); 2.5 mi. E Glencoe, 1 (OKSU); 2.5 mi. W Perkins Corner on Hwy 33, 1 (OKSU); 0.5 mi. W Stillwater Creek Bridge, 1 (OKSU); 4 mi. S Stillwater, 1 (OKSU); 6.5 mi. N Stillwater on US Hwy 177, 1 (OKSU). PONTOTOC COUNTY: 13 mi. W, 8 mi. N Ada, 1 (ECENT). ROGER MILLS COUNTY: Durham, 1 (OKSU); Roger Mills County, 2 (OKSU). TEXAS COUNTY: 5 mi. W Eva on US 64, 1 (OKSU); 3 mi. N, 4 mi. E Goodwell, 1 (KU). TILLMAN COUNTY: 6 mi. E, 0.5 mi. S Manitou, 1 (CAMCO). WOODS COUNTY: 6 mi. E

Alva, Oklahoma Territory, 1 (FMNH); jct. US 64 & SH 50, near Freedom, 1 (OMNH). WOODWARD COUNTY: 11 mi. S Freedom, 1 (OKSU); Ft. Supply, 1 (OKSU); 1 mi. E Woodward, 1 (OKSU); 14 mi. E Woodward, 1 (OKSU).

Urocyon cinereoargenteus.—Specimens examined (total 59): ADAIR COUNTY: 7 mi. W Stilwell, 1 (KU). BRYAN COUNTY: 1 mi. N Achille, 1 (OKSU); E Durant on US 70, 1 (OKSU). CADDO COUNTY: 6 mi. S, 1.85 mi. W Aetna, Kansas, 1 (KU); 8 mi. W Lookeba, 1 (KU); T10N, R10W, Sec. 34, 1 (OMNH). CHOCTAW COUNTY: 2 mi. E Grant, 1 (OKSU). CIMARRON COUNTY: Kenton, 1 (KU); Tesesquite Canyon Cave, 1 (OKSU). CLEVELAND COUNTY: Cleveland County, 1 (OMNH); T7N, R1W, Sec. 24, 3 mi. E, 5 mi. N Lexington, 2 (OMNH); 5 mi. E, 2 mi. N Lexington, 1 (OMNH); 9 mi. N Norman, 1 (OMNH); 16 mi. E Norman, 1 (OMNH); 20 mi. S Norman, 1,150 ft., 1 (OMNH); Mulden Ranch, 15 mi. E, 3 mi. N Purcell, 1 (OMNH). COAL COUNTY: 10 mi. SE Fittstown, 1 (OKSU). COMANCHE COUNTY: Lawton, 1 (CAMCO); Cache, 1.5 mi. E Brice Gate, Wichita Mountains, 1 (USNM); head of Panther Creek, Wichita Mountains, 1 (USNM); near Osago Lake, Wichita Mountains, 1 (USNM); 2 mi. E Easter Pageant, Wichita Mountains Refuge, 1 (USNM); Wichita Mountains Wildlife Refuge, 1 (OKSU), 1 (CAMCO). HUGHES COUNTY: Hughes County, 1 (OKSU), 1 (ECENT). KINGFISHER COUNTY: near Hennessey, 1 (OKSU). KIOWA COUNTY: 2 mi. S Lugert, 1 (OKSU); 3 mi. N Roosevelt, 1 (OKSU). LATIMER COUNTY: 3 mi. W, 3 mi. N Wilburton, 1 (OKSU). MARSHALL COUNTY: Dark Horse Corner, 1 (OUBS); 1.4 mi. N University of Oklahoma Biological Station, 1 (OUBS); 1.5 mi. W University of Oklahoma Biological Station, 1 (OUBS). MCCURTAIN COUNTY: 9 mi. W Idabel on SH 70, 1 (OKSU); 23 mi. S Smithville, 3 (USNM). MURRAY COUNTY: 3 mi. N Davis, 1 (ECENT). OKLAHOMA COUNTY: 2 mi. N Moore on US 35, 1 (OMNH); Nicoma Park (via State Health Rabies), 1 (CSUO); jct. N.W. 5th & Villa Sts., 1 (OMNH). PAWNEE COUNTY: near Ralston, 1 (OKSU); 1 mi. E, 6 mi. N Yale, 1 (OKSU). PAYNE COUNTY: Stillwater, 1 (OKSU); 8 mi. E Stillwater, 1 (OKSU). PONTOTOC COUNTY: 1 mi. SW Ada, 1 (ECENT); 6 mi. SE Ada, 2 (ECENT); 10 mi. N Ada, 1 (ECENT); 15 mi. W Ada, 2 (ECENT); Pontotoc County, 1 (ECENT). TULSA COUNTY: Tulsa Zoo, 2 (OKSU); 2 mi. W Tulsa, 1 (OKSU). WOODWARD COUNTY: Selman's Cave, 3 (OKSU).

Ursus americanus.—Specimens examined (total 4): COMANCHE COUNTY: southwest slope, Mt. Scott, 1 (USNM); Mt. Scott, 1 (USNM). HARPER COUNTY: Harper County, subfossil, 1 (OKSU). WOODS COUNTY: bed of Eagle Chief Creek, Alva, 1 (USNM).

Vulpes velox.—Specimens examined (total 28): BEAVER COUNTY: 7 mi.
SW Balko, 1 (OKSU); 3 mi. E Elmwood, 1 (OKSU); 3 mi. E, 0.5 mi. S
Gray, 1 (KU); 3 mi. E, 2 mi. S Gray, 1 (KU); 4 mi. E, 0.5 mi. S Gray, 11
(KU); Texas Line at Hwy 83, 2 (OKSU); T1N, R21E, Sec. 14, 1 (KU);
T1S, R21E, Sec. 15, 1 (KU); T1S, R21E, Sec. 19, 4 (KU); T1S, R21E,
Sec. 20, 2 (KU). TEXAS COUNTY: 5 mi. NW Goodwell, 1 (OKSU);
near Guymon, 1 (OKSU); 15 mi. E Hardesty, 1 (OMNH).

Vulpes vulpes.—Specimens examined (total 22): ADAIR COUNTY: Tyner
Creek, 4 mi. N US 62, 1 (OKSU). CHEROKEE COUNTY: 12 mi. N Tah-
lequah, 1 (UMMZ). DELAWARE COUNTY: Parker Ranch, 4 mi. W, 2.5
mi. N Jay, 1 (OKSU); 4 mi. W, 2.5 mi. N Parker Ranch, 1 (OKSU).
HUGHES COUNTY: Hughes County, 1 (OKSU). JACKSON COUNTY:
3 mi. N, 0.75 mi. E Altus, 1 (CAMCO). KIOWA COUNTY: 2 mi. E
Snyder on US Hwy 62, 1 (OKSU); 4 mi. E Snyder, 1 (CAMCO). LATI-
MER COUNTY: Brushy Narrows, 1 (OKSU). MARSHALL COUNTY:
Lake Texoma, 1 (OKSU). OKLAHOMA COUNTY: jct. N.E. 36th St. &
North Canadian River, 1 (OKSU). OKMULGEE COUNTY: Okmulgee
County, 1 (OKSU). PAYNE COUNTY: east side Stillwater, 1 (OKSU);
near Stillwater, 1 (OKSU); 2 mi. E Stillwater, 1 (OKSU); 2 mi. W Still-
water, 1 (OKSU). PITTSBURG COUNTY: near Krebs, 2 (CAMCO).
PONTOTOC COUNTY: near Lawrence, 1 (ECENT). PUSHMATAHA
COUNTY: 6 mi. S Clayton, 1 (OKSU). TILLMAN COUNTY: 1 mi. NE
Frederick, 1 (CAMCO); 4 mi. E Manitou, 1 (CAMCO).

Zapus hudsonius.—Specimens examined (total 2): TULSA COUNTY:
Mohawk Park, 2 (UMMZ).

Appendix 2
Etymology of Oklahoma Mammal Names

William Caire

Most people who have any acquaintance with the taxonomy of various groups of organisms know a number of scientific names and the meanings of the roots of at least a few of them. Such information is often both useful and intellectually satisfying, since in many cases the binomial which the author supplied reveals something of the color, morphology, habitat, or other characteristics—real or imagined—of the organism. We submit the following list of root meanings for the names of the mammals known to occur in Oklahoma with the expectation that it will be found to be helpful and interesting.

The list is alphabetical, with generic names and specific epithets listed independently. Abbreviations used in the list are: L = Latin, ML = Middle Latin, NL = New Latin, and G = Greek.

Alphabetical List of Generic Names and Specific Epithets (from Jordan, 1929; Jaeger, 1966).
albigula = *albus* (L), white + *gula* (L), throat
americana = America + *ana* (L), belonging to
americanus = America + *nus* (L), belonging to
antrozous = *antron* (G), a cave + zoon (G), an animal or living being
aquaticus = *aqua* (L), water + *icus* (L), belonging to
astutus = *astutus* (L), cunning
attwateri = for H. P. Attwater, who collected first specimen
audubonii = for J. J. Audubon, early naturalist and artist
austroriparius = *austro* (L), southern + *riparius* (L), frequenting banks of streams
bassariscus = *bassaris* (G), fox + *iskos* (G), diminutive form implying small
bison = Latin cognate of the old German *Wisunt* (modern German *Wisent*)
blarina = derivation unknown

499

borealis = *borealis* (L), northern

boylei = for C. C. Boyle, M.D. and naturalist

brasiliensis = Brazil + *ensis* (L), belonging to

brevicauda = *brevis* (L), short + *cauda* (L), tail

bursarius = *bursa* (L), pouch + *arius* (L), pertaining to

californicus = California + *icus* (L), belonging to

canadensis = Canada + *ensis* (L), belonging to

canis = *canis* (L), dog

castanops = *kastanos* (G), chestnut color + *opsis* (G), appearance

carolinensis = Carolina + *ensis* (L), belonging to

castor = *castor* (G), beaver

cervus = *cervus* (L), deer

cinereoargenteus = *cinereus* (L), ash-colored + *argenteus* (L), silvery

cinereus = *cinereus* (L), ash-colored

concolor = *con* (L), same + *color* (L), hue or tint

cooperi = for William Cooper, who collected first specimen

coypus = Latin for *coypu*, an Araucanian Indian word (Chile and Argentina)

crawfordi = for Dr. S. W. Crawford, who collected first specimen

cryptotis = *kryptos* (G), hidden + *otos* (G), ear

cynomys = *kynos* (G), dog + *mys* (G), mouse

dasypus = *dasy* (G), hairy + *pus* (G), foot

didelphis = *di* (G), double + *delphys* (G), womb

difficilis = *difficilis* (L), troublesome

dipodomys = *di* (G), two + *pod* (G), foot + *mys* (G), mouse

dorsatum = *dorsatus* (NL), with a back, backed

elaphus = *elaphos* (G), a deer, stag

elator = *elatus* (L), elevating

eptesicus = Greek word with obscure meaning; could be corruption of *ptetikos* (G), able to fly

erethizon = *erithizon* (G), to provoke, excite

eutamias = *eu* (G), good or true + *tamias* (G), a storer

felis = *felis* (L), cat

flavescens = *flavus* (L), yellow + *escens* (L), becoming or slightly

flavus = *flavus* (L), yellow

floridana (us) = Florida + *ana* (L), belonging to

frenata = *frenum* (L), bridle

fulvescens = *fulvus* (L), reddish yellow + *escens* (L), becoming or slightly

fuscus = *fuscus* (L), brown

geomys = *ge* (G), earth + *mys* (G), mouse

gossypinus = *gossypinus* (L), the cotton tree

grisescens = *griseus* (ML), gray + *escens* (L), becoming or slightly

hemionus = *hemi* (G), half + *onus* (G), mule or ass

hesperus = *hesperos* (G), of the evening, the west
hispidus = *hispidus* (L), rough, shaggy
hudsonius = Hudson (referring to the Hudson Bay) + *ius* (L), of or belonging to
humulis = probably a spelling error of word *humilis* (L), small
humeralis = *humerus* (L), upper arm + *alis* (L), pertaining to
keenii = for Rev. John Henry Keen, who collected first specimen
lasionycteris = *lasios* (G), hairy + *nykteris* (G), nocturnal
lasiurus = *lasios* (G), hairy + *oura* (G), tail
latrans = *latrans* (L), barker
leibii = for Dr. Leib, who collected first specimen
lepus = *lepus* (L), hare
leucogaster = *leukos* (G), white + *gaster* (G), belly
leucopus = *leuko* (G), white + *pus* (G), foot
lotor = *lotor,* washer
lucifugus = *lucis* (L), light + *fugio* (L), to flee
ludovicianus = of Louisiana (Purchase), where first specimen was collected
lupus = *lupus* (L), wolf
lutra = *lutra* (L), otter
lynx = *lynx* (G), the lynx
macrotis = *makros* (G), large + *otus* (G), ear
maniculatus = *manicula* (L), a small hand
marmota = *marmota* (L), marmot
megalotis = *megas* (G), large + *otos* (G), ear
mephitis = *mephitis* (L), bad odor
mexicana = Mexico + *ana* (L), belonging to
micropus = *mikros* (G), small + *pus* (G), foot
microtus = *mikros* (G), small + *otos* (G), ear
monax = American Indian name which means "the digger"
montanus = *mont* (L), mountain + *anus* (L), belonging to
mus = *mus* (L), mouse
musculus = *musculus* (L), small mouse
mustela = *mustela* (L), weasel
myocastor = *mys* (G), mouse + *kastor* (G), beaver
myotis = *mys* (G), mouse + *otos* (G), ear
neotoma = *neos* (G), new + *tomos* (G), cut
niger = *niger* (L), black
nigripes = *niger* (L), black + *pes* (L), foot
noctivagans = *noctis* (L), night + *vagans* (L), wanderer
norvegicus = Norway + *icus* (L), belonging to
notiosorex = *notio* (G), southern + *sorex* (L), shrew
novemcinctus = *novem* (L), nine + *cinctus* (L), banded or girdled

nutalli = for Thomas Nuttall, early naturalist

nutria = Spanish cognate of Latin word *lutra* (L), otter

nycticeus = *nychta* (G), night + *eius* (G), belonging to

ochrogaster = *ochro* (G), yellow + *gaster* (G), belly

ochrotomys = *ochra* (G), yellow + *otos* (G), ear + *mys* (G), mouse

odocoileus = *odous* (G), tooth + *koilia* (G), hollow

ondatra = Iroquois Indian name

onychomys = *onyx* (G), nail or claw + *mys* (G), mouse

ordii = for G. Ord, early U.S. naturalist

oryzomys = *oryza* (G), rice + *mys* (G), mouse

pallidus = *pallidus* (L), pale

palustris = *palustris* (L), of marshes

pappogeomys = *pappos* (G), grandfather, or the first down on chin + *geo* (G), land + *mys* (G), mouse

parva = *parva* (L), small

pectoralis = *pectoris* (L), breast + *alis* (L), pertaining to

perognathus = *pera* (G), pouch + *gnathos* (G), jaw

peromyscus = *pera* (G), pouch + *myskos* (G), little mouse

pinetorum = *pinetum* (L), a pine woods + *orum* (L), belonging to, place of

pipistrellus = Latin form of Italian word *pipistrello*, meaning "bat"

plecotus = *pleko* (G), to twist + *otos* (G), ear

procyon = *pro* (G), before + *kyon* (G), dog

putorius = *putorius* (L), of a foul odor

quadrivittatus = *quadrus* (L), fourfold + *vittatus* (L), striped

rattus = *rattus* (L), rat

rafinesquii = for Constantine Samuel Rafinesque, an early naturalist

reithrodontomys = *rheithron* (G), grooved + *odous* (G), tooth + *mys* (G), mouse

rufus = *rufus* (L), reddish

scalopus = *skalops* (G), mole, derived from *skallo* (G), to dig + *pus* (G), foot

sciurus = *sciurus* (L), squirrel (the word *sciurus* derived from *skia* [G], shadow + *oura* [G], tail, or creature that sits in the shadow of its tail)

seminolus = Latin for region inhabited by Seminole Indians from which the first specimen was taken

sigmodon = *sigma* (G), equivalent of English "s" + *odous* (G), tooth

sodalis = *sodalis* (L), companion

spermophilus = *sperma* (G), seed + *philos* (G), loving, fond of

spilogale = *spilos* (G), spot + *gale* (G), weasel

spilosoma = *spilos* (G), spot + *soma* (G), body

striatus = *striatus* (L), striped

subflavus = *sub* (L), below + *flavus* (L), yellow

sylvilagus = *sylva* (L), a wood + *lagos* (G), hare

synaptomys = *synapto* (G), to unite + *mys* (G), mouse
tadarida = word coined by Rafinesque, who gave no clue to its etymology
tamias = *tamias* (G), a storer
taxus = *taxus* (NL), badger
townsendii = for John K. Townsend, M.D. and naturalist
tridecemlineatus = *tridecem* (L), thirteen + *lineatus* (L), lined
truei = for F. W. True, former curator of mammals at U.S. National Museum
urocyon = *oura* (G), tail + *kyon* (G), dog
ursus = *ursus* (L), bear
variegatus = *vario* (L), varigated
velifer = *velum* (L), veil + *fero* (L), to bear
velox = *velox* (L), swift, speedy
virginiana = Virginia + *iana* (L), belonging to

Appendix 3
Scientific and Common Names of Plants Used in Text

William Caire and Jack D. Tyler

The following list contains the scientific and common names of the plants referred to throughout the text. The list is arranged alphabetically by scientific name. Many authors did not list complete scientific names, and therefore some species designations could not be made.

Scientific Name	*Common Name*
Acer supp.	Maples
Acer negundo	Box Elder
Acer saccharum	Sugar Maple
Agropyron smithii	Western Wheatgrass
Alnus serrulata	Smooth Alder
Amaranthus sp.	Pigweed
Ambrosia artemisiifolia	Lesser Ragweed
Andropogon spp.	Bluestems
Andropogon gerardi	Big Bluestem
Andropogon saccharoides	Silver Beard Grass
Aristida spp.	Three-awn Grasses
Aristida longiseta	Red Three-awn
Artemisia filifolia	Sand Sage
Arundinaria gigantea	Giant Cane
Asimina triloba	Pawpaw
Aster ericoides	White Heath-aster
Benzoin aestivale	Spicebush
Betula nigra	River Birch
Bouteloua spp.	Grama Grasses
Bouteloua curtipendula	Side-oats Grama
Bouteloua gracilis	Blue Grama

504

Bouteloua hirsuta	Hairy Grama
Brasenia spp.	Water Shields
Buchloë dactyloides	Buffalo Grass
Bumelia lanuginosa	Chittamwood
Callicarpa americana	French Mulberry
Campsis radicans	Trumpet Creeper
Carex spp.	Sedges
Carya spp.	Hickories
Carya illinoensis	Pecan
Carya texana	Black Hickory
Carya tomentosa	Mockernut Hickory
Cassia fasciculata	Partridge Pea
Ceanothus sp.	New Jersey Tea
Celtis spp.	Hackberries
Celtis laevigata	Lowland Hackberry
Celtis occidentalis	Sugarberry
Celtis reticulata	Thick-leaved Hackberry
Cephalanthus occidentalis	Buttonbush
Ceratophyllum sp.	Hornwort
Cercis canadensis	Redbud
Cercocarpus montanus	Mountain Mahogany
Chara spp.	Charas
Chenopodium sp.	Lamb's Quarter
Chionanthus sp.	Fringe Tree
Chloris verticillata	Windmill Grass
Chrysopsis stenophylla	Stiff-leaved Golden Aster
Chrysothamnus nauseosus	Rabbit Brush
Cirsium spp.	Thistles
Cleome sp.	Beeflower
Condalia obtusifolia	Lotebush
Coreopsis tinctoria	Prairie Tickseed
Corispermum hyssopifolium	Bugseed
Cornus spp.	Dogwoods
Cornus florida	Flowering Dogwood
Crataegus sp.	Hawthorne
Cycloloma atriplicifolium	Winged Pigweed
Cynodon dactyloides	Bermuda Grass
Cyperus spp.	Sedges
Desmodium sp.	Beggar's Lice
Dianthera	Water Willow
Diospyros virginiana	Persimmon
Eleocharis spp.	Spike-rushes

Equisetum spp.	Horsetails
Euphorbia spp.	Spurges
Euphorbia dentata	Toothed Euphorbia
Fagus sp.	Beechnut
Fraxinus americana	White Ash
Fuirena simplex	Sedge (Umbrella grass)
Grindelia sp.	Tarweed
Gymnocladus dioicus	Kentucky Coffee Bean
Helianthus sp.	Jerusalem Artichoke
Helianthus spp.	Sunflowers
Heteranthera sp.	Mud Plantain
Houstonia angustifolia	Narrow-leaved Houstonia
Ilex opaca	American Holly
Ipomoea spp.	Wild Potato Vines
Juglans nigra	Black Walnut
Juncus spp.	Rushes
Juncus torreyi	Torrey Rush
Juniperus monosperma	One-seeded Juniper
Juniperus virginiana	Red Cedar
Jussiaea sp.	Primrose Willow
Lemna spp.	Duckweeds
Lespedeza sp.	Bush Clover
Liquidambar styraciflua	Sweetgum
Lonicera sp.	Honeysuckle
Maclura pomifera	Osage Orange
Medicago sativa	Alfalfa
Monarda spp.	Horsemints
Morus spp.	Mulberries
Najas sp.	Bushy Pondweed
Nelumbo lutea	American Lotus
Nymphaea sp.	Water Lily
Nyssa sylvatica	Tupelo
Opuntia spp.	Prickly Pears
Opuntia davisii	Davis's Prickly Pear
Opuntia imbricata	Cholla Cactus
Opuntia leptocaulis	Pencil Cactus
Panicum virgatum	Switch Grass
Paspalum sp.	Paspalum
Phragmites spp.	Reeds
Phyllanthus polygonoidea	Knotweed
Pinus echinata	Shortleaf Pine
Pinus edulis	Piñon Pine

Pinus ponderosa	Western Yellow Pine
Pinus taeda	Loblolly Pine
Platanus occidentalis	Sycamore
Podophyllum peltatum	May Apple
Polygonum spp.	Smartweeds
Populus deltoides	Cottonwood
Populus sargentii	Cottonwood (Western)
Potamogeton spp.	Pondweeds
Prosopis glandulosa	Mesquite
Prunus sp.	Cherry
Prunus angustifolia	Sand Plum
Quercus spp.	Oaks
Quercus alba	White Oak
Quercus gambelii	Gambel's Oak
Quercus havardii	Shinnery Oak
Quercus marilandica	Blackjack Oak
Quercus mohriana	Mohr Oak
Quercus muhlenbergii	Chinquapin Oak
Quercus phellos	Willow Oak
Quercus shumardii	Spotted Oak
Quercus stellata	Post Oak
Quercus undulata	Rocky Mountain Shin Oak
Quercus velutina	Black Oak
Quercus virginiana	Live Oak
Rhododendron spp.	Azaleas
Rhus spp.	Sumacs
Rhus radicans	Poison Ivy
Rhus trilobata	Skunk Bush
Ribes spp.	Gooseberries
Robinia pseudo-acacia	Black Locust
Rubus sp.	Blackberry
Rudbeckia spp.	Coneflowers
Sabal glabra	Palmetto
Sagittaria sp.	Water Plantain
Salix spp.	Willows
Salix amygdaloides	Peachleaf Willow
Salix interior	Sandbar Willow
Sanguinaria canadensis	Bloodroot
Sassafras albidum	Sassafras
Saururus cernuus	Lizard's Tail
Schizachyrium scoparium	Little Bluestem
Schrankia uncinata	Sensitive Brier

Scutellaria resinosa	Resinous Skullcap
Senecio spp.	Groundsels
Setaria geniculata	Beard Grass
Smilax spp.	Greenbriers
Sorghastrum nutans	Indian Grass
Sorghum halapense	Johnson Grass
Sorghum vulgare	Sorghum
Sphaeralcea coccinea	Scarlet Globemallow
Sporobolus spp.	Dropseed Grasses
Sporobolus cryptandrus	Sand Dropseed
Stipa comata	Needle and Thread Grass
Strophostyles helvola	Wildbean
Symphoricarpos orbiculatus	Coralberry
Tamarix pentandra (gallica)	Tamarisk (Salt Cedar)
Taxodium distichum	Bald Cypress
Thelesperma trifidus	Three-cleft Greenthread
Tilia americana	Basswood
Tragia ramosa	Stinging Nettle
Trifolium spp.	Clovers
Triodia sp.	Purpletop
Triplasis purpurea	Purple Sandgrass
Triticum aestivum	Winter Wheat
Typha spp.	Cattails
Ulmus spp.	Elms
Ulmus alata	Winged Elm
Ulmus americana	American Elm
Utricularia spp.	Bladderworts
Vaccinium spp.	Huckleberries
Vaccinium vacillans	Lowbush Blueberry
Vernonia spp.	Ironweeds
Viburnum sp.	Viburnum
Vitis spp.	Grapes
Xanthium sp.	Cocklebur
Yucca glauca	Small Soapweed
Zea mays	Corn
Zizaniopsis miliacea	Southern Wild Rice

Literature Cited

Abert, J. W. 1845–46. Journal of J. W. Abert from Bent's Fort to St. Louis in 1845. U.S. Senate Doc. 8 (377–438):57; 29th Congr., 1st Sess.

Ables, E. D. 1969. Home-range studies of red foxes (*Vulpes vulpes*). J. Mamm., 50:108–120.

Adams, C. E. 1978. Ages of hunter-killed coyotes in southeastern Nebraska. J. Wildl. Mgmt., 42:425–426.

Aday, B., Jr., and A. Gennaro. 1973. Mammals (excluding bats) of the New Mexican Llano Estacado and its adjacent river valleys. Stud. Nat. Sci., E. New Mexico Univ., 1:1–33.

Ahshapanek, D. C., and R. D. Burns. 1960. Mammals associated with prehistoric people of Oklahoma. Proc. Oklahoma Acad. Sci., 40:16–19.

Allen, J. A. 1876. The American bisons, living and extinct. Mem. Harvard Mus. Comp. Zool., 4(10).

―――. 1891. Notes on new or little known North American mammals. Bull. Amer. Mus. Nat. Hist., 3:263–310.

Allen, R. W. 1962. Extent and sources of parasitism in pronghorn antelope. Pp. 48–51, *in* Interstate Antelope Conf. Trans., Reno, Nevada.

Andersen, K. W., and E. D. Fleharty. 1964. Additional fox records for Kansas. Trans. Kansas Acad. Sci., 67:193–194.

Anderson, R. C. 1962. The parasites of white-tailed deer. Pp. 163–173, *in* Proc. First Natl. White-tailed Deer Dis. Symp., Univ. Georgia, Athens.

Anderson, S., and B. C. Nelson. 1958. Additional records of mammals of Kansas. Trans. Kansas Acad. Sci., 61:302–312.

Anthony, A., and D. Foreman. 1951. Observations on the reproductive cycle of the black-tailed prairie dog (*Cynomys ludovicianus*). Physiol. Zool. 24: 242–248.

Armstrong, D. M. 1972. Distribution of mammals in Colorado. Monogr. Mus. Nat. Hist., Univ. Kansas, 3:1–415.

———, J. R. Choate, and J. K. Jones, Jr. 1986. Distributional patterns of mammals in the plains states. Occas. Pap., The Mus., Texas Tech Univ., 105:1–27.

———, and J. K. Jones, Jr. 1972. *Notiosorex crawfordi*. Mamm. Species, 17:1–5.

Armstrong, R. A. 1950. Fetal development of the northern white-tailed deer (*Odocoileus virginianus borealis* Miller). Amer. Midland Nat., 43:650–666.

Arvey, M. D., and B. P. Glass. 1950. The black-footed ferret in Oklahoma. J. Mamm., 31:460.

Asdell, A. S. 1964. Patterns of mammalian reproduction. Cornell Univ. Press, Ithaca, New York.

Ashbrook, F. G. 1948. Nutrias grow in the United States. J. Wildl. Mgmt., 12:87–95.

Atwood, E. L. 1941. White-tailed deer foods of the United States. J. Wildl. Mgmt., 5:314–332.

Baccus, J. T. 1968. Two noteworthy records of rodents from Baylor County. Southwestern Nat., 13:362.

———. 1971. The mammals of Baylor County, Texas. Texas J. Sci, 22: 177–185.

Bailey, E. P. 1974. Notes on the development, mating behavior, and vocalization of captive ringtails. Southwestern Nat., 19:117–119.

Bailey, V. 1898. Descriptions of eleven new species and subspecies of voles. Proc. Biol. Soc. Washington, 12:85–90.

———. 1905. Biological survey of Texas. No. Amer. Fauna, 25:1–222. Wash., D.C.

———. 1928. The red fox in America. Nature Mag., 28:269–272, 317.

———. 1931. Mammals of New Mexico. No. Amer. Fauna, 53:1–412. Wash., D.C.

Baker, R. H., and B. P. Glass. 1951. The taxonomic status of the pocket gophers, *Geomys bursarius* and *Geomys breviceps*. Proc. Biol. Soc. Washington, 64:55–58.

———, C. C. Newman, and F. Wilke. 1945. Food habits of the raccoon in eastern Texas. J. Wildl. Mgmt., 9:45–48.

Baker, R. J., L. W. Robbins, F. B. Stangl, Jr., and E. C. Birney. 1983. Chromosomal evidence for a major subdivision in *Peromyscus leucopus*. J. Mamm., 64:356–359.

———, and D. L. Spencer. 1965. Late fall reproduction in the desert shrew. J. Mamm., 46:330.

Barbour, R. W., and W. H. Davis. 1969. Bats of America. Univ. Kentucky Press, Lexington. 286 pp.

Barkalow, F. S., Jr. 1948. The status of the Seminole bat, *Lasiurus seminolus* (Rhoads). J. Mamm., 29:415–416.

Bartush, W. S., and G. W. Garner. 1978. Behavior of white-tailed does and fawns during the parturition periods. Proc. Ann. Conf. S.E. Assoc. Fish & Wildl. Agencies, 32:246–255.

——— and ———. 1979. Physical characteristics of white-tailed deer fawns in southwestern Oklahoma. Proc. Ann. Conf. S.E. Assoc. Fish & Wildl. Agencies, 33:250–258.

———, and J. C. Lewis. 1981. Mortality of white-tailed deer fawns in the Wichita Mountains. Proc. Oklahoma Acad. Sci., 61:23–27.

Base, D. L. 1986. Evaluation of experimental reintroduction of river otters into Oklahoma. Oklahoma Dept. Wildl. Conserv. Nongame Wildl. Prog.

Baumgardner, G. D. 1987. A recent specimen of the Texas kangaroo rat, *Dipodomys elator* (Heteromyidae), from Oklahoma. Southwestern Nat., 32:285–286.

Beale, D. M., and A. D. Smith. 1970. Forage use, water consumption, and productivity of pronghorn antelope in western Utah. J. Wildl. Mgmt., 34:570–582.

Bean, C. 1983. Mountain lion sightings growing with deer population. The Daily Oklahoman, December 12. Oklahoma City.

Beasom S. L., L. LaPlant, and V. W. Howard, Jr. 1981. Similarity of pronghorn, cattle and sheep diets in southeastern New Mexico. Proc. Wildl.-Livestock Relat. Symp., Coeur d'Alene, Idaho.

Bee, J. W., G. E. Glass, R. S. Hoffmann, and R. R. Patterson. 1981. Mammals in Kansas. Pub. Ed. Ser., Mus. Nat. Hist., Univ. Kansas, 7:ix + 1–300.

Bekoff, M. 1977. *Canis latrans*. Mamm. Species, 79:1–9.

———, ed. 1978. Coyotes: biology, behavior and management. Academic Press, New York. 384 pp.

Best, T. L. 1971. Notes on the distribution and ecology of five eastern New Mexico mammals. Southwestern Nat., 16:210–211.

———, and B. Hoditschek. 1982. Analysis of cheek pouch contents of Ord's kangaroo rat (*Dipodomys ordii*). Southwestern Nat., 27:117–124.

———, B. Hoditschek, and H. H. Thomas. 1981. Foods of coyotes (*Canis latrans*) in Oklahoma. Southwestern Nat., 26:67–92.

———, and M. L. Kennedy. 1972. The porcupine (*Erethizon dorsatum* Linnaeus) in the Texas panhandle and adjacent New Mexico and Oklahoma. Texas J. Sci., 24:351.

———, and G. D. Schnell. 1974. Bacular variation in kangaroo rats (genus *Dipodomys*). Amer. Midland Nat., 91:257–270.

Bever, W. 1957. The incidence and degree of the parasitic load among antelope and the development of field techniques to measure such parasitism. Pittman-Robertson Proj. 12-R-14, Job Outline No. A-5.2.

Bigham, S. R. 1966. Identification of the habitat of the cottontail rabbit in central Oklahoma. Okla. Dept. Wildl. Conserv. Publ.

Bird, R. D. 1930. Cottontail rabbits are insectivorous. J. Mamm., 11:240.

Birney, E. C. 1973. Systematics of three species of woodrats (genus *Neotoma*) in central North America. Misc. Publ., Mus. Nat. Hist., Univ. Kansas, 58:1–173.

———, and E. D. Fleharty. 1966. Age and sex comparisons of wild mink. Trans. Kansas Acad. Sci., 69:139–145.

———, W. E. Grant, and D. D. Baird. 1976. Importance of vegetative cover to cycles of *Microtus* populations. Ecology, 57:1043–1051.

———, J. K. Jones, Jr., and D. M. Mortimer. 1970. The yellow-faced pocket gopher, *Pappogeomys castanops*, in Kansas. Trans. Kansas Acad. Sci., 73:368–375.

Bissonette, J. A., and O. E. Maughan. 1978. Southeastern Oklahoma coal investigation: endangered species. Proj. No./14-16-002-77-080 Completed Rept. to U.S. Fish and Wildl. Serv. 101 pp.

Black, J. D. 1936. Mammals of northwestern Arkansas. J. Mamm., 17:29–35.

Black, J. H., and T. L. Best. 1972. Remains of a gray wolf (*Canis lupus*) from northwestern Oklahoma. Proc. Oklahoma Acad. Sci., 52:120.

———, R. Hunsicker, A. P. Blair, and T. Hunkapillar. 1977. The eastern chipmunk in central Oklahoma with validation of Howell's 1929 Red Fork record. Proc. Oklahoma Acad. Sci., 57:163–164.

Blair, W. F. 1936. The nine-banded armadillo in northeastern Oklahoma. J. Mamm., 17:293–294.

———. 1937. The burrows and food of the prairie pocket mouse. J. Mamm., 18:188–191.

———. 1938. Ecological relationships of the mammals of Bird Creek region, northeastern Oklahoma. Amer. Midland Nat., 20:473–526.

———. 1939. Faunal relationships and geographic distribution of mammals in Oklahoma. Amer. Midland Nat., 22:85–133.

———. 1942. Systematic relationships of *Peromyscus* and several related genera as shown by the baculum. J. Mamm., 23:196–204.

———. 1953. Population dynamics of rodents and other small mammals. Adv. Genetics, 5:1–41.

———. 1954. Mammals of the Mesquite Plains biotic district in Texas and Oklahoma, and speciation in the central grasslands. Texas J. Sci., 6:235–264.

————, and T. H. Hubbell. 1938. The biotic districts of Oklahoma. Amer. Midland Nat., 20:425–454.

Boddicker, M. L. 1968. Parasites of the black-footed ferret. Proc. South Dakota Acad. Sci., 47:141–148.

Bohlin, R. G., and E. G. Zimmerman. 1982. Genic differentiation of two chromosome races of the *Geomys bursarius* complex. J. Mamm., 63:218–228.

Bond, C. H. 1964. Game mammals of Oklahoma. Oklahoma Wildl. Comm. Educ. Pamp. No. 1. 38 pp.

Bridgewater, D. D. 1966. Laboratory breeding, early growth development and behavior of *Citellus tridecemlineatus* (Rodentia). Southwestern Nat., 11:325–337.

————, and D. F. Penny. 1966. Predation by *Citellus tridecemlineatus* on other vertebrates. J. Mamm., 47:345–346.

Bromley, P. T. 1969. Territoriality in pronghorn bucks on the National Bison Range, Moiese, Montana. J. Mamm., 50:81–89.

————, and D. W. Kitchen. 1974. Courtship in the pronghorn (*Antilocapra americana*). *In* The behavior of ungulates and its relation to management (V. Geist and F. Walther, eds.) Vols. I & II. IUCN Publ. No. 24. Morges, Switzerland.

Brown, C. E. 1936. Rearing wild animals in captivity and gestation periods. J. Mamm., 17:12.

Bruner, W. E. 1931. The vegetation of Oklahoma. Ecol. Monogr., 1:99–188.

Bruns, E. H. 1969. Winter predation of golden eagles and coyotes on pronghorn antelopes. Can. Field-Nat., 84:301–304.

Buechner, H. K. 1944. Helminth parasites of the gray fox. J. Mamm., 25:185–188.

————. 1950*a*. Life history, ecology and range use of the pronghorn antelope in Trans-Pecos Texas. Amer. Midland Nat., 43:257–354.

————. 1950*b*. Range ecology of the pronghorn on the Wichita Mountains Wildlife Refuge. Trans. N. Amer. Wildl. Conf., 15:627–644.

Burnett, C. D. 1983. Geographic and climatic correlates of morphological variation in *Eptesicus fuscus*. J. Mamm., 64:437–444.

Burnham, G. L. 1953. A study of the helminth parasites of the pocket gophers of Woods, Alfalfa, Grant, and Marshall counties, Oklahoma. Proc. Oklahoma Acad. Sci., 34:59–61.

Burns, J. C., J. R. Choate and E. G. Zimmerman. 1985. Systematic relationships of pocket gophers (genus *Geomys*) on the central Great Plains. J. Mamm., 66:102–118.

Buscher, H. N. 1975. *Raillietina* (*Raillietina*) *selfi* sp. (Cestoda: Davaineidae) from the desert cottontail in Oklahoma with notes on the distribution of

Raillietina from North American mammals. Proc. Oklahoma Acad. Sci., 55:103–107.

————, and J. D. Tyler. 1975. Parasites of vertebrates inhabiting prairie dog towns in Oklahoma, II. Helminthes. Proc. Oklahoma Acad. Sci., 55: 108–111.

Butts, K. O. 1973. Life history and habitat requirements of burrowing owls in western Oklahoma. MS thesis, Oklahoma State Univ., Stillwater. 188 pp.

————. 1976. Burrowing owls wintering in the Oklahoma Panhandle. Auk, 93:510–516.

————, and J. C. Lewis. 1982. The importance of prairie dog towns to burrowing owls in Oklahoma. Proc. Oklahoma Acad. Sci., 62:46–52.

Cahalane, V. H. 1932. Age variation in the teeth and skull of the white-tailed deer. Cranbrook Inst. Sci. Publ. 2.

————. 1961. Mammals of North America. MacMillan Co., New York.

Caire, W. 1985. Summer ecology of southeastern Oklahoma bats. Final Report—Oklahoma Dept. Wildl. Conserv. Nongame Wildl. Grant.

————, B. L. Cox, and B. Levesay. 1981. Some normal blood values of *Myotis velifer* (Chiroptera: Vespertilionidae). J. Mamm., 62:436–439.

————, H. Haines, and T. M. McKenna. 1982. Osmolality and ion concentration in urine of hibernating *Myotis velifer*. J. Mamm., 63:688–690.

————, R. M. Hardisty, and K. E. Lacy. 1986. Ecological notes on *Lasiurus cinereus* (Chiroptera: Vespertilionidae) in Oklahoma. Proc. Okla. Acad. Sci., 66:41–42.

————, and L. Hornuff. 1982. Wing morphology and flight behavior of the bat fly, *Trichobius major* (Diptera: Streblidae). Southwestern Nat., 27: 356–357.

————, and ————. 1986. Overwintering population dynamics of the bat fly, *Trichobius major* (Diptera: Streblidae). Southwestern Nat., 31:126–129.

————, ————, and M. Ports. 1981. Geographic variation in wing areas and femur lengths of the bat fly, *Trichobius major* (Diptera: Streblidae), in western Oklahoma. Southwestern Nat., 26:429–430.

————, ————, and N. Sohrabi. 1985. Stimuli used by *Trichobius major* (Diptera: Streblidae) to locate its bat host, *Myotis velifer*. Southwestern Nat., 30:405–412.

————, R. K. LaVal, and R. L. Clawson. 1979. Notes on the ecology of *Myotis keenii* (Chiroptera: Vespertilionidae) in eastern Missouri. Amer. Midland Nat., 102:404–407.

————, and M. A. Ports. 1981. An adaptive method of predation by the great horned owl on Mexican free-tailed bats. Southwestern Nat., 26:69–70.

————, J. F. Smith, S. McGuire, and M. A. Royce. 1984. Early foraging behavior of insectivorous bats in western Oklahoma. J. Mamm., 65:319–324.

————, and M. L. Thies. 1987. The Seminole bat, *Lasiurus seminolus*, (Chiroptera: Vespertilionidae), from central Oklahoma. Southwestern Nat., 32:273–289.

————, and E. G. Zimmerman. 1975. Chromosomal and morphological variation and circular overlap in the deer mouse, *Peromyscus maniculatus*, in Texas and Oklahoma. Syst. Zool., 24:89–95.

Cameron, G. N., and S. R. Spencer. 1981. *Sigmodon hispidus*. Mamm. Species, 158:1–9.

Carley, C. J. 1979. Status summary: the red wolf. Endang. Species Rept. No. 7, U.S. Fish & Wildl. Serv., Albuquerque, N.M.

Carpenter, J. W., J. C. Freeny, and C. S. Patton. 1972. Occurrence of *Demodex* Owen 1843 on a white-tailed deer from Oklahoma. J. Wildl. Dis., 8:112–114.

————, H. E. Jordan, and B. C. Ward. 1973. Neurologic disease in wapiti naturally infected with meningeal worms. J. Wildl. Dis., 9:148–153.

————, and R. P. Martin. 1969. Capturing prairie dogs for transplanting. J. Wildl. Mgmt., 33:1024.

Carter, D. C., W. D. Webster, J. K. Jones, Jr., C. Jones, and R. D. Suttkus. 1985. *Dipodomys elator*. Mamm. Species, 232:1–3.

Cary, M. 1911. A biological survey of Colorado. N. Amer. Fauna, 33:1–256. Wash., D.C.

Chapman, B. 1972. Food habits of Loring's kangaroo rat, *Dipodomys elator*. J. Mamm., 53:877–880.

Chapman, J. A., and G. A. Feldhamer. 1981. *Sylvilagus aquaticus*. Mamm. Species, 151:1–4.

————, J. G. Hockman, and W. R. Edwards. 1982. Cottontails. Pp. 83–123, *in* Wild mammals of North America: biology, management, and economics (J. A. Chapman and G. A. Feldhamer, eds.). Johns Hopkins Univ. Press., Baltimore, 1,147 pp.

————, J. G. Hockman, and M. M. Ojeda. 1980. *Sylvilagus floridanus*. Mamm. Species, 136:1–8.

————, and G. R. Willner. 1978. *Sylvilagus audubonii*. Mamm. Species, 106:1–4.

Chase, H. D. 1939. Two species of mammals from Cimarron County new for Oklahoma. Proc. Oklahoma Acad. Sci., 19:69.

————, and B. D. Barclay. 1939. A species of *Neotoma* new for Oklahoma. Proc. Oklahoma Acad. Sci., 20:37.

Chase, J. D., W. E. Howard, and J. T. Roseberry. 1982. Pocket gophers. Pp. 239–255, *in* Wild mammals of North America: biology, management, and economics (J. A. Chapman and G. A. Feldhamer, eds.). Johns Hopkins Univ. Press, Baltimore, 1,147 pp.

Chesemore, D. L. 1975. Ecology of fox and gray squirrels (*Sciurus niger* and

Sciurus carolinensis) in Oklahoma. Ph.D. dissert., Oklahoma State Univ., 370 pp.

Choate, J. R. 1987. Post-settlement history of mammals in western Kansas. Southwestern Nat., (in press).

———, E. K. Boggess, and F. R. Henderson. 1982. History and status of the black-footed ferret in Kansas. Trans. Kansas Acad. Sci., 85:121–132.

———, M. D. Engstrom, and R. B. Wilhelm. 1979. Historical biogeography of the least weasel in Kansas. Trans. Kansas Acad. Sci., 82:231–234.

———, E. D. Fleharty, and R. J. Little. 1973. Status of the spotted skunk, *Spilogale putorius*, in Kansas. Trans. Kansas Acad. Sci., 76:226–233.

———, C. J. Phillips, and H. H. Genoways. 1966. Taxonomic status of the brush mouse, *Peromyscus boylii cansensis* Long, 1961. Trans. Kansas Acad. Sci., 69:306–313.

———, and S. L. Williams. 1978. Biogeographic interpretation of variation within and among populations of the prairie vole, *Microtus ochrogaster*. Occas. Pap., The Mus., Texas Tech. Univ., 49:1–25.

Choquette, L. P. E., J. F. Gallivan, J. L. Byrnes, and J. Piliparicius. 1961. Parasites and diseases of bison in Canada I. Tuberculosis and some other pathological conditions in bison at Wood Buffalo and Elk Island national parks in the fall and winter of 1959–1960. Can. Vet. J., 2:168.

———, G. G. Gibson, E. Kuyt, and A. M. Pearson. 1973. Helminths of wolves, *Canis lupus* L., in the Yukon and Northwest Territories. Can. J. Zool., 51:1087–1091.

Churcher, C. S. 1959. The specific status of the new world red fox. J. Mamm., 40:513–520.

———. 1960. Cranial variation in the North American red fox. J. Mamm., 41:349–360.

Cinq-Mars, R. J., and L. N. Brown. 1969. Reproduction and ecological distribution of the rockmouse, *Peromyscus difficilis*, in northern Colorado. Amer. Midland Nat., 81:205–217.

Clark, T. W. 1966. Mammals of Boiling Springs State Park, Woodward County, Oklahoma. Proc. Oklahoma Acad. Sci., 46:36–38.

———. 1967. Habitat selection by transplanted mule deer in northwestern Oklahoma. M.S. thesis, Oklahoma State Univ., Stillwater.

———. 1968. Plants used as food by mule deer in Oklahoma in relation to habitat. Southwestern Nat., 13:159–166.

———. 1969. The life-form concept and mule deer habitat in Oklahoma. Proc. Oklahoma Acad. Sci., 48:23–27.

———, and D. D. Skryja. 1969. Further notes on the mammals of Black Mesa region, Oklahoma. Proc. Oklahoma Acad. Sci., 48:27–29.

Clark, W. K. 1951. Ecological life history of the armadillo in the eastern Edwards Plateau region. Amer. Midland Nat., 46:337–358.

————. 1953. Gray shrew, *Notiosorex*, from eastern Oklahoma. J. Mamm., 34:117.

Cockrum, E. L. 1948. The distribution of the hispid cotton rat in Kansas. Trans. Kansas Acad. Sci., 51:306–312.

————. 1952. Mammals of Kansas. Publ. Mus. Nat. Hist., Univ. Kansas, 7:1–303.

Coggins, J. R., and J. S. McDaniel. 1975. Helminth population dynamics in the cotton rat, *Sigmodon hispidus*. Proc. Okla. Acad. Sci., 55:112–115.

Cole, G. F. 1956. The pronghorn antelope, its range use and food habits in central Montana with special reference to alfalfa. Tech. Bull. 516, Montana State Coll. Agri. Expt. Sta., Bozeman, & Montana Fish and Game Dept., Helena.

Conaway, C. H. 1959. The reproductive cycle of the eastern mole. J. Mamm., 40:180–194.

Conover, G. W. 1927. Sixty years in southwest Oklahoma. N. T. Plummer, Printer, Anadarko, Oklahoma, 119 pp.

Constantine, D. G. 1961. Spotted bat and big free-tailed bat in northern New Mexico. Southwestern Nat., 6:92–97.

Cothran, E. G. 1983. Morphologic relationships of the hybridizing ground squirrels *Spermophilus mexicanus* and *S. tridecemlineatus*. J. Mamm., 64:591–602.

————, and E. G. Zimmerman. 1985. Electrophoretic analysis of the contact zone between *Geomys breviceps* and *Geomys bursarius*. J. Mamm., 66:489–497.

Crabb, E. D. 1925. The weight of an adult "coyote." Proc. Oklahoma Acad. Sci., 4:43.

Craighead, J. J., and J. A. Mitchell. 1982. Grizzly bear. Pp. 515–516, *in* Wild mammals of North America: biology, management, and economics (J. A. Chapman and G. A. Feldhamer, eds.). Johns Hopkins Univ. Press, Baltimore, 1,147 pp.

Cross, H. 1917. Animal life in Oklahoma, *in* Geography of Oklahoma. Oklahoma Geol. Surv. Bull. No. 27:183–213.

Currier, M. J. P. 1983. *Felis concolor*. Mamm. Species, 200:1–7.

Custer, J. W., and D. B. Pence. 1979. Ectoparasites of the ringtail, *Bassariscus astutus*, from west Texas. J. Med. Entomol., 15:132–133.

Cutter, W. L. 1958a. Denning of the swift fox in northern Texas. J. Mamm., 39:70–74.

————. 1958b. Food habits of the swift fox in northern Texas. J. Mamm., 39:527–532.

————. 1959. Notes on some mammals from north Texas. Southwestern Nat., 4:30–34.

Dalquest, W. W. 1947. Notes on the natural history of the bat, *Myotis yu-*

manensis, in California, with description of a new race. Amer. Midland Nat., 38:224–247.

———. 1968. Mammals of north-central Texas. Southwestern Nat., 13: 13–21.

———, and G. Collier. 1964. Notes on *Dipodomys elator*, a rare kangaroo rat. Southwestern Nat., 9:146–150.

Davis, W. B. 1942. The systematic status of four kangaroo rats. J. Mamm., 23:328–333.

———. 1974. The mammals of Texas. Texas Parks & Wildl. Dept. Bull. No. 41:1–294, Austin.

W. H. Davis. 1959. Taxonomy of the eastern pipistrel. J. Mamm., 40:521–531.

———, and H. B. Hitchcock. 1965. Biology and migration of the bat, *Myotis lucifugus*, in New England. J. Mamm., 46:296–313.

———, and W. Z. Lidicker. 1955. *Myotis subulatus leibii* in Missouri. J. Mamm., 36:288–289.

Desha, P. G. 1966. Observations on the burrow utilization of the thirteen-lined ground squirrel. Southwestern Nat., 11:408–410.

———. 1967. Variation in a population of kangaroo rats, *Dipodomys ordii medius* (Rodentia: Heteromyidae) from the high plains of Texas. Southwestern Nat., 12:275–289.

Dice, L. R. 1922. Some factors affecting the distribution of the prairie vole, forest deer mouse, and prairie deer mouse. Ecology, 3:29–47.

———. 1937. Fertility relations in the *Peromyscus leucopus* group of mice. Contrib. Lab. Vert. Genet., Univ. Michigan, 4:1–3.

———. 1940. Relationships between the wood-mouse and the cotton-mouse in eastern Virginia. J. Mamm., 21:14–23.

Dirschl, H. J. 1963. Food habits of the pronghorn in Saskatchewan. J. Wildl. Mgmt., 27:81–93.

Dodge, R. I. 1877. The plains of the Great West. New York.

Dolan, P. G., and D. C. Carter. 1977. *Glaucomys volans*. Mamm. Species, 78:1–6.

Dolgos, A. G., and G. A. Earls. 1973. Observations on a nutria (*Myocaster coypus*) population in southeastern Oklahoma. Proc. Oklahoma Acad. Sci., 53:109–110.

Dow, S. A., Jr. 1952. An evaluation of some criteria for age determination of the pronghorn (*Antilocapra americana* Ord). M.S. thesis, Montana State Univ., Missoula.

Downhower, J. F., and E. R. Hall. 1966. The pocket gopher in Kansas. Misc. Publ., Mus. Nat. Hist., Univ. Kansas, 44:1–32.

Drabek, C. M. 1977. Some population aspects of cricetid rodents in a central Oklahoma tall grass prairie. Proc. Oklahoma Acad. Sci., 57:25–28.

Drago, H. S. 1962. Red River valley. Chas. N. Potter Inc., New York.

Duck, L. G., and J. B. Fletcher. 1945. A survey of the game and furbearing animals of Oklahoma. Div. Wildl. Restor. & Res., Oklahoma Game & Fish Comm., Pittman-Robertson Ser. No. 2, State Bull. No. 3. Oklahoma City.

Egoscue, H. J. 1960. Laboratory and field studies of the northern grasshopper mouse. J. Mamm., 41:99–110.

———. 1962. Ecology and life history of the kit fox in Tooele County, Utah. Ecology, 43:481–497.

———. 1966. Description of a newborn kit fox. Southwestern Nat., 11: 501–502.

Einarsen, A. S. 1948. The pronghorn antelope and its management. Wildl. Mgmt. Inst., Wash., D.C.

Elder, W. H. 1951. The baculum as an age criterion in mink. J. Mamm., 32:43–50.

———, and C. M. Hayden. 1977. Use of discriminant function in taxonomic determination of canids from Missouri. J. Mamm., 58:17–24.

Elliot, D. G. 1899a. List of mammals obtained by Thaddeus Surber, collector for the museum, Oklahoma and Indian Territories. Field Columb. Mus. Zool. Ser. 1(16):291–303.

———. 1899b. Descriptions of apparently new species and subspecies of mammals from Oklahoma Territory. Field Columb. Mus. Publ. 37, Zool. Ser. 1(14):279–282.

Ellis, L. L., Jr. 1954. A tentative key to the mammalian ectoparasites of the Wichita Mountains Wildlife Refuge. Proc. Oklahoma Acad. Sci., 33:111–115.

———. 1955. A survey of the ectoparasites of certain mammals in Oklahoma. Ecology, 36:12–18.

Ellis, R. J. 1959. Food habits and control of coyotes in north-central Oklahoma. Oklahoma State Univ. Publ. Biol. Ser. 8, 31 pp.

———, and S. D. Schemnitz. 1958. Some foods used by coyotes and bobcats in Cimarron County, Oklahoma, 1954 through 1956. Proc. Oklahoma Acad. Sci., 38:180–185.

Engstrom, M. D., and J. R. Choate. 1979. Systematics of the northern grasshopper mouse (*Onychomys leucogaster*) on the central Great Plains. J. Mamm., 60:723–739.

———, D. J. Schmidly, and P. K. Fox. 1982. Nongeographic variation and discrimination of species within the *Peromyscus leucopus* species group (Mammalia: Cricetidae) in eastern Texas. Texas J. Sci., 34:149–162.

Erickson, A. B. 1944. Helminths of Minnesota Canidae in relation to food habits and a host list and key to the species reported from North America. Amer. Midland Nat., 32:358–372.

Errington, P. L. 1935. Food habits of mid-west foxes. J. Mamm., 16:192–200.

———. 1936. Food habits of a weasel family. J. Mamm., 17:406–407.

———. 1937. Summer food habits of the badger in northwestern Iowa. J. Mamm., 18:213–216.

———. 1963. Muskrat populations. Iowa State Univ. Press, Ames, 665 pp.

Fenton, M. B., and R. M. R. Barclay. 1980. *Myotis lucifugus*. Mamm. Species, 142:1–8.

Findley, J. S., A. H. Harris, D. E. Wilson, and C. Jones. 1975. Mammals of New Mexico. Univ. New Mexico Press, Albuquerque. 360 pp.

———, and C. Jones. 1964. Seasonal distribution of the hoary bat. J. Mamm., 45:461–470.

———, and G. L. Traut. 1970. Geographic variation in *Pipistrellus hesperus*. J. Mamm., 51:741–765.

Finley, R. B. 1958. The woodrats of Colorado: distribution and ecology. Mus. Nat. Hist. Publ., Univ. Kansas, 10:213–552.

Fisher, H. I. 1951. Notes on the red fox (*Vulpes fulva*) in Missouri. J. Mamm., 32:296–299.

Fitch, H. S., P. Goodrum, and C. Newman. 1952. The armadillo in the southeastern United States. J. Mamm., 33:21–37.

Fitch, J. H., and K. A. Shump, Jr. 1970. *Myotis keenii*. Mamm. Species, 121:1–3.

———, K. A. Shump, Jr., and A. U. Shump. 1981. *Myotis velifer*. Mamm. Species, 149:1–5.

Fleharty, E. D., J. R. Choate, and M. A. Mares. 1972. Fluctuations in population density of the hispid cotton rat: factors influencing a "crash." Bull. S. California Acad. Sci., 71:132–138.

Flyger, V., and J. E. Gates. 1982. Fox and gray squirrels, pp. 209–229, *in* Wild mammals of North America: biology, management, and economics (J. A. Chapman and G. A. Feldhamer, eds.). Johns Hopkins Univ. Press, Baltimore, 1,147 pp.

———, and E. Y. Levin. 1977. Congenital erythropoietic porphyria: normal porphyria of fox squirrels (*Sciurus niger*). Amer. J. Pathol., 87:269–272.

Foreman, G. 1926. Pioneer days in the early southwest. Arthur H. Clark Co., Cleveland, Ohio.

Frank, W. J. 1950. Rodent populations and their reactions to grazing intensities on sand sagebrush grasslands in the southern Great Plains region. Ph.D. dissert., Oklahoma State Univ., Stillwater. 204 pp.

Freeman, P. W. 1981. A multivariate study of the family Molossidae (Mammalia, Chiroptera): morphology, ecology, evolution. Fieldiana Zool., 7:1–173.

Freeman, R. C., and J. H. Shaw. 1979. Hybridization in *Canis* (Canidae) in Oklahoma. Southwestern Nat., 24:485.

Frick, E. J. 1951. Parasitism in bison. J. Amer. Vet. Med. Assoc., 119:387.

Fritts, S. H., and J. A. Sealander. 1978. Diets of bobcats in Arkansas with special reference to age and sex differences. J. Wildl. Mgmt., 42:533–539.

Fritzell, E. K., and K. J. Haroldson. 1982. *Urocyon cinereoargenteus*. Mamm. Species, 189:1–8.

Fujita, M. S., and T. H. Kunz. 1984. *Pipistrellus subflavus*. Mamm. Species, 228:1–6.

Fuller, W. A. 1960. Behavior and social organization of the wood bison of Wood Buffalo National Park. Arctic, 13:2.

———. 1962. The biology and management of the bison of Wood Buffalo National Park. Can. Wildl. Serv. Wildl. Mgmt. Bull., Ser. 1., No. 16.

Gardner, A. L. 1982. Virginia opossum. Pp. 3–36, *in* Wild mammals of North America: biology, management, and economics (J. A. Chapman and G. A. Feldhamer, eds.). Johns Hopkins Univ. Press, Baltimore, 1,147 pp.

Garner, G. W., and J. A. Morrison. 1977. Dirunal range and movements of young white-tailed deer fawns in southwestern Oklahoma. Proc. Ann. Conf. S.E. Assoc. Fish Wildl. Agencies, 31:126–133.

———, and J. A. Morrison. 1980. Observation of interspecific behavior between predators and white-tailed deer in southwestern Oklahoma. J. Mamm., 61:126–130.

———, ———, and J. C. Lewis. 1976. Mortality of white-tailed deer fawns in the Wichita Mountains, Oklahoma. S.E. Assoc. Game & Fish Comm. Ann. Conf., 30:493–506.

———, J. Powell, and J. A. Morrison. 1979. Vegetative composition surrounding daytime bedsites of white-tailed deer fawns in southwestern Oklahoma. Proc. Ann. Conf. S.E. Assoc. Fish & Wildl. Agencies, 33:259–266.

Garretson, M. S. 1938. The American bison. New York Zool. Soc., New York.

Gaut, J. S. 1904. Mammals of the Wichita Mountains, Oklahoma. Handwritten report to U.S. Biol. Surv. of visit in spring, 1904.

Geluso, K. N. 1970. Ecological distribution of *Peromyscus* (Rodentia: Cricetidae) in the Black Mesa region of Oklahoma. M.S. thesis, Univ. Oklahoma. 35 pp.

———. 1971. Habitat distribution of *Peromyscus* in the Black Mesa region of Oklahoma. J. Mamm., 52:605–607.

———. 1972. Western spotted skunk in Oklahoma. Southwestern Nat., 16:457–458.

Genoways, H. H., and J. R. Choate. 1972. A multivariate analysis of systematic relationships among populations of the short-tailed shrew (genus *Blarina*) in Nebraska. Syst. Zool., 21:106–116.

———, J. C. Patton III, and J. R. Choate. 1977. Karyotypes of shrews of the genera *Cryptotis* and *Blarina* (Mammalia: Soricidae). Experientia, 33:1294–1295.

———, and D. A. Schlitter. 1966. Northward dispersal of the hispid cotton rat in Nebraska and Missouri. Trans. Kansas Acad. Sci., 69:356–357.

George, S. B., J. R. Choate, and H. H. Genoways. 1981. Distribution and taxonomic status of *Blarina hylophaga* Elliot (Insectivora: Soricidae). Ann. Carnegie Mus., 50:493–513.

Gier, H. T. 1968. Coyotes in Kansas. Contrib. No. 994, Dept. Zool., Kansas Agri. Expt. Sta., Manhattan.

Gilbert, F. F. 1966. Aging white-tailed deer by annuli in the cementum of the first incisor. J. Wildl. Mgmt., 30:200–202.

Gipson, P. S. 1974. Food habits of coyotes in Arkansas. J. Wildl. Mgmt., 38:848–853.

———, and J. A. Sealander. 1972. Home range and activity of the coyote (*Canis latrans frustror*) in Arkansas. Proc. 26th Ann. Conf. S.E. Assoc. Game & Fish Comm., 1972.

———, ———, and J. E. Dunn. 1974. The taxonomic status of wild *Canis* in Arkansas. Syst. Zool., 23:1–11.

Glass, B. P. 1947. Geographic variation in *Perognathus hispidus*. J. Mamm., 28:174–179.

———. 1951. Report on the mammals of the Black Mesa region, Oklahoma. Proc. Oklahoma Acad. Sci., 30:26–30.

———. 1952. Factors affecting the survival of the Plains muskrat *Ondatra zibethicus cinnamomina* in Oklahoma. J. Wildl. Mgmt., 16:484–491.

———. 1953. A second *Notiosorex* from Oklahoma. J. Mamm., 34:118.

———. 1958. The Seminole bat in Oklahoma. J. Mamm., 39:587.

———. 1959. Status of the kit fox, *Vulpes velox*, in the High Plains. Proc. Oklahoma Acad. Sci., 37:162–163.

———. 1960. The taxonomic status of Oklahoma beavers, *Castor canadensis*. Southwestern Nat., 5:21–24.

———. 1961. Two noteworthy records of bats for Oklahoma. Southwestern Nat., 6:200–201.

———. 1966. Some notes on reproduction in the red bat, *Lasiurus borealis*. Proc. Oklahoma Acad. Sci., 46:40–41.

———. 1971. The type locality of *Dipodomys ordii richardsoni*. Southwestern Nat., 15:497–499.

———. 1982. Seasonal movement of Mexican freetail bats *Tadarida brasiliensis mexicana* banded in the Great Plains. Southwestern Nat., 27:127–133.

———. 1986. History of classification and nomenclature in Xenarthra (Edentata). Pp. 1–3, *in* The evolution and ecology of armadillos, sloths, and ver-milinguas (G. G. Montgomery, ed.), Smithsonian Inst. Press, (x) + 451 pp.

————, and R. J. Baker. 1968. The status of the name *Myotis subulatus* Say. Proc. Biol. Soc. Wash., 81:257–260.

————, and A. H. Halloran. 1960. Status and distribution of the red fox (*Vulpes vulpes*) in Oklahoma. Southwestern Nat., 5:71–74.

————, and ————. 1961. The small mammals of the Wichita Mountains Wildlife Refuge, Oklahoma. J. Mamm., 42:234–239.

————, and S. R. Humphrey. 1971. Distribution of the evening bat *Nyc-ticeius humeralis* in Oklahoma. Southwestern Nat., 15:399–400.

————, and R. C. Morse. 1959. A new pipistrel from Oklahoma and Texas. J. Mamm., 40:531–534.

————, and C. M. Ward. 1959. Bats of the genus *Myotis* from Oklahoma. J. Mamm., 40:194–201.

Goertz, J. W. 1962. A new marginal record for the fulvous harvest mouse in Oklahoma. Proc. Oklahoma Acad. Sci., 42:124–127.

————. 1963. Some biological notes on the plains harvest mouse. Proc. Okla-homa Acad. Sci., 43:123–125.

————. 1964. The influence of habitat quality upon density of cotton rat populations. Ecol. Monogr., 34:359–381.

————. 1965. Reproductive variation in cotton rats. Amer. Midland Nat., 74:329–340.

————. 1970. An ecological study of *Neotoma floridana* in Oklahoma. J. Mamm., 51:94–104.

————. 1971. An ecological study of *Microtus pinetorum* in Oklahoma. Amer. Midland Nat., 86:1–12.

————, L. V. Fitzgerald, and R. M. Nowak. 1975. The status of wild *Canis* in Louisiana. Amer. Midland Nat., 93:215–218.

Golz, E. 1961. Throw rug future for big cat killed on N.M. ranch. Amarillo Daily News, March 1. Amarillo, Texas.

Goodpaster, W. W., and D. F. Hoffmeister. 1954. Life history of the golden mouse, *Peromyscus nuttalli*, in Kentucky. J. Mamm., 36:16–27.

Grace, H. J. 1982. Kin recognition in white-footed deermice (*Peromyscus leu-copus*). Anim. Behav., 30:497–505.

Grau, G. A., G. C. Sanderson, and J. P. Rodgers. 1970. Age determination of raccoons. J. Wildl. Mgmt., 34:364–372.

Gray, F., and H. M. Galloway. 1959. Soils of Oklahoma. Misc. Publ., Okla-homa State Univ., Stillwater.

Green, P. M. 1964. Density of population as a regulating factor in the re-productive potential of *Sigmodon hispidus*. Ph.D. dissert., Oklahoma State Univ., Stillwater.

Gregg, J. 1844. Commerce of the prairies, *in* Early western travels, 1748–

1846, Vols. XIX & XX (R. G. Thwaites, ed.). Arthur H. Clark, Cleveland, Ohio, 1904–1907.

Grigsby, E. M., and W. L. Puckett. 1982. A study of three species of endangered bats occurring in Oklahoma. Prep. for U.S. Fish & Wildl. Serv., Contr. No. 14-16-0002-81-202.

Grinnell, J. 1921. Revised list of the species in the genus *Dipodomys*. J. Mamm., 2:94–97.

———, J. S. Dixon, and J. M. Linsdale. 1937. Fur-bearing mammals of California, their natural history, systematic status, and relations to man. Vol. 1. Univ. California Press, Berkeley.

Grubitz, G., III. 1963. The social behavior of the thirteen-lined ground squirrel (*Citellus tridecemlineatus*). M.S. thesis, Univ. Oklahoma, Norman.

Guthrie, M. J. 1933. The reproductive cycles of some cave bats. J. Mamm., 14:199–216.

Hafner, J. C., and M. S. Hafner. 1983. Evolutionary relationships of heteromyid rodents. Great Basin Nat. Mem., 7:3–29.

Hahn, H. C., Jr. 1945. The white-tailed deer in the Edwards Plateau region of Texas. Texas Game, Fish & Oyster Comm. Austin.

Hall, E. R. 1951. American weasels. Publ. Mus. Nat. Hist., Univ. Kansas, 4:1–466.

———. 1955. Handbook of mammals of Kansas. Univ. Kansas Mus. Nat. Hist., Misc. Publ. No. 7, Lawrence.

———. 1981. The mammals of North America. Vols. 1 and 2. John Wiley and Sons, New York, 1,181 pp.

Hall, J. S., and N. Wilson. 1966. Seasonal populations and movements of the gray bat in the Kentucky area. Amer. Midland Nat., 75:317–324.

Halloran, A. F. 1956. Last bears of the Wichitas. Oklahoma Game & Fish News, 12(7):3, 11.

———. 1957. Lion in Oklahoma—past and present. Oklahoma Game & Fish News., 13:6–8.

———. 1958. Longhorn cattle weights and horn measurements. Proc. Oklahoma Acad. Sci., 38:135–136.

———. 1961. American bison weights and measurements from the Wichita Mountains Wildlife Refuge. Proc. Oklahoma Acad. Sci., 41:212–218.

———. 1962. Additional longhorn cattle management records from Wichita Mountains Wildlife Refuge. Proc. Oklahoma Acad. Sci., 42:268–271.

———. 1963a. A melanistic coyote from Oklahoma. Southwestern Nat., 8:48–49.

———. 1963b. Specimens of the black bear (*Euarctos americanus*) from the Wichita Mountains of Oklahoma. Southwestern Nat., 8:174.

———. 1963c. History of the Wichita Mountains Wildlife Refuge Elk herd. Proc. Oklahoma Acad. Sci., 43:229–232.

————. 1965. Texas longhorn cattle weights and measurements from Wichita Mountains Wildlife Refuge, Oklahoma. Proc. Oklahoma Acad. Sci., 46: 228–233.

————. 1968a. The size and weight of elk from the Wichita Mountains Wildlife Refuge, Oklahoma. Proc. Oklahoma Acad. Sci., 47:406–413.

————. 1968b. Bison (Bovidae) productivity on the Wichita Mountains Wildlife Refuge, Oklahoma. Southwestern Nat., 13:23–26.

————. 1969. Deer live-trapping history on the Wichita Mountains Wildlife Refuge, Oklahoma. Proc. Oklahoma Acad. Sci., 48:205–207.

————, and B. P. Glass. 1959. The carnivores and ungulates of the Wichita Mountains Wildlife Refuge, Oklahoma. J. Mamm., 40:360–370.

————, and ————. 1964. Additional mammal notes from the Wichita Mountains region of Oklahoma. Proc. Oklahoma Acad. Sci., 44:56–58.

Hamilton, W. J., Jr. 1933. The weasels of New York. Amer. Midland Nat., 14:289–344.

————. 1937. Winter activity of the skunk. Ecology, 18:326–327.

————. 1943. The mammals of the eastern United States. Comstock Publ. Co., Inc. 432 pp.

————. 1946. The black persimmon as a summer food of the Texas armadillo. J. Mamm., 27:175.

————. 1955. Coprophagy in the swamp rabbit. J. Mamm., 36:303–304.

————. 1974. Food habits of the coyote in the Adirondacks. New York Fish and Game J., 21:177–181.

Handley, C. O., Jr. 1959. A revision of American bats of the genera *Euderma* and *Plecotus*. Proc. U.S. Natl. Mus., 110:95–246.

Hardisty, R. W., W. Caire, and K. E. Lacy. 1987. *Tadarida brasiliensis* (Chiroptera: Molossidae) from southeastern Oklahoma. Proc. Okla. Acad. Sci., 67:77–79.

Harriman, A. E. 1973. Self-selection of diet in northern grasshopper mice (*Onychomys leucogaster*). Amer. Midland Nat., 90:97–106.

Hart, B. J. 1972. Distribution of the pygmy mouse, *Baiomys taylori*, in north-central Texas. Southwestern Nat., 17:213–214.

Hart, E. B. 1978. Karyology and evolution of the plains pocket gopher, *Geomys bursarius*. Occas. Pap. Mus. Nat. Hist., Univ. Kansas, 71:1–20.

Hartman, S. E. 1980. Geographic variation analysis of *Dipodomys ordii* using nonmetric cranial traits. J. Mamm., 61:436–448.

Harvey, L. 1970. Black-footed ferret (*Mustela nigripes*): a bibliography. Bibl. Ser. No. 17, U.S. Dept. Int., Off. Lib. Serv.

Hatcher, R. T. 1975. Status of the red fox in Oklahoma and comparison of 3 furbearer survey techniques. MS thesis, Oklahoma State Univ., Stillwater, 72 pp.

————. 1982. Distribution and status of red foxes (Canidae) in Oklahoma. Southwestern Nat., 27:183–186.

————. 1984. River otters in Oklahoma. Proc. Oklahoma Acad. Sci., 64: 17–19.

Hatfield, D. M. 1936. A revision of the *Pipistrellus hesperus* group of bats. J. Mamm., 17:257–262.

Hays, H. A. 1958. The distribution and movement of small mammals in central Oklahoma. J. Mamm., 39:235–244.

————, and P. H. Ireland. 1967. A big free-tailed bat (*Tadarida macrotis*) taken in southeastern Kansas. Southwestern Nat., 12:196.

Heaney, L. R., and R. M. Timm. 1983. Relationships of pocket gophers of genus *Geomys* from the Central and Northern Great Plains. Misc. Publ., Mus. Nat. Hist., Univ. Kansas, 74:1–59.

Heard, W. R. 1959. Cotton rats, *Sigmodon hispidus*, as food of channel catfish, *Ictalurus punctatus*. Proc. Oklahoma Acad. Sci., 39:200–201.

Henderson, F. R., P. F. Springer, and R. Adrian. 1969. The black-footed ferret in South Dakota. South Dakota Dept. Game, Fish & Parks, Pierre. 37 pp.

Hermanson, J. W., and T. J. O'Shea. 1983. *Antrozous pallidus*. Mamm. Species, 213:1–8.

Hibbard, C. W. 1934. The occurrence of *Erethizon epixanthum bruneri* and *Mustela nigripes* in Kansas. J. Mamm., 15:70–71.

————. 1940. A new *Synaptomys* from the Pleistocene. Univ. Kansas Sci. Bull., 26:367–371.

————, and G. C. Rinker. 1942. A new bog-lemming (*Synaptomys*) from Meade County, Kansas. Kansas Univ. Sci. Bull., 28:25–35.

————, and G. C. Rinker. 1943. A new meadow mouse (*Microtus ochrogaster taylori*) from Meade County, Kansas. Univ. Kansas Sci. Bull., 29:255–268.

Hibbard, E. A. 1957. Age ratios in wild mink populations. J. Mamm., 38: 412–413.

Hill, J. E. 1942. Notes on mammals of New Mexico. J. Mamm., 23:75–82.

Hlavachick, B. D. 1968. Foods of Kansas antelope related to choice of stocking sites. J. Wildl. Mgmt., 32:399–401.

Hoditschek, B., and T. L. Best. 1983. Reproductive biology of Ord's kangaroo rat (*Dipodomys ordii*) in Oklahoma. J. Mamm., 64:121–127.

Hoffmeister, D. F. 1951. A taxonomic and evolutionary study of the piñon mouse, *Peromyscus truei*. Illinois Biol. Monogr., 21(4):1–104.

————. 1981. *Peromyscus truei*. Mamm. Species, 161:1–5.

————, and L. de la Torre. 1961. Geographic variation in the mouse *Peromyscus difficilis*. J. Mamm., 42:1–13.

Holle, D. G. 1977. Diet and general availability of prey of the coyote (*Canis latrans*) at the Wichita Mountains National Wildlife Refuge, Oklahoma. M.S. thesis, Oklahoma State Univ., Stillwater. 59 pp.

Hollister, N. 1911. A systematic synopsis of the muskrats. N. Amer. Fauna, 32:1–147. Wash., D.C.

Honacki, J. H., K. E. Kinman, and J. W. Koeppl. 1982. Mammal species of the world. Allen Press, Inc. Assoc. Syst. Col., Lawrence, Kansas, 694 pp.

Honeycutt, R. L., and D. J. Schmidly. 1979. Chromosomal and morphological variation in the plains pocket gopher, *Geomys bursarius*, in Texas and adjacent states. Occas. Pap., The Mus., Texas Tech Univ., 58:1–54.

———, and S. L. Williams. 1982. Genic differentiation in pocket gophers of the genus *Pappogeomys*, with comments on intergeneric relationships in the subfamily Geomyinae. J. Mamm., 63:208–217.

Hooper, E. T. 1958. The male phallus in mice of the genus *Peromyscus*. Misc. Publ., Mus. Zool., Univ. Michigan, 105:1–24.

Hoover, R. L., C. E. Till, and S. Ogilvie. 1959. The antelope of Colorado: a research and management study. Tech. Bull. No. 4, Colorado Dept. Game & Fish, Denver.

Hornaday, W. T. 1889. The extermination of the American bison, with a sketch of its discovery and life history. Smithson. Rept., 1887:367–548.

Howell, A. H. 1914. Revision of the American harvest mice. N. Amer. Fauna, 36:1–97.

———. 1938. Revision of the North American ground squirrels with a classification of the North American Sciuridae. N. Amer. Fauna, 56:1–256.

Hsu, T. C., and F. E. Arrighi. 1968. Chromosomes of *Peromyscus* (Rodentia, Cricetidae) I: evolutionary trends in 20 species. Cytogenetics, 7:417–446.

Hudson, P. 1959. Fetal recoveries in mule deer. J. Wildl. Mgmt., 23:234–235.

Humphrey, S. R. 1974. Zoogeography of the nine-banded armadillo (*Dasypus novemcinctus*) in the United States. Bioscience, 24:457–462.

———, and J. B. Cope. 1976. Population ecology of the little brown bat, *Myotis lucifugus*, in Indiana and north-central Kentucky. Spec. Publ., Amer. Soc. Mamm., 4:1–79.

———, and T. H. Kunz. 1976. Ecology of a Pleistocene relict, the western big-eared bat (*Plecotus townsendii*) in the southern Great Plains. J. Mamm., 57:470–494.

———, R. K. LaVal, and R. L. Clawson. 1977. Nursery populations of *Pipistrellus subflavus* (Chiroptera: Vespertilionidae) in Missouri. Trans. Illinois Acad. Sci., 69:367.

———, A. R. Richter, and J. B. Cope. 1977. Summer habitat and ecology of the endangered Indiana bat, *Myotis sodalis*. J. Mamm., 58:334–346.

Irving, W. 1835. A tour of the prairies. Cary, Lea and Blanchard, Philadelphia, 274 pp.

Jackson, H. H. T. 1961. Mammals of Wisconsin. Univ. Wisconsin Press, Madison, 504 pp.

———, and H. E. Warfel. 1933. Notes on the occurrence of mammals in the regions adjacent to the Salt Plains of northwestern Oklahoma. Publ. Univ. Oklahoma Biol. Surv., 5:65–72.

Jaeger, E. C. 1966. A source-book of biological names and terms. Charles C. Thomas Publ., Springfield, Ill.

Jahoda, J. C. 1973. The effect of the lunar cycle on the activity pattern of *Onychomys leucogaster breviauritus*. J. Mamm., 54:544–549.

James, E. 1823. Account of an expedition from Pittsburgh to the Rocky Mountains in the years 1819 and 1820 . . . under the command of Major Stephen H. Long. Carey and Lea, Philadelphia. 2 vols.

Jenkins, S. H., and P. E. Busher. 1979. *Castor canadensis*. Mamm. Species, 120:1–8.

Jennings, W. L. 1958. The ecological distribution of bats in Florida. Ph.D. dissert., Univ. Florida, Gainesville, 125 pp.

Johansen, K. 1962. Buoyancy and insulation in the muskrat. J. Mamm., 43:64–68.

Johnson, W. E., and R. K. Selander. 1971. Protein variation and systematics in Kangaroo rats (genus *Dipodomys*). Syst. Zool., 20:377–405.

Jones, C. 1965. Ecological distribution and activity periods of bats of the Mogollon Mountains area of New Mexico and adjacent Arizona. Tulane Stud. Zool., 12:93–100.

———. 1977. *Plecotus rafinesquii*. Mamm. Species, 69:1–4.

Jones, G. E. 1952. Survey of existing beaver range in Oklahoma. Oklahoma Game & Fish Dept. Fed. Aid. Div. Proj. W S1-R2, Completion Rept. 21 pp.

Jones, J. K., Jr. 1960. The hispid cotton rat in Nebraska. J. Mamm., 41:132.

———, and S. Anderson. 1959. The eastern harvest mouse, *Reithrodontomys humulis*, in Oklahoma. Southwestern Nat., 4:153–154.

———, D. C. Carter, H. H. Genoways, R. S. Hoffman, D. W. Rice, and C. Jones. 1986. Revised checklist of North American mammals north of Mexico. Occas. Pap., The Mus., Texas Tech. Univ., 107:1–22.

———, and B. P. Glass. 1960. The short-tailed shrew, *Blarina brevicauda*, in Oklahoma. Southwestern Nat., 5:136–142.

Jordon, D. S. 1929. Manual of the vertebrate animals. World Book Co., Yonkers-on-Hudson, N.Y.

Kalmbach, E. R. 1943. The armadillo: its relation to agriculture and game. Texas Game, Fish, & Oyster Comm., Austin, 60 pp.

Kennedy, M. L., M. L. Beck, and T. L. Best. 1980. Intraspecific morphologic variation in Ord's kangaroo rat, *Dipodomys ordii*, from Oklahoma. J. Mamm., 61:311–319.

————, and G. D. Schnell. 1978. Geographic variation and sexual dimorphism in Ord's kangaroo rat, *Dipodomys ordii*. J. Mamm., 59:45–59.

Kilgore, D. L., Jr. 1969. An ecological study of the swift fox (*Vulpes velox*) in the Oklahoma panhandle. Amer. Midland Nat., 81:512–534.

Kilpatrick, C. W., and W. Caire. 1973. The first record of the encinal mouse *Peromyscus pectoralis* for Oklahoma and additional records for northcentral Texas. Southwestern Nat., 18:351.

————, and E. G. Zimmerman. 1976. Biochemical variation and systematics of *Peromyscus pectoralis*. J. Mamm., 57:506–522.

Kimsey, A. 1953. Nutria. Oklahoma Wildl. News, 9(3):10–11.

King, J. A. 1955. Social behavior, social organization, and population dynamics in a black-tailed prairie dog town in the Black Hills of South Dakota. Contrib. Lab. Vert. Biol., Univ. Michigan, 67:1–123.

King, O. M. 1959. A list of mammals collected in west central Oklahoma. Proc. Oklahoma Acad. Sci., 37:52–53.

Kirkpatrick, R. D. 1965. Litter size and fetus numbers in the cotton rat. J. Mamm., 46:514.

Kitchen, D. W. 1974. Social behavior and ecology of the pronghorn. Wildl. Monogr., 38:1–96.

Klingener, D. 1963. Dental evolution of *Zapus*. J. Mamm., 44:248–260.

Kocan, A. A., M. G. Shaw, K. A. Waldrop, and G. J. Kubat. 1982. Distribution of *Parelaphostrongylus tenuis* (Nematoda: Metastrongyloidea) in white-tailed deer from Oklahoma. J. Wildl. Dis., 18:457–460.

Koford, C. B. 1958. Prairie dogs, whitefaces, and blue grama. Wildlife Monogr., 3:1–78.

Korschgen, L. J. 1957. Food habits of coyotes, foxes, house cats and bobcats in Missouri. Missouri Conserv. Comm., Fish & Game Div., Pittman-Robertson Ser. 15, 64 pp.

————. 1958. December food habits of mink in Missouri. J. Mamm., 39:521–527.

Krutzsch, P. H. 1954. North American jumping mouse (genus *Zapus*). Univ. Kansas Publ., Mus. Nat. Hist., 7:349–372.

Kunz, T. H. 1973. Population studies of the cave bat (*Myotis velifer*): reproduction, growth and development. Occas. Pap. Mus. Nat. Hist., Univ. Kansas, 15:1–43.

————. 1974. Feeding ecology of a temperate insectivorous bat (*Myotis velifer*). Ecology, 55:693–711.

————, and R. A. Martin. 1982. *Plecotus townsendii*. Mamm. Species, 175:1–6.

Landreth, H. F. 1972. Ecology of Norway rats, *Rattus norvegicus*, on a deserted farm in western Oklahoma. Proc. Oklahoma Acad. Sci., 52:45–48.

Larson, F. 1940. The role of bison in maintaining the shortgrass plains. Ecology, 21:113–121.

LaVal, R. K. 1970. Intraspecific relationships of bats of the species *Myotis austroriparius*. J. Mamm., 51:542–552.

———, R. L. Clawson, W. Caire, L. R. Wingate, and M. L. LaVal. 1977. An evaluation of the status of myotine bats on the proposed Meramec Park Lake and Union Lake project areas, Missouri. U.S. Army Corps Engineers, St. Louis Dist., 136 pp.

———, and M. L. LaVal. 1980. Ecological studies and management of Missouri bats, with emphasis on cave dwelling species. Missouri Dept. Conserv., Terrest. Ser., 8:1–53.

Lawrence, B., and W. H. Bossert. 1967. Multiple character analysis of *Canis lupus*, *latrans*, and *familiaris* with a discussion of the relationships of *Canis niger*. Am. Zool. 7:223–232.

Lechleitner, R. R. 1954. Age criteria in mink, *Mustela vison*. J. Mamm., 35:496–503.

———. 1969. Wild mammals of Colorado. Pruett Publ. Co., Boulder.

Lee, F. S., and J. B. Funderburg. 1982. Marmots. Pp. 176–191, *in* Wild mammals of North America: biology, management, and economics. (J. A. Chapman and G. A. Feldhamer, eds.). Johns Hopkins Univ. Press, Baltimore, 1,147 pp.

Lee, L. 1967. Bears, *in* New Mexico wildlife management. New Mexico Dept. Game & Fish, Santa Fe, 250 pp.

Leiby, P. D., P. J. Sitzmann, and D. C. Kritsky. 1971. Studies on helminths of North Dakota: parasites of the badger *Taxidea taxus* (Schreber). Proc. Helminth. Soc. Wash., 38:225–228.

Levenson, H., R. S. Hoffmann, C. F. Nadler, L. Deutsch, and S. D. Freeman. 1985. Systematics of holarctic chipmunks (*Tamias*). J. Mamm., 66:219–242.

Le Vick, J. P. 1982. Maternal response to neonate vocalizations in Ord's kangaroo rat (*Dipodomys ordii*). Southwestern Nat., 27:122–123.

Lewis, J. C. 1969. Evidence of mountain lions in the Ozarks and adjacent areas, 1948–1968. J. Mamm., 50:371–372.

———. 1970. Evidence of mountain lions in the Ozarks, Boston and Ouachita Mountains. Proc. Oklahoma Acad. Sci., 49:182–184.

———. 1973. Additional records of black-footed ferret in Oklahoma. Southwestern Nat., 18:350.

———. 1979. Techniques used to establish and limit prairie dog towns. Proc. Oklahoma Acad. Sci., 59:27–30.

———, and F. D. Hassien. 1974. Status of prairie dogs and black-footed ferrets in Oklahoma. Proc. Oklahoma Acad. Sci., 54:20–24.

Lindzey, J. S. 1950. The white-tailed deer in Oklahoma. Oklahoma Game & Fish Dept., Oklahoma City.

Linzey, D. W., and R. L. Packard. 1977. *Ochrotomys nuttalli*. Mamm. Species, 75:1–6.

Litton, G. 1957. History of Oklahoma. Vol. I. Lewis Hist. Publ. Co. Inc., New York.

Litvaitis, J. A. 1978. Movements and habitat use of coyotes on the Wichita Mountains National Wildlife Refuge. M.S. thesis, Oklahoma State Univ., Stillwater, 70 pp.

———, and W. S. Bartush. 1980. Coyote-deer interactions during the fawning season in Oklahoma. Southwestern Nat., 25:117–118.

Locker, B. 1953. Parasites of bison in the northwestern United States. J. Parasitol., 39:58–59.

Long, C. A. 1961. Woodchuck in Oklahoma and southeastern Kansas. J. Mamm., 42:255–256.

———. 1973. *Taxidea taxus*. Mamm. Species, 26:1–4.

———. 1975. Molt in the North American badger. *Taxidea taxus*. J. Mamm., 56:921–924.

———, and C. F. Long. 1964. Geographic records of the swift fox, *Vulpes velox*. Southwestern Nat., 9:108.

Lorr, D. F. 1974. Sexual and aggressive behavior of American bison (*Bison bison*) *in* The behavior of ungulates and its relation to management (V. Geist and F. Walther, eds.). Vols. I & II. IUCN Publ. No. 24, Morges, Switzerland.

Low, W. A., and I. M. Cowan. 1963. Age determination of deer by annular structure of dental cementum. J. Wildl. Mgmt., 27:466–471.

Lowery, G. H., Jr., 1943. Check-list of the mammals of Louisiana and adjacent waters. Occas. Pap. Mus. Zool., Louisiana State Univ., 13:213–257.

———. 1974. The mammals of Louisiana and its adjacent waters. Louisiana State Univ. Press, Baton Rouge, 565 pp.

Lucker, J. T., and G. Dikmans. 1945. The distribution of *Pseudostertagia bullosa* and some new records of nematodes from pronghorn antelope (*Antilocapra americana*). Proc. Helminth. Soc. Wash., 12:2–4.

Marcy, R. B. 1854. Exploration of the Red River of Louisiana in the year 1852 (Appendix F, Zoology, pp. 200–201, Mammals). B. Tucker, Senate Printer, Wash., D.C., 310 pp.

Marshall, W. H. 1936. A study of the winter activities of the mink. J. Mamm., 17:382–392.

Martin, A. C., H. S. Zim, and A. L. Nelson. 1951. American wildlife and plants. McGraw-Hill Book Co. Inc., New York.

Martin, C. O., and D. J. Schmidly. 1982. Taxonomic review of the pallid bat, *Antrozous pallidus* (Le Conte). Spec. Publ., The Mus., Texas Tech Univ., 18:1–48.

Martin, E. P., and G. F. Sternberg. 1955. A swift fox, *Vulpes velox* (Say), from western Kansas. Trans. Kansas Acad. Sci., 58:345–346.

Martin, R. E., and K. G. Matocha. 1972. Distributional status of the kangaroo rat, *Dipodomys elator*. J. Mamm., 53:873–877.

———, and J. R. Preston. 1970. The mammals of Harmon County, Oklahoma. Proc. Oklahoma Acad. Sci., 49:42–60.

McBee, K., and R. J. Baker. 1982. *Dasypus novemcinctus*. Mamm. Species, 162:1–9.

McCarley, H. 1952. The ecological relationships of the mammals of Bryan County, Oklahoma. Texas J. Sci., 4:102–112.

———. 1954. Natural hybridization in the *Peromyscus leucopus* species group of mice. Evolution, 8:314–323.

———. 1959. A study of the dynamics of a population of *Peromyscus gossypinus* and *P. nuttalli* subjected to the effects of X-irradiation. Amer. Midland Nat., 61:447–469.

———. 1960. The rice rat in southern Oklahoma. J. Mamm., 41:130–131.

———. 1961. New locality records for some Oklahoma mammals. Southwestern Nat., 6:108–109.

———. 1962. The taxonomic status of wild *Canis* (Canidae) in the south central United States. Southwestern Nat., 7:227–235.

———. 1966. Annual cycle, population dynamics, and adaptive behavior of *Citellus tridecemlineatus*. J. Mamm., 47:294–316.

———, and P. Free. 1962. A new record of the woodchuck from Oklahoma. J. Mamm., 43:272.

McCarley, W. H. 1951. Color mutation in a small, partially isolated population of pocket gophers (*Geomys breviceps*). J. Mamm., 32:338–341.

———, and C. J. Carley. 1979. Recent changes in distribution and status of wild red wolves (*Canis rufus*). Endang. Species Rept. No. 4, U.S. Fish & Wildl. Serv., Albuquerque, N.M.

McCarty, R. 1978. *Onychomys leucogaster*. Mamm. Species, 87:1–6.

McClung, P. 1972. Startled teachers report spotting mountain lion. Lawton, Oklahoma Constitution, June 8, p. 2B.

McCracken, G. F. 1984. Communal nursing in Mexican free-tailed bat maternity colonies. Science, 223:1090–1091.

McCulloch, C. Y., Jr., and J. M. Inglis. 1961. Breeding periods of the Ord kangaroo rat. J. Mamm., 42:337–344.

McCullough, D. R. 1969. The Tule elk: its history, behavior, and ecology. Univ. California, Publ. Zool., 88:1–209.

McHugh, T. 1958. Social behavior of the American buffalo. Zoologica, 43:1–40.

McManus, J. J. 1974. *Didelphis virginiana*. Mamm. Species, 40:1–6.

McMurray, F. B. 1944. Porcupine records in Oklahoma. J. Mamm., 25:413.

———. 1945. Three shrews, *Cryptotis parva*, eaten by a feral house cat. J. Mamm., 26:94.

———. 1947. An unusual winter record of *Citellus spilosoma* in Oklahoma. J. Mamm., 28:292.

Mead, J. R. 1899a. *Felis concolor*. Trans. Kansas Acad. Sci., 16:278–279.

———. 1899b. Some natural history notes of 1859. Trans. Kansas Acad. Sci., 16:280–281.

Mead, R. A. 1968. Reproduction in western forms of the spotted skunk (genus *Spilogale*). J. Mamm., 49:373–390.

Mech, L. D. 1970. The wolf. Nat. Hist. Press (Doubleday), New York.

———. 1974. *Canis lupus*. Mamm. Species, 37:1–6.

Meinzer, W. P., D. N. Ueckert, and J. T. Flinders. 1975. Food niche of coyotes in the Rolling Plains of Texas. J. Range Mgmt. 28:22–27.

Merrifield, G. C. 1955. Occurrence of a mountain lion in Oklahoma. Proc. Oklahoma Acad. Sci., 34:75.

Miller, F. W. 1925. A new hog-nosed skunk. J. Mamm., 6:50–51.

Miller, G. S., Jr., and G. M. Allen. 1928. The American bats of the genera *Myotis* and *Pizonyx*. Bull. U.S. Natl. Mus., 144:1–218.

Miller, R. S. 1964. Ecology and distribution of pocket gophers (Geomyidae) in Colorado. Ecology, 45:256–272.

Mitchell, G. J. 1971. Measurements, weights and carcass yields of prong-horns in Alberta. J. Wildl. Mgmt., 35:76–85.

Morris, J. W., C. R. Goins, and E. C. McReynolds. 1976. Historical atlas of Oklahoma. Univ. Oklahoma Press, Norman.

Morrison, E. E., and H. T. Gier. 1979. Parasitic infection of *Filaroides osleri*, *Capillaria aerophila* and *Spirocera lupi* in coyotes from the southwestern United States. J. Wildl. Dis., 15:557–559.

Morse, R. C., and B. P. Glass. 1960. The taxonomic status of *Antrozous bunkeri*. J. Mamm., 41:10–15.

Moulton, M. P., J. R. Choate, and S. J. Bissell. 1983. Biogeographic relationships of pocket gophers in southeastern Colorado. Southwestern Nat., 28:53–60.

Mower, N. A., and D. Russell, eds. 1972. The plains: the journal of François des Montaignes (Isaac Cooper) of an expedition in 1845. Univ. Oklahoma Press, Norman.

Murie, A. 1936. Following fox trails. Misc. Publ., Univ. Michigan Mus. Zool., 32:1–x.

————. 1940. Ecology of the coyote in the Yellowstone. U.S. Natl. Parks Fauna Ser. No. 4, Wash., D.C.

Murphy, M. F. 1952. Ecology and helminths of the Osage woodrat, *Neotoma floridana osagensis*, including the description of *Longistrata neotoma* n. sp. (Trichostrongylidae). Amer. Midland Nat., 48:204–218.

Murray, G. B., and B. M. Vestal. 1979. Effects of environmental structure on the burrow distribution of thirteen-lined ground squirrels, *Spermophilus tridecemlineatus* (Sciuridae). Southwestern Nat., 24:79–86.

Myers, R. F. 1964. Ecology of three species of myotine bats in the Ozark Plateau. Unpubl. Ph.D. dissert., Univ. Missouri, 210 pp.

Nelson, E. W. 1925. Status of the prong-horned antelope, 1922–24. Bull. U.S. Dept. Agric., 1346:1–x.

————, and W. A. Goldman. 1930. Six new raccoons of the *Procyon lotor* group. J. Mamm., 11:453–459.

Newman, C. C., and R. H. Baker. 1942. Armadillo eats young rabbits. J. Mamm., 23:450.

Nice, M. M. 1931. The birds of Oklahoma. Rev. ed. Publ. Univ. Oklahoma Biol. Surv., 3:1–224.

Novakowski, N. S., J. G. Cousineau, G. B. Kolenosky, G. S. Wilton, and L. P. E. Choquette. 1963. Parasites and diseases of bison in Canada II. Anthrax epizooty in the Northwest Territories. Proc. 28th N. Amer. Wildl. & Nat. Resources Conf., Detroit, Michigan.

Nowack, R. M. 1976. The cougar in the United States and Canada. U.S. Fish & Wildl. Serv., Wash., D.C. & N.Y. Zool. Soc., 190 pp.

Nunley, G. L. 1978. Present and historical bobcat population trends in New Mexico and the west. Proc. 8th Vert. Pest Conf., March 7–9. Univ. California, Davis.

Nuttall, T. 1821. A journal of travels into the Arkansas Territory during the year 1819, *in* Early western travels, 1748–1846, Vol. VIII. (R. G. Thwaites, ed.). Arthur H. Clark Co., Cleveland, Ohio, 1904–1907.

O'Gara, B. W. 1978. *Antilocapra americana*. Mamm. Species, 90:1–7.

————, and G. Matson. 1975. Growth and casting of horns by pronghorns and exfoliation of horns by bovids. J. Mamm., 56:829–846.

O'Melia, M. E. 1980. Competition between prairie dogs and beef cattle for range forage. M.S. thesis, Oklahoma State Univ., Stillwater, 33 pp.

Ockenfels, R. A. 1980. Habitat requirements of white-tailed deer in the post oak–blackjack oak habitat type. M.S. thesis, Oklahoma State Univ., Stillwater.

Oklahoma Dept. Wildl. Conserv. 1981. Panhandle bear. Outdoor Oklahoma, 37(5):55.

————. 1982. Deer hunter's handbook. Oklahoma City, 24 pp.

Oklahoma Game and Fish Dept. 1952. Furbearers and game mammals of Oklahoma. Oklahoma City.

Orr, R. T. 1954. Natural history of the pallid bat, *Antrozous pallidus* (Le Conte). Proc. California Acad. Sci., 4th Ser., 28:165–246.

Osborn, B., and W. H. Kellogg. 1943. Wildlife occurrence and habitat conditions in Roger Mills and Custer counties, Oklahoma. Proc. Oklahoma Acad. Sci., 23:41–46.

Packard, R. 1960. Speciation and evolution of the pygmy mice, genus *Baiomys*. Mus. Nat. Hist., Univ. Kansas Publ., 9:579–670.

Packard, R. L. 1969. Taxonomic review of the golden mouse, *Ochrotomys nuttalli*. Misc. Publ., Mus. Nat. Hist., Univ. Kansas, 51:373–406.

———, and J. H. Bowers. 1970. Distributional notes on some foxes from western Texas and eastern New Mexico. Southwestern Nat., 14:450–451.

———, and H. W. Garner. 1964*a*. Arboreal nests of the golden mouse in eastern Texas. J. Mamm., 45:369–374.

———, and ———. 1964*b*. Records of some mammals from the Texas high plains. Texas J. Sci., 16:387–390.

Palmer, R. S. 1954. The mammal guide. Doubleday & Co., Garden City, N.Y., 384 pp.

Palmer, T. S. 1916. Our national herds of buffalo. Ann. Rept. Amer. Bison Soc., 10:40–62.

Paradiso, J. L., and R. M. Nowak. 1971. A report on the taxonomic status and distribution of the red wolf. U.S. Fish & Wildl. Serv. Spec. Sci. Rept. Wildl., 145:1–36.

———, and ———. 1972. *Canis rufus*. Mamm. Species, 22:1–4.

———, and ———. 1982. Wolves. Pp. 460–474, *in* Wild mammals of North America: biology, management, and economics (J. A. Chapman and G. A. Feldhamer, eds.). Johns Hopkins Univ. Press, Baltimore, 1,147 pp.

Park, E. 1969. The world of the bison. J. B. Lippincott Co., New York.

Patterson, B. D. 1984. Geographic variation and taxonomy of Colorado and Hopi chipmunks (genus *Eutamias*). J. Mamm., 65:442–456.

Pearson, O. P., M. Koford, and A. K. Pearson. 1952. Reproduction of the lump-nosed bat (*Corynorhinus rafinesquei*) in California. J. Mamm., 33:273–320.

Peden, D. G. 1976. Botanical composition of bison diets on shortgrass prairie. Amer. Midland Nat., 96:225–229.

Pelton, M. R. 1982. Black bear. Pp. 504–514, *in* Wild mammals of North America: biology, management, and economics (J. A. Chapman and G. A. Feldhamer, eds.). Johns Hopkins Univ. Press, Baltimore, 1,147 pp.

Pelzer, L. 1917. Marches of the dragoons in the Mississippi Valley: an account of marches and activities of the First Regiment, U.S. Dragoons, between 1833 and 1850. State Hist. Soc. Iowa, Iowa City.

Pence, D. B., and R. C. Dowler. 1979. Helminth parasitism in the badger, *Taxidea taxus* (Schreber, 1778), from the western Great Plains. Proc. Helminthol. Soc. Wash., 46:245–253.

———, and J. E. Stone. 1977. Lungworms (Nematoda: Pneumospiruridae) from west Texas carnivores. J. Parasitol., 64:979–991.

———, and K. D. Willis. 1978. Helminths of the ringtail, *Bassariscus astutus*, from west Texas. J. Parasitol., 64:568–569.

Penfound, W. T. 1962. The savanna concept in Oklahoma. Ecology, 43:774–775.

Penny, D. F., and E. G. Zimmerman. 1976. Genic divergence and local population differentiation by random drift in the pocket gopher genus *Geomys*. Evolution, 30:473–483.

Perry, H. P., Jr. 1982. Muskrats. Pp. 282–325, *in* Wild mammals of North America: biology, management, and economics (J. A. Chapman and G. A. Feldhamer, eds.). Johns Hopkins Univ. Press, Baltimore, 1,147 pp.

Pfister, A. 1984. Annual report on the deer herd, Fish and Wildlife Services, Dept. Eng. and Housing, Fort Sill, Oklahoma.

Phillips, P. G. 1936. The distribution of rodents in overgrazed and normal grasslands of central Oklahoma. Ecology, 17:673–679.

Polderboer, E. B., L. W. Kuhn, and G. O. Hendrickson. 1941. Winter and spring habits of weasels in central Iowa. J. Wildl. Mgmt., 5:115–119.

Pournelle, G. H. 1968. Classification, biology, and distribution of the venom apparatus of insectivores of the genera *Solenodon, Neomys*, and *Blarina, in* Venomous animals and their venoms. (W. Burcherl, E. A. Buckley, and V. Deulofen, eds.). Acad. Press, New York.

Pratt, H. D., and N. E. Good. 1954. Distribution of some common domestic rat ectoparasites in the United States. J. Parasitol., 40:113–129.

Prenzlow, E. J. 1965. A literature review on pronghorn behavior. Colorado Dept. Game, Fish & Parks Spec. Rept. No. 3, Denver.

———, D. L. Gilbert, and R. W. Glover. 1968. Some behavior patterns of the pronghorn. Colorado Dept. Game, Fish & Parks Spec. Rept. No. 17, Denver.

Preston, J. R., and R. E. Martin. 1963. A gray shrew population in Harmon County, Oklahoma. J. Mamm., 44:268–270.

Puckette, W. L. 1976. Notes on the occurrence of the short-faced bear (*Arctodus*) in Oklahoma. Proc. Oklahoma Acad. Sci., 56:67–68.

Pyle, R. A., and W. Caire. 1979. Second record of *Tadarida macrotis* (Gray) (Chiroptera: Molossidae) in Oklahoma. Southwestern Nat., 24:389.

Ranson, A. B. 1966. Determining age of white-tailed deer from layers of cementum in molars. J. Wildl. Mgmt., 30:197–199.

Rausch, R. 1963. Geographic variation in size in North American brown bears, *Ursus arctos* L., as indicated by condylobasal length. Canadian J. Zool., 41:33–45.

Reed, K. M., and J. R. Choate. 1986. Geographic variation in the plains pocket mouse (*Perognathus flavescens*) on the Great Plains. Texas J. Sci., 38:227–240.

Reilly, J. R., and W. Curren. 1961. Evaluation of certain techniques for judging the age of red foxes (*Vulpes fulva*). New York Fish and Game J., 8:122–129.

Reynolds, R. E. 1977. Distribution of beaver in Oklahoma. Proc. Okla. Acad. Sci., 57:83–85.

———, and J. C. Lewis. 1976. Evaluating beaver guards on restricted flow risers of flood control impoundments. Ann. Conf. Southeast. Assoc. Fish and Game Comm., 13:455–462.

Rhodes, L. K. 1980. Oklahoma Geol. Notes, 40:47–62.

Rice, D. W. 1957. Life history and ecology of *Myotis austroriparius* in Florida. J. Mamm., 38:15–32.

Richards, R. E. 1976. The distribution, water balance, and vocalization of the ringtail, *Bassariscus astutus*. D.A. dissert., Univ. N. Colorado, Greeley.

Richardson, W. B. 1942. Ring-tailed cats (*Bassariscus astutus*): their growth and development. J. Mamm., 23:17–26.

Riddle, B. R., and J. R. Choate. 1986. Systematics and biogeography of *Onychomys leucogaster* in western North America. J. Mamm., 67:233–255.

Riley, G. A., and R. T. McBride. 1972. A survey of the red wolf (*Canis rufus*). U.S. Dept. Int. Spec. Sci. Rept. Wildl. No. 162.

Robbins, L. W., M. H. Smith, M. C. Wooten, and R. K. Selander. 1985. Biochemical polymorphism and its relationship to chromosomal and morphological variation in *Peromyscus leucopus* and *Peromyscus gossypinus*. J. Mamm., 66:490–510.

Roberts, J. D. 1969. Ecological study of the Texas kangaroo rat. M.S. thesis, Texas Tech Univ., 56 pp.

Roe, F. G. 1970. The North American buffalo. 2nd ed. Univ. Toronto Press, Toronto, Canada, 991 pp.

Roest, A. I. 1979. Subspecies of North American red foxes (*Vulpes vulpes*). Paper read at 59th Ann. Mtg. Amer. Soc. Mamm., 18 June 1979, Oregon State Univ., Corvallis.

Rohwer, S. A., and D. L. Kilgore, Jr. 1973. Interbreeding in the arid-land foxes, *Vulpes velox* and *V. macrotis*. Syst. Zool., 22:157–165.

Rolley, R. E. 1983. Behavior and population dynamics of bobcats in Oklahoma. M.S. thesis, Oklahoma State Univ., Stillwater, 98 pp.

———. 1985*a*. Dynamics of a harvested bobcat population in Oklahoma. J. Wildl. Mgmt., 49:283–292.

————. 1985b. Bobcat habitat use in southeastern Oklahoma. J. Wildl. Mgmt., 49:913–920.

Rorabacher, J. A. 1970. The American buffalo in transition: a historical and economic survey of the bison in America. North Star Press, St. Cloud, Minnesota.

Roth, E. E., W. V. Adams, G. E. Sanford, Jr., B. Greer, K. Newman, M. Moore, P. Mayeax, and D. Linder. 1963. The bacteriologic and serologic incidence of leptospirosis among striped skunks in Louisiana. Zoonoses Res., 2:13–39.

Roudabush, R. L. 1936. Arthropod and helminth parasites of the American bison (Bison bison). J. Parasitol., 22:517–518.

Rouse, C. H. 1941. Notes on winter foraging habits of antelope in Oklahoma. J. Mamm., 22:57–60.

Rue, L. L., III. 1978. The deer of North America. Crown Publ. Inc., N.Y.

Ruffer, D. G. 1964a. A checklist of the mammals of the Oliver Wildlife Preserve, Cleveland County, Oklahoma. Proc. Oklahoma Acad. Sci., 44:66–68.

————. 1964b. Studies on the ethology of the northern grasshopper mouse (Onychomys leucogaster). Ph.D. dissert., Univ. Oklahoma, Norman, 104 pp.

————. 1968. Agonistic behavior of the northern grasshopper mouse (Onychomys leucogaster breviauritus). J. Mamm., 49:481–487.

Russel, R. J. 1953. Mammals of Cooke County, Texas. Texas J. Sci., 5:454–464.

————. 1968. Revision of pocket gophers of the genus Pappogeomys. Univ. Kansas Publ., Mus. Nat. Hist., 16:581–776.

Russell, D. N., and J. H. Shaw. 1971. Notes on the red wolf (Canis rufus) in the coastal marshes and prairies of eastern Texas. Contrib. Fed. Aid Wildl. Restor. Texas W-103-R.

Russell, T. P. 1964. Antelope of New Mexico. New Mexico Dept. Game & Fish Bull. 12, Santa Fe.

Samuel, D. E., and B. B. Nelson. 1982. Foxes. Pp. 475–490, in Wild Mammals of North America: biology, management, and economics (J. A. Chapman and G. A. Feldhamer, eds.). Johns Hopkins Univ. Press, Baltimore, 1,147 pp.

Sanderson, G. C. 1949. Growth and behavior of a litter of captive long-tailed weasels. J. Mamm., 30:412–415.

————. 1950. Methods of measuring productivity in raccoons. J. wildl. Mgmt., 14:389–402.

Scheck, S. H., and E. D. Fleharty. 1979. Daily energy budgets and patterns of activity of the adult thirteen-lined ground squirrel, Spermophilus tridecemlineatus. Physiol. Zool., 52:390–397.

Scheffer, T. H. 1949. Ecological comparison of three genera of moles. Trans. Kansas Acad. Sci., 52:30–37.

Schendel, R. R. 1940. Life history notes of *Sigmodon hispidus texianus* with special emphasis on populations and nesting habits. M.S. thesis, Oklahoma State Univ., Stillwater, 40 pp.

Schmidly, D. J. 1971. Population variation in *Dipodomys ordii* from western Texas. J. Mamm., 52:108–120.

———. 1972. Geographic variation in the white-ankled mouse, *Peromyscus pectoralis*. Southwestern Nat., 17:113–138.

———. 1973. Geographic variation and taxonomy of *Peromyscus boylii* from Mexico and the southern United States. J. Mamm., 54:111–130.

———. 1974. *Peromyscus attwateri*. Mamm. Species, 48:1–3.

———. 1983. Texas mammals east of the Balcones fault zone. Texas A&M Univ. Press, College Station, 400 pp.

Schwartz, A. 1955. The status of the species of the *brasiliensis* group of the genus *Tadarida*. J. Mamm., 36:106–109.

Schwartz, C. C., and J. G. Nagy. 1976. Pronghorn diets relative to forage availability in northeastern Colorado. J. Wildl. Mgmt., 40:469–478.

Schwartz, C.W., and E. R. Schwartz. 1981. The wild mammals of Missouri. Univ. Missouri Press, Columbia, 356 pp.

Scott, T. G. 1955. An evaluation of the red fox. Illinois Nat. Hist. Surv. Biol. Note No. 35, Urbana.

Scott, W. E. 1951. Wisconsin's first spotted skunk, and other notes. J. Mamm., 32:363.

Sealander, J. A. 1952. *Notiosorex* in Arkansas. J. Mamm., 33:105–106.

———. 1956. A provisional check-list and key to the mammals of Arkansas (with annotations). Amer. Midland Nat., 56:257–296.

———. 1979. A guide to Arkansas mammals. River Road Press, Conway, Arkansas, 313 pp.

———. and P. S. Gipson. 1973. Status of the mountain lion in Arkansas. Proc. Arkansas Acad. Sci., 27:38–41.

Self, J. T., and T. J. McKnight. 1950. Platyhelminths from the fur bearers in the Wichita Mountains Wildlife Refuge, with a special reference to *Oochoristica* spp. Amer. Midland Nat., 43:58–61.

Seton, E. T. 1925–1928. Lives of game animals. Doubleday, Doran and Co. Inc., Garden City, New York. 4 vols.

Setzer, H. W. 1949. Subspeciation in the kangaroo rat, *Dipodomys ordii*. Univ. Kansas Publ., Mus. Nat. Hist., 1:473–573.

Severinghaus, C. W. 1949. Tooth development and wear as criteria of age in white-tailed deer. J. Wildl. Mgmt., 13:195–216.

———. 1974. Notes on the history of wild canids in New York. New York Fish & Game J., 21:117–125.

Sexson, M. L., and J. R. Choate. 1981. Historical biogeography of the pronghorn in Kansas. Trans. Kansas Acad. Sci., 84:128–133.

———, J. R. Choate, and R. A. Nicholson. 1981. Diet of pronghorn in western Kansas. J. Range Mgmt., 34:489–493.

Sharp, W. M., and L. H. Sharp. 1956. Nocturnal movements and behavior of wild raccoons at a winter feeding station. J. Mamm., 37:170–177.

Shaver, W. M. 1973. Skeletal morphology as an index of variation among selected subspecies of Ord's kangaroo rat, *Dipodomys ordii* (Rodentia, Heteromyidae). M.S. thesis, Univ. Mississippi, Oxford. 47 pp.

Shaw, J. H. 1975. Ecology, behavior, and systematics of the red wolf (*Canis rufus*). Ph.D. dissert., Yale Univ., New Haven, Connecticut.

Shaw, M. G., and A. A. Kocan. No date. The parasites of white-tailed deer in Oklahoma. Fed. Aid Wildl. Restor. Act, Proj. W-80-R and W-130-R, Oklahoma Dept. Wildl. Conserv., Oklahoma City, 23 pp.

Sheets, R. G., and R. L. Linder. 1969. Food habits of the black-footed ferret, *Mustela nigripes*, in South Dakota. Proc. South Dakota Acad. Sci., 48:58–61.

———, ———, and R. B. Dahlgren. 1972. Habits of two litters of black-footed ferrets in South Dakota. Amer. Midland Nat., 87:249–251.

Sheldon, W. G. 1949. Reproductive behavior of foxes in New York State. J. Mamm., 30:236–246.

———. 1950. Denning habits and home range of red foxes in New York State. J. Wildl. Mgmt., 14:33–42.

Shirk, G. H. 1950. Peace on the plains. Chron. Oklahoma, 28(1):2–41.

Shump, K. A., Jr., and A. U. Shump. 1982a. *Lasiurus borealis*. Mamm. Species, 183:1–6.

———, and ———. 1982b. *Lasiurus cinereus*. Mamm. Species, 185:1–5.

Sibley, G. C. 1812. George C. Sibley's journal of a trip to the Salines in 1811. (G. R. Brooks, ed.) Bull. Missouri Hist. Soc., 59:172–178, 1965.

Sisk, M. E., and C. J. McCoy. 1964. Stomach contents of *Natrix r. rhombifera* (Reptilia: Serpentes) from an Oklahoma lake. Proc. Oklahoma Acad. Sci., 44:68–71.

Skinner, M. P. 1922. The pronghorn. J. Mamm., 3:82–105.

Slonaker, J. R. 1902. The eye of the common mole, *Scalopus aquaticus machrinus*. J. Comp. Neurol., 12:335–366.

Smith, C. C. 1940a. The effect of overgrazing and erosion upon the biota of the mixed-grass prairie of Oklahoma. Ecology, 21:381–397.

———. 1940b. Notes on the food and parasites of the rabbits of a lowland area in Oklahoma. J. Wildl. Mgmt., 4:429–431.

Smith, C. F. 1954. Four new species of cestodes of rodents from the High Plains, central and southern Rockies and notes on *Catenotaenia dendritica*. J. Parasitol., 40:245–254.

Smith, J. D. 1964. Second record of the eastern harvest mouse in Oklahoma. Trans. Kansas Acad. Sci., 67:204–205.

Smith, R. E. 1967. Natural history of the prairie dog in Kansas. Misc. Publ., Mus. Nat. Hist., Univ. Kansas, 16:1–36.

Smolen, M. J. 1981. *Microtus pinetorum*. Mamm. Species, 147:1–7.

Snead, E., and G. O. Hendrickson. 1942. Food habits of the badger in Iowa. J. Mamm., 23:380–391.

Snow, C. 1972. Habitat management series for endangered species. Rept. No. 2: black-footed ferret (*Mustela nigripes*). U.S. Bur. Land Mgmt. Tech. Note.

Snyder, D. P. 1982. *Tamias striatus*. Mamm. Species, 168:1–8.

Snyder, J. C. 1977. Description of the reproductive tract and its uses in determining productivity in the ringtail (*Bassariscus astutus*). M.S. thesis, Texas A&M Univ., College Station.

Spencer, D. L. 1968. Sympatry and hybridization of the eastern and southern plains wood rats. Ph.D. dissert., Oklahoma State Univ., Stillwater, 85 pp.

Spencer, S. R., and G. N. Cameron. 1982. *Reithrodontomys fulvescens*. Mamm. Species, 174:1–7.

Sperry, C. C. 1941. Food habits of the coyote. U.S. Dept. Int., Fish & Wildl. Serv. Wildl. Res. Bull., 4:1–70, Wash., D.C.

Spillet, J. J. 1964. A synopsis of the literature and miscellaneous observations on the pronghorn antelope (*Antilocapra americana*). Utah Coop. Wildl. Res. Unit Spec. Rept. No. 13, Logan.

Stains, H. J. 1956. The raccoon in Kansas: natural history, management, and economic importance. Misc. Publ., Mus. Nat. Hist., Univ. Kansas, 10:1–76.

Stangl, F. B., Jr. 1986. Aspects of a contact zone between two chromosomal races of *Peromyscus leucopus* (Rodentia: Cricetidae). J. Mamm., 67:465–473.

———, and W. W. Dalquest. 1986. Two noteworthy records of Oklahoma mammals. Southwestern Nat., 31:123–124.

Stanley, W. C. 1963. Habits of the red fox in northeastern Kansas. Misc. Publ., Mus. Nat. Hist., Univ. Kansas, 34:1–x.

Stevens, P. G., and J. L. E. Erickson. 1942. The chemical constitution of the musk of the Louisiana muskrat. J. Amer. Chem. Soc., 64:144–147.

Stiles, C. W., and C. E. Baker. 1935. Key-catalogue of parasites reported for Carnivora (cats, dogs, bears, etc.) with their possible public health importance. U.S. Natl. Inst. Health Bull. No. 163:913–1223.

Stock, A. D. 1974. Chromosome evolution in the genus *Dipodomys* and its taxonomic and phylogenetic implications. J. Mamm., 55:505–526.

Stone, J. E., and D. B. Pence. 1978. Ecology of helminth parasitism in the bobcat from west Texas. J. Parasitol., 64:295–302.

Storm, G. L. 1965. Movements and activities of foxes as determined by radio-tracking. J. Wildl. Mgmt., 29:1–13.

Storrs, E. E. 1971. The nine-banded armadillo: a model for leprosy and other biomedical research. Internat. J. Leprosy, 39:703–714.

———. 1973. Leprosy in the armadillo: new model for biomedical research. Science, 183:851–852.

———, and B. Labadies. 1982. The astonishing armadillo. Natl. Geogr. Mag., 161(6):820–830.

Stout, G. G. 1982. Effects of coyote reduction on white-tailed deer productivity on Fort Sill, Oklahoma. Wildl. Soc. Bull., 10:329–332.

———, F. C. Lowry, and F. Carlile. 1972. The status of elk transplants in eastern Oklahoma. Proc. 26th Ann. Conf. S.E. Assoc. Game & Fish Comm., pp. 202–203.

Strecker, J. K. 1926. The extension of the range of the nine-banded armadillo. J. Mamm., 7:206–214.

Streubel, D. P., and J. P. Fitzgerald. 1978. *Spermophilus spilosoma*. Mamm. Species, 101:1–4.

Stuewer, F. W. 1943. Reproduction of raccoons in Michigan. J. Wildl. Mgmt., 7:60–73.

Stutzenbaker, C. D. 1970. Coastal marsh management survey job no. 6, mottled duck status. Job Prog. Rept., Fed. Aid Proj. No. W-96-R-3.

Sudman, P. O., J. C. Burns, and J. R. Choate. 1986. Gestation and postnatal development of the plains pocket gopher. Texas J. Sci., 38:91–94.

Sullivan, E. G., and A. O. Haugen. 1956. Age determination of foxes by X-ray of forefeet. J. Wildl. Mgmt., 20:210–212.

Tate, R. C., and L. B. Nice. 1928. Say's chipmunk, *Eutamias quadrivittatus quadrivittatus* in Cimarron County. Proc. Okla. Acad. Sci., 7:134.

Taylor, R. J. 1964. Additional mammals for Bryan County, Oklahoma. J. Mamm., 45:640–642.

———, and H. McCarley. 1963. Vertical distribution of *Peromyscus leucopus* and *P. gossypinus* under experimental conditions. Southwestern Nat., 8: 107–108.

———. 1965. The badger from Johnston County, Oklahoma. Proc. Oklahoma Acad. Sci., 45:80.

Taylor, W. P. 1954. Food habits and notes on life history of the ring-tailed cat in Texas. J. Mamm., 35:55–63.

Terrel, T. L. 1972. The swamp rabbit (*Sylvilagus aquaticus*) in Indiana. Amer. Midland Nat., 87:283–295.

Tester, J. R. 1953. Fall food habits of the raccoon in the South Platte valley of northeastern Colorado. J. Mamm., 34:500–502.

Thompson, J. N., Jr. 1969. Variations in the interparietal of the kangaroo rat, *Dipodomys ordii*. Amer. Midland Nat., 82:625–628.

———, and S. D. Barrett. 1969. A nest complex of *Perognathus hispidus* (Rodentia: Heteromyidae) in Oklahoma. Proc. Oklahoma Acad. Sci., 48: 105–108.

Thompson, W. K. 1949. Predation on antelope. J. Wildl. Mgmt., 13: 313–314.

Thornton, W. A., G. C. Creel, and R. E. Trimble. 1971. Hybridization in the fox genus *Vulpes* in west Texas. Southwestern Nat., 15:473–484.

Tiemeier, O. W. 1955. Winter foods of Kansas coyotes. Trans. Kansas Acad. Sci., 58:196–207.

Tigner, J. R., and D. L. Gilbert. 1960. A contribution toward a bibliography on the black bear. Tech. Bull., Colorado Dept. Game & Fish, 5:1–42.

Tihen, J. A., and J. M. Sprague. 1939. Amphibians, reptiles and mammals of the Meade County State Park. Trans. Kansas Acad. Sci., 42:499–512.

Tileston, J. V. 1962. A resumé of Colorado big game research projects, 1939–1957. Fed. Aid Wildl. Restor. Proj. W-38-R. Colorado Dept. Game and Fish Tech. Bull. No. 9, Denver.

Timm, R. M., and R. D. Price. 1980. The taxonomy of *Geomydoecus* (Mallophaga: Trichodectidae) from the *Geomys bursarius* complex (Rodentia: Geomyidae). J. Med. Entomol., 17:126–145.

Tomich, P. Q. 1982. Ground squirrels. Pp. 192–208, *in* Wild mammals of North America: biology, management, and economics (J. A. Chapman and G. A. Feldhamer, eds.). Johns Hopkins Univ. Press, Baltimore, 1,147 pp.

Toweill, D. E. 1976. Movements of ringtails in Texas' Edwards Plateau region. M.S. thesis, Texas A&M Univ., College Station.

———, and M. A. Price. 1976. Ectoparasites of ringtails collected from Kerr County, Texas. Southwestern Entomol., 1 (1):20.

———, and J. G. Teer. 1977. Food habits of ringtails in the Edwards Plateau region of Texas. J. Mamm., 58:660–663.

———, and D. B. Toweill. 1978. Growth and development of captive ringtails. Carnivore, 1:46–53.

Trail, M. A., and R. Tumlison. 1984. Anomalies of bobcat skulls from Oklahoma. Proc. Oklahoma Acad. Sci., 64:46–47.

Trapp, G. R. 1972. Some anatomical and behavioral adaptations of ringtails, *Bassariscus astutus*. J. Mamm., 53:549–557.

———. 1973. Comparative behavioral ecology of two southwest Utah carnivores: *Bassariscus astutus* and *Urocyon cinereoargenteus*. Ph.D. dissert., Univ. Wisconsin, Madison.

Trowbridge, A. H., and H. L. Whitaker. 1940. A new kangaroo rat from Oklahoma. J. Mamm., 21:343–345.

Tuttle, M. P. 1976. Population ecology of the gray bat (*Myotis grisescens*) philopatry, timing and patterns of movement, weight loss during migration, and seasonal adaptive strategies. Occas. Pap. Mus. Nat. Hist., Univ. Kansas, 54:1–38.

Twente, J. W. 1955. Some aspects of habitat selection and other behavior of cavern-dwelling bats. Ecology, 36:706–732.

Tyler, J. D. Occurrence of the ringtail in Oklahoma. (in prep).

———. 1968. Distribution and vertebrate associates of the black-tailed prairie dog in Oklahoma. Ph.D. dissert., Univ. Oklahoma, Norman.

———. 1970. Vertebrates in a prairie dog town. Proc. Oklahoma Acad. Sci., 50:110–113.

———. 1979. Occurrence of the red fox (*Vulpes vulpes*) in western Oklahoma. Proc. Oklahoma Acad. Sci., 59:124–125.

———, and A. R. Gilliland. 1979. Status of *Notiosorex crawfordi* in Oklahoma, and new distributional records. Southwestern Nat., 24:375–376.

———, and J. F. Jensen. 1981. Notes on foods of great horned owls (*Bubo virginianus*) in Jackson County, Oklahoma. Proc. Oklahoma Acad. Sci., 61:28–30.

———, and M. J. Lodes. 1980. Distributional status of the eastern spotted skunk, *Spilogale putorius interrupta*, in Oklahoma. Proc. Oklahoma Acad. Sci., 60:102–104.

———, and L. Payne. 1982. Second Oklahoma record for the silver-haired bat, *Lasionycteris noctivagans*. Southwestern Nat., 27:245.

———, and C. M. Scott. 1982. Status and distribution of *Lasiurus cinereus* (Chiroptera: Vespertilionidae) in Oklahoma. Proc. Oklahoma Acad. Sci., 62:91–92.

Udy, J. R. 1953. Effects of predator control on antelope populations. Utah Dept. Game & Fish, Fed. Aid. Div., Publ. No. 5.

Urban, E. K., and R. B. Wimmer. 1959. *Reithrodontomys megalotis* and *Urocyon cinereoargenteus* from western Oklahoma. J. Mamm., 40:450.

Van Devender, T. R. 1977. Holocene woodlands in the southwestern deserts. Science, 198:189–192.

Van Gelder, R. G. 1959. Taxonomic revision of the spotted skunks (genus *Spilogale*). Bull. Amer. Mus. Nat. Hist., 117:229–329.

———. 1978. A review of canid classification. Amer. Mus. Novit., 2646:1–10.

Van Volkenberg, H. L., and A. J. Nicholson. 1943. Parasitism and malnutrition of deer in Texas. J. Wildl. Mgmt., 7:220–223.

Van Wormer, J. 1966. The world of the black bear. J. B. Lippincott Co., Philadelphia.

———. 1969. The world of the pronghorn. J. B. Lippincott Co., Philadelphia.

Van Zyll de Jong, C. G. 1979. Distribution and systematic relationships of long-eared *Myotis* in western Canada. Canadian J. Zool., 57:987–994.

――――. 1984. Taxonomic relationships of Nearctic small-footed bats of the *Myotis leibii* group (Chiroptera: Vespertilionidae). Canadian J. Zool., 62: 2519–2526.

――――. 1985. Handbook of Canadian mammals. 2. Bats. Nat. Mus. Canada, Ottawa, 212 pp.

Veal, R. A. 1983. Ecological aspects of the ectoparasitic fauna of hibernating *Myotis velifer*. M.S. thesis, Indiana State Univ., Terre Haute, 63 pp.

Verts, B. J. 1967. The biology of the stripped skunk. Univ. Illinois Press, Urbana, 218 pp.

Wade-Smith, J., and B. J. Verts. 1982. *Mephitis mephitis*. Mamm. Species, 173:1–7.

Waldrip, G. P. 1975. Elk habitat use during calving season with possible effects on white-tailed deer at the Wichita Mountains National Wildlife Refuge. M.S. thesis, Oklahoma State Univ., Stillwater, 81 pp.

Walker, E. P. 1975. Mammals of the world. Johns Hopkins Univ. Press, Baltimore. 1,500 pp.

Walker, M. L., and W. W. Becklund. 1970. Checklist of the internal and external parasites of deer, *Odocoileus hemionus* and *O. virginianus*, in the United States and Canada. Index-catalogue of Med. & Vet. Zool., Spec. Pub. No. 1, Nat. Animal Paras. Lab., Agri. Res. Serv., U.S. Dept. Agric., 45 pp.

Ward, J. W. 1934. A study of some parasites of rabbits of central Oklahoma. Proc. Oklahoma Acad. Sci., 14:31–32.

Warren, E. R. 1909. A new chipmunk from Colorado. Proc. Biol. Soc. Wash., 22:105–106.

Watkins, L. C. 1972. *Nycticeius humeralis*. Mamm. Species, 28:1–4.

Webster, W. D., and J. K. Jones, Jr. 1982. *Reithrodontomys megalotis*. Mamm. Species, 167:1–5.

――――, and ――――. 1985. Nongeographic variation, reproduction, and demography in the Texas kangaroo rat, *Dipodomys elator* (Rodentia: Heteromyidae). Texas J. Sci., 37:51–61.

Whitaker, H. L. 1937. Occurrence of the Texas rice rat in Oklahoma. J. Mamm., 18:102.

Whitaker, J. O. 1972. *Zapus hudsonius*. Mamm. Species, 11:1–7.

Whitlock, S. C. 1939. The prevalence of disease and parasites in whitetail deer. Trans. 4th N. Amer. Wildl. Conf.:244–249.

Wilcomb, M. J., Jr. 1954. A study of prairie dog burrow systems and the ecology of their arthropod inhabitants in central Oklahoma. Ph.D. dissert., Univ. Oklahoma, Norman.

Wilcomb, M. J., Jr., M. E. Griffith, and L. L. Ellis. 1952. Commensal rat ectoparasite collection. Public Health Monogr., 5:31–37.

Wiley, R. W. 1980. *Neotoma floridana*. Mamm. Species, 139:1–7.

Willey, R. B., and R. E. Richards. 1981. Vocalizations of the ringtail (*Bassariscus astutus*). Southwestern Nat., 26:23–30.

Williams, A. R. 1937. Observations on antelope in Texas. Spec. Rept., Texas Game, Fish & Oyster Comm., Austin, 6 pp. (typewritten).

Williams, D. F. 1978. Systematics and ecogeographic variation of the Apache pocket mouse (Rodentia: Heteromyidae). Bull. Carnegie Mus. Nat. Hist., 10:1–57.

Willner, G. R. 1982. Nutria. Pp. 1059–1076, *in* Wild mammals of North America: biology, management, and economics (J. A. Chapman and G. A. Feldhamer, eds.). Johns Hopkins Univ. Press, Baltimore, 1,147 pp.

———, G. A. Feldhamer, E. E. Zucker, and J. A. Chapman. 1980. *Ondatra zibethicus*. Mamm. Species, 141:1–8.

Wilson, D. E. 1968. Ecological distribution of the genus *Peromyscus*. Southwestern Nat., 13:267–274.

———. 1973. The systematic status of *Perognathus merriami* Allen. Proc. Biol. Soc. Wash., 86:175–192.

Wistrand, H. 1974. Individual, social, and seasonal behavior of the thirteen-lined ground squirrel (*Spermophilus tridecemlineatus*). J. Mamm., 55:329–347.

Wittrock, D. D., and M. J. Ulmer. 1974. Helminths of badgers, *Taxidea taxus* (Schreber), in northwest Iowa. Iowa State J. Res., 48:319–327.

———, and N. Wilson. 1974. Ectoparasites of the badger, *Taxidea taxus* (Schreber, 1778), in northwestern Iowa with a list of species recorded from North America. Iowa State J. Res., 49:9–15.

Wolfe, J. L. 1982. *Oryzomys palustris*. Mamm. Species, 176:1–5.

———, and A. V. Linzey. 1977. *Peromyscus gossypinus*. Mamm. Species, 70:1–5.

Wood, J. E. 1954. Food habits of furbearers of the upland post oak region in Texas. J. Mamm., 35:406–415.

———. 1958. Age structure and productivity of a gray fox population. J. Mamm., 39:74–86.

Woodhouse, S. W. 1853. Report on the natural history of country passed over by exploring under command of Capt. L. Sitgreaves, U.S. Topogr. Engrs., 1851. 32nd Congr., 2nd Sess., Sen. Ex. Doc., 59:37–47. Wash., D.C.

Woods, C. A. 1973. *Erethizon dorsatum*. Mamm. Species, 29:1–6.

Wright, P. L. 1948. Breeding habits of captive long-tailed weasels (*Mustela frenata*). Amer. Midland Nat., 39:338–344.

———. 1966. Observations on the reproductive cycle of the American badger (*Taxidea taxus*). Symp. Zool. Soc. London, 15:37–45.

————. 1969. The reproductive cycle of the male American badger (*Taxidea taxus*). J. Reprod. Fert. Suppl., 6:435–445.

————, and S. A. Dow, Jr. 1962. Minimum breeding age in pronghorn antelope. J. Wildl. Mgmt., 26:100.

Wyman, R. L., and K. Schaefer. 1972. The ectoparasites of *Peromyscus maniculatus* in Texas County, Oklahoma. Southwestern Nat., 16:435–436.

Yates, T. L., and D. J. Schmidly. 1977. Systematics of *Scalopus aquaticus* (Linnaeus) in Texas and adjacent states. Occas. Pap., The Mus., Texas Tech Univ., 45:1–36.

————, and D. J. Schmidly. 1978. *Scalopus aquaticus*. Mamm. Species, 105:1–4.

Young, S. P. 1946a. Our rare "black boots" of the prairies. Pp. 13–20, *in* Sketches of American wildlife. Monumental Press, Baltimore.

————. 1946b. The wolf in North American history. Caxton Printers Ltd., Caldwell, Idaho, 149 pp.

————. 1958. The bobcat of North America. Stackpole Co., Harrisburg, Pennsylvania, and Wildl. Mgmt. Inst., Washington, D.C. 193 pp.

————, and E. A. Goldman. 1944. The wolves of North America. Amer. Wildl. Inst., Wash., D.C., 636 pp.

————, and ————. 1946. The puma, mysterious American cat. Amer. Wildl. Inst., Wash., D.C., 358 pp.

————, and H. H. T. Jackson. 1951. The clever coyote. Stackpole Co., Harrisburg, Pennsylvania, and Wildl. Mgmt. Inst., Wash., D.C.

Zimmerman, E. G., B. J. Hart, and C. W. Kilpatrick. 1975. Biochemical genetics of the *truei* and *boylei* groups of the genus *Peromyscus* (Rodentia). Comp. Biochem. Physiol., 50B:1–5.

Zimmerman, J. W. 1982. The common long-nosed armadillo (*Dasypus novemcinctus*) in northcentral Oklahoma. M.S. thesis, Oklahoma State Univ., Stillwater, 106 pp.

Zumbaugh, D. M., and J. R. Choate. 1985. Historical biogeography of foxes in Kansas. Trans. Kansas Acad. Sci., 88:1–13.

————, ————, and L. B. Fox. 1985. Winter food habits of the swift fox on the Central High Plains. Prairie Nat., 17:41–47.

Index

548